NATIONAL GEOGRAPHIC SOCIETY

Research Reports

Bradford and Barbara Washburn observing angles from the top of Dana Butte, Grand Canyon (see page 1).

NATIONAL GEOGRAPHIC SOCIETY

Research Reports

VOLUME 15

On research and exploration projects
supported by the National Geographic Society,
for which an initial grant or continuing support
was provided in the year

1971, 1973, or 1974

Compiled and edited by
Paul H. Oehser, John S. Lea, and Nancy Link Powars
under the direction of the
Committee for Research and Exploration

NATIONAL GEOGRAPHIC SOCIETY

WASHINGTON, D. C.

Statement by the Chairman

The National Geographic Society was founded in 1888 by a group, composed largely of Washington scientists, to increase and diffuse geographic knowledge and to promote research and exploration. The Society's activities toward achieving its second objective date from 1890, when the society sponsored a geographic and geologic expedition to study the Mount St. Elias Range of Alaska. Since then it has made more than 2,500 grants in support of approximately 1,900 projects in research and exploration. The work has encompassed the broad scope of geography, including such scientific disciplines as geology, paleontology, astronomy, geophysics, oceanography, biology, anthropology, archeology, ethnology, and geographic exploration. The research program has increased as the Society has grown, until today the budget of the Society provides $2,750,000 annually in support of the program.

To assist in the task of selecting from among the hundreds of applicants those best qualified to continue the high standards of accomplishment set by recipients of grants during the past nine decades, the Society has assembled the panel of distinguished scientists and scholars listed above.

This is the fifteenth in a series of volumes presenting summary reports on the results of all the research and exploration projects sponsored by the Society since it was established. These are being published volume by volume, as rapidly as the material can be assembled. The present volume contains 67 accounts covering work for which the initial grant was made in 1971, 1973, or 1974. In instances when a continuing research program has been supported by grants over a number of years, and a breakdown of results by year is impracticable, it has seemed best to report on the subsequent grants in one résumé, with cross references to the main account inserted in other volumes as appropriate. The volumes now in print, and the grant years covered in them, are listed in the Editor's Note that follows.

In presenting the reports, no attempt has been made to standardize the style and specific approach of the investigator, other than to confine each account to reasonable space limitations. In many cases fuller but scattered reports on the work have been, or will be, published elsewhere—in technical and scientific journals, occasionally in the *National Geographic,* or in book form. Published accounts emanating from the research projects are included in the literature references, which each author has been encouraged to supply.

Although the editors of these Reports make every reasonable effort to obtain a timely report from every grantee, so that the results of all projects supported in a given year will be accounted for in one volume, circumstances occasionally interfere. In these instances the delayed report will be published in a later volume. Grantees generally have been most cooperative in this publication project: the Committee for Research and Exploration takes this opportunity to thank them for their support, and we solicit their continued help.

Experience with the preceding volumes of this series has convinced us that the presentation of research findings as given in these books is of significant value to the scientific community. Scholars the world over find this record of the accumulating results of National Geographic Society research grants of real assistance in their own investigations and in the preparation of scientific publications. The general reader also gains new and important knowledge about the current state of research related to geography from each of these volumes.

MELVIN M. PAYNE

Editor's Note

The accounts in this volume are arranged alphabetically under the name of the principal investigator, who is not necessarily the senior author named in the Contents (p. xi). Lists of the grants on which these are based is to be found in the Appendices of the volumes of *National Geographic Society Research Reports* indicated on p. x of this note.

The following accounts published in *National Geographic Society Research Reports,* vol. 11 (*1970 projects*), vol. 12 (*1971 Projects*), vol. 13 (*1971* and *1972 Projects*), and vol. 14 (*1973 Projects*) deal with research that continued into 1974 and was supported by grants in that year. Since these accounts cover this 1974 research, no further treatment is required here.

"Studies of Pre-Columbian American Diseases, 1971-1976," by *Marvin J. Allison, vol.* 12, pp. 1-11.

"Biological Colonization of a Newly Created Volcanic Island and Limnological Studies on New Guinea Lakes, 1972-1978," by *Eldon E. Ball* and *Joe Glucksman, vol.* 13, pp. 89-97.

"Survey of Ancient Shipwrecks in the Mediterranean," by *George F. Bass, vol.* 14, pp. 45-48.

"Archeological, Paleontological, and Geological Research at the Lubbock Lake Site, Texas, 1973-1974," by *Craig C. Black, Eileen Johnson,* and *Charles A. Johnson II, vol.* 14, pp. 57-64.

"Behavior of Vertebrate Populations on Abandoned Strip-mine Areas," by *Fred J. Brenner, vol.* 12, pp. 67-74.

"In Search of Garifuna, Beachfolk of the Bay of Honduras," by *William V. Davidson, vol.* 14, pp. 129-142.

"Search for the *Monitor* and Development of a Camera for Horizontal Underwater Photography," by *Harold E. Edgerton* and *John G. Newton, vol.* 14, pp. 157-160.

"The Cooperative Breeding System of African Bee-eaters," by *Stephen T. Emlen, vol.* 14, pp. 167-170.

"Petrology and Origin of the Mount Stuart Batholith, Cascade Mountains, Washington," by *Erik H. Erikson, Jr., vol.* 12, pp. 175-184.

"The 'Acropolis' of Aphrodisias in Caria: Investigations and Excavations of the Theater and the Prehistoric Mounds, 1971-1977," by *Kenan T. Erim, vol.* 12, pp. 185-204.

"Systematic Study of the Hesperiidae of Mexico," by *Hugh Avery Freeman, vol.* 14, pp. 259-260.

"Wild Orangutan Studies at Tanjung Puting Reserve, Central Indonesian Borneo, 1971-1977," by *Birute M. F. Galdikas,* vol. 13, pp. 1-10.

"Ecology of the Wolverine in Northwestern Montana," by *Maurice G. Hornocker,* vol. 14, pp. 341-350.

"Anthropological Research in Mali," by *Johan Huizinga, R.M.A. Bedaux,* and *J. D. van der Waals,* vol. 11, pp. 281-307.

"The Submerged Sanctuary of Apollo at Halieis in the Argolid of Greece," by *Michael H. Jameson,* vol. 14, pp. 363-367.

"Population Ecology of the Flamingos of the World," by *M. Philip Kahl,* vol. 12, pp. 407-415.

"Continuing Research East of Lake Turkana in Northern Kenya, 1973-1976," by *Richard E. F. Leakey,* vol. 14, pp. 399-423.

"The Taxonomy, Distribution, and Ecology of Australian Freshwater Turtles (Testudines: Pleurodira: Chelidae)," by *John M. Legler,* vol. 13, pp. 391-404.

"Archeological Research in the Ariari River Basin, Western Meta, Colombia," by *John P. Marwitt,* vol. 14, pp. 463-471.

"The Quintana Roo Mural Project," by *Arthur G. Miller,* vol. 13, pp. 443-457.

"The Chan Chan-Moche Valley Archeological Project, Peru," by *Michael E. Moseley,* vol. 11, pp. 413-425.

"Natural History of Vertebrates on the Brazilian Islands of the Mid South Atlantic," by *Storrs L. Olson,* vol. 13, pp. 481-492.

"Research on the Behavior of Various Species of Whales," by *Roger S. Payne,* vol. 12, pp. 551-564.

"Vision and Orientation in Aquatic Animals," by *Talbot H. Waterman,* vol. 11, pp. 547-566.

Reports on the 1974 grants listed below were not available at the time this volume went to press. They will appear in later volumes as they are received.

798, 1360: To Dr. Maynard M. Miller, Michigan State University, East Lansing, Michigan, for a regimen investigation of a prototype inland glacier system, Atlin Park, British Columbia.

1288: To Dr. Susan E. Riechert, University of Tennessee, Knoxville, Tennessee, for a study of ontogeny and diversification of feeding behavior in the desert funnel web spider.

1291: To Dr. James E. Carpenter, Kent State University, Kent, Ohio, for excavation of an early Bronze Age settlement in Cyprus.

1311: To Dr. Raymond E. Clarke, Sarah Lawrence College, Bronxville, New York, for a study of niche overlap and species diversity of coral reef fish.

1315: To Dr. Marie-Helene Sachet, Smithsonian Institution, Washington, D. C., for collection of materials for a flora of the Marquesas Islands.

1322: To Dr. Elwyn L. Simons, Peabody Museum of Natural History, Yale University, New Haven, Connecticut, for an expedition for fossil ancestors of man in the Kathmandu Valley, Nepal.

1324, 1376: To Dr. Peter S. Rodman, University of California, Davis, California, for a population study of nonhuman primates in East Kalimantan, Indonesia.

1328: To Dr. Kalman A. Muller, National Institutes of Health, Bethesda, Maryland, for a research film elicitation project on Tanna, New Hebrides.

1364: To Dr. Ned K. Johnson, Museum of Vertebrate Zoology, Berkeley, California, for a study of systematics of sibling species of birds in northwestern South America.

1379: To Dr. Donald R. Johnson, University of Idaho, Moscow, Idaho, for radiotracking Idaho's last mountain caribou.

1380: To Mr. Augusto Ruschi, Museu de Biologia, Santa Teresa, E. E. Santo, Brazil, for a study of ecology and geographical distribution of the hummingbird in South America, Central America, and Mexico.

1389: To Dr. Robert G. Douglas, University of Southern California, Los Angeles, California, for a study of abyssal deep sea foraminifera in the Pacific Ocean.

1399: To Dr. Deane M. Petersen, State University of New York at Stony Brook, for studies of peculiar early type stars.

1411: To Julia M. Wentworth-Shepard, Cornell University, Ithaca, New York, for a study of behavior differences among lekking male ruffs in Sweden.

Libraries and institutions regularly receiving copies of these reports will note that this one bears the volume number 15 and that this practice of numbering is now being used to identify volumes. For their convenience, the earlier ones may be considered to bear numbers (shown in parentheses) as follows:

Vol. no.	Covering grant years	Date issued
(1)	1890-1954	1975
(2)	1955-1960	1972
(3)	1961-1962	1970
(4)	1963	1968
(5)	1964	1969
(6)	1965	1971
(7)	1966	1973
(8)	1967	1974
(9)	1968	1976
(10)	1969	1978
(11)	1970	1979
12	1971	1980
13	1971, 1972	1981
14	1973	1982

To aid researchers, the Society's grants made from 1966 onward are listed numerically in the Appendix of *Research Reports* volumes as indicated below:

Grants (year made)		In volume	(project year)
550 - 600	(1966)	(4)	1963
601 - 670	(1967)	(5)	1964
671 - 743	(1968)	(5)	1964
744 - 822	(1969)	(6)	1965
823 - 917	(1970)	(6)	1965
918 - 1036	(1971)	(7)	1966
1037 - 1136	(1972)	(8)	1967
1137 - 1285	(1973)	(9)	1968
1286 - 1421	(1974)	(10)	1969
1422 - 1568	(1975)	(11)	1970
1569 - 1701	(1976)	(11)	1970
1702 - 1844	(1977)	12	(1971)
1845 - 1974	(1978)	12	(1971)
1975 - 2130	(1979)	13	(1972)
2131 - 2287	(1980)	14	(1973)
2288 - 2420	(1981)	15	(1974)

Contents

Resurvey of the Heart of the Grand Canyon, 1971-1978

Principal Investigator: Bradford Washburn, The Museum of Science, Boston, Massachusetts.

Grant Nos.1024, 1094, 1137, 1355, 2022.   For mapping the Grand Canyon of the Colorado River.

The first formal map of the Bright Angel area of the Grand Canyon, published in 1903, was a result of the extraordinary survey of 1902-03 by parties of the U. S. Geological Survey, (USGS) under the leadership of E. M. Douglas—with topography by François Matthes and control by H. L. Baldwin, Jr., and J. T. Stewart. This excellent "reconnaissance" map (scale 1:48,000, with 40-foot contours) was not materially improved until the new USGS Bright Angel Quadrangle (scale 1:62,500, with 80-ft. contours), published in 1960, was made by photogrammetric methods from aerial photographs taken in 1954 and 1960.

I enjoy making maps. I was an instructor of cartography before I came to the Museum of Science in 1939, and I have tried to keep up with the great advances in cartographic techniques which have occurred in the past forty years; and whenever the opportunity arose, I have become involved in an interesting exploratory mapping project. When my wife and I visited the Grand Canyon in fall 1969, we were disturbed by the fact that no large-scale maps of the area existed. For either the hiker or the scientist who has any desire or need to know precisely where he is or, indeed, precisely where he is going, a map with a scale of an inch to a mile (1:62,500) is simply inadequate to depict such incredibly rough country, with extremely intricate trails involving hundreds of tight switchbacks. This is also far too small a scale for the accurate plotting of the geology, botany, or archeology of the heavily-frequented and much-studied heart of the Canyon.

After considerable research, it became clear that neither the National Park Service (NPS) nor the U. S. Geological Survey planned to remap the Canyon area on a larger scale, and I became intrigued with the idea of making a number of new sheets of the most intensely used part of the Canyon on a manuscript scale of 1:4800 (roughly, a foot to a mile) with the long-range hope of eventually coalescing these large sheets into a single map on a scale partway between this and that of the small-scale government sheets.

1

Mrs. Washburn and I discussed this project with Harry R. Feldman of Boston, one of New England's top professional surveyors, with whom we had worked before on the control of our large-scale maps of Squam Lake, New Hampshire, and the Squam Range, and he expressed keen interest in working with us at the Canyon. The Museum of Science has owned a Wild T-3 theodolite for many years and Feldman had just acquired a new Laser Ranger II, which appeared to be ideally suited to making precise distance measurements across the Canyon and between its dramatic pinnacles and buttes.

It was our plan to work together as volunteers, encouraging other volunteers to help us, and to finance the project with any grants-in-aid that we could secure as the project progressed. Before plunging into a major commitment, we decided to visit the area once more, using a modest grant from my Museum of Science research fund, to see what the working conditions were, to investigate the availability and cost of reliable helicopter support, and to make a few preliminary observations along and near the South Rim. We also speculated further by having Mark Hurd Aerial Surveys of Goleta, California, take vertical photographs of the entire area under consideration. These were made with a Zeiss camera from an altitude of 16,000 ft. (above sea level) and flown both north-south and east-west in order to cover every detail of the terrain.

We studied the existing maps thoroughly and secured all available control from the U. S. Coast and Geodetic Survey (USC&GS) and U. S. Geological Survey. The area that interested us extended westward from Yaki Point eight miles to Hermit Creek, northward across the Canyon to Point Sublime and then eastward again to the vicinity of Bright Angel Point on the North Rim. This was a large area—well over one hundred square miles—and it covered most of the "heart" of the Canyon which was then being visited by nearly three million tourists and hikers each year.

There was very little precisely marked government control in this area. The USC&GS had first-order triangulation stations at Yaki Point (44. Middle; see Table 1 on p. 8, listing stations), Point Sublime, and Cape Royal. The positions of these stations were very accurate, but their altitudes were far less precisely known. The USGS had a triangulation station near Hopi Point (70. Rowe), another one (Angel) at the North Rim Ranger station and another at Obi Point. Rowe and Obi were easily accessible, but Angel lay amid huge trees, and a high tower would have been needed in order to observe from it. A very accurate line of levels had been run down the Bright Angel Trail to the Colorado River by François Matthes's party in 1902 and a number of bench marks from this work still remained. Also, the NPS had done considerable additional leveling in the Inner Canyon and along ten miles of the lower course of Bright Angel Creek, in connection with the establishment of the water pipeline between Roaring Springs (on the North Kaibab Trail) and the South Rim complex.

In short, all the control of the existing maps of this part of the Canyon depended on baseline measurements made in the desert many miles away, and except for a small number of widely separated points, no reliable and marked control existed in our area of interest. We therefore decided to start the work with a clean sheet of white paper on which we marked the grid coordinates of Yaki Point (44. Middle USC&GS) and Point Sublime (81. Sublime USC&GS). We assumed these stations to be precisely positioned—and this of course yielded the azimuth between them. This azimuth was also checked in the field with theodolite work at Middle to USC&GS station Royal, which lay east of our network.

For the only time in the whole project, we abandoned our policy of an all-volunteer group of field workers in connection with precise leveling, and hired Edward A. Krahmer of Sun Lakes, Arizona (highly recommended to us by the USGS), to establish a very solid datum for our project by running two level-loops for us from USC&GS Bench Mark S-61 (6878.136 ft.)* at the head of the Santa Fe railroad yard at Grand Canyon Village. One of these closed loops ran out to Yaki Point, and established the altitude of Middle as 7261.882 ft. The other, passing USGS station Rowe (7068.829 ft.) on the way, ran out to Hopi Point and established an altitude of 7044.962 ft. at a new triangulation station which we set up at the tip of the point, in full view of the other great points along the central part of the South Rim (Yaki, Yavapai, and Pima), as well as virtually all of our key points on the North Rim and in the Canyon itself. Our entire map was to be hung on the positions of Middle and Sublime, the azimuth of the line between them, and the altitudes brought to Middle and Hopi from Bench Mark S-61. Krahmer also swung past a new station which we set on the roof of Yavapai Museum (firmly related to its stone foundation) and gave it an altitude of 7084.202 ft. Also accepted as vertical control down in the Canyon were those of Matthes's 1902 bench marks related to the Bright Angel Trail, and all of the NPS level stations between Roaring Springs and Indian Gardens.

We are extremely grateful for assistance given to us in this regard by staff members of the USC&GS, the USGS, and the NPS, particularly Robert Lovegren and Merle Stitt, superintendents of Grand Canyon National Park, and also by the others listed in the Acknowledgments on page 33.

---

* See Postscript (p. 32) explaining how this bench mark was erroneously moved some years ago, and the consequences thereof.

Our first trip to the Canyon was made in 1971 (February 18-27) before we had developed solid plans for the project, in part to appraise the whole situation and in part actually to start some of the work if conditions looked favorable and Park Service interest in what we hoped to do appeared high. Those in our party, besides Mrs. Washburn and myself, were our daughter Betsy, who lived in Denver, and Wendell Mason of Boston, a longtime friend, professional surveyor, and Harry Feldman's chief assistant.

This first trip was extremely successful: we experienced the usual incredibly fine Canyon weather (a pleasant change from the myriad weather problems encountered when working in Alaska and the Yukon); we established solid relations with the Park Service; we located all the key survey stations on the South Rim described in the lists given to us by the government; and we set up a number of our new stations, both along the South Rim and somewhat out into the Canyon. We also set up a good working relationship with Grand Canyon Helicopters who performed most of our support for the first three years in the field. Late winter is an excellent time to work at the Canyon and we accomplished a great deal, despite the fact that we were in the field for only 10 days. Needless to say, because we were all busily employed on other major jobs and doing this "on the side," it was clear from the start that it would take us a long time to reach our goal, a tiny bite on each trip, but we enjoyed it this way and we rapidly developed a delightful spirit of camaraderie between the two of us who were "regulars" on each trip and the many volunteers who worked so enthusiastically with us. (See Acknowledgments, p. 33.)

After the first trip, we reviewed progress and were very pleased. We had spent only $2400, already had set up a very sound composite base along the South Rim (Yaki-Yavapai-Hopi-Pima), and had used the helicopter and laser enough to be certain that they were the basic tools needed for our success. The Laser Ranger II, however, was not powerful enough to measure distances over 5 miles, whereas several of the sights that we needed to develop a sound network across to the other side of the Canyon ranged between 7 and 13 miles. So we sought the help of Laser Systems and Electronics of Tullahoma, Tennessee, which had made Feldman's Ranger II. From this contact developed a working relationship that has been of extraordinary importance, not only to this Grand Canyon project but also to our subsequent work both in Alaska and New Hampshire.

Fig. 1.   Buddy Cutshaw and Barbara Washburn sighting northward with the Rangemaster across the Grand Canyon from the survey station at Yavapai Point. Below: Bradford Washburn measuring angles on the South Rim with the Wild T-3 theodolite. In certain sights that required great precision an umbrella was used to shade the instrument's level bubble.

Our second trip was planned for almost a full month (June 16 to July 11, 1971) and this time our volunteer ranks were expanded to include not only Mason and Feldman but also Buddy Cutshaw and Wayne McQueen of Laser Systems, who were to field test a new laser instrument under development at the time.

It would take many, many pages of intricate text to cover the day-to-day work of each of these trips, all of which, of course, is recorded in our logs of the project. This account will simply deal with the basic steps of progress as we went forward and will recount the principal techniques used in our work.

Again, we invested little time down in the Canyon, concentrating instead on measuring the long lines, so essential to the development of a strong over-all survey network, and of which some reached significantly beyond the limits that we had first set for our project. We continued to add to the control out in the Canyon by measurements to and from Zoroaster, Cheops, Set, and Ra, all points that rose dramatically above the Canyon floor, yet were easily accessible by helicopter.

Each of our survey stations (see Table 1 for a complete listing) consisted of a 1-inch hole, 3 inches deep, drilled in the rock by means of a Black and Decker Rotohammer, operated by current supplied by a Homelite generator. This gear, contributed to our project by the manufacturers, was hauled by helicopter to almost all of our stations, but a half-dozen holes were cut by using an old-fashioned hand drill and sledge hammer.

When the hole was completed, we drove into it a 3 x $^3/_4$ in. galvanized pipe nipple, then added a coupling and a section of pipe, varying in length from 2 to 5 ft., to which we attached our targets, as in figure 3. Those which we had to see from a number of different directions were 16-in. plastic spheres (National Geographic world-globe cores!). Those which were to be sighted from only one direction were simply rectangular plywood targets bolted to the iron pipes. All were painted flat white, then spray-painted with fluorescent orange, which appeared to be the most practical color for visibility against the complex Canyon backgrounds. Repainting was necessary about twice each year, as the paint rapidly faded in the intense desert sunlight.

As our stations were established, they were marked with large white cloth targets staked out on the ground, and photographed from the air at low altitude, so that they could be precisely related to our 1970 high-altitude photography. This was obviously not the normal way to mark control, all of which should have been targeted in advance and photographed before field measurements started, but this orderly procedure could not be followed on an informal project such as ours, inching slowly forward, with exceedingly limited finances and a modest contingent of volunteers.

FIG. 2. Bradford and Barbara Washburn observing angles from the top of Dana Butte, probably the most dramatic of all the stations that were occupied. A view of this from the other side appeared in the *National Geographic* (July 1978, p. 36).

At the conclusion of the two trips in 1971, all of our vacation time was exhausted and we retreated to Boston to sum up the results of our work. We had spent, in all, 26 days in the field, had made 85 helicopter landings; and were now sure that what we were doing made sense. Our preliminary calculations were yielding excellent results. Our trusted Wild T-3 theodolite was working perfectly and the two Laser Rangers had made distance measurements (see Table 2) speedy and simple. But it was clear that, unless we wanted to whittle away gently on our project for years, we would need much more financial assistance than my small Museum research fund could provide, particularly because a great deal more helicopter work lay ahead as we progressed farther and farther away from the South Rim; and we had not yet started the costly phase of photogrammetric control-proliferation and contouring.

Accordingly, in the fall of 1971, we approached the National Geographic Society to see if we could enter into a collaborative arrangement with its Committee for Research and Exploration to split our future expenses equally

TABLE 1. Grand Canyon Survey Stations, Location Data

1. See Postscript (p. 32) for explanation of corrections. The *elevation* of 12 stations was determined by leveling, and the letter following the elevation indicates how this was done: a, from USC&GS Bench Mark S-61 (6878.136 ft.); b, from USGS Bench Mark (3870.292 ft.) on Bright Angel Trail; c, from USNPS Pipeline level line.

2. Of the 92 stations used for *control*: 33 were occupied by both theodolite and Laser Ranger (TLO); 42 were fixed by theodolite and laser distances (TL); 7 were occupied by theodolite and intersected by theodolite from one or more other stations (TO); 8 were targeted by helicopter or afoot and fixed by theodolite sights from two or more other points (HT); 2 were not visited at all, but their peaks intersected from two or more theodolite stations (INT).

| No. and name | Altitudes (in ft.) and positions of control | | | Survey station marks (left in field) | Control[2] |
	Old elevation[1]	Corrected elevation[1]	Grid coordinates		
1 Angel A	8145.5	8147.5	N1889707.98 E461254.60	USGS bronze disc	TLO
2 Boulder	5683.7	5685.7	N1878200.58 E406359.21	Drill-hole in rock	TO
3 Clear	4030.4	4032.4	N1855151.25 E464972.88	Drill-hole, pipe and sphere	TL
4 Cheops	5386.6	5388.6	N1862418.82 E439687.26	Concrete observing stand and bronze disc	TLO
5 Colonnade	6238.6	6240.6	N1875818.23 E438797.79	Drill-hole with pipe	TO
6 Confucius	7073.0	7075.0	N1884912.95 E410129.23	Drill-hole with pipe	TLO
7 Cope	3522.0	3524.0	N1853206.42 E418127.89	Drill-hole with pipe	HT
8 Corner	4967.2	4969.2	N1832044.23 E471583.41	Drill-hole with pipe	TL
9 Cremation	3894.2	3896.2	N1853533.79 E453051.54	Drill-hole with pipe	TO
10 Crystal	3991.7	3993.7	N1873333.06 E404795.83	Drill-hole with pipe	TL
11 Dana	5033.6	5035.6	N1852652.10 E431163.00	Drill-hole with pipe	TO
12 Dragon	4450.8	4452.8	N1888276.70 E426637.95	Drill-hole with pipe	TL
13 Dragon (North)	7661.1	7663.1	N1898037.84 E424626.74	Drill-hole with pipe	TL
14 Gorge	3820.3	3822.3	N1847006.32 E469075.33	Drill-hole, pipe and sphere	TL

15 Grama	7733.4	7735.4	N1895867.32	E411753.34	Drill-hole, pipe and sphere	HT
16 Grandeur	7032.4	7034.4	N1842898.79	E439381.14	Drill-hole	TL
17 Greenland	8315.0	8317.0	N1897209.67	E475233.95	Drill-hole with pipe	TL
18 Hattan	5967.2	5969.2	N1868638.30	E460207.55	Drill-hole with pipe	TLO
19 Hermit	6650.4	6652.4	N1841946.69	E413139.78	Bronze disc	TLO
20 Hopi	7042.99 (a)	7044.962 (a)	N1846394.62	E429774.70	Bronze disc	TLO
21 Horsethief	6346.3	6348.3	N1836184.03	E409380.76	Drill-hole with pipe	TL
22 Horus	6130.2	6132.2	N1870417.15	E423315.40	Drill-hole, pipe and sphere	TO
23 Howlands	5571.4	5573.4	N1854099.78	E472703.87	Drill-hole with pipe	TLO
24 Indian Gardens	3849.56 (b)	No. chg.	N1847577.94	E438117.70	Bronze disc	TLO
25 Indian Gds. A	3939.9	No. chg.	N1846661.08	E437138.79	Drill-hole	TL
26 Indian Gds. B	3924.2	No. chg.	N1847540.78	E437023.19	Drill-hole	TL
27 Indian Gds. C	3871.8	No. chg.	N1848012.20	E437681.45	Drill-hole	TL
28 Indian Gds. D	3815.8	No. chg.	N1848401.72	E437954.53	Drill-hole	TL
29 Indian Gds. E	3734.4	No. chg.	N1849276.63	E438361.92	Drill-hole	TL
30 Indian Gds. F	3799.3	No. chg.	N1848258.57	E438740.16	Drill-hole	TL
31 Indian Gds. G	3913.8	No. chg.	N1849759.46	E438142.65	Drill-hole	TL
32 Isis	7013.9	7015.9	N1870665.40	E435072.80	Nothing left	INT
33 Johnson	5298.2	5300.2	N1866916.30	E449923.20	Drill-hole, pipe and sphere	HT
34 Knee	5401.2	5403.2	N1860262.85	E469883.62	Drill-hole, pipe and sphere	TL
35 Komo	7987.4	7989.4	N1882943.45	E469551.71	Drill-hole with pipe	TL
36 Laser	4038.9	4040.9	N1880209.02	E416491.93	Drill-hole with pipe	TL
37 Ledge	6534.8	6536.8	N1878406.28	E448988.11	Drill-hole with pipe	TL
38 Lookout	4499.9	4501.9	N1846127.66	E412950.68	Drill-hole with short pipe	TL
39 Lyell	5348.1	5350.1	N1836531.15	E467180.17	Drill-hole with pipe	TLO
40 Manzanita	8108.8	8110.8	N1887512.32	E475296.34	Drill-hole with pipe	TL
41 Maricopa	6988.06 (a)	6990.032 (a)	N1841574.19	E432137.51	Drill-hole	TLO
42 Maricopa A	6994.93 (a)	6996.902 (a)	N1841903.13	E432213.88	Drill-hole	TLO
43 Mesa	4836.7	4838.7	N1862394.43	E414839.81	Drill-hole with pipe	TLO
44 Middle (USC&GS)	7259.91 (a)	7261.882	N1840705.52	E450811.59	USC&GS bronze disc	TLO
45 Newton	5918.8	5920.8	N1841545.53	E459955.73	Drill-hole with pipe	HT
46 Obi (USGS)	7928.6	7930.6	N1876730.86	E471902.45	USGS bronze disc	TLO

TABLE 1. Grand Canyon Survey Stations, Location Data—*Continued*

No. and name	Altitudes (in ft.) and positions of control			Survey station marks (left in field)	Control[2]
	Old elevation[1]	Corrected elevation[1]	Grid coordinates		
47 O'Neill	5308.8	5310.8	N1844968.00 E448830.00	Cairn with pipe in it	HT
48 Osiris	6637.2	6639.2	N1872253.77 E420375.84	Nothing left	INT
49 Ottoman	4382.9	4384.9	N1864992.68 E473354.87	Drill-hole with pipe	TL
50 Parapet	6923.868 (a)	6925.840 (a)	N1840470.37 E435259.15	Bronze disc	TLO
51 Pattie	5308.8	5310.8	N1845240.01 E459107.22	Drill-hole with pipe	HT
52 Perch	6269.1	6271.1	N1875618.37 E426727.80	Drill-hole, pipe and sphere	HT
53 Pima	6765.0	6767.0	N1845459.90 E416473.41	Bronze disc	TLO
54 Phantom Ranch	2546.21 (c)	No chg.	N1857788.53 E447705.03	Bronze disc	TLO
55 Phantom (USGS)	2518.20 (c)	No chg.	N1857099.48 E447415.02	Nothing left (corner of house)	TO
56 Phantom A	3724.9	3726.9	N1858246.21 E450012.58	Drill-hole with pipe	TLO
57 Phantom B	3874.6	3876.6	N1854086.88 E450221.32	Drill-hole with pipe	TLO
58 Phantom C	3885.7	3887.7	N1853850.03 E445335.45	Drill-hole with pipe	TLO
59 Phantom D	4117.2	4119.2	N1857588.51 E443995.55	Drill-hole with pipe	TLO
60 Phantom E	4091.1	4093.1	N1861121.06 E447281.91	Drill-hole with pipe	TL
61 Phantom F	4123.8	4125.8	N1861328.90 E441893.03	Drill-hole with pipe	TL
62 Phantom H	4104.8	4106.8	N1860932.54 E446587.22	Drill-hole with pipe	TL
63 Phantom J	4058.7	4060.7	N1861749.80 E444199.65	Drill-hole with pipe	TL
64 Phantom K	3760.1	3762.1	N1857369.96 E453317.25	Drill-hole with pipe	TL
65 Plateau Point	3781.66 (b)	No chg.	N1853215.59 E441312.68	Bronze disc	TLO
66 Powell	5427.3	5429.3	N1872091.30 E453071.20	Drill-hole with pipe	TL
67 Powell Point (USGS/BM)	7043.88	No chg.	B 1846054.90 E430964.40	USGS bench mark (bronze disc)	TL
68 Ra	6077.9	6079.9	N1870649.10 E415445.26	Drill-hole with pipe	TLO
69 Ribbon	3715.7	3717.7	N1877119.37 E460043.11	Bronze disc	TLO

70 Rowe (USGS)	7066.857 (a)	7068.829 (a)	N1846085.30	E430055.65	Buried disc marked with iron pipe	TLO
71 Set	6016.4	6018.4	N1863435.00	E423147.40	Drill-hole with pipe	TLO
72 Set A	5290.3	5292.3	N1862232.55	E425895.71	Drill-hole with pipe	HT
73 Shiva	5254.3	5256.3	N1871940.07	E429024.87	Drill-hole with pipe	TL
74 Shoshone	7278.5	7280.5	N1835770.07	E458113.13	Bronze disc	TLO
75 S. Rim Hq. 1	6978.7	6980.7	N1837418.08	E436323.18	No permanent mark left	TL
76 S. Rim Hq. 2	6856.8	6858.8	N1837625.66	E432928.44	No permanent mark left	TL
77 S. Rim Hq. 3	6833.0	6835.0	N1839738.03	E432882.87	No permanent mark left	TL
78 S. Rim Hq. 4	7162.4	7164.4	N1840369.34	E444804.75	No permanent mark left	TL
79 S. Rim Hq. 6	7075.3	7077.3	N1839557.93	E442214.17	No permanent mark left	TL
80 S. Rim Hq. 8	6912.3	6914.3	N1840450.57	E434909.86	No permanent mark left	TL
81 Sublime (USC&GS)	7457.50	No chg.	N1891602.88	E401712.28	USC&GS bronze disc	TLO
82 Sumner	5156.1	5158.1	N1860474.73	E453179.96	Drill-hole with pipe	TLO
83 Tiyo (USGS)	7762.8	7764.8	N1884934.72	E437701.55	Drill-hole, pipe and sphere	TLO
84 Tiyo (NW)	7944.8	7946.8	N1895514.10	E433181.03	Drill-hole, pipe and sphere	TL
85 Tonto	3702.4	No chg.	N1853088.15	E438351.55	USGS bronze BM disc	TO
86 Transept	8101.8	8103.8	N1896059.49	E450350.11	Drill-hole, pipe and sphere	TL
87 Transept (Lower)	4774.3	4776.3	N1883795.10	E463452.18	Drill-hole, pipe and sphere	TL
88 Uncle Jim	8244.1	8246.1	N1896252.12	E465135.42	Drill-hole, pipe and sphere	TL
89 Valhalla	8202.6	8204.6	N1893980.55	E473083.76	Drill-hole with pipe	TL
90 Yaki	7262.235 (a)	7264.207 (a)	N1840710.69	E450855.25	Bronze disc	TLO
91 Yavapai	7082.225 (a)	7084.197 (a)	N1843324.42	E440864.64	Bronze disc on top of concrete column	TLO
92 Zoroaster	7121.7	7123.7	N1862447.60	E462151.65	Bronze disc	TLO

1, 2 See head notes.

TABLE 2. Grand Canyon Survey, Laser Observation Data

Horizontal and vertical angles measured with a Wild T-3 theodolite; slope distances with a
Laser Ranger II, a Ranger III, or a Rangemaster I, loaned to the project by Laser Systems and
Electronics Inc. of Tullahoma, Tennessee, now a division of Keuffel & Esser, Inc.

From Station (Altitude[1], ft.)	To	Slope distance (ft.)	Grid distance (ft.)
1 Angel A (8147.5)	17 Greenland	15,873.67	15,864.98
	18 Hattan	21,217.09	21,095.68
	35 Komo	10,711.73	10,705.18
	40 Manzanita	14,219.41	14,212,37
	46 Obi	16,796.04	16,786,37
	86 Transept	12,625.63	12,619.41
	88 Uncle Jim	7,612.65	7,608.32
	89 Valhalla	12,583.41	12,577.12
4 Cheops (5388.6)	92 Zoroaster	22,539.52	22,464.40
6 Confucius (7075.0)	36 Laser	8,478.20	7,912.70
	68 Ra	15,261.03	15,222.27
	81 Sublime	10,763.35	10,751.75
9 Cremation (3896.2)	61 Phantom F	13,617.18	13,611.40
	64 Phantom K	3,849.27	3,845.80
10 Crystal (3993.7)	12 Dragon	26,476.62	26,464.89
	36 Laser	13,571.53	13,567.52
	81 Sublime	18,856.52	18,528.21
	68 Ra	11,182.24	10,982.44
13 Dragon (North) (7663.1)	6 Confucius	19,573.54	19,556.08
	81 Sublime	23,812.35	23,800.86
	84 Tiyo (NW)	8,927.41	8,918.81
18 Hattan (5969.2)	4 Cheops	21,457.37	21,442.11
	37 Ledge	14,892.35	14,875.79
19 Hermit (6652.4)	10 Crystal	32,596.80	32,476.54
	81 Sublime	50,982.09	50,954.14
	83 Tiyo	49,543.95	49,510.11
20 Hopi (7044.962 L)	4 Cheops	18,922.83	18,842.34
	10 Crystal	36,877.28	36,737.22
	53 Pima	13,342.73	13,334.09
	68 Ra	28,199.07	28,171.13
	71 Set	18,320.25	18,283.75
	73 Shiva	25,628.98	25,556.45
	81 Sublime	53,234.55	53,209.83
	83 Tiyo	39,371.32	39,346.84
	44 Middle	21,803.29	21,792.58
	90 Yaki	21,844.07	21,833.38
	91 Yavapai	11,512.09	11,507.08
	67 Powell Point[2]	1,237.70	1,237.25
21 Horsethief (6348.3)	43 Mesa	26,824.89	26,772.86

From Station (Altitude¹, ft.)	*To*	*Slope distance (ft.)*	*Grid distance (ft.)*
23 Howlands (5573.4)	39 Lyell	18,424.47	18,416.51
	34 Knee	6,782.31	6,777.70
	49 Ottoman	10,980.49	10,912.37
	3 Clear	7,954.87	7,802.17
	8 Corner	22,099.99	22,083.99
	14 Gorge	8,160.60	7,967.65
	46 Obi	22,777.29	22,645.26
24 Indian Gardens (3849.56 L)	25 Ind. Gds. A	1,344.36	1,341.23
	26 Ind. Gds. B	1,097.71	1,095.14
	27 Ind. Gds. C	615.98	615.55
	28 Ind. Gds. D	840.89	839.79
	29 Ind. Gds. E	1,720.80	1,716.16
	30 Ind. Gds. F	924.22	922.34
41 Maricopa (6990.032 L)	75 S. Rim Hq. 1	5,901.11	5,898.56
	76 S. Rim Hq. 2	4,030.96	4,026.97
	77 S. Rim Hq. 3	1,988.92	1,981.68
	78 S. Rim Hq. 4	12,731.07	12,724.41
	91 Yavapai	8,905.12	8,900.79
	79 S. Rim Hq. 6	10,281.16	10,276.40
	50 Parapet	3,313.33	3,365.48
	80 Rim Hq. 8	2,993.75	2,991.40
	16 Grandeur	7,239.28	7,236.08
42 Maricopa A (6996.902 L)	24 Indian Gardens	8,776.94	8,188.93
43 Mesa (4838.7)	38 Lookout	16,385.31	16,376.10
44 Middle (7261.882 L)	20 Hopi	21,803.29	21,792.58
	70 Rowe	21,452.06	21,441.80
	81 Sublime	70,751.20	70,719.75
	83 Tiyo	46,154.87	46,131.28
50 Parapet (6925.842 L)	4 Cheops	22,452.50	22,390.95
	42 Maricopa A	3,367.90	3,365.48
	61 Phantom F	22,074.61	21,888.37
56 Phantom A (3726.9)	57 Phantom B	4,148.42	4,164.56
	58 Phantom C	6,422.85	6,418.87
	60 Phantom E	3,982.81	3,965.01
58 Phantom C (3887.7)	54 Phantom Ranch	4,788.43	4,596.70
59 Phantom D (4119.2)	65 Plateau Point	5,143.03	5,130.32
	60 Phantom E	4,825.36	4,824.84
	56 Phantom A	6,067.79	6,052.87
	58 Phantom C	3,979.18	3,971.34
	57 Phantom B	7,149.30	7,142.94
	63 Phantom J	4,167.96	4,166.29
	62 Phantom H	4,232.02	4,239.76
	61 Phantom F	4,292.38	4,291.14
64 Phantom K (3762.1)	57 Phantom B	4,516.47	4,512.58
	61 Phantom F	12,100.45	12,091.65
	56 Phantom A	3,421.34	3,418.87

TABLE 2. Grand Canyon Survey Stations, Location Data—Continued

From Station (Altitude[1], ft.)	To	Slope distance (ft.)	Grid distance (ft.)
53 Pima (6767.0)	10 Crystal	30,358.83	30,220.50
	68 Ra	25,229.73	25,210.17
	81 Sublime	48,472.09	48,446.52
	83 Tiyo	44,851.37	44,820.70
	43 Mesa	17,128.40	17,013.14
	20 Hopi	13,342.73	13,334.09
65 Plateau Point (3781.66 L)	82 Sumner	13,983.61	13,911.41
	50 Parapet	14,460.23	14,109.61
	90 Yaki	16,115.57	15,730.01
	58 Phantom C	4,074.90	4,072.49
	56 Phantom A	10,052.91	10,049.65
	64 Phantom K	12,707.87	12,703.09
	61 Phantom F	8,143.51	8,134.12
70 Rowe (7068.829 L)	44 Middle	21,452.06	21,441.80
	91 Yavapai	11,160.76	11,156.02
71 Set (6018.4)	4 Cheops	16,589.49	16,571.05
	68 Ra	10,557.08	10,553.02
74 Shoshone (7280.5)	4 Cheops	32,466.89	32,398.59
	82 Sumner	25,291.66	25,192.39
	8 Corner	14,172.52	13,976.06
	39 Lyell	9,305.71	9,098.92
	23 Howlands	23,499.73	23,427.93
81 Sublime (7457.50)	10 Crystal	18,856.52	18,528.21
	68 Ra	25,101.03	25,053.06
82 Sumner (5158.1)	39 Lyell	27,746.50	27,736.27
	23 Howlands	20,549.81	20,538.33
	61 Phantom F	11,370.52	11,319.63
87 Transept (Lower) (4776.3)	18 Hattan	15,551.60	15,500.20
90 Yaki (7264.207 L)	1 Angel A	50,119.67	50,088.72
	20 Hopi	21,844.07	21,833.38
	70 Rowe	21,493.06	21,482.78
	82 Sumner	20,018.98	19,900.29
	92 Zoroaster	24,508.24	24,496.97
	56 Phantom A	17,915.33	17,555.76
	23 Howlands	25,691.01	25,624.79
	61 Phantom F	22,707.76	22,481.53
91 Yavapai (7084.197 L)	20 Hopi	11,512.09	11,507.08
	54 Phantom Ranch	16,635.61	16,000.17
	69 Ribbon	39,016.76	38,857.59
	70 Rowe	11,160.76	11,156.02
	44 Middle	10,292.05	10,285.93
92 Zoroaster (7123.7)	46 Obi	17,321.00	17,294.21

[1] L=leveled elevation.
[2] USGS-BM.

TABLE 3. Preliminary Trail Distances
(Subject to minor adjustments, correct probably within less than 100 ft.)

Trail	To	Distance (miles)
Bright Angel Trail:	First rest house	1.58
	Second rest house	3.01
	Indian Gardens	4.61
	Pipe Creek crossing (below switchbacks)	6.77
	River Trail fork (just below Rest House)	7.74
	River's edge	7.80
River Trail (added to Bright Angel; starts at River Trail fork):		
	S. end of pipeline bridge	(1.18 from fork) 8.92
	Junction with Kaibab Trail	(1.46 from fork) 9.20
	Phantom Ranch dining room	(1.94 from fork) 9.68
South Kaibab Trail:	Cedar Ridge	1.45
	Top of switchbacks	2.93
	Tonto Trail junction	4.42
	The Tip-Off	4.59
	S. end of bridge	6.34
	Inner Canyon junction	6.73
	Phantom Ranch dining room	7.23
North Kaibab Trail:	Tunnel	1.73
	Bridge	2.68
	Top of cliff zig-zags	3.60
	Campground fork	4.72
	Bridge	5.43
	Cottonwood (main building)	6.84
	Ribbon Falls (S. fork)	8.34
	Phantom Creek	12.59
	Phantom Ranch dining room	13.69
	Inner Canyon junction	14.18
Hermit Trail:	Hermit Basin (Waldron Trail junction)	1.30
	Crest of Hermit Gorge (sign)	1.70
	Lookout Point	4.01
	Top of Cathedral stairs	5.40
	Tonto Trail junction	6.63
	Hermit Creek (first crossing)	7.65
	Colorado River	8.96
Tonto Trail:	Bright Angel to South Kaibab (Checked twice H. Sharpe 21821/21744)	4.13
	Bright Angel to Hermit-Tonto Junction (Henry Sharpe—Unchecked)	11.84

FIG. 3.   Attaching a survey target at one of the survey stations on the South Rim. The sphere is a National Geographic plastic globe core.

between the Museum and the Society. This first proposal envisaged a map that would cover 84 square miles, 10.5 miles east-west and 8 miles north-south, stretching from the South Rim to a point approximately 3.5 miles north of the Colorado River. To our delight, this proposal was accepted by the Society, and on December 10, 1971, the remapping of what we called the "Heart of the Grand Canyon" became a formal reality.

Our third trip (February 19 to March 1, 1972) continued our station-marking and angular measurements in the southern half of our area and started the detailed mapping of the Bright Angel, Hermit, and Waldron trails. In this we were assisted by our longtime friend Jack Pechman of Denver. No laser work was done on this trip.

As we became more familiar with the area, it also became more and more apparent that, although much more fieldwork would be involved, it would make no sense to have our northern limit so far short of the North Rim. So we reapproached the National Geographic about the advisability of extending our work one mile farther northward, to encompass Ribbon Falls, and Shiva and Buddha Temples. This enlargement of the project, approved by the Society on June 8, 1972, increased the size of the area to be mapped by 10.5 square miles to a total of 94.5 square miles, and we arranged to have an additional strip of east-west aerial photos made to cover this new area.

While this fieldwork was progressing, Lockwood Mapping was at work contouring the parts of our map on which the control had been completed. This work, at a scale of 1:4800, was done between March and July 1972, and 50-ft. contours were scribed directly from a Wild A-7 plotter onto plastic "scribecoat" sheets, thus avoiding the loss of detail and quality inevitable when contours are first marked in pencil and then later scribed onto the final manuscript by another draftsman.

Our fourth trip (May 29 to June 15) involved a great deal of activity with both laser and theodolite. In addition to Mason, Cutshaw rejoined us with a very powerful new instrument, the Rangemaster, with which, for the first time, we were able to make the long sights between Yavapai and Bright Angel points (10 miles) and from Yaki Point to Point Sublime (13.5 miles). Our work afoot on the trails intensified, and was done whenever we had windy days which made helicopter work impractical. In 1972, working with nearby Landis Aerial Surveys of Phoenix, we completed a complex series of low-altitude (8500 ft.) vertical stereo-photo-strips along the trails, as it was impossible to secure the desired detail in them from 16,000-ft. photography.

Although a considerable amount of control still remained to be added (as well as a massive amount of trailwork) the early summer trip in 1972 essentially broke the back of the overall project. We were now thoroughly familiar with the area and how to work in it. We had a top-notch group of volunteers, and the helicopter pilots, led by Daniel Nicholson, had now become expert at the demanding sort of pinnacle-landing work that was essential to our project.

Trip 5 (August 30 to September 17, 1972) took a tremendous slice out of our agenda. Krahmer carried out a line of levels for us along a 3-mile section of wood road northward from Tiyo Point, thus giving us strong vertical control across the middle of the wooded North Rim plateau. This level-line also had a strong start, as our figures and those of the USGS for the altitude of Tiyo Point agreed within a foot. This simply reconfirmed what repeatedly had happened to date: wherever we zeroed in on a precise spot which was also in the USGS survey, our figures and theirs virtually coincided; the major difference between our maps lay in the enormous detail that our low-altitude photography and large-scale contouring yielded, and this was the reason for our work. In addition, because of this large scale, we were forced to add a great deal more control spread throughout the area. On this trip we completed all of our observations in the new northern extension and also made a precise large-scale survey of the tree-covered area around Indian Gardens. Feldman and Mason helped us throughout this period, and Richard Hinderlie and Margo Sweet assisted by making a large number of distance measurements along the trails. One of the most delightful high points of the whole project was the discovery, by Ranger Gary Howe's two young sons Rusty (age 11) and Ronnie (age 9), of an ancient bench mark on the Bright Angel that had been "lost" for many years. We told them more or less where they had to search, offered a $10 reward for finding it, and their sharp young eyes, coupled with a lot of patient scrambling among rocks and bushes, won them the prize!

As fall 1972 deepened, great progress had been made, and by October 30 we were able to send the first nine sheets of our manuscript to the National Geographic, covering 94.35 square miles, complete topographically, but still missing a substantial amount of trail detail. This photogrammetric work was done by Lockwood Mapping, Inc., of Rochester, New York, under the direction of Ray Byrne and Keith Adams.

When we forwarded these sheets to the National Geographic, we recommended one further major addition to the map: to extend it northward another 3.88 miles, to take in the whole southern edge of the forested North Rim plateau as well as the Grand Canyon Lodge and the NPS North Rim Ranger Station. While this proposal was under consideration, a pleasant bolt of lightning struck. During consideration of our proposed addition by the Committee for Research and Exploration, Conrad Wirth, eminent past director of the National Park Service and member of the National Geographic's Board of Trustees, recommended that we also add a strip all along the eastern edge of the map in order to include most of Bright Angel Creek and all of the course of the North Kaibab and Clear Creek Trails. Although this meant extending our work for at least another year, we were delighted at this proposal, approved on December 20, 1972, which added 70.24 square miles to our map, bringing the total to 164.602 square miles.

With the completion of the first nine of the large-scale sheets involved in the original survey plan, it was exciting to see the end-result of all of our

---

FIG. 4.   Laying out cloth "panel" at survey station Lyell. Clearly visible in the photographs taken from a flight altitude of 16,000 feet, these were used for precise positioning of stations. Below: A signal panel seen from the air at low altitude.

labors in the field beginning to take shape. We now prepared a battle-plan for completing the entire twice-expanded project: four more sheets were needed to complete the first expansion to the North Rim. Then four more were required to cover the eastern edge. Trip 5 had yielded the control still needed to contour the entire North Rim area, and Lockwood proceeded with work on these four sheets in spring and summer 1973.

In the midst of this activity, the National Park Service decided that a new very-large-scale map of the South Rim headquarters area was needed. Low-altitude pictures of this had already been flown by Hurd, so we provided the needed laser-control and it, too, was contoured by Lockwood Mapping during the period April through November 1973 at U. S. Government expense. This proved extremely valuable from our standpoint, as it yielded a detailed, up-to-date map of an intricate part of our sheet and we were glad to contribute our control-work for it in order to speed its completion.

In fact 1973 was the busiest year of the whole project. Three more trips were made to the Canyon. Trip 6 (March 22 to April 2) closely followed a helicopter flight by Hinderlie and Nicholson on February 24 to drill and target six of the new stations required to control the central part of the eastern addition. Heavy snows, of course, prevented effective work on either rim at that time of year. Mrs. Washburn and I, with Wendell Mason, joined Hinderlie for two intensive weeks of late winter helicopter-and-laser work that nailed down our needs in the dramatic region of the Ottoman Amphitheatre, Howlands Butte, and Zoroaster Canyon. Then we returned in early summer 1973 for Trip 7 (June 13 to July 4) to complete both the northern and southern ends of the eastern edge, after the snows had melted and foot-travel again became easy on the rims.

During this period of intense activity in the field, additional volunteers were very important to us, particularly on the North Rim; Feldman joined us to help with many key laser-sights, and Frederick Eidsness and Lindsey Happel worked for scores of hours with Hinderlie and us on this most complex and difficult part of the whole map, because steep slopes and dense forest made it impossible to use helicopters, and most of our final stations had to be marked, drilled, and occupied afoot. We also reconnoitered the entire 14-mile length of the North Kaibab Trail and started the seemingly endless task of marking accurately on our low-altitude aerial photographs the parts of the trail that

---

FIG. 5.   Cartographers at Lockwood Mapping scribing the original Grand Canyon map manuscript from the aerial photographs. Below: Rudi Dauwalder scribing the cliffs for the Grand Canyon manuscript at the Swiss Federal Topographic Service in Wabern, a suburb of Berne.

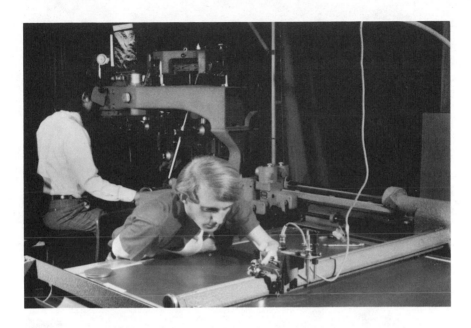

FIG. 6. The Bright Angel Trail descends steeply through the vertical cliffs of the Coconino Sandstone at the location of the Bright Angel fault. This photograph illustrates the intricacy of the Canyon's trails and cliffs. Note that the top of the Coconino cliff to the right (west) of the fault is some 189 feet higher than the top of the same feature to the left (east) of the fault.

were concealed by trees or deep shadows. Daniel Nicholson, our close friend and leader of most of our helicopter flying up to this point, had left to teach helicopter pilots in Iran early in summer 1973 and shortly after this Jerry McMullin, an equally competent pilot from Madison Aviation, took over the bulk of flying for us.

Trip 8 was the shortest of all, only three days (October 21-23, 1973). I had a lecture in Seattle and returned to Boston via the Canyon, meeting Mrs. Washburn there for an intensive attack on the complex details of the upper 5 miles of the North Kaibab trail before winter snows engulfed them. David Ochsner, NPS ranger and gifted photographer, accompanied us on this trip. Of all of our many forays to the Canyon, this was the most beautiful—with the brilliant blue skies of fall, chilly nights, thrilling stars, and the aspens in all their autumn splendor.

As fall 1973 progressed, Lockwood's photogrammetrists were busily plotting the contours of our last sheets. On September 24 sheet 13, covering Bright Angel Point and the North Rim headquarters area, was completed and work then progressed southward along the eastern edge of the map, till sheet 17 was finished on January 8, 1974. As these sheets arrived in Boston, one by one, they had to be meticulously checked for accuracy of detail. Long sections of the trails were still incomplete, although the drainage, topography, and buildings were essentially finished by early 1974.

Trip 9 (February 22 to March 1, 1974) dealt almost entirely with the trails, and we did scores of miles of walking along the Bright Angel, Tonto, River, North Angel, and Clear Creek trails (Table 3 shows some of the results of this undertaking). Long segments of these trails were invisible on our vertical pictures, either because they were obscured by shadows or because they were so infrequently traveled that there were not the slightest traces of them on even the low-altitude pictures. On two past trips we had found that late February and early March is a perfect time for work in the depths of the Canyon, and this one simply reinforced that conviction. Also, we had new and congenial hiking companions in Charles Hovey and his son from Boston, and Ron and Ann Merritt of Russell, Massachusetts.

On July 26, 1974, we returned to the South Rim en route to Boston from Alaska and stayed through July 29 for Trip 10. These were four extremely intensive days of work: out to Widforss Point and back to detail this 5-mile trail afoot and under a broiling sun; over to Uncle Jim Point and back to finalize the invisible parts of this little-traveled North Rim path; down slowly and meticulously the upper five miles of the North Kaibab Trail to check its final manuscript; then, on July 29, down the Bright Angel trail to check the intricate contortions of its upper $4\frac{1}{2}$ miles as far as Indian Gardens. It was 2 miles down the trail on this beautiful final morning that we had the most exciting moment of our whole project. As we rounded a sharp curve, we came upon two young men walking up the trail hand-in-hand. One asked me what we were doing and how our measuring wheel worked. His companion expressed avid interest and said that a good map would have made their trip more interesting. Then the first turned to him and said, "Joe, how'd you like to *feel* it?" Not until then did we realize that his companion, Joe, was totally blind! I led his deft fingers to the wheel, its spokes, the Veeder-counter, and the tiny "tripper" which logs off each foot of distance. We chatted for a few minutes about accurate maps and how helpful they are to hikers. Then we said goodbye and they headed briskly off up the trail beneath the searing summer sun. As we resumed our descent, our hearts welled with respect for that brave young fellow and his generous guide, on an adventure that will never be forgotten, either by them or by us.

As 1975 arrived, our work was drawing to a close. We had already made 10 trips to the Canyon and spent 122 days in the field. We made our last winter trip (no. 11) from February 22 to March 1 and focused it on introducing Paul Witzler to the Canyon. He had flown there from Berne, Switzerland, where he worked at the Landestopographie, Switzerland's Federal Topographic Service, as the world's top expert on shaded relief, the subtle shadows that give a three-dimensional feel to a flat map. He spent two weeks at the Canyon as our guest, studying its shapes and colors, and made important recommendations to us later about the colors needed to depict the Canyon's savage relief most effectively on our new map. On one day we walked the entire 9-mile length of the Clear Creek Trail, checking every detail of it in our final manuscript. On another, we completed the lower half of the Bright Angel, 5 hours to do $3\frac{1}{2}$ miles. Then down the lower two-thirds of the steep Hermit Trail, completing it too, all the way to the Colorado River. When we left, Witzler had developed a marvelous understanding of the terrain, both from the air and on the ground, and the end of our work was in sight.

Our final trip (no. 12, from June 28 to July 6) involved two weeks of picking up loose ends, very low altitude aerial photography of a number of intricate spots on the trails, and final coordination and farewells to all the volunteers from the Park Service (see p. 33, Acknowledgments) who had helped us so much during the last four eventful years. How much of our own time had been occupied by this undertaking is suggested by the tabulation (opposite) of our trips to the Canyon and the number of helicopter flights we made.

Although the public has always had the illusion that one moves directly from work in the field to the printing press in map production, a long, complex, frustrating interval always lies between these two extremes. The Grand

Canyon map was no exception to this rule. Up to this point, the Museum and the Society had shared the expense equally. From here on, this map was entirely a National Geographic project.

Four steps remained: The final coalescing of all of Lockwood's 17 sheets of contouring into a single sheet at 1:24,000 (one-fifth the original scale); completion of the large-scale maps of the trails and their reduction and integration into the final manuscript; the lengthy work of cliff-drawing; and, finally, the equally time-consuming and demanding task of drawing the shaded relief.

During the final phases of our fieldwork, Raytheon-Autometrics of Sudbury, Massachusetts, had been preparing strip-maps of the trails at 1:2400, twice the scale of the 17 manuscript sheets. These strips were made of the Bright Angel, the South Kaibab, the Hermit, the North Kaibab, and the lengthy Tonto Trail. The detailed work on these trail-sheets consumed a large part of our final weeks in the field. An immense amount of work had to be done on foot, checking details and, as mentioned before, filling in scores of gaps caused by shadows and trees and in areas where the terrain was so bare and rocky that the paths were invisible even in enlargements of the low-altitude photographs. It was not until April 23, 1976, that I had completed the drafting of the last of these trail-sheets on my own drafting table in Belmont. This was slow, meticulous, fascinating work that I enjoyed immensely. With this accurate detail it would be possible for a hiker to find his exact posi-

Year	Trip No.	Time at the Canyon	Workdays	Helicopter landings
1971	1	February 18–27	10	27
1971	2	June 16–July 11	16	58
1972	3	February 19–March 1	12	48
1972	4	May 29–June 15	18	76
1972	5	August 31–September 17	18	124
1973	-	February 24 (R. Hinderlie)	1	7
1973	6	March 24–31	8	101
1973	-	May 4 (Krahmer)	2	4
1973	-	May 21 (Krahmer)	2	4
1973	-	May 27 (Nicholson)	1	4
1973	7	June 13–July 4	21	101
1973	8	October 21–23	3	11
1974	9	February 21–March 4	12	114
1974	10	July 26–29	4	7
1975	11	February 22–March 1	8	13
1975	12	June 28–July 6	8	13
		TOTALS	144	712

tion on these wonderful trails, and this was one of the main objectives of our whole project. Later on it is our plan to publish very large scale strip-maps of at least two of the most important of the trails, but that will be another story.

While this last fieldwork was going on, the final contours and drainage were being scribed at the National Geographic, by Norbert and Walter Vasques, and Thomas Gray was working on the intricate problems of nomenclature and compilation of all this data. The cliff-drawing was executed for us by Rudi Dauwalder and Alois Flury at the Swiss federal office of topography (Landestopographie) in Berne during the period from July 23, 1976, to February 1, 1977. A map of the Grand Canyon without considerable use of cliff-hachures would involve a huge amount of meaningless concentrations of brown ink where dozens of parallel contours were jammed together on the steep slopes and, even worse, in areas where hundreds of feet of utterly vertical cliffs were encountered. Dauwalder and his associates were the top people in the world in this exacting frontier between art and science and they did the work superbly, often investing more than a day of intense labor to produce a few square centimeters of cliffs. The illustration clearly shows how a typical cliff-drawing problem was handled on the slopes of Isis Temple. The only drawback of this technique from the standpoint of pure science is that in areas where cliffs are perpendicular, or even overhang, there is no room to do the hachuring and some artistic license must be exercised, i.e., a bit of space must be stolen for this purpose from the slope immediately above and below the cliff.

This work was all done on a scale of 1:24,000, a huge reduction in which the 17 original sheets were coalesced into a single manuscript 33 x 34 in. If our scale had been larger, the sheet would have been hopelessly unwieldly for use in the field, or we would have had to resort to two sheets. Had it been smaller, we would have sacrificed most of the fine detail that was, after all, the basic objective of the whole project.

Dauwalder's work was done on four small sheets that were fitted together and sent to Washington in February 1977. There expert craftsmen at the National Geographic Society's Department of Cartography coordinated them with the contour manuscript, carefully removing the thousands of crammed contours whenever they were to be replaced by cliff drawing (see figs. 5 and 7).

Then another year of demanding artwork followed, as National Geographic artist Tibor Toth, trained a dozen years ago by Swiss expert Paul Ulmer, carried out the relief-shading. Unlike the cliff-drawing, which is cut into a manuscript emulsion by a sharp scribing tool, shaded relief is produced by employing both the airbrush and a variety of pencils of differing degrees of hardness. The basic burden of managing the many stages of this lengthy and

F<small>IG</small>. 7. Elements that were combined to produce the Isis Temple section of the Grand Canyon Map. Above, contours, with areas eliminated where cliff-drawing is to be added. Over, left top, cliff-drawing; left, bottom, contours and cliffs combined; right, top, shaded relief; right, bottom, all combined.

intricate process fell on the able shoulders of William Peele, the National Geographic's chief cartographer, who tragically had a severe heart attack on August 10, 1977, right at the peak of the activity. His assistant, Richard Rogers, carried the burden superbly in an anguishing interregnum before Richard Darley became the new chief cartographer on September 11, 1978.

In late fall 1977, the editors decided that the map would be published as an insert in the July 1978 National Geographic Magazine, and the next eight months saw a veritable tempest of cartographic activity: final coordination of the contours, drainage, cliffs, shadows, and trails; addition of titles and nomenclature after the most careful checking with local experts of the National

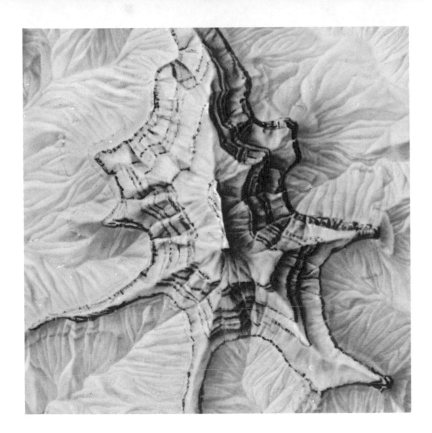

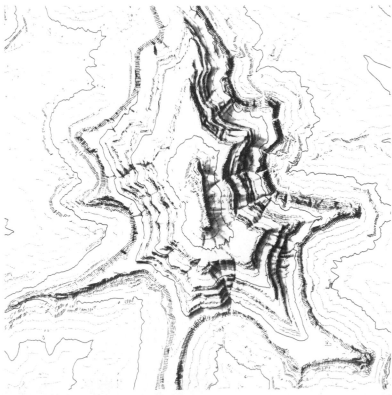

Park Service and Professor Harvey Butchart, the clearly acknowledged authority on place-names, the location of reliable springs, and other essential details.

Finally the new map, *The Heart of the Grand Canyon,* went to press on May 4, 1978. It was printed in six colors by R. R. Donnelley & Sons Co., 10,400,000 copies on 1,084,000 pounds of paper, using 35,272 pounds of printer's ink. This edition, which appeared in the National Geographic Magazine for July 1978, as planned, had to be considerably narrower than the full area that we had mapped, as the full size (east and west) would not fit onto the "web presses" needed to print an edition of this size. In June 1978 a separate edition of 34,500 sheets was printed on waterproof paper in the full 33 x 34 in. size by Lebanon Valley Offset Co., and was placed on sale at the National Geographic Society, the Grand Canyon, and the Museum of Science.

This project accomplished substantially more than simply the production of a new 1:24,000 map of the central part of the Grand Canyon. In the long run, the 17 manuscript sheets that were reduced and coalesced to make this medium-scale composite map of the area may have more value than the 1:24,000 sheet, for the manuscript sheets contain a vast wealth of fine detail (even individual rocks, trees, bushes, and tiny undulations of the footpaths) that could not possibly be reduced to a significantly smaller scale than 1:4800.

Such detail could easily have been omitted from the master manuscripts at a considerable saving in cost. However, their production on this scale and with this fine detail was a basic part of this project, which, in addition to yielding the 1:24,000 sheet for hikers, campers, and tourists, envisaged substantial professional value to geologists, botanists, archeologists, and other scientists for precise plotting of their fieldwork in years to come.

These sheets were meticulously studied and revised during 1979. The scribed manuscripts, completed on November 12, 1979, are now stored at the Cartography Department of the National Geographic Society in Washington. One set of Cronaflex positive prints is there and a second is kept at the Museum of Science in Boston. Copies of these sheets may be purchased at cost from the Museum by those wishing to pursue serious scientific studies in the field. Two similar manuscript sheets covering the complex and extremely precipitous Inner Canyon area on a scale of 1:2400 were prepared during 1975-76 by

FIG. 8.   Tibor Toth's hand and airbrush work on the shaded relief, final stage in the preparation of the Grand Canyon manuscript.

Swissair Photo & Vermessungen, in Zurich, and are also available at the Museum of Science.

Finally, pencil manuscripts by Raytheon/Autometrics of the five famous trails (Bright Angel, Hermit, North and South Kaibab, and Rim) on a scale of 1:2400 are filed and available for reference at the Museum of Science. These large-scale manuscripts and those of the Inner Canyon were used in conjunction with the 1:4800 sheets to assume maximum possible accuracy of the trails, and they are certain to prove very useful to those doing any sort of fieldwork along the trails that requires a precise knowledge of position.

In conclusion, I wish to express the utmost gratitude to the National Geographic Society and to my Museum, without whose full and generous support we could never have attempted this project, as well as to the scores of volunteers, listed in the Acknowledgments, whose enthusiastic and selfless cooperation made the fieldwork successful. I doubt whether a surveying project of this scope and complexity ever before has been attempted by an all-volunteer group.

And lastly, I cannot close without expressing my admiration for the extraordinary work of the topographers who preceded us at the Canyon over a period of almost exactly 100 years. What they produced, working afoot and on horseback with plane tables and transits instead of theodolites, lasers, and helicopters was, of course, one of the greatest accomplishments in all topographic history. It was a thrill and a privilege to travel in their footsteps in this epicenter of our world's most awe-inspiring scenery.

POSTSCRIPT

In June 1981, three years after *The Heart of the Grand Canyon* appeared as a map supplement in the July 1978 issue of the *National Geographic* magazine, it was finally verified that the published and long accepted elevation (6876.164 ft.) of National Geodetic Survey Bench Mark S-61 was in error by 1.972 feet.

The error apparently was caused, at an undetermined date between 1934 and 1971, by a wall-building party that had removed the bench mark disc from its original position, had built a low rock wall over the spot, and had re-installed the disc on the top of the new wall at a new and higher elevation (6878.136 ft.).

This erroneous and illegal resetting of the bench mark was first discovered by a National Park Service survey party working on the area in 1979, a year after publication of the map, and was subsequently reported to the National Geodetic Survey. Not until spring 1981 was this finding formally confirmed by a National Geodetic Survey field party, which officially re-leveled Bench Mark S-61 at 6878.136 feet.

As a result of this 1981 announcement, which came long after the map had been printed and at a moment when this report was in the final stages of publication, many, but not all, of the elevations given on the map must be increased by 1.972 feet. Publication of this report was delayed so that appropriate changes could be made in the text where elevations are cited (as on page 3) and in Table 2 (p. 12). Also, Table 1 (p. 8), which lists the survey stations, now shows their correct elevations in a column next to that giving the elevations that appear on the map.

Appropriate changes of these elevations on the map itself, which is still available at the Grand Canyon, at the National Geographic Society, and at the Museum of Science in Boston, will have to await publication of a later edition.

ACKNOWLEDGMENTS

I take this opportunity to express my special personal thanks to those who gave extraordinary support, advice, and assistance to this project through the National Geographic Society: Dr. Melville B. Grosvenor, Dr. Melvin M. Payne, Robert E. Doyle, Dr. Leonard Carmichael, William T. Peele, and Richard K. Rogers.

The following organizations, through their special facilities and their talented and cooperative staff members, contributed significantly to the success of this project: Museum of Science, Boston, Massachusetts; National Geographic Society; Harry R. Feldman, Inc.; Laser Systems and Electronics, Inc.; Lockwood Mapping, Inc.; Raytheon-Autometrics, Inc.; Swissair Photo & Vermessungen; Landis Aerial Surveys, Inc.; Mark Hurd Aerial Surveys, Inc,; Federal Topographical Survey of Switzerland; Museum of Northern Arizona; U. S. Coast & Geodetic Survey; U. S. Geological Survey; U. S. National Park Service; Grand Canyon Helicopters, Inc.; Arizona Helicopters, Inc.; and Madison Aviation, Inc.

Gratitude is likewise expressed to the individuals listed below, who contributed in so many ways to the success of this project. (Principal collaborators in italics; * indicates volunteers; †, helicopter pilots.)

Keith Adams	*William J. Breed
*Bruce and Mary Aikens	*John O. Brew
Werner Altherr	*Jean Buitekan*
†Michael Antonelli	†Gale Burak
John Baber	*Harvey Butchart
†Joseph Baginski	*Raymond Byrne*
*Robert Beaucamp	*Steven Carothers
*Edgar W. Blair	Ronald Chiccano
†Douglas Blakeley	*Ed Clancy

†Marvin Connaway
*Earl Cram
*Buddy Q. Cutshaw
Mrs. Diana Dahart
*Edward B. Danson
Rudi Dauwalder
†James Edgins
*Frederick A. Eidsness, Jr.
*Harry R. Feldman
Alois Flury
*Benjamin T. Foster
*Lee Francis
*Vincent Gleason
John Glynn
Thomas Gray
†Steven Grooms
Jessica Gugino
Burnell Hamlin
*William Hanson
*Lindsey Happel
*Dr. and Mrs. James Haycox
*Louise Hinchliffe
*Richard R. Hinderlie
*Kenneth Hockelberg
*Neil Hoener
*Mr. and Mrs. Gary Howe
*Ronnie Howe
*Rusty Howe
Ernst Huber
*Roy Johnson
William Kemper
*James W. Keogh
*Emery Kolb
Edward A. Krahmer
Jerry Landis
*Wesley Leishman
†Benjamin Locke
Robert Lovegren
†Robert Lusigman
†Bradley Martin
†Michael Mason
*Wendell Mason
*William Matteson

†Frederick Maurer
*Richard C. McLaren
†Jerry L. McMullin
*Wayne McQueen
*Ronald and Ann Merritt
Peter Nichols
†Daniel Nicholson
*Mr. and Mrs. David Ochsner
†Daniel O'Connell
Charles O'Rear
*Jack R. Pechman
William Peele
*William Rall
Jamie Ramirez
*John Ray
*Richard S. Rayner
Richard Rogers
Jan Rolff
*Ray Rosales
Gary Settle
*Henry Sharpe III
*William and Rosella Shelton
*Philip and Katherine Shoemaker
†Lee Siddons
†Donald Sides
Harsh Singh
Linda Smith
*Roy Starkey
Merle Stitt
*Stan Stockton
*Margo Sweet
Daniel Tortorell
Tibor Toth
†Joseph Ugliano
Norbert Vasques
Walter Vasques
*Victor Vieira
*Victor Watahomigie
*Jack Watson
*Millard W. Wilcox
John N. Wilford
Paul Witzler
*Robert Yearout

BRADFORD WASHBURN

Systems of Kinship and Marriage in South Asia:
A Comparative Analysis

Principal Investigator: Anthony T. Carter, Department of Anthropology, The University of Rochester, Rochester, New York.

Grant No. 1212:   To study hierarchy and amity in South Asian kinship and marriage.

The purpose of this research was to identify some of the elements of a generic paradigm that will account for the diversity found in South Asian systems of kinship and marriage and that will assist in delineating the connections between these systems and segmentary caste systems.

Background

The kinship and marriage systems of India and Sri Lanka differ one from another in many important respects. Rules of unilineal descent, for example, are part of the kinship systems of some South Asian communities, but are absent from others. Where unilineal descent does occur, it is sometimes patrilineal and sometimes matrilineal. Hypergamous marriage systems, not infrequently involving breaches of caste endogamy, are found among many communities in North India as well as among the Nayars in some areas of Kerala. Elsewhere marriage is isogamous. Cross-cousin marriage occurs commonly in South India and Sri Lanka but is prohibited in the north. In the kinship terminologies used in most of South India and Sri Lanka cross-cousins are distinguished from parallel cousins and classed with siblings-in-law, while in the terminologies used in the north all cousins are classed with siblings.

Although there is considerable diversity among rules of descent and marriage and systems of kin classification in South Asia, especially as regards the contrast between North and South India, other features of Indian and Sinhalese social structure remain constant. In particular, the structure of the segmentary caste systems of the region is remarkably homogeneous. Throughout the region the principle of hierarchy, in which pure is opposed to impure (Dumont, 1970), orders the external relations of castes conceived of as separate, endogamous kindreds. Certain aspects of the internal structure of castes also are ordered by the principle of hierarchy, expressed in this context in the sphere of marriage and affinity.

35

In the light of the functionalist hypothesis that the parts of a social system are interdependent, the seeming discontinuity between the relatively homogeneous caste systems and the heterogeneous kinship systems of South Asia raises a number of fundamental issues. Is there, in fact, a common generic paradigm underlying the seemingly diverse kinship systems of India and Sri Lanka? If there is a common paradigm, of what elements is it composed and how are they connected? Finally, in what manner and to what extent are the caste and kinship systems of the region connected?

These questions frequently are answered in the negative with the assertion that there is no connection between caste and kinship. Leach, for example, has argued (1960) that kinship is internal to caste while political, economic, and ritual relations are external. He also argues that "the kinship systems of caste-ordered societies vary, but all types are readily duplicated in other societies historically unconnected with the Indian world" (1960, p.7). The so-called "Dravidian" kinship systems of South India and Sri Lanka can be regarded, then, as unrelated to the "Indo-European" systems of North India and instead can be examined in the context of other "two-section" systems or "elementary marriage systems" in Melanesia and elsewhere (see Scheffler, 1971 and 1972).

Work along these lines has produced valuable contributions to our understanding of kinship terminology per se, but recent research suggests that such global comparisons are subject to limitations resulting from important connections between caste and kinship, and that other useful results can be obtained by controlled comparison and paradigmatic analysis within the Indian region. Thus Dumont (1957) has shown that the principle of hierarchy operates within, as well as between, castes, and that as an isolate in isogamous and hypergamous marriage it is an important element of Indian kinship systems in both the north and the south. Conversely, Yalman (1960) and Fox (1971, p.23) suggest that principles derived from South Asian kinship are an important part of the caste systems of the region.

Methods of Analysis

The principal method of analysis in this study was controlled comparison within the South Asian setting. The research began with a careful analysis of ethnographic material obtained from non-Brahmin castes in and around Girvi, a large agricultural village in Phaltan Taluka, Satara District, Maharashtra State, by the principal investigator during field studies in 1965-67 (see Carter, 1974a). Results derived from this analysis were tested in a two-stage comparison, first with other isogamous systems in South India and then with hypergamous systems in North India and in Kerala.

In addition, extensive use was made of a model for the formal semantic analysis of systems of kintype classification developed, in its most elaborate form, by Scheffler and Lounsbury (1971).

Results

The results of the analysis of the Maharashtrian materials may be summed up as follows. Externally, the Maharashtrian caste is conceived of as consisting of all those persons related to one by ties of filiation pushed to their extreme limit. All one's caste mates are thus regarded as equals vis-a-vis other castes by virtue of the principle of kinship amity. Internally, however, the kindred of recognition divides into two categories, *bhauki* and *soyre*. The *bhauki* segment of the kindred consists of all those who are equal in status because they are blood relatives in the marked or strong sense. Since ritual status is transmitted from generation to generation unilineally according to a rule of cumulative patrifiliation, primary emphasis is given to agnates, but matrilateral parallel relatives and the *soyre* of one's *soyre* also are included. Ritual status is maintained and protected from loss by entering into proper, i.e., isogamous, affinal relations with persons in the *soyre* segment of the kindred—relations involving a variety of ritual services and prestations as well as marriage. Although there is a slight stress on wife-givers, both wife-givers and wife-takers are included among one's *soyre*. Both are invited to the ceremonies which end death pollution, for example, but the turban which marks the end of mourning is normally presented to the chief mourner by one of his wife-givers.

More particularly, it was demonstrated that systems of kintype classification are distinct from categories of kinship relations, and that non-Brahmin systems of kintype classification in Maharashtra do not involve (*pace* Scheffler, 1971 and 1972) any two-section MBD-FZS-spouse equation rule which reduces "affinal" kintypes to "consanguineal" foci, but instead are based upon a two-class equivalence rule which divides the kintypes of ego's own generation and of the adjacent generations into two intermarrying classes.

Controlled comparison confirmed the analysis of the Maharashtrian materials and suggested that the apparently diverse kinship systems of India and Sri Lanka are based upon a single, rather simple, generic paradigm. The principal features of these systems, i.e., the external boundary and the internal organization of the status-bearing caste or kindred, and the expression of these features in kinship terminology, beliefs concerning kinship and marriage, and ritual relationships, may be understood in terms of two main variables, each with two alternate values. A rule of cumulative filiation, either patrilineal or matrilineal, determines the manner in which ritual status or caste identity is

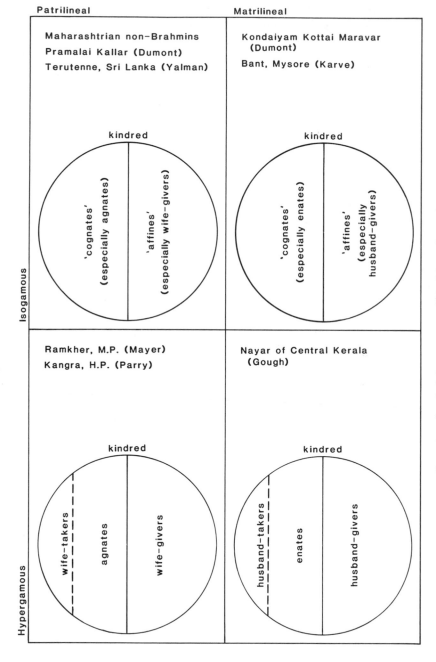

FIG. 1. South Asian systems of kinship and marriage.

transmitted from generation to generation. A rule of marriage, either isoga-mous or hypergamous, determines the manner in which status may be pre-served or enhanced. It would appear that many of the South Asian kinship systems on which we now have adequate reports may be assigned to one or an-other of the four possible combinations of the two values of each variable (see fig. 1).

More particularly, again, the research demonstrated that the Hindi sys-tem of kintype classification is based on a three-class equivalence which (1) ex-presses the propositions that "persons married to same-sex 'siblings' are 'siblings' to one another" (Vatuk, 1969, p. 101) and that persons married to opposite-sex 'siblings' may be regarded as 'spouses,' and (2) is related to hy-pergamous systems in the same way that the two-class equivalence rule is re-lated to isogamous marriage systems. The lack of terms for certain kintypes among aristocratic Nayar in Central Kerala, moreover, may be understood as the outcome of an attempt to combine matrilineal cumulative filiation with hypergamous marriage.

In general, it is simply not true that kinship is "inside" caste and other-wise independent of it. South Asian kinship and caste are equally segmentary systems and both are based on intersecting principles of hierarchy and equal-ity. Although other factors of course are involved, birth and filiation have to do with the manner in which caste status is shared and transmitted from gen-eration to generation while marriage has to do with the way in which caste sta-tus is preserved and enhanced. Externally, therefore, in the sphere of inter-caste relations, the unity of ranked units in relation to other ranked units is based upon filiation or sibling equality pushed to its furthest limits, while separation is maintained by endogamous marriage. Throughout India and Sri Lanka, in other words, a caste is in principle equivalent to an endogamous, bi-lateral kindred. Internally, however, the South Asian paradigm permits greater variation, depending upon whether status is regarded as transmitted primarily patrilineally or matrilineally and as best preserved and enhanced by isogamy or hypergamy.

Publications

The full results of this project are contained in an essay entitled "A Com-parative Analysis of Systems of Kinship and Marriage in South Asia," which was awarded the 1973 Curl Essay Prize of the Royal Anthropological Institute (Carter, 1974b).

REFERENCES

CARTER, ANTHONY T.
1974a. Elite politics in rural India, 207 pp., illus. Cambridge University Press.
1974b. A comparative analysis of systems of kinship and marriage in south Asia. Proceedings of the Royal Anthropological Institute for 1973, pp. 29-54.

DUMONT, LOUIS
1957. Hierarchy and marriage alliance in south Indian kinship, 45 pp. Royal Anthropological Institute, Occasional Paper 12. London.
1970. Homo hierarchicus: The caste system and its implications (transl. from French by M. Sainsbury), 386 pp. University of Chicago Press.

FOX, RICHARD G.
1971. Kin, clan, raja and rule, 187 pp. University of California Press.

GOUGH, E. KATHLEEN
1961. Nayar: central Kerala. Pp. 298-384, *in* "Matrilineal Kinship," 761 pp., D. Schneider and E. Kathleen Gough, eds. University of California Press.

KARVE, IRAWATI
1965. Kinship organization in India, 389 pp. Asia Publishing House, Bombay.

LEACH, EDMUND R.
1960. Introduction. Pp. 1-10 *in* "Aspects of Caste," 148 pp., E. R. Leach, ed. Cambridge Papers in Social Anthropology, no. 2, Cambridge University Press.

MAYER, ADRIAN C.
1960. Caste and kinship in central India, 295 pp. University of California Press.

PARRY, JONATHAN P.
1979. Caste and kinship in Kangra, 354 pp. Routledge and Kegan Paul, London.

SCHEFFLER, HAROLD W.
1971. Dravidian-Iroquois: the Melanesian evidence. Pp. 231-255 *in* "Anthropology in Oceania," 290 pp., L. R. Hiatt and C. Jayawardena, eds. Angus and Robertson, Sydney.
1972. Systems of kin classification: a structural typology. Pp. 113-133 *in* "Kinship Studies in the Morgan Centennial Year," 190 pp., P. Reining, ed. The Anthropological Society of Washington, Washington, D. C.

SCHEFFLER, HAROLD W., and LOUNSBURY, FLOYD G.
1971. A study in structural semantics: The Siriono kinship system, 260 pp. Prentice-Hall, Englewood Cliffs, N.J.

VATUK, SYLVIA
1969. A structural analysis of the Hindi kinship terminology. Contributions to Indian Sociology, new ser., no. 3, pp. 94-115.
1972. Kinship and urbanization, 219 pp. University of California Press.

YALMAN, NUR
    1960.   The flexibility of caste principles in a Kandyan community.   Pp. 78-
             112 *in* "Aspects of Caste," 148 pp., E. R. Leach, ed.   Cambridge Pa-
             pers in Social Anthropology, no. 2, Cambridge University Press.

ANTHONY T. CARTER

Status and Ecology of the Mauritius Fody *Foudia rubra*, an Endangered Species

Principal Investigator: Anthony S. Cheke, Edward Grey Institute, Oxford, England. (Presently at Moorcote, Ellingstring, Near Ripon, North Yorkshire, England.)

Grant No. 1263: For ecological and behavioral study of an avian endangered species in Mauritius.[1]

The Mauritius fody *Foudia rubra* has long been a rare bird; fears for its future were already being expressed a hundred years ago (Slater in Hartlaub, 1877), Meinertzhagen (1912) wrote it off as doomed, and it is listed as endangered in both editions of the Red Data Book (Vincent, 1966; King, 1977) and remains a priority species in the conservation programs of the International Council for Bird Preservation (ICBP; anon., 1981).

The British Ornithologists' Union Mascarene Islands Expedition, mounted in 1973 to study the ecology of the rare and declining endemic birds of Mauritius, Réunion, and Rodrigues, was able, with the help of the National Geographic Society, to pay special attention to the Mauritius fody, whose habitat was being drastically reduced by a forestry project (Procter and Salm, 1975). During 1972-74 an area of some 28 km^2 of habitat formerly supporting the species was lost—probably resulting in the loss of some 200 pairs, or over half the pre-1972 total population (see p.45, below). It was therefore urgent to census the birds in the remaining habitat and assess the species' ecological requirements. This report is the result of that investigation.

Distribution, Numbers, and Density

There is no useful information as to the Mauritius fody's original range on the island, though to judge by present habitat preferences it would have been widespread in the forest that covered the uplands before these were cut by man for timber and for growing sugarcane.

---

[1] When the British Ornithological Union Expedition arrived in Mauritius, it was discovered that a study of the pink pigeon was in progress under Dr. Stanley A. Temple, whose work was being funded by another source. Ultimately, therefore, the National Geographic Society's grant was used to support the study of another endangered species, the Mauritius fody *Foudia rubra*, by Anthony S. Cheke.

During the 1973-74 breeding season, all areas of native forest on the island were explored, as were many localities dominated by exotic vegetation, spontaneous and planted. The areas harboring fodies were noted, and I familiarized myself with the habits of the bird to facilitate censusing the following season. In the breeding season Mauritius fodies are highly territorial, rather vocal, and the males respond well to playback of their calls; out of season they are much quieter (pers. obs.; Newton, 1959), more secretive, and less responsive. Repeated observations in one place suggested that two long visits (all day exploring a small area) or three line transects would normally reveal nearly all territories present. In 1974-75 all but one of the areas with resident fodies were revisited, and accessible areas were covered by means of line transects, with more detailed coverage by exploration in certain sample plots.

The Mauritius fody in 1973-75 was confined to the high plateau southwest of Curepipe and the upper parts of its south-facing slopes, with a tiny outlying group on the Piton du Fouge, an isolated peak of similar elevation (1956 ft; 594 m) in the extreme southwest, opposite Le Morne peninsula (fig. 1). Most of the present distribution is over 1500 ft (455 m), but descends to about 1000 ft (304 m) in Bel Ombre and Combo on the southern slopes. The present distribution seems also to be contained almost entirely within the zone where the mean January temperature is below 23°C and the annual rainfall is above 280 cm (fig. 2). Native forest outside that zone contained few or no fodies (the summit climate of the Piton du Fouge seems to be ignored in the maps issued by the Mauritius Meteorological Services; all data from Padya, 1972).

A total of 121 territories were found in the 1974-75 season, and there were three found in 1973-74 that were not rechecked the following season. The 1974-75 census agreed very closely with the indications for the previous season. Given suitable habitat not censused, and taking into account the varying density (see below), I estimate the total breeding population to have been close to 250 pairs, or about double those actually counted (table 1). Over half of these (59 counted, 137 estimated) were along the forested south-facing slopes between Bel Ombre and Combo. Some 57 pairs (estimated; 31 counted) were on land actually being cleared or threatened with clearance shortly.

Carié (1904) observed during his lifetime a decrease in the birds (apparently unrelated to habitat destruction), and by 1910 Meinertzhagen (1912) was writing the fody's epitaph: "this . . . species is fast disappearing from Mauritius and is now a rare bird even in the south-west of the island." Newton (1959) remarked that it was "not uncommon" in the right habitat, though very local. By 1973 new massive clearances of native vegetation on the plateau for forestry (fig. 1) were causing alarm and the threat to this species was em-

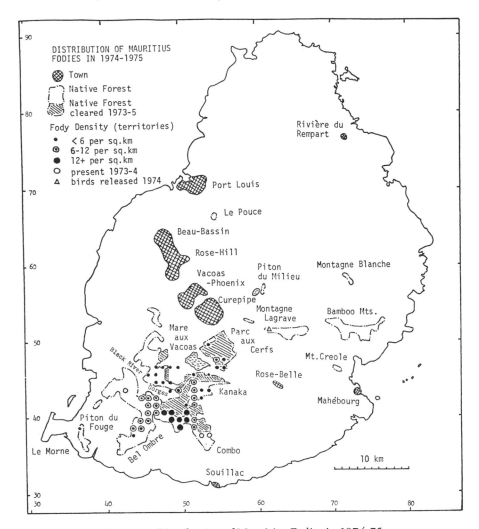

FIG. 1.   Distribution of Mauritius Fodies in 1974-75.

phasized by Temple (1974; *in* Procter and Salm, 1975, Appendix 6) and myself (Cheke, 1974a, b.) Returning to the island in 1978, I noted a sharp decline in fody numbers (Cheke, 1979), and Jones (1980) estimated the population as only 20-40 pairs.

The census revealed very substantial variations in fody density in different parts of the range, from a low of < 1/km², to as many as 27/km² on the southern scarp of the plateau between Alexandra Falls and Montagne Savanne (table

TABLE 1. Summary of Mauritius Fody Census Data, 1974-75

Locality	Area (km^2)	Territories Counted	Territories Estimated	Density per km^2 (approx.)
Crown Land Monvert	0.6	2	2-4	3-7
Parc-au-Cerfs -Mare aux Vacoas area	a	9	11	-
Kanaka	4.5	11	21-28	[2]4.5-6[8] [c]
Ghouly Block	a	8	10	-
Southern Slopes (Alexandra Falls -Mt. Savanne)	5.25	41	100	[14]19[27] [c]
Combo (upper)	1.5	[2] [d]	7	4-5
Plaine Champagne	4.1	17	27-29	6.5-7
Bel Ombre (scarp)	1.1	7	12	11
Bel Ombre (forest)	4.75 [b]	11	31	[3.5]6.5[9] [c]
Black River Peak	1	0[1] [d]	1	1
Petrin	1.1	5	6	[2]5.5[8-10] [c]
Mare Longue/ Brise Fer area	6.3	6	11-12	[<1]2[4-5] [c]
Macabé	3	3	7	2-2.5
Piton du Fouge	0.5	1	1-2	2-4
Totals	33.7+	124	247-260	-

[a] These areas were being cleared, so no meaningful estimate of habitat area or density is possible.

[b] Only the forest above 1000 ft (304 m) is included.

[c] The density varied over the area from the lower to higher bracketed figures given.

[d] Figure from 1973-74 season.

1). It was not clear in 1974 whether the high density on the southern slopes was due to this being the optimal habitat or whether the large numbers were simply due to an influx of birds displaced from the adjacent Les Mares area which had very recently been clear cut (Procter and Salm, 1975). A return visit in October 1978 revealed a dramatic decrease in fodies along this "high density" slope. This led me to conclude that the relatively high densities in this area in 1973-75 were an artifact of the adjacent habitat destruction and that by 1978 the numbers had returned to normal (Cheke, 1979); i.e., a density of nearer 6-7/km^2, as in Plaine Champagne and Bel Ombre in 1974-75. If this is so, the carrying capacity of the habitat existing in 1974 was probably only

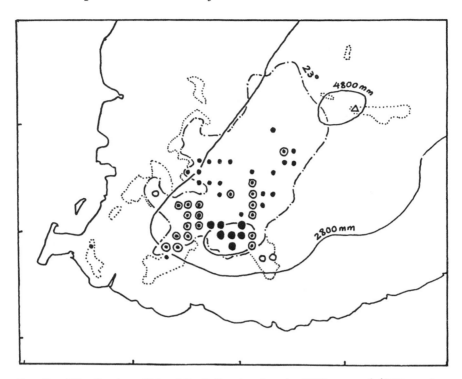

FIG. 2.   Distribution of Mauritius fodies showing the 2800 mm and 4800 mm iso-
hyets and the 23° January isotherm. Fine dotted lines indicate native forest outside
the climatic limits indicated.

about 150-170 territories (not the 247-260 estimated in 1974), so the clearances of 1972-74 actually eliminated habitat supporting over half the fody's
previous population.

Territory size is not a function of density except above about 20 pairs per
km^2. At lower densities territories remain 4-8 hectares (ha) in area whether or
not they are contiguous with others, so that there are gaps where there are no
fodies. Even at the highest densities territories never drop below 3 ha. Mention of "8-20 ha" as the territory size in an earlier paper (Cheke, 1980) was an
overestimate based on density before the data were fully examined.

Habitat

Mauritius fodies occur in all types of native forest within the climatic limitations already described. The highest densities found in 1974-75 were in the
forests along the southern scarp of the high plateau: very wet, 20-30 ft (7-10

m) tall, heavily dominated by *Calophyllum tacamaha*. As mentioned above, however, the concentration in this zone was probably an artifact of the destruction of the dwarf forest of Les Mares, on the plateau above. Medium densities (6-12 territories per square kilometer), probably the norm in Mauritius at present, occurred in the remaining dwarf forest (Plaine Champagne), high forest (but only in Bel Ombre) and in various degraded habitats invaded by exotics (especially *Psidium cattleyanum,* sens. lat., and *Ligustrum walkeri*) and interplanted with imported timber trees (notably *Eucalyptus robusta* and *Cryptomeria japonica*). Only one territory was found in almost entirely exotic vegetation *(Psidium* scrub with *Ravenala madagascariensis).* There is no reason to suppose that the fody's feeding habits (see below) should confine it to native vegetation, provided appropriate substitutes were present, so it seems that the bird is limited by the structure of the forest and the nature of introduced species. A characteristic of the native dwarf forest (Procter and Salm, 1975 = *"Sideroxylon* thicket" of Vaughan and Wiehé, 1937) is a very open canopy, with bushy vegetation between the trees, themselves only 10-25 ft (3-8 m) tall. The structure of the degraded forest is usually similar, some tallish trees emerging from a low (6-10 ft; 2-3 m) scrubby thicket. Territorial fodies use the tall trees as vantage points for singing and as lookouts, often flying from point to point within the territory. However, fodies are all but absent from structurally similar native habitat on the drier western edge of the plateau between Brise Fer and Simonet, and scarce around Mare Longue reservoir in the same general area, suggesting that rainfall (or some consequence of it) is a more powerful limiting factor than structure. Likewise, the typical upland climax forest (Vaughan and Wiehé, 1937) on the north side of Black River Gorges supports very few fodies (fig. 2), while similar forest in the upper part of Bel Ombre harbors good numbers. The latter area is mostly wetter (the rainfall increases very fast toward the north and east in Bel Ombre; Padya, 1972), but has a very similar temperature regime. In forests high humidity is usually associated with a good growth of epiphytes and rapid rotting of dead wood, both of which are necessary for the fody's feeding habits. It is probably the absence of epiphytes and lack of dead wood that makes forestry plantations within their range unsuitable for fodies: monocultures of pine or eucalypts simply do not harbor the necessary insect fauna. Where pine plantations border native forest the birds sometimes use the pines *(Pinus elliotti)* for nesting but feed in the indigenous vegetation. Pines and *Cryptomerias* in mixed indigenous/exotic forest are also chosen for nest sites, the nests there possibly being less vulnerable to arboreal predators. The dominant spontaneous exotics in the uplands, guava and privet, are smooth-barked and rarely support epiphytes, providing few feeding opportunities for fodies. I have commented elsewhere on the possibility of providing, through suitable hardwood mixtures and/or tree-fruit plantations, an artificial habitat suitable for Mauritius fodies and other native birds (Cheke, 1978). The existence of large areas of native forest on Réunion similar in structure to the upland dwarf forest in Mauritius led me to suggest transferring some fodies to that island to establish a second population (Cheke, 1974a, b). This was agreed to by all the relevant authorities and a trapping program to remove birds from areas at risk of clearance for transfer started in January 1975. Three birds were translocated, being released at Bébour on February 12, 1975 (Cheke, 1975a). In November 1974 some birds (2♂♂ 1♀) were also translocated to Montagne Lagrave (fig. 1) in the hope of extending the bird's range in Mauritius.

Feeding Ecology

Mauritius fodies feed on insects, fruit, and nectar from flowers from near the ground to the tops of trees. Insects are largely taken by probing or stripping dead wood and searching the bark of living trunks, branches and epiphytes, like a nuthatch (*Sitta* sp.); though some capture from foliage and flowers also takes place. Observations are summarized in Table 2. All observations of these feeding techniques were on native species; the following were identified: *Sideroxylon bojerianum, Mimusops glaucus, M. petiolaris, Calophyllum tacamaha* and *Eugenia glomerata.* It was rarely possible to identify insects captured, but the following were observed: Orthoptera (both grasshoppers and crickets), 4; "long grub" (? beetle larva), 1; "small larvae," 1; and an entire small spider's web complete with attached insects (and? the spider).

One of the best ways of detecting fodies in an area is to see if the berries of the small introduced undershrub *Ardisia crenata* have been "treated." Fodies feed on this fruit in a very characteristic manner, perching on the plant, peeling the fruit skin and then chiselling the flesh off the stone (i.e., pit) with the beak, leaving the stripped seeds still attached to the plant. The fruit is about 1 cm across, about half of which is the hard stone, presumably too large to swallow. Native *Eugenia* sp. berries are treated similarly, but the birds swallow whole little blue fruits of *Ossea marginata,* an introduced shrub. *Ardisia* is in fruit throughout the year, but native *Eugenia* spp. are seasonal, and *Ossea* is in fruit only briefly in midsummer (January-February).

Fodies were also seen taking nectar from the flowers of native *Eugenia, Aphloia theaeformis* and the introduced *Eucalyptus robusta* and *Callistemon speciosus.* All these flowers have shallow floral discs easily accessible to the bird's tongue. More time is spent by the birds foraging for insects than feeding in other ways, but whether this is reflected in the quantity of food taken is impossible to say.

Mauritius fodies often form temporary feeding associations with groups of grey white-eyes, *Zosterops borbonica,* passing through their territory. Outside the breeding season some fodies appear to wander with white-eye flocks. On these occasions the foraging sites generally remain separate, the fodies probing trunk and branches, the white-eyes gleaning on twigs and in the foliage.

TABLE 2.   Insect-feeding Methods of Mauritius Fodies

NOTES: (1) Observations during 1973-75 by the author, R. E. Ashcroft, M. de L. Brooke, A. W. Diamond, J. Shopland, and J. M. Vinson, all at various times associated with the expedition. (2) One observation of foraging on dead wood on the ground is included in the table. (3) All observations of males gleaning by searching on flowers or leaves were when they were feeding in close company with their mates. In one case the male kept with the female but did not feed, later going off to forage on trunks and branches.

Sex	Searching along, up or down trunks and branches			Gleaning from leaves, leaf-bases, and flowers		Totals
	Dead wood	Live wood	Unspecified	Methodical searching	Watch, see, & jump	
Male	11	11	2	3	1	28
Female	3	3	2	4	-	12
Totals	14	14	4	7	1	40

Breeding

Activity leading to breeding begins in August, male fodies becoming vocal and territorial, and pairs associating closely together. The earliest observations of nest building are in the second week of October though S. A. Temple (pers. comm.) heard birds with (? free-flying) young on October 21, 1973, which suggests egg-laying in mid to late September. At least in some years nesting continues until late March; on March 22, 1973, two pairs were carrying food to (presumed) nests at Petrin. By April 13 there was no longer any nesting activity. The end of the season may depend on the incidence of cyclones; in 1973-74 there were none, but in 1974-5 breeding was brought to an abrupt stop by the violent storm *Gervaise* on February 6 (see below).

All the indications are that breeding success in this species is extremely low. Nests were rarely found, and I have observations on only five for which the outcome is known; none progressed beyond incubation, four being destroyed by predators and one by cyclone Gervaise. Horne (in press) also failed to observe a successful nest. In each season there was only one observation of free-flying young, in October 1973 and January 1975.

The principal predator is probably the common introduced monkey *Macaca fascicularis,* though the ship rat *Rattus rattus* is also likely to be very significant. No actual acts of predation were observed, but monkeys were often seen "bird-watching" and the fact that two of the predated nests were completely destroyed (one missing, the other torn to shreds) suggests monkeys rather than rats. The other two, less extensively damaged, might have been attacked by either predator. Newton (1959) and Guérin (1940-53) also implicated monkeys as the major predator on fodies.

I believe the very low densities of fodies are attributable to the very low nesting success, and this would explain why the distribution is often patchy— there are simply not enough fodies to occupy available habitat, and those that there are retain a territory size related to a natural condition of higher density.

The nests observed in this study, and two more observed by D. A. Turner (unpubl. obs.), were all in trees, placed 7-30 ft (2-9 m) up, usually in the thickest foliage in the tree's canopy. Three nests were in indigenous trees (*Calophyllum tacamaha,* 2; unspecified (Turner), 1). Others were in introduced species (*Cryptomeria japonica,* 2; *Pinus* spp., 2; unspecified conifer (Turner), 1). The lowest nest (7 ft up) was in a *Cryptomeria* which had thick foliage at all levels; the pines and native trees usually had thick foliage only in the canopy. Newton (1959) recorded nests from as low as 3 ft (1 m) in brambles, but usually 20-50 ft (7-16 m).

Four nests of which the construction material could be observed were made primarily of grass. The nest is domed with a lateral entrance like other *Foudia* nests and sometimes has a "porch" extending the entrance somewhat, a feature which Lafresnaye (1850) considered a diagnostic distinction from the nest of the introduced cardinal *Foudia madagascariensis.* However I have found this detail to be variable.

The relative roles of the sexes in building the nest are unclear. In four cases only the female was seen bringing nest material and working on the nest, the male actively fussing around and pursuing her but not helping; this is exactly as described by Newton (1959). In another case, however, both members of the pair were working together on a nest.

No clutches or nestlings were observed in this study. Nests which reached the incubation stage were inaccessible, and all were destroyed before hatching. Newton (1959) stated that "the usual number [of eggs] appears to be three," though he may (Newton, 1958) have seen only one clutch. There are four clutches in the Cambridge University Zoology Museum collected by or for Edward Newton in October and December 1865—two with three eggs and two with two, though one cannot be sure the latter were complete. Hartlaub (1877; Guérin, 1940-53) citing Newton as source, gave the clutch as three. The brood size remains unknown. Staub (1976), not citing a source, gave the incubation period as 14 days and the nestling period as 18 days.

Mauritius fody eggs, like those of cardinals, are pale blue (Newton, 1959), measuring about 20 x 14 mm (Hartlaub, 1877).

Plumage Sequences and Molt

The adult male Mauritius fody has a bright red head, throat, and rump. The female is dull grey-brown, as are newly-fledged young. As Staub (1976) has already pointed out, this species does, like other fodies, (contra Newton, 1959; and Moreau, 1960), have an eclipse plumage, with the red areas becoming a sparrowlike brown, as in the female. A complete molt occurs at the end of the breeding season and, the males, at least, change only the contour feathers to regain red plumage, just before the next breeding season. I have several observations in April 1974 of males actively undergoing a complete molt (some had lost all tail feathers simultaneously), the red being replaced by brown. Two birds seen on May 20 had only a few scattered red feathers; all others seen were entirely brown, their sex indeterminable. Only one dated museum specimen examined was in molt—a male one-third through wing molt on March 15, 1863 (in Cambridge). I was out of the island for most of June and July so have no pertinent observations, but by early August many males were back in red plumage; the same was true in 1973 (J. M. Vinson obs.). Throughout the breeding season, however, birds are to be seen molting into red plumage, and I suspect these are young from the current or the previous season.

Freshly fledged young are recognizable by their pale horn-colored bills (black in adults). The bill presumably normally darkens after a few months, like that of the Rodrigues Fody (Cheke, in press).

Weight and Measurements

The range of afternoon weights of Mauritius fodies trapped in the field was 16.0-20.1 g in males (ave. 17.8, n=13) and 16.1-19.7 in females (ave. 17.3, n=4). Males of the closely related introduced congeneric cardinals are, in Mauritius, about the same weight (pers. obs.): males 16.3-20.4 g (ave. 18.1, n=24) and females 14.0-18.3 g (ave. 16.3, n=13).

Brown-plumaged fodies behaving as females had shorter wing-length

TABLE 3. Wing Length and Sex in Mauritius Fodies

Note: Moreau (1960) gave a range of only 69-71 mm for 6 males.

Wing length (mm)	Red plumaged males		Brown plumaged birds		
	Museum specimens [a]	Living	Museum specimens [a]		Living [b]
			Sexed female	Unsexed	
63			1		1
64			1		1
65					1
66	1 [c]				
67		1		1	1
68	2	5		1	
69	5	3			
70	2				
71	1	1		1	
72	2	1			
73	1	1			
74	1				
Totals	15	12	2	3	4

[a] Museum material: from Staub (1973b: 2 males, 1 female) and from specimens examined in Cambridge (6 males, 1 female, 1 unsexed), London (BM(NH), (2 males, 2 unsexed), and Paris (5 males); no specimens in Edinburgh, Liverpool, and Oxford zoology museums (all visited). Specimens also exist at Vienna (2), Leiden (1), American Museum of Natural History (New York, 1), Smithsonian Institution (4), Academy of Natural Science of Philadelphia (2) (various curators, in litt.), the Mauritius Institute (several) and probably also Berlin.

[b] The three brown birds with wings 63-65 mm were all paired with red males and behaving as females. The 67-mm bird was holding a territory in which a female and a juvenile were present.

[c] The male in the 66 mm column actually measured 66.5 mm.

(<66 mm) than red-plumaged males (67 + mm). I attempted to confirm this relationship on museum specimens, but of 17 specimens in Cambridge, London (BM(NH)), and Paris only four are in brown plumage and only one of these was sexed by examination; Staub (1973) gives measurements of a further specimen. Details of living birds and museum specimens measured by me are given in Table 3.

Males are more visible and easier to trap than females, a condition that accounts for the great disparity between the sexes, both in museums and in my trapping records. Males, as with the Rodrigues fody (Cheke, 1979) respond well to playback of their song and are easily mist-netted as they home in on the tape-recorder. Females also respond to playback of male song but they do not approach so closely nor so impetuously.

Relationship and Interactions with the Cardinal and Other Species

Slater (in Hartlaub, 1877) attributed the decline of the Mauritius fody to the introduction and spread of the cardinal, *Foudia madagascariensis,* but as Carié (1904) soon pointed out, their habits are very different. Newton (1959) concluded that rarity of the endemic form was due to predation and forest destruction as much as to any possible competition. With this view I agree.

Although it occurs throughout the island, the cardinal, as Newton (1959) noted, is at its lowest breeding density in upland forests, being at a lower density in 1974 than the native bird along the southern scarp of the plateau. It is almost entirely absent from the Macabé area north of the Black River Gorges where the endemic fody is also scarce. In the very few interactions with *F. rubra* that I observed the native species often displaced territorial cardinals from songposts or perches.

Given the catholicity of feeding and plasticity of habitat tolerance exhibited by the cardinal, it is not impossible that over time it has been able to displace the native bird from introduced or marginal habitat over much of the island. I doubt, however, if it is responsible for any of the endemic fody's difficulties within its present distribution and native habitat.

Despite the near-disappearance of the only resident raptor, *Falco punctatus,* fodies well outside its range retain a brisk response to potential aerial predators: a male quietly preening vanished tittering into the undergrowth when a dove *(Streptopelia sinensis)* glided over, a bird much the same size and color as the rare kestrel (Parc aux Cerfs, April 6, 1974).

Acknowledgments

This study, supported by National Geographic Society grant No. 1263, in 1973, formed part of the work of the British Ornithologists' Union Mascarene Islands Expedition led by the author. The following assisted this study in the field at various times: R. E. Ashcroft, M. de L. Brooke, R. A. Cheke, A. W. Diamond, M. A. Peirce, J. Shopland, S. A. Temple, and J.-M. Vinson. The cooperation and support of the Mauritius Forestry Services and the Conservator of Forests, Mr. A. W. Owadally, made the study possible and is gratefully acknowledged. F.R.G. Rountree and A. Forbes-Watson very kindly allowed me to use unpublished data, the latter lending me, with his permission, D. A. Turner's field notes.

REFERENCES

ANONYMOUS
1981.   Special issue on bird conservation priorities.   International Council for Bird Protection [ICBP], Newsletter, vol. 3, no. 1.

CARIÉ, P.
1904.   Observations sur quelques oiseaux de l'Île Maurice.   Ornis, vol. 12, pp. 121-128.

CHEKE, A. S.
1974a.   British Ornithologists' Union Mascarene Islands Expedition: Interim report on the Mauritian fody *Foudia rubra*.   Cyclostyled, (mimeographed) memorandum, unpublished.   British Ornithologists' Union, London.

1974b.   Proposition pour introduire à la Réunion des oiseaux rares de l'Île Maurice. Memorandum circulated to ICBP, Paris.   (Published later in Info-Nature, Île Réunion, no. 12, pp. 25-29, 1975.)

1975a.   Official report on the introduction of the Mauritius fody *Foudia rubra* to Réunion. Cyclostyled (mimeographed) memorandum, unpublished. British Ornithologists' Union (BOU) Mascarene Islands Expedition, Oxford.

1978.   Recommendations for the conservation of Mascarene vertebrates. Conservation memorandum No. 3 arising out of the British Ornithologists' Union (BOU) Mascarene Islands Expedition, 13 pp.   Publ. by the author, Oxford.   (Published 1978, in French translation, in Info-Nature, Île Réunion, no. 16, pp. 69-83.)

1979.   The Rodrigues fody *Foudia flavicans:* A brief history of its decline and a report on the 1978 expedition.   Dodo, vol. 15, pp. 12-19.

1980.   Urgency and inertia in the conservation of endangered island species illustrated by Rodrigues.   Pp. 355-359 *in* "Proceedings of the 4th Pan-African Ornithological Congress," D. N. Johnson, ed.   South African Ornithological Society.

_____.   Observations on the surviving endemic land-birds of Rodrigues.   British Ornithologists' Union. (In press.)

GUÉRIN, R.
1940-1953.   Faune ornithologique ancienne et actuelle des Îles Mascareignes, Seychelles, Comores et des îles avoisinantes, 3 vols.   Publ. by the author, Port Louis.

HARTLAUB, G.
1877.   Die Vögel Madagascars und der benachbarten Inselgruppen, 425 pp.   H. W. Schmidt, Halle.

HORNE, J.
_____.   Vocalisations of the endemic land-birds of the Mascarene Islands.   *In* "The Birds of the Mascarene Islands," A. W. Diamond and H.F.I. Elliott, eds.   British Ornithologists' Union. (In press.)

JONES, C. G.
1980.   The conservation of the endemic birds and bats of Mauritius and Rodrigues, 47 pp. plus appendices.   Cyclostyled (mimeographed) report, unpublished. ICBP, Washington.

KING, WARREN B., compiler
  1977-1979. Red data book. 2nd ed., revised. Vol. 2, Aves. International Union for the Conservation of Nature and Natural Resources (IUCN)/International Council for Bird Preservation (ICBP), Morges.
LAFRESNAYE, F.
  1850. Sur la nidification de quelques espèces d'oiseaux de la famille des Tisserins (Ploceinae). Rev. Mag. Zool., ser. 2, vol. 2, pp. 315-326.
MEINERTZHAGEN, R.
  1912. On the birds of Mauritius. Ibis, ser. 9, vol. 6, pp. 82-108.
MOREAU, R. E.
  1960. The ploceine weavers of the Indian Ocean Islands. Journ. Orn., vol. 101, pp. 29-44.
NEWTON, R.
  1958. Ornithological notes on Mauritius and the Cargados Carajos archipelagos. Mauritius Hist. Bull., vol. 2, pp. 39-71.
  1959. Notes on the two species of *Foudia* in Mauritius. Ibis, vol. 101, pp. 240-243.
PADYA, B. M., ed.
  1972. Climate of Mauritius, unpaginated. Mauritius Meteorological Services, Vacoas.
PROCTER, J., and SALM, R.
  1975. Conservation in Mauritius 1974. Cyclostyled (mimeographed) report, International Union for the Conservation of Nature and Natural Resources, Morges.
STAUB, F.
  1973b. Birds of Rodriguez Island. Proc. Roy. Soc. Arts and Sci., Mauritius, vol. 4, pp. 17-59.
  1976. Birds of the Mascarenes and Saint Brandon, 110 pp. Organisation Normale des Entreprises, Port Louis.
TEMPLE, S. A.
  1974. Wildlife in Mauritius today. Oryx, vol. 13, pp. 584-590.
VAUGHAN, R. E., and WIEHÉ, P. O.
  1937. Studies on the vegetation of Mauritius. I. A preliminary survey of the plant communities. Journ. Ecol., vol. 25, pp. 289-343.
VINCENT, J.
  1966. Red data book, vol. 2, Aves. International Union for the Conservation of Nature and Natural Resources/International Council for Bird Preservation, Morges.

ANTHONY S. CHEKE

Social Organization and Ecology of the Green Jay in Colombia

Principal Investigator: Humberto Alvarez-Lopez, Universidad del Valle, Cali, Colombia.

Grant No. 1362:   In support of a study of the social organization of the green jay in Colombia.

From August 1974 to September 1975 I conducted field studies of the green jay (Aves: Corvidae, *Cyanocorax yncas*) in northwestern Colombia. The results of fieldwork on this species during 1972-1973, as well as a detailed description of the study area, were the subject of a previous article (Alvarez, 1975).

Green jays live the year around in small flocks (from 4 to 9 individuals) which communally maintain and defend permanent all-purpose territories. Only one pair of each flock breeds but nest building and feeding of the young are communal affairs in which other members of the flock participate—both immatures and unmated adults. Apparently green jays do not reproduce until they are at least 2 years old. In none of the 4 flocks under observation did the young disperse from the parental groups, and all increments in numbers came from reproduction within the flock.

During the second part of my studies (1974-1975) I intended to refine the available information on aspects such as flock dynamics, relationships between flock size and reproductive success and survival, and on relationships between quality and size of territories and reproductive success and survival, as well as on life-table statistics on the basis of color-banded individuals of known age and origin.

I spent 3 to 11 days per month at the study area during the 12-month period, and concentrated on censusing, identifying of banded birds, plotting and mapping of routes and territories, and nest watching.

I found only 2 nests during the March-April-May 1975 breeding season. One of them contained 3 young of 4 to 5 days of age, and was attended by a female that had been captured and color banded as a juvenile on June 1973 in the same general area, and an unbanded male of unknown origin. This female had been wandering and perhaps defending the same territory since October 1974, accompanied by an unbanded jay, probably her male at this nest. The 3

57

color-banded young abandoned the nest on April 2 to stay around for 10 days and then disappear while their parents were to be seen until the end of the year.

The second nest contained 4 eggs. From the day of their hatching the young were fed by 2 adults and a blue-naped immature. This nest was destroyed by some unknown predator when the young were 8 days old. None of the jays involved were banded, and the nest was well outside of the previously known and mapped territories.

By the middle of March a pair of unbanded green jays were feeding a young of the parasitic giant cowbird, *Scaphydura oryzibora*. I saw them for 4 days within the territory of a flock of which all members except one had been color banded during 1972-1973. I did not record any territorial interactions and I did not see any of the banded jays nearby; the parasitized pair, therefore, was intruding from an adjacent territory.

Out of 20 green jays that I had captured and color banded only 2 were seen in the study area during 1974-1975. One of them was the female at one of the nests, and the second was a male captured and banded as an adult, the male at a nest, in November 1973. The widespread disappearance of banded jays corresponded with an over-all decrease of the population, from some 30 individuals in 4 flocks by September 1973, to perhaps less than 10 by December 1974-January 1975, with at least a few of them contributed by neighboring flocks.

Some three-fourths of the study area are under silvicultural management for the purpose of watershed protection and cellulose pulp production. At the end of 1973 the pine plantations were subjected to severe defoliation by the larvae of a geometrid moth, *Glena bisulca*. During 1974 and 1975 a treatment followed consisting of chemical control of the moth at the affected young stands, as well as extensive clear cutting of the older stands. Most of the second-growth forest of native species were burned in the process of re-setting the plans of management. The study area was thus extensively and adversely modified as a habitat for the green jays and, therefore, for the purpose of my studies. By December 1977-January 1978 the local population of green jays had not yet shown any noticeable recovery.

REFERENCE

ALVAREZ, HUMBERTO
    1975.   The social system of the green jay in Colombia.   The Living Bird, vol.
            14, pp. 5-44.

HUMBERTO ALVAREZ-LOPEZ

The Turner Farm Archeological Project

Principal Investigator: Bruce J. Bourque, Maine State Museum, Augusta, Maine.

Grant No. 1331, 1477, In support of archeological research at the Turner Farm site,
   and 1909.   North Haven, Maine.

Introduction

The Turner Farm Archeological Project began in 1971 as part of the larger Fox Islands Archeological Project. Goals of the Fox Islands Archeological Project are to extend and amplify the cultural chronological sequence for central coastal Maine and to gain understanding of human adaptational changes evident in that sequence. The geographic focus of the project includes North Haven, Vinalhaven, and surrounding smaller islands clustered in the center of Penobscot Bay on the coast of Maine.

The Fox Islands were chosen as a research universe for three reasons. First, they are centrally located in the Gulf of Maine, near concentrations of many known Archaic sites, especially those of the late Archaic Moorehead Phase (Bourque, 1971:63-101). Second, well-documented amateur collections from the islands indicated an unusually large number of Archaic sites, as well as numerous later ones. Third, excellent stratification and faunal preservation are characteristic of the shell middens that make up most of the site sample.

As the Fox Islands Project began, the Turner Farm site was one of four shell middens identified from local collections that possessed potentially early components. Test excavations conducted there in 1971 confirmed this potential and led to continued work between 1972 and 1975. Research conducted in 1974 and 1975 was supported by National Geographic Society grants 1331 and 1477. The site was placed on the National Register of Historic Places in 1973.

In 1977 a final phase of excavation was conducted in submerged deposits adjacent to the currently dry portions of the midden. Through these excavations we hoped to ascertain whether the site's dimensions had been reduced by coastal submergence. We also hoped to encounter organic cultural materials preserved in waterlogged condition. Intact occupation floors were discovered beneath a salt-marsh deposit adjacent to the midden's eastern margin and beneath 7 feet of beach deposit at its southeastern limit. However, no uncarbonized vegetable matter was recovered.

As analysis of the Turner Farm data began in 1975, the great potential of the site's faunal sample became apparent. Since 1978, detailed analysis of this material has been conducted with support from National Geographic Society grant 1909. To date, most basic phases of analysis are complete, though faunal analysis of shell and fish remains is still under way, and a final group of radiocarbon samples is in process. Data pertaining to the Turner Farm site have appeared in Bourque 1975 and 1976, as well as in a series of student theses (B.A. and M.A.). A final comprehensive report is in preparation.

Setting

The central portion of the Turner Farm site consists of a half acre shell-midden deposit that occupies the shoreward portion of a low terrace at the southern tip of Fish Point on North Haven Island. This terrace borders a crescentic gravel beach along its southern margin and a salt marsh on its western edge. As mentioned above, in places the midden extends well below the modern high-water mark but is eroding along most of its shoreward margin. To the north of the site lies a 60- to 80-foot-high bedrock ridge that is oriented east-west. Soil underlying the site is an intermittent glacial till, which overlies highly fractured acid-volcanic bedrock of the Castine Volcanic Belt.

Local topography protects the site from cooling north winds and heavy surf, while assuring maximum solar exposure the entire year. These factors, common to most large Fox Islands sites, create comfortable living areas and seem to have been determining criteria for settlement location.

Description

Coastal middens of the Gulf of Maine are composed largely of well-stratified, manmade deposits, which include marine mollusk shell, beach gravel, rock, humus, and artifactual debris, all introduced directly by humans. At the Turner Farm site, these deposits reach a maximum depth of 6 feet.

The site's earliest occupants (Occupation 1) excavated a series of pits into the subsoil, probably for cooking food. It appears that they also deposited some of the thinner basal midden lenses. Radiocarbon dates from charcoal found in these pits range from 4,970 to 5,290 B.P.

The next major occupation of the site (Occupation 2), radiocarbon dated between 4,390 and 4,555 B.P., left an extensive series of shell-midden deposits interbedded with dark gravel lenses, probably the remains of house floors and activity areas. From these deposits have come a large series of bone and

FIG. 1. Oblique aerial photograph of the Turner Farm site looking eastward. The shell midden occupies the area in the center to the left of the beach between the line of trees (left) crossing the road and the bog (lower right).

stone tools that resemble artifacts from "Red Paint" or Moorehead Complex cemeteries of Maine and New Brunswick. I have designated the culture that produced these remains as the Moorehead phase (1971: 78-93).

Following Occupation 2, the site was inhabited by groups referrable to the Susquehanna Tradition, who deposited additional extensive shell lenses and gravel "floors," as well as a series of cremation burials placed in shallow subsoil pits (Occupation 3). Dates from these strata range from 3,515 to 4,020 B.P. Associated artifacts are predominantly large, bifacially chipped, stemmed blades that closely resemble Susquehanna forms from southern New England and New York. The near absence of bone tools stands in marked contrast to both Occupation 2 and to later ceramic period occupations.

Superimposed upon Occupation 3 deposits were a series of midden lenses and gravel floors that yielded ceramics. Other artifacts recovered from these strata include bone and stone implements of styles previously found in association with ceramics at other coastal shell-midden sites. Radiocarbon dates for these later strata range between ca. 3,000 and 875 B.P.

Animal Exploitation Patterns

Although faunal analysis is not yet complete, general patterns for most periods are emerging. Faunal remains for all occupations include marine mollusks, and all but Occupation 1 include marine mammals, terrestrial mammals, fish, and birds. In addition, it is assumed that crustaceans such as lobster *(Homarus americanus)* and crabs played a significant role in the diets of many or all inhabitants. Unfortunately, skeletal elements of these species are rarely preserved, even in shell middens.

Thus, all occupants appear to have exploited similar, rather wide ranges of animal species. However, the relative importance of some species changed markedly during the site's history. In Occupation 2 white-tailed deer *(Odocoileus virginianus),* groundfish (especially cod, *Gadus morrhua),* and swordfish *(Xiphias gladius)* account for the great majority of live-weight animal flesh, though seal *(Phoca vituline* and *Halocoserus grypus)* are also present. By Occupation 3 times, swordfish exploitation had virtually ceased, the few associated specimens possibly being cases of stratigraphic ambiguity. Furthermore, the importance of groundfish species declined, whereas flounder and other shoalwater species showed relative increases.

After Occupation 3, two clear trends continued throughout the stratigraphic sequence. Measured in terms of weight, moose *(Alces alces)* replaced deer as the predominant cervid species, and fish (especially flounder species) rose markedly.

Our faunal analysis emphasizes season-of-death determinations in order to delimit the periods during which the site was in use and ultimately to determine the relative importance of coastal settlement and exploitation through time. One important result of this work has been the discovery that from ca. 4,500 B.P. onward, occupation at the site was apparently year round, or nearly so, during its periods of use. Furthermore, whereas deer, seal, and probably swordfish were hunted during specific seasons by Occupation 2 hunters, later hunting patterns increasingly spread the pursuit of deer, moose, seal, and fish throughout much of the year.

Significance of the Turner Farm Site

LOCAL FACTORS

Analysis of material recovered from thirty other sites during the Fox Islands Project is just beginning, and detailed intersite comparisons lie in the future. It is currently apparent, however, that the Turner Farm site was more frequently occupied than any other extant site on the Fox Islands. It also seems likely that it supported larger populations.

REGIONAL FACTORS

Technological comparisons between the Turner Farm artifact sample and other materials from the region have focused upon Archaic Occupations 1, 2, and 3. Occupation 1 appears to relate to a small series of components only recently recognized in central and western Maine. As a group, they have produced assemblages that resemble Ritchie's Small-Stemmed Point Tradition in point morphology and the preponderance of quartz as a raw material (Ritchie, 1965). The approximate chronological range of this tradition in areas to the south and west of Maine is 4,500-4,000 B.P., significantly later than Occupation 1. However, small-stemmed Merrimac points occurred in 5,000-6,000 B.P. contexts at the Neville site in Manchester, New Hampshire, suggesting that this technological tradition has considerable antiquity in the southwestern Gulf of Maine. The primary significance of Occupation 1, then, is its demonstration that populations using small-stemmed points exploited coastal resources, including shellfish, by ca. 5,000 B.P.

As mentioned earlier, Occupation 2 appears to represent a coastal habitation component of the Moorehead Phase, to whom are attributed the "Red Paint" cemeteries of Maine and New Brunswick. Technological and mortuary ceremonial resemblances between these sites and those of similar age in Newfoundland and Labrador have led some to include the former in Tuck's Maritime Archaic Tradition (Tuck, 1971). However, Occupation 2 subsistence patterns included strong reliance upon white-tailed deer, fish, and swordfish, whereas Maritime Archaic economies are regarded as caribou and seal oriented.

In light of this discrepancy, the utility of such an attribution seems questionable. Rather, the Turner Farm sequence together with other Maine data suggests that close relationships between the two areas were confined to a period between 4,500 and 3,800 B.P., were also confined to a narrow range of ideas, and did not include basic similarities in subsistence strategies.

Occupation 3 provides clear evidence that technologies and mortuary ceremonialism associated with the Susquehanna Tradition in southern New England and New York extend as far northeast as the central Maine coast, considerably beyond their formerly known range. Furthermore, the Susquehanna Tradition shows little relationship to the technology and mortuary practices of the preceding Moorehead Phase. The mechanisms that brought about this discontinuity are not clear, and it is possible that population replacement accompanied the introduction of Susquehanna tradition traits in territory previously occupied by the Moorehead Phase.

Comparisons between subsistence strategies during Occupation 3 and Susquehanna occupations to the south are difficult at present, owing to a scarcity of relevant data in the latter area.

BROADER IMPORTANCE

Recent years have witnessed increased archeological interest in northern maritime adaptations. Commenting upon a series of papers dealing with such cultures, Fitzhugh hypothesized several properties that should be manifested by such cultures (1975:342-86). These properties include increased absolute population density, large semipermanent or permanent settlements, intensified religious expression, trends toward specialized labor, and increased external contacts.

We feel that the central Maine coast, lying as it does in the biologically rich central Gulf of Maine, is an appropriate test for Fitzhugh's criteria. Many of his criteria appear to be satisfied here, particularly at the Turner Farm site. Population density on the coast, and perhaps along major river drainages as well, appears to increase substantially after ca. 4,500 B.P. The late Archaic mortuary ceremonial complexes of the Moorehead Phase and the Susquehanna Tradition suggest intensified religious expression, increased external contacts, and perhaps specialized labor in the form of religious specialists. But most important is the fact that from ca. 4,500 B.P. onward, the Turner Farm site components appear to represent year-round occupation. The significance of this conclusion is further enhanced by the site's location on an island that probably sustained more limited terrestrial food resources per unit area than adjacent portions of the mainland.

Finally, the long-standing pattern of sedentism at the Turner Farm site, combined with the shift from apparently selective hunting patterns (Occupations 1 and 2) to more intensive pursuit of important species (Occupation 3 and later), suggests that Archaic populations were not limited primarily by resource availability.

Problems for Future Research

The data recovered by the Turner Farm Archeological Project, although filling many archeological needs in the Gulf of Maine region, are limited in their usefulness by two factors. First, Turner Farm is one of comparatively few sites in the region to receive sustained attention by professional archeologists. Archeology is a comparative discipline, and many data categories at the Turner Farm exceed the quality of data from surrounding areas. Therefore, completion of analysis of the whole Fox Islands sample remains a high priority. Second, our control of paleoclimatic data for the coastal region is currently inadequate to provide a detailed backdrop for the archeological record. Particularly, data on coastal vegetation and sea-level rise are badly needed. As these data become available in the future, we expect the Turner Farm site to provide further insights on aboriginal coastal adaptations in the Gulf of Maine.

REFERENCES

BOURQUE, BRUCE J.
   1971.   Prehistory of the central Maine coast.   Unpublished Ph.D. thesis, Harvard University, Cambridge, Massachusetts.
   1975.   Comments on the Late Archaic populations of central Maine: The view from the Turner farm.   Arctic Anthrop., vol. 12, no. 2, pp. 35-45.
   1976.   The Turner farm site: A preliminary report.   Man In The Northeast, no. 11, pp. 21-30.
FITZHUGH, WILLIAM
   1975.   A comparative approach to northern maritime adaptations.   Pp. 339-386 *in* "Prehistoric Maritime Adaptations of the Circumpolar Zone," William Fitzhugh, ed.   The Hague: Mouton.
RITCHIE, WILLIAM A.
   1965.   The "small stemmed point" in New England.   Pennsylvania Archaeologist, vol. 35, nos. 3-4, pp. 134-158.
TUCK, JAMES A.
   1971.   An Archaic Indian cemetery at Port Au Choix, Newfoundland.   American Antiquity, vol. 36, no. 3, pp. 343-358.

BRUCE J. BOURQUE

The Archeology of the Tunica: Trial on the Yazoo and the Tunica Treasure II Projects

Principal Investigator: Jeffrey P. Brain, Peabody Museum, Harvard University, Cambridge, Massachusetts.

Grant Nos. 1340 and 1737. In support of archeological investigations conducted by the Lower Mississippi Survey in 1974 and 1977.

Introduction

The Lower Mississippi Survey (LMS), Peabody Museum, Harvard University, conducted archeological research in the Lower Mississippi Valley during 1974 and 1977. The respective areas of attention were the loess bluffs in the vicinity of Vicksburg, Mississippi, and the grounds of the Louisiana State Penitentiary (Angola), West Feliciana Parish, Louisiana. The expeditions were funded by research grants from the National Geographic Society, and operated as joint ventures with the Mississippi Department of Archives and History, and the Louisiana Archaeological Survey and Antiquities Commission. The LMS crews consisted of Jeffrey P. Brain, field director, and students from Harvard, Brown, and Michigan Universities. This core was augmented by professional staff from the state organizations and labor drawn from local resources.

The over-all objective of the fieldwork was to establish the Indian and French presence in the Vicksburg and Angola regions during the early historic contact period at the beginning of the 18th century. Special emphasis was placed upon the location and excavation of Tunica Indian sites relating to this period.

The research reported upon here is an important input into our Tunica studies. Long concerned with anthropological problems of culture contact and change (Brain, 1969, 1978, 1979, in press, and in prep.), we have selected the Tunica as a case study in the Lower Mississippi Valley because of their high archeological profile (Brain, 1976). We may trace the Tunica across 400 miles of space, from northern Mississippi to central Louisiana, during 400 years of often dramatic culture contact and change (Brain, 1977). Our research objectives have concentrated upon the archeological exposition of a series of stages in the odyssey of the Tunica, and then to use these as units of measure in a case study of acculturation by a native American Indian group.

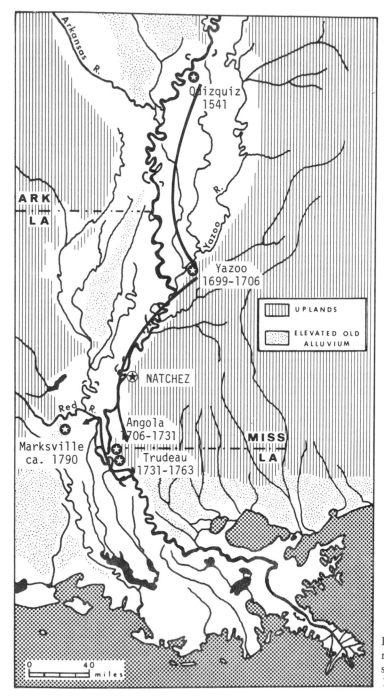

FIG. 1. Tunica migrations and settlements, ca. 1541 to the present.

Within the map:

Arkansas R.

Quizquiz
1541

ARK
LA

Yazoo
1699–1706

Yazoo R.

UPLANDS

ELEVATED OLD
ALLUVIUM

NATCHEZ

Red R.

Angola
1706–1731

MISS
LA

Marksville
ca. 1790

Trudeau
1731–1763

0   40
miles

The Tunica were one of the more important historic tribes discovered by the French in the Lower Mississippi Valley. Not only were they one of the larger and better organized of the valley tribes, but they had a curious history of migrating from place to place at irregular intervals. The scale of these movements, and their identification with important events, was of sufficient magnitude to suggest that the Tunica could provide a firm reference point and integrating factor for the protohistoric-historic archeology of the valley. The first step was the archeological establishment of the Tunica themselves.

The several migrations of the Tunica, and the intermediate places of settlement are known (ethno) historical facts (fig. 1). In the protohistoric period, the Tunica have been identified as living in northwestern Mississippi where they were discovered by De Soto in 1541. The narratives of that expedition record enough information to make the identification of the "province" of Quizquiz with the Tunica reasonably secure (Brain et al., 1974), and archeological work in the region provides a sample of protohistoric Tunica material culture (Phillips, 1970: 941-942; Brown, 1978).

The Tunica moved to the lower Yazoo River sometime before 1699 when they were first encountered by the French. It was believed, but not yet proven, that the principal village of the Tunica on the Yazoo was located at the Haynes Bluff site, 12 miles north of Vicksburg.

In 1706, the Tunica moved farther down river, again, to the vicinity of the confluence with the Red River. Their provenience there had not been precisely determined until one of their principal villages was discovered in 1968. Looted graves produced an extraordinary amount of European and native artifacts relating to the Tunica material culture of the mid-18th century (1731-1763), the "Tunica Treasure" (Brain 1970, 1979). Excavations conducted at this site, Trudeau, in 1972 by the LMS verified the archeological context of this important collection, and served to enhance its value as a firm datum for the middle historic period (Brain, 1973).

Toward the end of the 18th century, the Tunica moved yet again, this time across the river to central Louisiana. Recent amateur excavation of early 19th-century Tunica burials at the Pierite site near Marksville has provided another valuable reference point, this time relating to the late historic contact period.

The next obvious research was to return to the intermediate points that had not yet been well documented archeologically: the 1699-1706 site on the Yazoo, and the 1706-1731 settlement near the Red River confluence. The identification of the Tunica in this crucial early historic contact period hopefully would serve to integrate the data from the protohistoric and middle historic periods, and so reinforce the scale against which developments and events in the Lower Mississippi Valley could be measured (table 1).

TRIAL ON THE YAZOO

The special objectives of the 1974 field investigation were designed to fulfill the over-all objectives discussed above. Thus, the primary field objectives were the location and excavation of the historic Indian villages along the lower Yazoo River, with particular attention to the isolation of protohistoric and historic Tunica components. The major results of these excavations were expected to be the collection of representative samples of early 18th-century French and Indian artifacts which could be used as artifactual datums for the study of culture contact and change.

The principal village of the Indians in this region had already been identified with the archeological site of Haynes Bluff. Other contemporary sites nearby were known, and additional ones were located during the course of the investigations. Haynes Bluff was the focus of the excavation program, but three of the satellite sites also were tested. [The partially contemporary French Fort St. Pierre a few miles away was excavated at the same time as part of the over-all program, but since that operation was funded separately by the State of Mississippi it is not reported upon here.]

The Excavations

The emphasis in excavation was directed to Haynes Bluff since it was believed to have been the most important village of the Tunica while they lived in the Yazoo region. Four major locations at the site were extensively tested.

TABLE 1. The Places of Haynes Bluff Angola in the History and Archeology of the Tunica

Archeological periods	*Historical periods*		*Type of interaction*	*Archeo- logical- historical sites*	*Patterns of culture change*	*Description*
	(Quimby 1966)	*(In this report)*	*(Fontana 1965)*			
				Marksville	Assimilation	All Euro-American artifacts and traits in Euro-American configurations. Potentially good archeological recovery, but probably indistinguishable from nonnative remains.

		VI		Pierite		3	All Euro-American artifacts and traits, but predominantly in native configurations. Good archeological recovery.
	Late						
		V		James Village			
Historic		IV	Postcontact	Trudeau	Acculturation	2	Considerable array of European artifacts and traits, but still a strong native representation. All in native configurations. Good archeological recovery.
	Middle	III		ANGOLA			
		II	Contact	HAYNES BLUFF		1	Predominantly native assemblage, with European trinkets and hardware, in native configurations. Difficult archeological recovery.
Protohistoric		I	Initial Contact (exploration)	Quizquiz			Occasional European trinkets in otherwise native assemblage and configurations. Very difficult archeological recovery.
Prehistoric	Early						

These locations were chosen according to the types of data they could be expected to produce that would contribute most directly to the primary objectives listed above. The choice in each case was determined generally by information derived from prior work at the site by amateurs, and by intuitive conclusions drawn from survey observations. Specific placements of the excavations were determined by instrument survey which pinpointed the types of

FIG. 2. Early 18th-century burial of adult male at Haynes Bluff. Grave accompaniments included a flintlock musket, catlinite pipe, and ditty bag containing assorted oddments.

features which were being searched for, thus saving considerable effort in excavation.

A large pyramidal mound feature was the most intensively investigated location at Haynes Bluff. The principal reason for this was that it, and its immediate surroundings, appeared to be the best preserved part of the site. Thus, it was hoped that evidence of the latest occupations would be present there if anywhere. Furthermore, previous surveys had indeed turned up native and European artifacts appropriate to the early historic contact period on the surface of the mound.

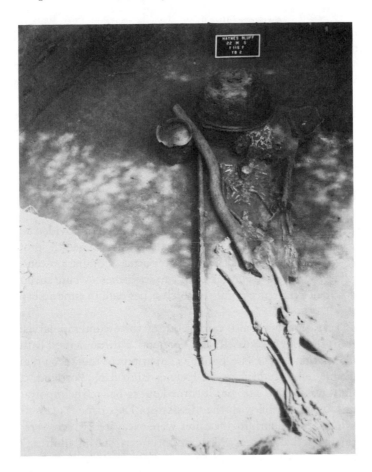

FIG. 3.   Burial of second adult male at Haynes Bluff. This important individual was
accompanied by native pots, a brass kettle, thousands of glass trade beads and other
ornaments, and both a musket and a pistol. The inverted kettle protected a beaded
feather headdress.

The mound summit was cleared, and instrument surveys detected a number of interesting anomalies. Two loci at the summit gave strong indications
of burials with metal artifacts, while a third locus was determined to have a
high content of small metallic objects spread over a wide area. All appeared to
be good contexts for the historic occupation and so were targeted for excavation. As predicted, two burials were discovered (figs. 2 and 3). These were accompanied by European and native artifacts which could be dated to the early
historic contact period. Both individuals had been important personages, as
determined by their provenience at the top of the mound and the nature and

variety of mortuary accompaniments. As discrete assemblages, they provide important datums for the early historic component at the site.

The third locus at the summit also provided a good historic assemblage; although the original context had been destroyed by natural agency, and so no features could be recognized, the first 15-20 cm of topsoil yielded a large number of European and native artifacts. This surface layer was stripped from a large part of the summit (approximately one-third of the total horizontal area). On the vertical scale, a strata cut over 4 meters deep was sunk down into the mound near the northern edge. This cut revealed that while the historic component was restricted to the uppermost level, already extensively explored, the top half of the mound itself was a very late construction relating to the protohistoric period.

Three other locations on the site were also tested and provided additional stratigraphic and artifactual data which further discriminated the protohistoric and historic occupations. As the most important population center of the period in the Yazoo region, Haynes Bluff thus becomes a secure anchor for our researches: a major reference point to which other data in time and space may be related.

Small excavations were also carried out at three contemporary sites near Haynes Bluff: Burroughs, Russell, and Portland. Burroughs and Russell both yielded information on the late Indian occupations of the Yazoo region, and were a valuable reinforcement to the Haynes Bluff data. Portland, closest to Haynes Bluff, was a small site, but it turned out to be vitally important to our study. In a joint operation with the Mississippi Department of Archives and History, a number of aboriginal features were excavated which were remarkably rich in artifactual content. Most important is that in addition to a fine sample of early contact European items we discovered the purest complex of native ceramics which could definitely be identified as Tunica (fig. 4). The result was an imporant aboriginal datum for the early 18th century, and specifically a Tunica component dating to the 1699-1706 period.

TUNICA TREASURE II

The most important village of the Tunica during the period 1706-1731 was located on what is now a part of the Louisiana State Penitentiary (Angola). The general location of the settlement has been known for some time, and a small portion of it was excavated in 1934 (Ford, 1936: 129-140). But most of it lay in wild, heavily overgrown country which appears to have been relatively untouched since the 18th century. Brief attempts by the LMS to discover other archeological contexts in 1975 were thwarted by the rugged natural conditions. However, in the fall of 1976 two burials with an impressive array of grave goods were unearthed by an inmate of the prison. Most of these finds were confiscated by the authorities and turned over to the state archeologist, who in turn brought them to our attention. The prospect of forging another missing link was sufficient encouragement to bring us to the field posthaste.

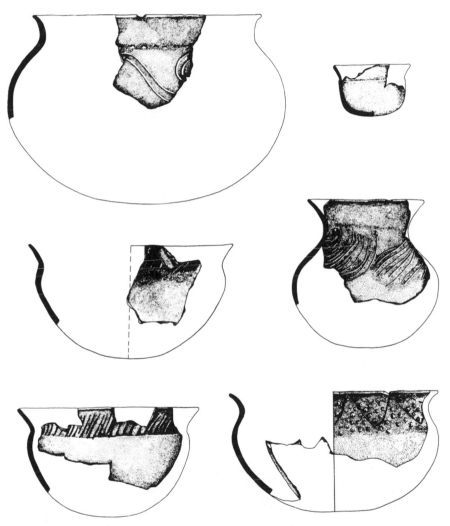

FIG. 4.   Tunica pottery of the early 18th century from Portland.

FIG. 5. Burial of adult female at Angola. She was accompanied by an aboriginal bowl and European brass kettle. Personal adornments included marine shell ear pins of native manufacture and glass trade beads.

FIG. 6.   Detail of child burial at Angola. Of considerable interest was the crucifix, a token of Christian missionizing, found beneath the elaborate marine shell necklace, an indication of high status in the native society.

The Excavations

The first investigation, conducted during the spring of 1977, focused upon the excavation of what we anticipated to be an early 18th-century cemetery of the Tunica. Unfortunately, the cemetery location was not as pristine as had been hoped, and in fact it came to our attention during the excavations that it had been despoiled clandestinely over a 2-year period prior to its official reporting to state authorities. However, with the help of the Louisiana Archaeological Survey and prison labor we completely exposed the entire location and conducted an electronic survey. We were able to pinpoint and remove four undisturbed burials, as well as three more which had been partly looted. These burials were extremely informative and contained artifactual materials consistent with French contact during the first third of the 18th century (table 2; see also Brain, 1977: 9-13).

Even more important for our over-all researches on the Tunica, we were also able to locate a village occupation area adjacent to the cemetery. We put

TABLE 2. Burials Excavated by the Lower Mississippi Survey at Angola in 1977

Age/Sex	Accompaniments	Orientation
Adult male	Musket, shot and powder, spare gun parts; aboriginal stone tools	East
Adult female	Brass kettle, containing an aboriginal Natchezan bowl; white glass beads and native columella shell ear pins; and she was wearing a cuffed dress coat of European origin	East (fig. 5)
Adolescent (female?)	Two iron axes, and a quantity of blue glass beads apparently strung and woven into the hair	East
Child (male?)	Lavishly accompanied with hundreds of beads of many types, copper bells, two steel clasp knives, and other European miscellany; aboriginal Caddoan pottery vessel, and elaborate marine shell necklace	West (fig. 6)

in several exploratory trenches during the final week of operations and discovered a zone of undisturbed midden and features. Artifactual materials included European items similar to those from the cemetery, as well as a fine assemblage of Tunica Indian pottery.

The second stage of investigation was carried out in October as a continuation of the excavation at the promising village occupation area. Prison labor was again employed, and within a 2-week period the remaining undisturbed midden and associated features were removed. Altogether, 200 square meters of surface area was opened to an average depth of 50 cm.

The cultural remains added considerably to our artifactual data for the French and Indians of the early 18th century. The European artifacts included known period pieces, as well as a variety of other items which could now be placed solidly in time. The native artifacts were still plentiful at this stage of early European contact, and provide a valuable measure of material acculturation (see table 1). Furthermore, particular ceramic and lithic types form a solid link between the Yazoo and Trudeau sites, and make possible a certain ethnic identification.

In sum, we are satisfied that we have pinned down a Tunica settlement dating to the period 1706-1731. While the location is not likely to have been the site of the principal village of the Tunica during this period, it was certainly one of the outlying villages mentioned in the contemporary accounts. In any case, it is a valuable addition to the history and archeology of the Tunica, neatly tying together our work on the Yazoo and the Tunica Treasure site (Trudeau).

Conclusion

The major result of these projects is a secure archeological recognition of the various kinds of cultural remains relative to the participant traditions, native and European, during the early historic contact period in old French Louisiana. Furthermore, we can organize this archeological data into specific events that provide a tightly controlled datum for the study of Indian and French interaction in this context.

The information thus generated is vitally important to the over-all Tunica project. Once again, the Tunica may be placed solidly in time and space, thus strengthening the key role we have designed for them as the prime ethnohistoric datum during the dynamic events of the protohistoric-early historic contact period in the Lower Mississippi Valley. Two more very important parts to this case study of cultural interaction and change have been given substance as a result of our archeological work during 1974 and 1977.

REFERENCES

BRAIN, JEFFREY P.
 1969.   Winterville: a case study of prehistoric culture contact in the Lower Mississippi Valley.   Ph.D. dissertation, Yale University. New Haven.
 1970.   The Tunica treasure.   Lower Mississippi Survey, Bulletin, no. 2. Peabody Museum. Cambridge.
 1973.   Trudeau: an 18th century Tunica village.   Lower Mississippi Survey, Bulletin, no. 3. Peabody Museum. Cambridge.
 1976.   From the words of the living: the Indian speaks.   Pp. 74-103, *in* "Clues to America's Past." National Geographic Society Special Publication. Washington.
 1977.   On the Tunica trail.   Louisiana Archaeological Survey and Antiquities Commission, Anthropological Study, no. 1. Baton Rouge.
 1978.   Late prehistoric settlement patterning in the Yazoo Basin and Natchez Bluffs regions of the Lower Mississippi Valley.   *In* "Mississippian Settlement Patterns," B. D. Smith, ed.   Academic Press. New York.
 1979.   Tunica Treasure.   Papers of the Peabody Museum, vol. 71. Cambridge.
 ———.   Cultural dynamics in the Lower Mississippi Valley, A.D. 1000-1700: a case study of Mississippian impact on the southern periphery.   *In* "Reviewing Mississippian Development," S. Williams, ed.   School of American Research and University of New Mexico Press. Santa Fe. (In press.)
 ———   Tunica Archaeology.   Papers of the Peabody Museum. Cambridge. (In preparation.)
BRAIN, JEFFREY P.; TOTH, ALAN; and RODRIGUEZ-BUCKINGHAM, ANTONIO
 1974.   Ethnohistoric archaeology, and the De Soto entrada into the Lower Mississippi Valley.   Conference on Historic Site Archaeology, Papers, vol. 7, pp. 232-289.
BROWN, IAN W.
 1975.   Archaeological investigations at the historic Portland and St. Pierre sites in the lower Yazoo Basin, Mississippi, 1974.   M.A. thesis, Brown University. Providence.
 1978.   An archaeological survey of Mississippi period sites in Coahoma County, Mississippi.   Ms. Lower Mississippi Survey, Peabody Museum. Cambridge.
FORD, JAMES A.
 1936.   Analysis of Indian village site collections from Louisiana and Mississippi.   Louisiana Geological Survey, Anthropological Study, no. 2. New Orleans.
PHILLIPS, PHILIP
 1970.   Archaeological survey in the lower Yazoo Basin, Mississippi, 1949-1955.   Papers of the Peabody Museum, vol. 60. Cambridge.

JEFFREY P. BRAIN

Recovery of Hominid Skeletal Remains from Upper Pliocene Localities in Ethiopia

Principal Investigators: Francis H. Brown, University of Utah, Salt Lake City, Utah, and F. C. Howell, University of California, Berkeley, California.

Grant Nos. 1348 and 1413.   In support of a study of hominid skeletal remains from upper Pliocene localities in Ethiopia, and to assist in publication of the conference, "Stratigraphy, Paleoecology and Evolution in the Lake Rudolf Basin."

The Omo Research Expedition of 1974 was complicated by political problems in Ethiopia. The reign of Haile Selassie was nearing its end, and at first, it appeared that permission to enter the lower Omo Valley via Kenya would not be granted. In the end, permission was received, but the expedition was allowed only 3 Kenyan staff members of the 13 who had been trained for several years by our expedition. Consequently, work proceeded less rapidly than had been hoped, but nonetheless a great deal was accomplished.

The objectives of the 1974 expedition were to clear up a few remaining stratigraphic problems, to continue excavations at a number of sites which had yielded hominids in 1973, to continue collection of micromammals, and to take further samples for paleomagnetic polarity determination. The scientific personnel involved were Dr. N. T. Boaz (University of California, Berkeley), Dr. F. H. Brown (University of Utah), Dr. J. de Heinzelin and Dr. P. Haesaerts (both of the University of Ghent). Kenyan staff members were Mr. Januari Kithumbi, Mr. John Munyoki, and Mr. John Kaumbulu. The representative from the National Museum of Ethiopia was Ato Allemayhu Asfa. A number of local people were hired to help with the excavations.

Excavations

Locality 894, situated in a fossiliferous horizon of silty sand in the middle of unit G-28 of the Shungura Formation, yielded a fragmentary hominid cranium with teeth in August 1973. In 1973 and 1974 the surface area around the original find was sieved by Dr. Boaz, and in 1974 the fossiliferous deposit was removed in its entirety. Fifty cranial fragments, many of them articulated, and a partial dental series were recovered.

81

The hominid cranium (L.894-1) is derived from a dark orange to reddish sesquioxide layer overlying a paleoland surface. The microstratigraphical relationships of the fossiliferous horizon were examined by Dr. de Heinzelin in 1974 in a trench cut through the deposits. The sediments of G-28 are faulted in the west and abut an unfossiliferous section of lacustrine sediments in unit G-9. The site is thought to represent a land surface, which lies between shallow lacustrine sediments, that was probably exposed by a small regression of the lake.

All of the cranial fragments show fresh breaks along their margins, and as all areas of the skull are represented, it is thought that the entire cranium was preserved in the deposit and only broken up and disarticulated upon exposure by erosion.

In 1973 a hominid mandible was found at locality 860, in unit F-1 of the Shungura Formation. Two quartz artifacts were found during surface survey of this locality in early July 1974. A step trench of 2.5-meter width was opened at this locality on July 3, 1974, at the site of the mandible find after sieving of the surface surrounding the original find had been completed. Dr. de Heinzelin drew a profile at the locality, and studied the microstratigraphy. It is nearly certain that the mandible is derived from a gravelly sand at the base of unit F-1 which has an age of about 2 million years.

The trench at L.860 was taken to a depth of 5 meters, and extended below the level of the mandible find, but the sparseness, derived nature, and abraded condition of the fossils, and the lack of artifacts in a primary context argued against further excavation at this site.

Locality 105 yielded a lumbar vertebra, originally though to be hominid but later decided to be that of a baboon. A richly fossiliferous horizon could not be located at this locality with certainty, and it was decided not to re-excavate during the 1974 field season. Many of the surface fossils could have derived from higher in the sequence, which was an additional factor in not extending the small excavation made at the site in 1973.

Locality 899 in unit C-8 was sieved for the remains of a large cercopithecine proximal humerus found through surface survey. Only one small fragment of the shaft was recovered.

Excavation was begun at locality F-400 in the southern Kalam exposures in unit L-2 after the discovery of a largely intact elephant cranium during surface survey on July 9, 1974. A bone level was located at this locality and excavation continued through July with some 20 square meters being exposed. Unfortunately, bone was sparse and fragmentary, and with the exception of the elephant cranium little of interest was recovered.

F-507, a locality in unit H-1, yielded a suid limb bone and teeth, and an excavation of some 15 square meters was carried out in late July. A partial cranium of the bovid *Menelikia lyrocera* and a nearly complete palate with teeth of a possibly new species of *Mesochoerus* were recovered among other fossils.

Hominid Discoveries

Further cranial fragments were recovered from locality 894. This is the most complete of the Omo hominids to date, with both cranial parts and dentition known.

F.511-16, a hominid left third metatarsal from middle Member H (H-4 to H-6), was found in July. Based on its size and morphology it is probably the first *Australopithecus boisei* foot bone known from East Africa.

The locality P.996 was reinvestigated in 1974, but unsuccessfully. In 1973 the locality yielded the first firm evidence of *Homo erectus* in the lower Omo Valley.

Geological Work

In addition to determination of the microstratigraphy at the excavated sites, a number of geological tasks were completed. Dr. P. Haesaerts rechecked the stratigraphic levels of all fossil sites established previously. As nearly 1,000 sites were involved, distributed over about 30 square kilometers, the task was a large one, but successfully concluded.

Drs. de Heinzelin and Brown managed to securely weld the Shungura Formation exposures which occur south and west of Kalam to the type sections established to the north. So in the final field season, all exposures were placed into a single stratigraphic framework.

An additional 600 samples were taken for paleomagnetic polarity determination from levels where the magnetostratigraphy was unclear. The laboratory work has been completed, and the results have been published in the *Geophysical Journal* of the Royal Astronomical Society.

Paleontological Collections

An attempt was made to enhance the collections of fossil vertebrates from the upper members of the Shungura Formation (members H, J, K, and L) by intensive collections in these members whenever time permitted. The faunal assemblages from these members are critical to an understanding of the ecological conditions in the lower Omo Valley from about 1.8 to 0.8 million years ago. The effort was rewarding, although further collection is still desirable.

An attempt also was made to enhance the micromammal collections. To this end, a large amount of sediment from known micromammal localities was washed to remove the fine particles, and the concentrate shipped to Addis Ababa for further sorting.

REFERENCES

BOAZ, N. T., and HOWELL, F. C.
 1977. A gracile hominid cranium from upper Member G, Shungura Formation, Ethiopia. Amer. Journ. Phys. Anthrop., vol. 46, pp. 93-108.

BROWN, F. H., SHUEY, R. T., and CROES, M. K.
 1978. Magnetostratigraphy of the Shungura and Usno Formations: Additional data and comprehensive reanalysis. Geophys. Journ. Royal Astron. Soc., vol. 54, pp. 519-538.

ROGERS, R. J., and BROWN, F. H.
 1979. Authigenic mitridatite from the Shungura Formation, southwestern Ethiopia. Amer. Mineral., vol. 64, pp. 169-171.

FRANCIS H. BROWN

Archeological Investigations at Quiriguá, Guatemala

Principal Investigators: William R. Coe (1975), University Museum, University of Pennsylvania, Philadelphia; Robert J. Sharer (1976), University Museum, University of Pennsylvania, Philadelphia.

Grant Nos. 1384 and 1534.   In support of archeological investigations of the ruins and setting of Quiriguá, Guatemala.

Quiriguá is a major Maya lowland archeological site located in the vast alluvial flood-plain of the Lower Motagua Valley in eastern Guatemala (see maps, figs. 1 and 2). As such, it dominates a large, but almost unknown, region in the southeast lowlands of the Maya area.

Quiriguá first came to public attention through the visit of Frederick Catherwood in 1840. Since that time the site has been visited and studied by numerous scholars, most of whom have devoted a good part of their attention to the magnificent sculptured monuments. Between 1881 and 1894 Alfred P. Maudslay (1889-1902) recorded the known monuments, using photography and molds. Maudslay also instigated the first probes into the ruined structures at Quiriguá. In the 20th century, much of the central area of the site (now known as the Acropolis) was cleared of debris by successive field projects of the Archaeological Institute of America and the Carnegie Institution of Washington (see Hewett, 1911, 1912, 1913, 1916; Morley, 1914). The latter institution sponsored restoration of one structure (Str. 1B-1), studies of the hieroglyphic inscriptions (Morley, 1937-1938), and the resetting of several stelae (Stromsvik, 1941). During this period also the principal groups of ruins were set aside as a park, thanks to the United Fruit Co., owners of the land. In recent years, the monumental inscriptions have received renewed epigraphic attention (Kelley, 1962; Hatch, 1975).

Despite this past work, we had as of 1973 (when the Quiriguá Project was formulated) little basic archeological data from Quiriguá. Apart from the relatively short (ca. 80 years) time span indicated by the monuments, little published information was available bearing upon the time and duration of occupation at the site; no artifactual sequences existed for either Quiriguá or the lower Motagua Valley. Furthermore, we knew almost nothing about the constructional sequence and function of the variety of architectural features at the site. Nevertheless, a variety of hypotheses had been proposed to account for the location, and explain the function, of Quiriguá. Quiriguá has been most commonly considered a satellite of Copán, located some 50 kilometers to the south (Morley, 1920; Kelley, 1962). But also Quiriguá has been portrayed as a "breakaway" or rebel center that severed its ties from its larger parent site (Proskouriakoff, 1973; Hatch, 1975). From another perspective, Quiriguá has often been viewed as a trading center, controlling highland-lowland commerce (e.g., obsidian) along the Motagua Valley route (Hammond, 1972). Yet, because of the dearth of data from Quiriguá, these hypotheses have not gone beyond the status of mere possibilities. Indeed, adequate data for the entire southeastern periphery of the Maya area—including Quiriguá—are only now beginning to be acquired (Voorhies, 1972; Sharer, 1974, 1975; Willey, Coe, and Sharer, 1976). In this light, an understanding of Quiriguá and its ancient role within the southeastern periphery is of vital importance for an ultimate understanding of this entire region (Sharer, 1978).

The Quiriguá Project

The Quiriguá Project was established in 1973 through a contract between the Ministry of Education (Government of Guatemala) and the University Museum, University of Pennsylvania, in order to initiate the first systematic archeological investigations at Quiriguá. The Project undertook two broad responsibilities: archeological research (funded by the University Museum, the National Geographic Society, and other institutions) and a consolidation/renovation program (funded by the Guatemalan Government) to be discharged over five seasons of work (1974 through 1978).

The research goals of the Project were cast in culture-historical as well as functional and explanative terms (Sharer and Coe, 1979). The first of these aims was to document the basic chronology of activity (constructional, occu-

---

KEY TO FIGURE 1
Archeological Sites

1. Quiriguá	6. Guaytan	11. Seibal	16. Uaxactun
2. Copán	7. Chalchuapa	12. Lubaantun	17. Tikal
3. Playitas	8. Kaminaljuyu	13. Caracol	18. Yaxha
4. Naco	9. Palenque	14. Barton Ramie	19. Dzibilchaltun
5. Los Naranjos	10. Altar de Sacrificios	15. San Jose	20. Cozumel Island

Geological Resource Areas
a. Ixtepeque (obsidian)
b. El Chayal (obsidian)
c. Middle Motagua (jadeite)

pational, ritual, political, and so forth) at the site via both deep stratigraphic and lateral excavations. The resulting artifactual and architectural sequences could be linked, if possible, to a refined monument sequence based upon epi-

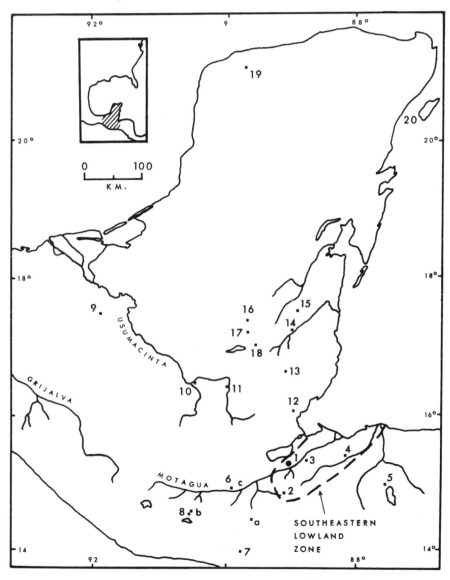

FIG. 1. Map showing location of Quiriguá in eastern Guatemala.

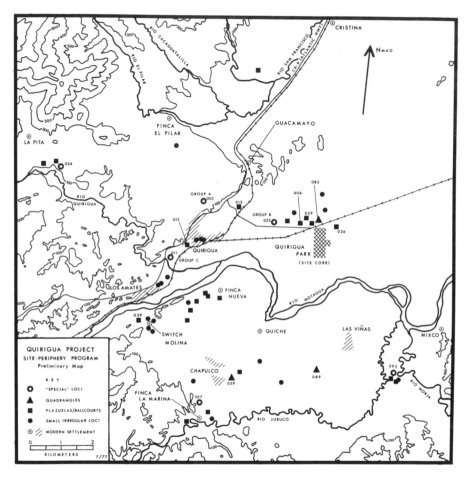

FIG. 2. Map of the area investigated by the Quiriguá Project site-periphery program.

graphic data. The second objective was to define (map) and determine the function(s) of the site of Quiriguá, based upon the nature and patterning of structures as well as epigraphic studies, within the site-core (see fig. 3). A third goal was to define and determine the function(s) and relationships of the site periphery via investigation of the nature and distribution of outlying structures or activity loci. The final objective was to test and refine the various hypotheses (see above) in order to better explain the origins, location, function, and demise of Quiriguá. The Project's consolidation and renovation re-

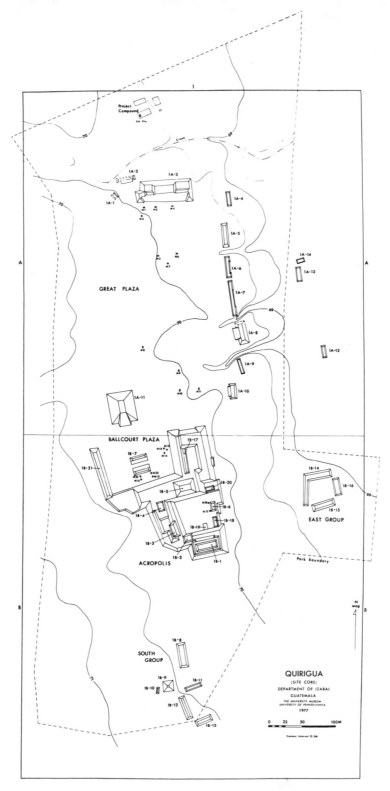

FIG. 3.   Map of the site core. Quiriguá.

sponsibilities were to be met by two programs: the preservation of all monuments and the consolidation of selected structures within the park.

At the present writing the Project has completed its research. The 1974 operations were limited to preliminary mapping and testing at Quiriguá and in outlying groups within the lower Motagua Valley. The following report summarizes research conducted in 1975 and 1976. Full-scale research at Quiriguá and its peripheries was launched in the 1975 season. The 1976 season continued this research and saw the initiation of the Guatemalan Government's structural consolidation program. The remainder of the research will be treated in subsequent reports.

The 1975 Season

In January 1975, working under a 5-year contract between the University Museum and the Guatemalan Government—through the Ministry of Public Education and its dependency, the Institute of Anthropology and History (IDAEH)—a research staff of seven began the arduous but exciting work of unraveling the details of development and decline of this site. Funds for the full-scale first season were supplied by the University Museum, the Ford Foundation, and the National Geographic Society, of the United States; and in Guatemala by the National Government and the independent Tikal Association.

For purposes of summary presentation, investigations are here divided into topical categories: mapping, excavation and architectural recording, sculptural and epigraphic recording, peripheral reconnaissance and settlement studies, and laboratory processing and analysis (see Coe and Sharer, 1979).

The Map. Since none of the extant maps was fully adequate, we undertook the remapping of epicentral Quiriguá—that is, the area included within Quiriguá Park, or what Morley calls the Main Group. After fixing a primary bench mark in the cement floor of the laboratory, we imposed a 500-meter square, magnetically oriented grid on the site; the system of designation of squares is infinitely expandable. We have now all but completed the plane-table-and-alidade mapping of the $\frac{1}{2}$ square-kilometer core of Quiriguá, and when completed the result will be published at a 1:2000 scale with 1-meter contour intervals.

As a part of the mapping project (fig. 3), we changed the designation for structural entities at Quiriguá, dropping a series of ill-defined names in favor of the simple, inferentially uncluttered label of "structure" (Coe and Sharer, 1979).

The Excavations and Architectural Recording. During the 1975 season, excavations were planned so as to achieve as comprehensive a view as possible of constructional stratigraphy and composition, physical articulations, and variations in structural design. There were four foci of activity: Structure 1A-3, Structure 1A-2, the Acropolis, and the South Group and Structure 1B-8.

(1). Structure 1A-3. With its long axis set east-west, this massive feature dominates the north end of the half-kilometer-long Plaza and forms the visible backdrop for the four northernmost monuments. No prior excavations had been done here and we were optimistic that its principal recorded characteristic (Morley, 1937-1938, vol. 4, p. 180), the apparent lack of cut-stone masonry, was an accident of decay and mound-formation. What emerged from our excavations (as Operation 2) was a truly complex entity, wherein the presumed original structure (1A-3-2d) had been almost totally stripped of masonry in preparation for superimposing a new structure (1A-3-1st) over the whole. Only on the northern flanks did we find the masonry of 2d still in place. But construction of 1st was halted permanently at about the halfway point; using huge quantities of fill, workers had managed to inter only the north face and central upper portions of the old structure before the project was abandoned.

In brief, 2d was a steeply pitched substructure, with a low basal molding along its sides and rear, and a massive, continuous second molding rising from the first to the summit. The aproned terrace, with floor surfaces of crushed rhyolite "plaster," carried shortly around the southeast and southwest corners, terminating at the extremities of the broad inset stairway. The summit was occupied by a platform running its entire length, probably with short southern extensions at the ends to match the very broad "U" form of the structure as a whole. Facing masonry throughout was a mix of small, finely cut marble and rhyolite blocks set in a dense mud mortar. The fill had been staged in vertical and horizontal units and consisted of immense amounts of riverine muds and silts as matrix for probably an equal volume of variegated rubble.

Demolition destroyed the entire stairway except the basal riser: the stairway appears to have been pried out block by block rather than stripped away via a deep top-to-bottom excavation. The north face was expanded by marked construction units some 16 meters to the north in line with the ends of the old structure, concealing the apron terrace of 2d. In the center, a low rhyolite-faced platform was begun but apparently left unfinished. And the north face and sides of the massive addition, designated as Structure 1A-3-1st, were never formally walled: the faces we found were rough retaining walls sealing interior fill units. Moreover, the stairway of 1st, if we presume it was to have been south-oriented like its demolished predecessor, was apparently never begun.

A thick layer of undisturbed riverine silt sealed the basal remains of the stairway and adjacent terraces of 2d. What appeared to be post-demolition wash from the stripped south slope of 2d was also found to drift out onto the old riverstone Plaza. Here, the wash admixed with the disintegrated crushed rhyolite surfacing of the Plaza, all overlain by the silt. These various features appear to preclude modern robbery of 2d. Similarly this silt, which had accumulated basally against the expansion known as 1st, sealed nothing that could be treated as finished masonry. But this still leaves unexplained the need to destroy so much of 2d, unless the scheduled replacement of its stairway was to duplicate the original position and pitch but in new masonry. The latter might have been planned as large sandstone blocks, for we suspect that such was favored in late times at the site.

Axial trenching at the front of the structure and at Plaza level was carried south, intersecting the far west edge of a previously unknown platform surrounding Monument 4 (formerly Stela D; see below). This clearly had been anciently disturbed, for the naturally deposited layer of silt overlay not only a demolition line across the surface of the platform but also large blocks of seemingly dislodged sandstone masonry resting on disintegrated Plaza flooring and outwash from Structure 1A-3 alongside the platform. Oddly enough, the basal masonry along the west side was rhyolite. And while we believe the visible perimeter of the platform to have consisted of a single course of sandstone blocks, our trench disclosed an insufficient number of such blocks to restore it.

A test pit extending west from the central trench disclosed the expected 0.60-meter-thick silt layer overlying the formal Plaza. The upper limit of the Plaza consisted of a one-stone-thick layer of flat river rocks that carried bits of disintegrated granulated rhyolite surfacing; the same layer of cobbles abutted both the stela platform and the surviving first step of Structure 1A-3-2d. Directly beneath this layer and separated from it by some 10 centimeters of packed earth and mud was a 1.6-meter-thick stratum, with clear "pause lines," of pure rounded cobbles interspersed by dark mud. This foundation overlay what appeared to be sterile silt. Attempts to deepen the cut were thwarted at this point by the high water table.

In the course of this work the possibility of a monument having been removed east of Monument 4 was tested. We found no evidence for this, a result that makes us ponder all the more the asymmetrical arrangement of monuments along the south side of Str. 1A-3 (see fig. 3).

The various related excavations centering on this structure brought us to realize, early in the season, certain marked complexities of Quiriguá. First, since most fills, as just seen, were devoid of sherd material (let alone burials and other special deposits), the usual ceramic dating of construction seemed precluded. Conceivably, however, materials and methods of installation used in building underwent sequent and reconstructable changes. In line with this question, we also pondered the cost of construction material here: the sedimentary sandstones came from 3.5 kilometers north of the site, marble from a much greater distance (some 20 kilometers), metamorphic serpentines from up to 10 kilometers away, and rhyolite from a totally unknown volcanic source, to say nothing of the staggering volume of mud and stone fill material brought in from the river. And even granting that the raw materials were possibly collected from natural taluses, we must still add the labor costs of dressing marble and rhyolite. To our minds the greatest extravagance was the presence in fill of marble and rhyolite, in chunks probably too large to represent masons' detritus: weighty pieces apparently were brought into the site along with more easily available sandstones simply as volume-making fill. Structure 1A-3 also raised the puzzle of why construction work should have been permanently halted, leaving a major edifice in a shambles, and, of course, the question of whether (and if so, how) such disruption related to abandonment of the site.

(2). Structure 1A-2.   This feature drew our attention first by a combination of its odd location and orientation, just north of the west end of Structure 1A-3, and, later, by the possibility that it was not a structure at all but rather the stockpiled missing masonry of Structure 1A-3, just discussed. A few hours of digging (as Operation 5) disclosed steps of a south-oriented stairway, and thus, our tentative explanation collapsed.

The structure proved to comprise a substructure featuring two terraces with simple vertical walls and marked by a broad central south-projecting stairway, the latter littered with pottery. The whole was faced with mixed rhyolite and marble blocks, masonry essentially matching that of nearby Structure 1A-3. On the summit was a badly ruined platform, which yielded no evidence of masonry walls. The west end and rear of the structure were gone, presumably demolished in cutting adjacent (modern) drainage ditches. Our axial trench disclosed a unitized fill, like that of Str. 1A-3, composed of river cobbles, sandstone, and marble rubble in a largely mud matrix. Neither cobblestone foundation nor formal flooring was found about or under the substructure.

(3). Acropolis.   Although long-published in plan, the awesome size and intricate conformation of the Acropolis became apparent to us only after the high underbrush covering it was cleared early in the season. Also revealed, however, were the depressing extent of its deterioration and the enormous amounts of old excavation "spoil" left about the area of the court (Morley's

"Temple Plaza"). As had long been known, the five buildings exposed between 1894 and 1919 by Maudslay, then Hewett, Morris, and finally Morley, had seriously deteriorated and rooms once cleared had become half-obscured with fresh debris.

Our initial step, that of digging out the collapsed interiors of buildings, merely exacerbated the problem of accumulated debris, for after we had stockpiled all recoverable masonry nearby, the huge balances of dirt had to be dumped into the already inundated court area. Thanks to the timely loan of trucks and a gigantic front-end loader, we were able—over a period of several weeks—to free the court of 90 percent of old debris, as well as of all that produced by our fresh excavations. The literally thousands of cubic meters of dirt and stone were trucked beyond the Acropolis and piled for eventual use—for instance, in backfilling trenches and later repair work. In future seasons, a dump truck and a small front-end loader lent by the current Proyecto Tikal should suffice to keep clearing abreast of excavation.

Although most prior excavations were (fortunately) confined to a late, shallow level, the virtual lack of records from such work makes determination of the original condition of the mounds and "inter-mound" areas a serious problem. Many surface details—such as original debris line and the sequence of mound-forming collapse—have been irretrievably lost. To add to the difficulty, we must contend with other modern activities, from well-intentioned partial resetting of the great central stairway facing the Plaza, to post-excavational collapse, to illegal digging and even robbery of once-recorded sculpted stones. While at times we began to feel the Acropolis had been hopelessly brutalized, we continue to believe that it remains archeologically salvageable.

Excavations down in the court have verified four distinct stages in a complex history of growth. The earliest court overlies an apparently natural silt, which, by its level, should be the same stratum encountered beneath Plaza foundations to the north. The first court was constructed of fill floored twice by a crushed rhyolite plaster. The second and third stages of construction repeated this fill-plus-plaster-flooring sequence. But the final stage of growth differed in that the fill was capped first by a continuous, tightly fitted paving of large, relatively thin schistose slabs. Then, as before, it was sealed by the familiar rhyolite-based plaster; there are traces of two subsequent refurbishings of this floor.

The same four stages—incorporating close to 4 meters of vertical growth—were found both to the west and south to integrate with a series of terraces and associated stairways, often with secondary additions. Partially dismantled buried buildings and major structural rip-outs add to the analytic complexity. From an architectural standpoint, most surprising were two cases of free-standing, nonbearing walls. Both were buried by later construction and one was decorated by an imposing row of five monumentally scaled masks, carved in deep relief in mixed sandstone and rhyolite, which alternate between depictions of "Kinich Ahau" and a serpent with human arms.

As part of the over-all investigation of the Acropolis this year, excavations were carried out about the great zoomorphs and their altars (Mons. 15, 16, 23, 24). This work (Operation 4) was geared principally to relating the monuments stratigraphically to their supporting platform, to the Plaza proper, to the ballcourt, and, via the great sandstone staircase, to the Acropolis itself. Although research was impeded by earlier cache-oriented cuts here, it seems reasonably certain we are dealing with a sequence proceeding from basal natural silt, to the formation of a cobble plaza-foundation, then to construction of the monument platform, and finally to the addition of the Acropolis stairway. It remains for future work to tie the ballcourt to this series and to relate both Plaza and platform directly to the Acropolis by tracing their extent south beneath the great staircase.

(4). The "South Group" and Structure 1B-8. To provide a possible functional contrast, a compact group of structures lying south of the Acropolis was investigated in a limited manner (see map, fig. 2). The six mounds that make up this potentially domestic group were relocated and bushed, but excavation this season was confined to Structure 1B-8 (Operation 7A). Various cuts disclosed a substructure built first of cobble fill, encased by sandstone rubble in mud, and the whole finally faced by sandstone block masonry and schistose slabs that likely were once sealed by plaster. In plan, the substructure appears as three superimposed platforms. The basal and uppermost platforms are simple rectangles, but the intermediate one has inset corners on its east side. On the west is a stairway that runs basally the entire length of the substructure, but contracts markedly with each ascending level. No signs of a masonry substructure were detected, and the possibility of a perishable one was left unconfirmed owing to our inability to locate postholes on the eroded summit.

While most masonry had toppled from position, little of it was found in excavation. This raises the possibility of deliberate removal for reuse elsewhere, as if this structure—like Structure 1A-3 to the north—had been largely dismantled. If so, demolition was selective, for the southern part of the basal platform was still essentially intact.

Epigraphic and Sculptural Records. As with construction entities, the carved monoliths of Quiriguá have borne a confusing assortment of labels. To simplify, we have converted past systems to a single series incorporating all free-standing stone elements, each now bearing the same reasonably noncommittal name of "monument" (Coe and Sharer, 1979).

Concerning extant records of the monuments—and other sculptural material—we have come to the reluctant conclusion that we ought to assemble a fresh and comprehensive photographic file on this material. From these photographs inked diagrams in line and stipple could be prepared at a standard scale, as has been done at Tikal and elsewhere by others. Actual recording following these procedures began in the 1975 season with the famous but poorly documented Monuments 23 and 24. Their sculptured surfaces were plotted, then photographed, and converted finally, in Philadelphia, to quarter-scale, inked, standardized diagrams. Because of the new drawings, Christopher Jones has been able to initiate epigraphic study of these important texts. Recording was begun for the small, mirror-image Monuments 18 and 19, but only provisional drawings are possible until more cleaning is completed and critical photography is done with artificial light.

Settlement Survey. Our understanding of Quiriguá requires that attention be paid not only to the elites and to sumptuous ceremonial remains of the "core" of the site but also to the modest homes, workshops, and burial sites of the general population as well. In 1973, Timothy Nowak of Harvard University began an archeological survey in the Lower Motagua Valley, including the Quiriguá area but focusing on regional distribution of settlement. Not until the present Quiriguá Project has there been a study specifically designed to examine the nature of the greater Quiriguá "community." Reconnaissance, mapping, surface-collection, and selective excavation for such a study were begun in 1975 by Wendy Ashmore as part of the site periphery program (fig. 2). Settlement remains appear to be abundant both on the valley floor and along the benches to the north. Survey is hindered, however, by modern settlement and, on the Motagua floodplain, by alluviation. We hope in future seasons to employ a number of survey techniques to overcome these obstacles—from aerial photography to magnetometer and resistivity surveys, to interval coring and examination of extant ditch faces.

Along the first bench, structures were found located close to the low but precipitous drop to the valley floor. All mounds are small, occurring close to present-day water sources in irregular groups of less than 10. Surface collections at such loci were generally sparse, but one group of six mounds yielded abundant obsidian *débitage*. Time permitted the test-pitting of only one mound on the bench (Operation 8Q), work that yielded a few coarse sherds and some obsidian. With sparse cobble inclusions, fill consisted mainly of tamped earth. The summit had been floored no more than twice, but positive evidence of a building was lacking on the platform. Other disturbed mounds adjacent to the Project's camp in Los Amates show evidence of a nearly pure riverstone fill (cf. Operation 8R). Interestingly enough, the flat sweeps of the Río Motagua fronting Los Amates continue today to be "mined" commercially for cobbles to be used in construction.

On the valley floor mounds are distributed singly as well as in clusters of fewer than five. A possible ballcourt occurs northwest of the Park. Such still observable mounds, alone and grouped, are generally separated by distances on the order of 100 meters. The visibility afforded by recent conversion of former banana land to cattle pasture helps sighting, and we are impressed by the number of mounds evident. But, as noted before, alluvial accumulation buries all but the highest pre-Columbian remains. With this in mind, we tested a mound merely 0.6 meters high (Operation 8P) northwest of the Park. Accounting for this elevation were slumped masonry walls and benches; the 1-meter-high substructure lay 0.2 meter below the present ground surface. The potentials of the valley were further tested by reconnoitering an old drainage canal running north-south about a kilometer east of the Park (Operation 8S). Fairly large numbers of surface sherds were collected quite continuously along the roughly 1,000 meters of embankments inspected.

Morley's outlying Groups A, B, and C were all visited in 1975. In Group A, high on the second bench with a splendid sight of the entire valley, it was found that Morley had omitted a long, narrow mound along the west side of the platform-plaza as well as a probable mound at the end of a possibly natural ridge running north from the platform. Early Monuments 20 and 21, long toppled and abandoned, were relocated in Group A. (It is planned that these be moved to the Park for safety and study.)

As regards Group B, the mounds were found not to be so symmetrically arranged as Morley (1937-1938: pl. 215b) shows them. Monument 19 also appears in plan too far south. This incomplete stela strikes us as likely having been reset here.

Group C, barely described in the literature (ibid.: IV, 241), is today visible from the Atlantic Highway and consists of five substantial mounds, four of which occupy a plaza overlooking the Quiriguá River. Midway between the two largest mounds is the fallen Monument 25, Morley's Unsculptured Stela. This is a plain cylindrical shaft of yellow sandstone (not whitish schist as Morley states). Two lower mounds lie south of the monument and, south of these, flat, possibly artificial terracing drops several meters to the river. Set on the crest of a natural rise, the fifth mound of the group is about 120 meters north of the plaza. No surface sherds or other artifacts were found in this group.

Laboratory Analyses. In 1975 a field laboratory was established under the direction of Mary R. Bullard. Obsidian promises to be a major study category and one that is additionally intriguing in the light of the hypothesized role of Quiriguá in the trade of Ixtepeque material (Hammond, 1972). Pottery censers also impress us by their frequency, especially those of a stratigraphically intermediate part of the Acropolis. Strikingly, we have yet to see flint in any form appear in the day-to-day collections, and pottery figurines have so far proved to be most rare.

A preliminary study of the 1975 collections of Quiriguá ceramics was done by Sharer in the last weeks of the season in order to assess the possibilities of chronological change and functional differentiation within the site. To do this, a rough typological classification was made following the procedures of the type-variety method. The sherd sample consisted of (a) material from two test pits within the laboratory compound (Operations 3C and 3D) and (b) sherds recovered in sequent constructional and occupational units within the south trench in the Acropolis (Operation 6I). These two sources have to date been the most productive, for most excavation lots have been in fills either sterile or nearly so.

From the limited results obtained thus far, it appears that the pottery from Quiriguá proper is limited in both time span and diversity. With the exception of a few Preclassic examples from the test pits on the north edge of the site (Ops. 3C and 3D), all sherds examined appear to be Late Classic or possibly (in some cases) Early Postclassic. The number of types is quite limited, and there is a surprising lack of decorative elaboration; to date there are no examples of the usual Late Classic polychrome types usually encountered at Maya lowland sites. The most striking omission, considering the purported close ties to nearby Copán, is the surprising rarity of Copador pottery, the diagnostic Late Classic ware of Copán (Longyear, 1952).

The pottery picture at Quiriguá contrasts with that emerging from the surrounding valley. The Project settlement survey and the work of Timothy Nowak, who conducted a site survey of the Lower Motagua, have both revealed considerable ceramic diversity. A fuller range of Preclassic (Middle and Late), some Early Classic and Postclassic wares—all absent or feebly represented at the Quiriguá site—seems to be present in the valley.

Further testing at Quiriguá and the surrounding area should establish whether or not this apparent disparity in ceramic distribution is real. If the pattern is substantiated, the pottery evidence should provide information concerning Quiriguá's temporal position, its degree of sociopolitical integration with the rest of the Lower Motagua Valley, and its relationship to Copán.

FIG. 4.   Earthquake damage. Quiriguá workmen erecting temporary bracing to support Monument 10, snapped at the base on February 4, 1976.

The 1976 Season

Support for the 1976 season's work was supplied by the University Museum (Francis Boyer Museum Fund), the National Geographic Society, and the National Science Foundation (grant 7602185 and doctoral dissertation grant 7603283), as well as by several private benefactors.

The most conspicuous event of the 1976 season was the disastrous earthquake of February 4. Fortunately, although located near the Motagua fault, the Quiriguá area was spared much of the devastation that struck the central and eastern highlands of Guatemala. No one associated with the Project was injured, and damage to Project facilities was minimal. The ruins were more affected; two stelae snapped from their bases and parts of several walls tumbled (see fig. 4). Despite the national state of emergency in Guatemala, however, the supervisory staff of 10 and the 60 Project workmen were able to accomplish all of our basic objectives for the season.

The objectives and results can be summarized under five programs: site mapping, site-core excavation, site-periphery program, monument preservation and recording, and pottery analysis.

(1). In the mapping program, the goal was to complete the contour map of the area within Quiriguá Park begun in 1975. The map was finished early in the season and will be published at a scale of 1:2000.

(2). The goals of excavation within the site core (see map, fig. 2) were to continue the 1975 investigations in the Acropolis and in Structure 1A-3, along with initiating excavations in several untested structures, in order to understand the basic construction sequence and, we hope, the function of these entities, as well as their chronological position relative to the dated monuments.

Work in the Acropolis area commenced with investigation of the east and south stairways flanking the Ballcourt Plaza (Morley's "Ceremonial Plaza"). The first construction phase revealed here was the erection of Platform 1B-3-2d on the east side of this Plaza, featuring the basal course of a presumed large-stone block staircase, side terraces, and frontal terrace. A large sandstone slab, placed on the early terrace floor axial to the stairway, was probably the pedestal stone for one of the three monuments found in the vicinity (Monuments 12, 13, and 14), and, therefore, provides a tentative link with their associated hieroglyphic dates. Monument 13, the most likely candidate because its shape is similar to that of the pedestal slab, bears probable dates of 9.15.0.0.0 and 9.15.3.2.0 (both ca. A.D. 730).

In the second phase of construction, the stairway of Platform 1B-3-2d was largely removed and a new stair (with a new frontal terrace) built over it, enveloping the pedestal stone. This renovation occurred at the same time that Structure 1B-5 was built: while the "pyramid" substructure of the latter abuts the southern terraces of the earlier platform, the uppermost terraces of Str. 1B-5 and Platform 1B-3-1st dovetail and rise in an unbroken line 2.5 meters higher than Platform 1B-3-2d. Platform 1B-3 ultimately was topped by construction of Str. 1B-17, a building platform whose cobble surface is reminiscent of the unfinished north face of Str. 1A-3-1st, at the north end of the Monument Plaza.

The final construction phase included setting the southern stairway of the Ballcourt Plaza, that of Platform 1B-2. The zoomorph terrace appears to run under this stairway. If the terrace was built to receive the zoomorphs, then this suggests that the monuments were in place by the time the stairway was constructed. In other words, it appears that the stairway was built after 9.18.5.0.0. (ca. A.D. 795, the date of Monuments 16 and 24).

After three weeks' research in the Ballcourt Plaza area, a plan for suggested reconstruction work was presented to and adopted by the Instituto de Antropología e Historia; this work began, under Instituto direction, before the close of the 1976 season.

No excavations were undertaken in the western part of the Ballcourt Plaza (Platform 1B-1), and research in the ballcourt itself was postponed until 1977.

Description of excavations in the Acropolis will proceed counterclockwise from Str. 1B-5 on the north, along the west rim of the complex to Str. 1B-6 on the east.

Interior excavation of Str. 1B-5 consisted of checking room step-ups and benches for secondary construction (none was found) and removing the roof stones of the rear chamber (heavily damaged in the February 4 earthquake). On the exterior, the west and north terraces of the substructure were traced to the level of the Ballcourt Plaza (see above), indicating that 1B-5 had originally been more isolated from the structures along the west side of the Acropolis. Investigations continued on the buried Structure 1B-5-2d, discovered in 1975 to underlie the western portion of Str. 1B-5. Although the west side of Str. 1B-5-2d had been partially destroyed during subsequent construction activities, enough remained to establish its plan as a single-room structure, facing south, atop a platform with wide inset stairway and sloping end terraces. A second buried structure (1B-Sub. 3) of comparable exterior dimensions was encountered farther to the northwest, but time permitted only preliminary clearing. Preserved in one corner to its plastered vaulted roof, Str. 1B-Sub. 3 has yielded the only complete building profile yet discovered at Quiriguá.

West of Str. 1B-Sub. 3, a third buried structure (1B-Sub. 2) was discovered by investigating the masonry lines visible on the surface of Platform 1B-2. These lines were the remains of the upper zone of a single-room vaulted building facing north. Str. 1B-Sub. 2 had the unusual features of a geometric mosaic frieze in its upper zone, as well as an exceptionally wide (3.8 meter) central doorway. The well-preserved structure had received a series of massive buttresses on all but the central part of its northern face. Before the construction of the final northern stairway of Platform 1B-2 (see above), the vaulted roof of Str. 1B-Sub. 2 was partly razed and its room and northern and eastern facades were buried by cobble fill.

Of the three buried structures discussed above, the two western examples stand in contrast to the one under Str. 1B-5. Strs. 1B-Sub. 2 and 3 are built of different style masonry, appear to rest at a lower level, and face north instead of south. And when Str. 1B-5-2d was buried by Str. 1B-5, its two companions were left uncovered. They were later buried, as noted, by the final stair of Platform 1B-2; no evidence of a later superstructure has been encountered.

The focus of 1976 Acropolis excavation was Platform 1B-4 (see fig. 5), the massive unit supporting Structures 1B-3 and 4. Platform 1B-4-2d, the earlier of the two stages presently recognized, had a broad central stairway on its eastern face leading up to three upper terraces (or broad steps) and topped by Str. 1B-Sub. 1, the free-standing mosaic-mask wall discovered in 1975 (see below). The wall may have been built at the same time as or later than the platform. The upper eastern terraces of Platform 1B-4-2d abut the wall of Structure 1B-2 to the south; its south and west sides rose in single steep and high terraces, forming a platform some 23 meters wide (east/west), which then narrowed to 7 meters in the center. Its total northern extent is not yet known, but it has been traced beyond the axis of Str. 1B-4, and since its surface is at about the same elevation as that of the platform of Str. 1B-5-2d (see above), the two may have been continuous. Platform 1B-4-1st consists of the latest stairway to the Acropolis court, the walls, floors, and western platforms which completely cover the earlier platform and its many structures and additions.

Excavations on the axis and the southeast corner of Str. 1B-4 revealed an earlier and similarly oriented platform beneath it, with an eastern stairway leading down to the level of Platform 1B-4-2d. The southern flanking terrace of this stairway both abuts and acts as a buttress for the northern part of Str. 1B-Sub. 1. A second, southern-facing stair leads down to Platform 1B-4-2d along the west face of Str. 1B-Sub. 1. Str. 1B-4 was built directly over this earlier platform and has the same axis and dimensions; new eastern and southern stairs were also superimposed on the old. Subsequent construction here

FIG. 5.   Air view of excavations in the Acropolis at Quiriguá, 1976. Looking east, Structure 1B-4 in the foreground; 1B-1 in upper right corner.

consisted of additions (especially buttressing) to and renovation of existing features, much of which work seems to have been occasioned by the severe structural deterioration of Str. 1B-4 during the period of its use. The source of the problems is unknown but could have been earthquakes combined with poor underpinnings (suggested by cracks and slumps in the underlying platform floor).

Structure 1B-3, to the south, was found to be later in the sequence of construction on the west side of the Acropolis. A large platform, northwest of Str. 1B-3 proper, was built after Str. 1B-4, and the rear cornice of Str. 1B-3 rests directly upon this platform. The latter thus resembles the buttresses of Str. 1B-Sub. 2, but it was built before rather than after the walls they support. Although Str. 1B-3 was more solidly constructed than Str. 1B-4, it too has a series of later buttress additions.

The mosaic frieze of Str. 1B-Sub. 1, which antedates both Strs. 1B-3 and 4, continued to be visible throughout these constructions. This wall began as a simple rectangle (in plan) but acquired platforms extending west at its south and north ends, forming a three-sided court on Platform 1B-4-2d. A series of four fill operations, each involving alternate halves (north or south) of the court, were associated with constructions in the areas of Strs. 1B-3 and 4 and resulted progressively in the burial of the lower reaches of the western face of Str. 1B-Sub. 1 (i.e., up to the base of the masks), then the lower parts of the southern mask, and finally in the complete interment of the wall.

Structure 1B-2, in the southwest corner of the Acropolis, is one of the earliest constructions in this complex. It rests on the lowest level of the Acropolis court and, like its later neighbors, evidences a series of added buttresses. Constructional weakness was thus a problem that Quiriguá builders learned early to patch but never to prevent. Medallions, identical to the one located by Morley on the front of Str. 1B-2, were also uncovered on the side and rear walls in a fine state of preservation.

Excavation in the vicinity of Str. 1B-1 revealed, in 1975, an east-west free-standing wall abutting the southeast corner of a north-south structure. The wall was traced this season to the east. The structure appears to be an earlier equivalent of Str. 1B-1, located slightly west of the latter, but similarly oriented to the north. It is almost opposite Str. 1B-5-2d at the north end of the Acropolis and is similarly built of white rhyolite masonry. The structure is early in the Acropolis sequence (before Platform 1B-4-2d) but still postdates Str. 1B-2. (See fig. 5.)

Structure 1B-6, which Morley thought to be early, is actually contemporary with the final level of the Acropolis court. Antecedent constructions were discovered here, though, and will be further investigated in later seasons.

Over-all, the sequent constructions revealed in the Acropolis in 1975 and 1976 suggest attempts at fortifications or at least the restriction of access to the inner plaza. Specifically, the free-standing wall north of Str. 1B-1, the buttresses of Str. 1B-2, the south and west walls of Platform 1B-4-2d, and the buttresses of Str. 1B-Sub. 2 formed an unbroken exterior face for the west and south sides of the Acropolis. The north side, with its line of buried structures, might have been defensible as well; the east side has yet to be investigated. Phases before and after these walls, on the other hand, do not appear to be as useful for restricting access, and such changes in inferred motivation will be further explored as they surely imply changes in the function of the site-core of Quiriguá.

Another pattern that has emerged is the patchwork nature of much of Quiriguá construction. Each platform or structure has many additions to it, buttresses and otherwise. Also, old features were reused as part of later constructions rather than being replaced (as at Tikal). In spite of the apparently short time depth of Acropolis construction, therefore, the stratigraphy is extremely complex.

North of the Acropolis, excavation continued the 1975 investigation of Str. 1A-3, especially focusing on location of the western end of Str. 1A-3-2d. The 1976 test was predicated on the proposition that the structure had been reoriented, with the earlier version centered on the earlier monuments (4 and 6) and the later on the over-all group (Monuments 1 through 7). The summit excavations were inconclusive, and no break (to demonstrate expansion to the west) could be found in the frontal stairway. Possible probes in later seasons would seek a rear corner for 1A-3-2d and an axial tomb in line with the latest associated monument (Monument 7, which seems to allude to death and accession events).

In Str. 1A-11, new excavations were initiated near the close of the season, clearing the base of the southern outset stairway and side terraces. This work will be continued in subsequent seasons.

Finally, tests were begun in two structures along the northeast border of the Monument Plaza. A central outset stairway, with side terraces, was cleared on Str. 1A-8. Str. 1A-10 also had an outset western stairway, but many of its stones had been ripped out. A low frontal platform was discovered by magnetic survey and confirmed by excavation. Further excavation is also planned here in the future.

(3). The goals of the site-periphery program were to complete identification and mapping of sites peripheral to Quiriguá and to begin excavation tests in a scientific sample of these activity loci. The survey aspect is essentially complete now, with 113 loci of pre-Columbian activity recorded within a roughly quadrilateral zone bounded by La Pita, Cristina, Mixco, and Finca La Marina (see map, fig. 3). Aerial reconnaissance of these 95 square kilometers in late March confirmed the reliability of the foot survey for locating surficial remains.

The loci vary considerably in form, size, and complexity, and a preliminary typology recognizes five formal categories. Nonarchitectural loci (total: 56) include primarily surface sherd scatters but also one probable midden; of course, subsequent excavation might reveal buried architecture. Small irregular groups have provisionally been classed with single mounds (presumably architectural platforms) representing the least "arranged" (and probably often partly destroyed) architectural remains (total: 30). Small, regularly arranged groups (total: 18) include both presumed ballcourts (3) and small open plazuelas (plazas bounded on at least two sides by platforms). Quadrangles (total: 3) are like plazuelas but are bounded on at least three sides and are larger in all dimensions, with access to the central court more restricted than in the smaller groups. That is, the court is closed on two or more corners. The final category (total: 6) shows no formal consistency among its constituents; these loci are temporarily segregated as a unit for "special/complex" characteristics such as unusually large size (e.g., Locus 092) or the presence of stone monuments (e.g., Locus 002).

All loci tend to be located on raised ground within $\frac{1}{4}$ kilometer of water and near modern trails or roads. Spacing between units is variable, and many loci have likely been destroyed. The social continuum implied by the formal typology is perhaps reflected in the placement of "higher order" units at least 2 kilometers apart; the most extensive and complex loci outside of Quiriguá Park are also farthest from it (Loci 024, 057, and 092).

Bruce Bevan, of the Museum Applied Science Center for Archaeology (MASCA), spent one month surveying in and adjacent to Quiriguá Park with a cesium magnetometer to try to locate structures and monuments buried by alluvium (see fig. 6). The strongest anomaly was tested by excavation in 1976 and found to represent a schist pavement. Traced magnetically for ca. 90 meters, it may have served as a "causeway" linking the seven loci that form a rough east-west line, about 2 kilometers long, north of the Park (see map, fig. 3).

Settlement excavations included ceramic test-pitting, tests of the "causeway," and extensive excavation in two architectural loci. The ceramic tests sought to gather stratified ceramic samples from the site periphery but were largely unsuccessful. Tests of the "causeway" feature established its orientation. The final month of settlement work focused on excavation of one irregularly arranged group (Locus 029) and one regularly arranged (plazuela) group (Locus 026), both located on the valley floor north of the Río Motagua.

Locus 029 is a group of three irregularly oriented mounds, Structures 3C-1 through 3 in the Quiriguá grid-designation system. Str. 3C-1 was constructed of earth and cobbles, faced with cut sandstone and rhyolite blocks. Basal coursing for two parallel walls at the summit surface of the mound represents either the uppermost terrace of the substructure or possibly the vestiges of a masonry superstructure. Associated artifacts suggest that this structure was residential.

Str. 3C-2, on the other hand, seems to have served only ceremonial functions. It consisted of an earthen mound covering a centrally located schist-and-sandstone chamber. Although the chamber was of a size appropriate for a burial crypt, and was constructed like such crypts known from the area of San Agustín Acasaguastlán (Smith and Kidder, 1943), its only contents were three pottery vessels. All are apparently Terminal Classic.

The only other construction encountered in Locus 029 (Str. 3C-3 was not

FIG. 6.   Magnetometer survey. Bruce Bevan testing magnetism of an apparent causeway feature discovered in 1976 northeast of Quiriguá.

tested) were two cobble pavements and part of a wall at the north end of Str. 3C-2. The upper pavement and the wall, both near ground level, appear to be contemporaneous and may be related to the final form of Str. 3C-2; lack of stratigraphic connections between them and linking them to the stone chamber preclude final judgment here. The lower pavement, about 1 meter below the level of the first, both seals and is littered with sherds, which appear to date to the Late or Terminal Preclassic, thus representing the first excavated sample of Preclassic materials from the immediate Quiriguá area. There was no surface indication at Locus 029 of this early occupation.

FIG 7.   Site-periphery program. Excavation of Structure 2C-3, northeast of the main
ruins at Quiriguá.

Locus 026 is composed of three structures (Strs. 2C-1 through 3), an extension of Str. 2C-3 closing the fourth (south) side of the central court. Str. 2C-3 (fig. 7) appears to have been a Terminal Classic or Early Postclassic residence, constructed of earth fill with a veneer of sandstone and schist masonry. The upper portion of the superstructure may have been built of perishable materials. A male in his early twenties was interred in a pit cut through the floor on the center line of the structure. Six buttonlike discs of oxidized copper were found on the skeleton, but no other mortuary goods were encountered.

Str. 2C-2 was not tested, but the central part of the south (front) face of Str. 2C-1 was cleared, revealing a broad ruined sandstone staircase. The overburden of debris on the stairs was rich in sherds and censer fragments, apparently Terminal Classic, and suggests a more "ceremonially" oriented use for this structure than for Str. 2C-3, whose pottery was generally more utilitarian.

FIG. 8.   Small clay bat pendant discovered in 1976 in the Acropolis excavations at Quiriguá. Late Classic. (Approximately twice actual size.)

(4). The goals of the monument preservation and recording program are (a) eradication of the destructive botanical growths that have colonized the monuments and prevention of recolonization, and (b) compilation of accurate scale renderings (photographs, drawings, molds, and/or rubbings) of monumental sculpture and inscriptions. The preservation work (now supported by the National Geographic Society) was begun in 1975 by Dr. Mason E. Hale of the Smithsonian Institution, when he determined the safest and most effective agents for killing the microflora (Hale, 1979). Eight of the 20 monuments within the Park have now been sprayed at least once, and periodic applications to all monuments over the next few years should completely destroy the growths. In addition, Dr. Daniel Butterbaugh of MASCA has begun tests of a possible stabilizing compound for sandstone.

Monument recording in 1976 gave priority to those sculptures with the poorest extant records and those most threatened with loss of detail through erosion. These included Monuments 13, 17, and 18 (Morley's Altars M, Q, and R). Attention was given also to recording the full-figure glyphs of Monuments 2, 4, and 23 (Zoomorph B, Stela D [east side] and Altar of Zoomorph O). In Str. 1B-1, the 17 in situ blocks of the hieroglyphic benches were photographed, as were 46 hieroglyphic blocks and 110 miscellaneous carved stones fallen from the upper facade of this structure.

(5). The laboratory analysis program was begun in 1976 with the classification of pottery as its first objective. The first step undertaken was to formulate a basic typology for assessing ceramic lots, such assessments to contribute to temporal and functional evaluation of occupation in and around Quiriguá. The approach adopted was a combination of the type-variety-mode method (Smith, Willey, and Gifford, 1960) and classification by vessel form. Sixty-two provenience lots, from both surface and excavation contexts, both within and outside the site core, were analyzed in 1976. With a few exceptions, all were essentially the same in content. These data suggest that, aside from the tantalizing but limited Preclassic finds, the bulk of occupation at Quiriguá is referable to the Late and Terminal Classic (fig. 8) and (perhaps) the beginning of the Postclassic periods (ca. A.D. 700-1000). As noted in 1975, polychrome pottery (including Copador) is unexpectedly rare in this ceramic assemblage. Internal differences in form distribution include a prevalence of "domestic" jars in peripheral loci and of certain bowl forms and censers within the site core; these differences probably reflect an anticipated functional distinction between the two areas.

REFERENCES

COE, WILLIAM R.
　1975.　Archeological investigations of the ruins and setting of Quiriguá, Guatemala.　Proposal submitted to the National Science Foundation.
COE, WILLIAM R., and SHARER, ROBERT J.
　1979.　The Quiriguá Project 1975 field season.　Quiriguá Papers I, University Museum Monograph 37, pp. 13-32.　Philadelphia.
HALE, MASON E.
　1979.　Control of the lichens on the monuments of Quiriguá.　Quiriguá Papers I, University Museum Monograph 37, pp. 33-38.　Philadelphia.
HAMMOND, NORMAN
　1972.　Obsidian trade routes in the Mayan area.　Science, vol. 178, pp. 1092-1093, map.
HATCH, M. P.
　1975.　A study of hieroglyphic texts at the Classic Maya site of Quiriguá, Guatemala.　Unpublished doctoral dissertation, University of California, Berkeley.

HEWETT, EDGAR L.
1911. Two seasons' work in Guatemala.   Bull. Archaeol. Inst. Amer., vol. 2, pp. 117-134.
1912. The third season's work in Guatemala: The excavations at Quiriguá in 1912. Bull. Archaeol. Inst. Amer., vol. 3, pp. 163-171.
1913. The excavations at Quiriguá, Guatemala, by the School of American Archaeology. Proc. 18th Int. Congr. Americanists, pt. 2, pp. 241-248. London.
1916. Latest work of the School of American Archaeology at Quiriguá. Holmes Anniversary Volume, pp. 157-162. Washington.
KELLEY, DAVID H.
1962. Glyphic evidence for a dynastic sequence at Quiriguá, Guatemala. Amer. Antiq., vol. 27, no. 3, pp. 323-335, illus.
LONGYEAR, JOHN M., III
1952. Copán ceramics: A study of southeastern Maya pottery. Carnegie Inst. Washington Publ. 597, 114 pp., 118 figs., 3 maps.
MAUDSLAY, ALFRED P.
1889-1902. Archaeology, 4 vols. and atlas. *In* "Biologia-Centrali-Americana." London.
MORLEY, SYLVANUS G.
1914. Prehistoric Quiriguá: The unfinished city. El Palacio (Santa Fe), vol. 1, no. 3, pp. 1-3.
1920. The inscriptions at Copán. Carnegie Inst. Washington Publ. 219, 643 pp, illus.
1935. Guidebook to the ruins of Quiriguá. Carnegie Inst. Washington Suppl. Publ. 16, 205 pp., illus.
1937-1938   The inscriptions of Petén. Carnegie Inst. Washington Publ. 437, 5 vols., vol. 1, 466 pp.; vol. 2, 608 pp., vol. 3, 494 pp.; vol. 4, 497 pp.; vol. 5, plates.
PROSKOURIAKOFF, T.
1973. The hand-grasping-fish and associated glyphs on Classic Maya monuments. Pp. 165-173 *in* "Mesoamerican Writing Systems," E. P. Benson, ed. Dumbarton Oaks, Washington.
SHARER, ROBERT J.
1974. The prehistory of the southeastern Maya periphery. Current Anthrop., vol. 13, no. 2, pp. 165-187.
1975. The southeast periphery of the Maya area: A prehistoric perspective. Paper presented at 74th annual meeting of the American Anthropological Society, San Francisco.
1978. Archaeology and History at Quiriguá, Guatemala. Journ. Field Archaeology, vol. 5, no. 1, pp. 51-70.
SHARER, ROBERT J., and COE, WILLIAM R.
1979. The Quiriguá Project: Origins, objectives, and research in 1973 and 1974. Quiriguá Papers I, University Museum Monograph 37, pp. 1-11. Philadelphia.
SMITH, A. L., and KIDDER, ALFRED V.
1943. Explorations in the Motagua Valley, Guatemala. Carnegie Inst. Washington Publ. 546. Pp. 101-182 *in* Contr. to Amer. Anthrop. and Hist., vol. 8, no. 41.

SMITH, ROBERT E.; WILLEY, GORDON R.; and GIFFORD, JAMES C.
  1960.   The type-variety concept as a basis for an analysis of Maya pottery.
          Amer. Antiq., vol. 25, no. 3, pp. 330-340.
STROMSVIK, G.
  1941.   Substela caches and stela foundations at Copán and Quiriguá.   Carnegie
          Inst. Washington Publ. 528, contr. 37, 110 pp.
VOORHIES, BARBARA
  1972.   Settlement patterns in two regions of the southern Maya lowlands.
          Amer. Antiq., vol. 37, no. 1, pp. 115-126, maps.
WILLEY, GORDON R.; COE, WILLIAM R.; and SHARER, ROBERT J.
  1976.   Un proyecto para el desarrollo de investigacion y preservacion arqueoló-
          gica en Copan (Honduras) y vecindad, 1976-81.   YaxKin, vol. 1, no.
          2, pp. 10-29.   Tegucigalpa.

WILLIAM R. COE
ROBERT J. SHARER

The Central African Megaliths Project

Principal Investigator: Nicholas David, Department of Archaeology, University of Ibadan, Nigeria.

Grant No. 1396:   In support of a study of Central African megaliths.

Whereas research into the archeology of most other parts of Africa has intensified over the past 20 years, this has scarcely been the case in the Central African Empire (CAE) and surrounding regions. The aim of this project, supported by a grant from the National Geographic Society, was to investigate a group of megalithic monuments recently discovered in the Bouar-Niem region of the western CAE and first described by Pierre Vidal (1969) in a short preliminary monograph. Dr. Vidal, of the Université de Paris X and on secondment to the Université Bokassa in Bangui, collaborated with the staff and students of the Department of Archaeology, University of Ibadan, in the research described below.

Our search for living sites associated or contemporary with the megalithic monuments—henceforth referred to as *Tazunu,* their name in the language of the Gbaya who now occupy the region—proved unsuccessful, but we were able to excavate two large Tazunu and a third, much smaller one, and initiate a concentrated search for megaliths in a 100-square-kilometer area. In addition, a large Iron Age village site at the confluence of the Nana and Modé Rivers (6°19′N, 15°6′E) was located and tested during my preliminary visit in December 1974-January 1975. This site, dating to the 7th/8th centuries A.D., has proved of critical importance in the study of the eastwards spread, from Cameroon to the margins of intralacustrine East Africa, of the Ubangian (or Eastern) branch of the Adamawa-Ubangian linguistic subfamily. A full report on this aspect of our work, which was primarily supported by a University of Ibadan Senate Research Grant, is published in volume 7 of the West African Journal of Archaeology (David and Vidal, 1977).

The zone in which the Tazunu are concentrated lies along an arc some 120 kilometers long, running generally northwest from Bouar to Niem and then north to the source of the Pende River (fig. 1). Within this zone, the monuments are found along and on either side of the Chad-Congo watershed. The cataloguing of Tazunu is being carried out by Vidal but is not yet complete; this aspect of our work will be reported elsewhere. In the following sections, our excavations are described and briefly compared with Vidal's previous

113

work, and some tentative conclusions are drawn concerning the function of
the structures, the culture responsible, and its possible significance in African
culture history.

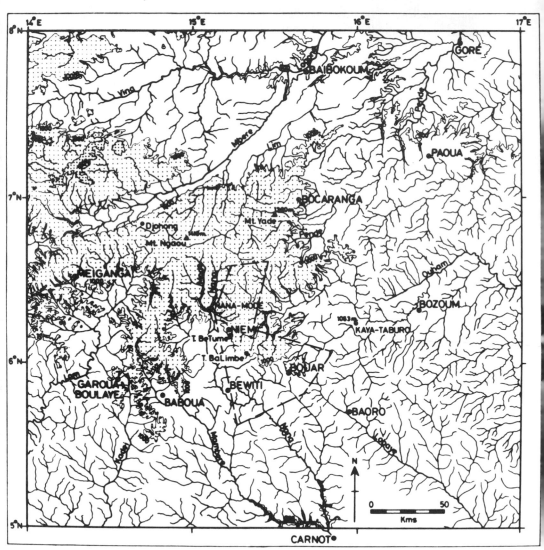

FIG. 1.   Map of the northwestern Central African Empire and parts of Cameroon
and Chad. Topography and drainage, main towns and certain archeological sites.
The megalithic zone is delimited by dashed lines.

FIG. 2. Tazunu BeTume. View from the south after removal of most of level 1. Part of the enclosing wall is visible at bottom left behind the blackboard which rests on a probable fallen "cist" capstone.

Tazunu BeTume and Tazunu BaLimbe II and III

Excavations at Tazunu BeTume and Tazunu BaLimbe II and III were carried out in July and August 1975. T. BeTume (6°10′N, 15°14′E) is one of the largest of the monuments and had already been the subject of testing by Vidal in 1971. At the start of the excavation it appeared as a low mound, overgrown with vegetation, rising 1.3 meters above the general land surface and 18 meters long by 16 meters wide. From its surface projected some 40 upright or tilted megaliths (fig. 2), while others were broken or fallen, and on the southern edge of the site a low shelter-like construction or "cist" was visible, open to the exterior and formed of three monolithic slab walls and a heavy capstone (fig. 3). Our excavations were limited to the southeastern quadrant of the site.

The stratigraphy is summarized below:

Level 1 (5-50 cm.)—Yellowish-brown clay and compact sandy clay with numerous roots and rootlets and much evidence of ant and termite activity.

Level 2 (maximum thickness 125 cm.)—Tightly packed granite rubble, used to support the megalithic uprights, with interstitial matrix similar to that of level 1.

Level 3   (75 cm. and continuing below the base of excavation)—Yellowish-red fine gravel in clayey matrix.

Level 3   predates the monument while there is strong stratigraphic evidence that level 1 and the clayey matrix of level 2 accumulated by natural causes after the monument had been built.

The raw material for both megaliths and rubble is granite. The uprights, all of undressed stone, are set at various levels within level 2 or rest on the disturbed surface of level 3. Excavated examples vary in length between 63 and 291 centimeters (median 161 cm.) and in estimated weight between 25 and 1450 kilograms (median 225 kg.). Besides the uprights there are a number of other megalithic features including a three sided "cist" (stones 61-64 on fig. 3) near the center of the monument, special settings for certain of the largest uprights, and an enclosing wall around the northern, eastern, and southern sides of the site. This is made of megalithic slabs laid on their sides in shallow foundation trenches and buttressed on the exterior by smaller stones. Sections of this wall were capped with slabs to form "cists."

With considerable difficulty we were able to reconstruct the following sequence of construction (see fig. 3):

(1)   Lowering of the ground surface in the central part of the site.
(2)   Building of the small inner "cist."
(3)   Installation of the uprights and rubble packing.
(4)   Construction of the exterior wall and "cist" complex.
(5)   Rubble packing between the wall and the main body of the monument.

Tazunu BaLimbe II (6°4′N, 15°20′E) was chosen for excavation because it had a much higher proportion of standing megaliths than BeTume, and, therefore, might be of significantly later date (fig. 4). It measures 18 meters north-south and 11 meters east-west. Only the northern half was excavated, revealing stratigraphy and features and a sequence of construction closely similar to BeTume (fig. 5; note that the rubble at this site is designated level 3). The uprights are of sizes comparable to those of BeTume (median length 181 cm., median estimated weight 275 kg.) The largest single excavated stone from either site is a "cist" capstone found broken and estimated to weigh 3¼ tonnes (fig. 6). Tazunu BaLimbe III, 36 meters south-southwest of BaLimbe II, measured only 12 square meters in area, lacked any "cists" or walls, and only one stump of a small megalith protruded above the surface of its 30-centimeter rubble mound. Nevertheless, the combination of rubble packing and upright, its proximity to T. BaLimbe I and II, the eroded state of the sherds found in the rubble, and our knowledge, derived from survey work by Vidal, of the very wide size range of Tazunu allow us to classify it in the Tazunu category.

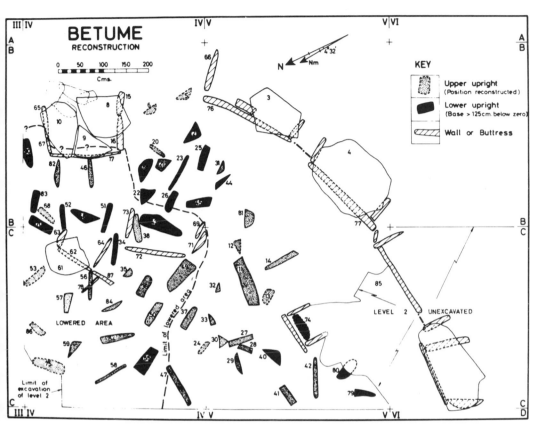

FIG. 3. Tazunu BeTume. Plan: attempted reconstruction of original positions of megaliths.

The distribution of Tazunu sizes is of significance in determination of their function and will be further discussed below. With regard to their dating, our excavations demonstrated that (a) the monuments were planned and constructed as units rather than being the product of a series of additions over a long period, and (b) at the time of their construction they were not covered with earth, the deposits overlying and in the interstices of the rubble having accumulated subsequently by colluvial and biological action. Before this deposit had formed, charcoal and small artifacts could have infiltrated into the rubble from the surface. Similarly the collapse of uprights or other megalithic features at a later date would also have facilitated penetration of materials foreign to the structures.

A series of four charcoal samples from BeTume gave, for the underlying level 3, two dates in the 3rd millennium B.C., and, for the rubble, two dates in the 6th century B.C. The implication is that the monument was built at or before the later date. A fifth sample from Vidal's excavation gave a date in the 18th century A.D. but should be disregarded as it is associated with level 1. BaLimbe II gave three dates in the 7th-9th century B.C. range, and one in the 3rd and one in the 5th century A.D. There are, however, reasonable stratigraphic arguments for the view that the two latter samples had been contaminated by charcoal penetrating the Tazunu after its construction. The good agreement between the three early dates and the two from the BeTume rubble is satisfactory, and, with dendrochronological correction, would indicate that both sites were built in the period 1100-700 B.C. BaLimbe III produced inadequate material for dating.

Material Culture and Economy

Only very few artifacts were recovered from the three sites. At BeTume, a number of pieces of quartz, mostly natural but including a few artifacts and for the most part associated with level 3 and an intermediate zone (2-3) disturbed in the building of the Tazunu, testify to the presence of Late Stone Age hunter-gatherers in the region *before* the megalithic phase. Only one piece of worked quartz was found at BaLimbe II. It is uncertain, therefore, whether the builders made use of flaked stone tools. Both the larger sites provided evidence of ground stone technology. Lower grindstones were found, incorporated into the rubble, at both sites, and from a "cist" at BaLimbe II came a ground stone axe, probably lost during construction. There were also a few pieces of heavily eroded pottery, mostly plain, at all three sites, and one pot decorated by grooves and probable comb-stamping from BaLimbe II (fig. 7). The pottery is of interest in that it is markedly different in preservation and decoration from the Iron Age pottery of the region, which is characterized by carved wood rouletting.

These meager data nevertheless allow us to say something of the material culture and economy of the megalith builders. First, there is no evidence of iron-working or iron-using; the technology is Neolithic. They may have made use of flaked stone tools. The presence of grinding equipment and the axe shows that they had the means of clearing forest and woodland, and suggests that their economy included cereal, presumably sorghum, cultivation. As no ancient bone was preserved, we cannot evaluate the potential contributions of hunting and pastoralism to the economy. The former is likely to have been of importance, while cattle herding, if it existed, can only have been practiced

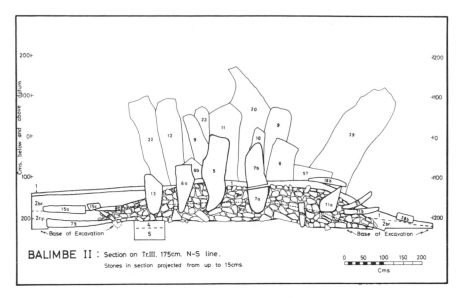

FIG. 4. Tazunu BaLimbe II. View from the north after removal of level 1. The collapsed wall and "cist" complex is visible to the left of the photograph.

FIG. 5. Tazunu BaLimbe II. East-west section.

FIG. 6. Tazunu Ba-Limbe II. View of wall and "cist" complex from the south. The picture, taken from the large tree seen in figure 4, shows the largest excavated megalith, a "cist" capstone broken into three pieces and estimated to weigh $3\frac{1}{4}$ tons.

on a small scale since, in the late 2d/early 1st millennium B.C., the region would have been much more thickly wooded than it is today (Sillans, 1958). It may be noted that the indirect evidence of cereal agriculture suggests that by this time the rain forest, which must have invaded the region during the main Holocene wet phase, had already retreated south of Bouar.

Comparisons with Sites in the Bouar Locality

Since rather different dates and artifactual materials have been recovered from sites excavated by Vidal around Bouar, only 30 kilometers southeast of

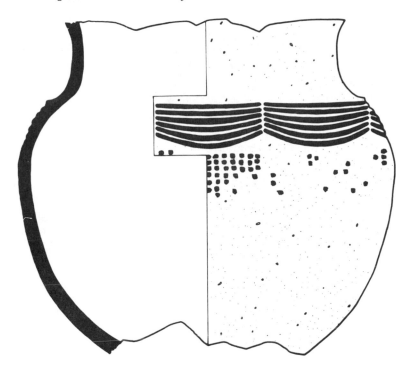

FIG. 7.   Tazunu BaLimbe II. Pot decorated with grooved scallops and probable comb-stamping.

BaLimbe, we shall briefly compare the two bodies of data. These comparisons are based upon the available publications (Vidal, 1969; Bayle des Hermens, 1975), inspection of the sites and discussions with Vidal. All the Tazunu so far excavated in the Bouar locality show features essentially similar to those of BeTume and BaLimbe. These include the use of the same raw materials and the presence in several sites of "cists" and exterior wall-"cist" complexes. Vidal did not, however, recognize that the stratigraphic units equivalent to Be-Tume level 3 *pre-dated* the monuments, even though they were on occasion disturbed or dug into during the course of Tazunu construction. It is from such contexts that a date in the 6th millennium B.C. was obtained from T. Be-Foro I and another in the 5th millennium from the unpublished T. ZuPaya. Against these, there are three dates of the 1st millennium B.C. and, from T. Tia I, one dubiously associated date of A.D. 30 ± 100. Rough contemporaneity of these sites and BeTume and BaLimbe seems probable.

The Bouar sites were equally poor in artifactual material, though the few sherds published could have been drawn from the same population as that described above, and are definitely pre-Iron Age. Two fragments of smoking pipe found in an apparently sealed context at T. Gam may reflect recent interference or attempted plundering of the site, while a group of ceremonial iron objects from T. BeForo I are likely to be intrusive. Bouar is now a sizable town, the environs of which were already relatively heavily populated at the time of the first European penetration of the area. Especially since Tazunu are still used by the Gbaya as places of offering, a higher incidence of intrusive objects in the monuments of this locality is not unexpected. We may, therefore, conclude that the differences in dates and artifacts between the Bouar sites and those we excavated are more apparent than real, and that all the Tazunu so far investigated form part of the same cultural complex dating to the late 2d and 1st millennia B.C.

The Function of Tazunu

Since no habitation sites of the Tazunu builders have as yet been discovered, we are left, if we wish to learn more about their culture, with the evidence of the monuments themselves, their sizes, their distribution in space, and the inferred manpower requirements necessary for their construction. Although full data on size and distribution are not yet available, the following generalizations can be made:

1.   Although there are outliers, as for example in Cameroon at Djohong (Marliac, 1973), Tazunu appear to be densely distributed in a limited area (fig. 1). There may well be surprises in store, but it is fairly certain that in other neighboring granite areas, for example on the Adamawa Plateau of Cameroon, Tazunu are absent or virtually absent. (The possibility remains that there and elsewhere less resistant raw materials might have been employed to build structures intended for a similar cultural role, but none such have as yet been found.)

2.   Tazunu are, at least in some localities, densely distributed. Vidal's attempt to record all the monuments in an area only 10 km by 10 km had already produced over twenty before it was half completed.

3.   Tazunu are less confined to locations near the headwaters of streams on either side of the Chad-Congo watershed than previously supposed. Several sites are now known from the larger valleys, and it would now appear that the association with headwaters was in part an artifact of research, in that the few access roads tend to run along the ridges.

4.   All Tazunu seem to have been built according to a single pattern, al-

though it is one that allowed a number of options. On the other hand, they vary greatly in size—from 12 square meters in the case of BaLimbe III to nearly 400 square meters at T. Tia II. They thus reflect a wide range of labor inputs.

It is only when sources of raw material are limited and thus definable that we can make any potentially useful estimate of the labor required for Tazunu construction. Such is fortunately the case at BeTume, where the megaliths were almost certainly collected—no quarrying was needed—from the surface of a granite whaleback some 650 meters north-northeast of the site. The nearest sources of rubble are small outcrops of granite lying west of the site at an average distance of 400 meters. Very gross calculations based on data on Neolithic technological capabilities summarized by Coles (1973) suggest that a force of 30 workers (the number required to transport the largest recorded upright) could have brought all the excavated as well as the unexcavated BeTume megaliths to the site over a 13-day period. Most could have been carried using ropes and poles; rough branch sleds or rollers may have been used to haul the largest stones. The same number of workers would have needed a further 22 days to transport the estimated 120 cubic meters of rubble to the site. The time required, using only ropes, wooden levers, log slides, axes, digging sticks and, possibly, sheerlegs to install the uprights and construct the "cists" and enclosing wall is impossible to estimate realistically without experimentation (to be conducted by Vidal). Perhaps a further 10 days would be a reasonable guess. In any case the whole process of construction could have been carried out during a single dry season, when underemployment is normal, either by the population of a small village or hamlet or by the members of a large lineage. BeTume is one of the largest known Tazunu.

We may now attempt to identify the function of Tazunu. This can hardly have been economic. Their large numbers, the wide variation in size, and the fact that they are sometimes found in close proximity to each other or even in groups suggest that they are not temples or shrines but are associated in some way with individual or family status. Whether this was ascribed or achieved and whether the monuments testify to such status at birth, initiation, marriage, death, or any other landmark in the people's lives cannot as yet be determined. If, as would at first sight seem most probable, they are tombs, then bio-pedological action has destroyed all evidence of burials. There were no grave goods or at least none preserved, and, since not all Tazunu are equipped with "cists," which in any case do not appear to have been closed in any permanent fashion on all four sides, the body or bodies must either have been placed in "cists" and allowed to decay, or have been lain on the ground before the rubble began to be accumulated. Although features within the underlying deposits have been recorded by Vidal, there is no evidence of graves beneath the monuments.

Conclusions

Further work will contribute to the resolution of the problem of function and to the more interesting questions that can be raised concerning the non-monumental aspects of the Neolithic culture of the region. We can, however, note two facts of significance.

First, this is an area characterized ethnographically by small-scale, hamlet and lineage, political units and by the difficulty of delimiting "tribal" groupings—which in reality reflect dialects spoken within the vast area occupied by speakers of Gbaya. From what we know of the distribution of the megaliths it would appear as if cultural boundaries were much more precisely defined in the 1st millennium B.C.

Second, there is at present a gap of some one thousand years between the latest relatively reliable Tazunu date and that of the Iron Age Nana-Modé village. While the latter site is most unlikely to represent the earliest appearance of iron-working peoples in the region, the disappearance of the Tazunu builders or the collapse of their culture into archeological invisibility before the arrival of their Ubangian successors is a possibility. There are here interesting parallels with the Kintampo culture which appeared in central Ghana about 1500 B.C. only to vanish some 500 years later (Flight, 1976), to be followed by a period of a millennium during which there is little evidence of occupation in spite of archeological reconnaissance more intensive than in any other part of West or Central Africa. Other parallels between the two cultures include the following: (a) both derive a significant part of their technology and economy from the northern savannas, where, at least in certain areas, mixed farming combining cereal cultivation and herding had been practiced since the 3rd millennium B.C. if not before—indeed, both cultures may represent immigrant populations; (b) both appear to have been the first food-producers in their respective areas—there is proof that the Kintampo people herded cattle and small stock and the evidence is strongly suggestive of cereal and pulse growing; (c) both cultures inhabited an environment which is now characterized as relatively moist woodland and savanna and which at the time must have been more thickly wooded or even have supported closed canopy dry forest; and (d) both cultures are marginal to the main center of African yam cultivation (Coursey, 1976; Harris, 1976), Kintampo lying to the west and the megalithic zone to the east.

This last parallel suggests a possible cause for the apparent failure of the two cultures to maintain themselves; it may also be of relevance to the vexed question of the antiquity of the food-producing economy based upon the African yams and the oil palm. As a working hypothesis, therefore, I would conclude by suggesting that the economy of both the Kintampo and the Tazunu cultures, initially developed farther to the north, proved inefficiently adapted to more southerly and wetter environments, and that the yams, later staple cultigens in both regions (though now largely replaced in the CAR by cassava [manioc]), had not yet diffused to them as part of an agricultural system, and that as a result of this and no doubt other factors, including epidemiological ones, both these pioneering societies failed to survive. If this is so, then it would in turn imply that the synthesis of the yam-oil palm economy is a relatively late development in African prehistory, attributable to a period no earlier than the 2d millennium B.C.

Acknowledgments

Besides generous financial support from the National Geographic Society, I wish to thank Professor E. de Dampierre, who first encouraged me to work in the Central African Empire; M. le Ministre de l'Education Nationale et de la Réforme Educative of the Central African Republic, who allowed this project to be realized within the framework of an agreement between the Université de Paris X and the Central African Government; Dr. Pierre Vidal without whose generous collaboration little or nothing would have been achieved; and Dr. Robert Stuckenrath of the Radiation Biology Laboratory, Smithsonian Institution, Washington, D. C., who kindly processed our charcoal samples. The Prefect of Nana-Mambéré and the Sub-Prefect of Bouar both gave us their full cooperation and took a keen interest in our work.

REFERENCES

BAYLE DES HERMENS, R. DE
    1975.   Recherches préhistoriques en République centrafricaine.   Klincksiek, Paris.
COLES, J.
    1973.   Archaeology by experiment.   Hutchinson University Library, London.
COURSEY, D. G.
    1976.   The origins and domestication of yams in Africa.   Pp. 383-408 *in* Harlan et al., 1976.
DAVID, N., AND VIDAL, P.
    1977.   The Nana-Modé village site (Sous-Préfecture de Bouar, Central African Republic) and the prehistory of the Ubangian-speaking peoples.   W. Afr. Journ. Archaeol., vol. 7, pp. 17-56.

FLIGHT, C.
   1976.   The Kintampo culture and its place in the economic prehistory of West
           Africa.   Pp. 211-222 *in* Harlan et al., 1976.
HARLAN, J. R.; DE WET, J. M. J.; AND STEMLER, A. B. L., eds.
   1976.   Origins of African plant domestication.   Mouton, The Hague and
           Paris.
HARRIS, D. R.
   1973.   Traditional systems of plant food production and the origins of agricul-
           ture in West Africa.   Pp. 311-356 *in* Harlan et al., 1976.
MARLIAC, A.
   1973.   L'état des connaissances sur le paléolithique et le néolithique du Camer-
           oun.   ORSTOM, Yaoundé.
SILLANS, R.
   1958.   Les savanes de l'Afrique centrale.   Encyclopédie Biologique, tome LV.
           Chevalier, Paris.
VIDAL, P.
   1969.   La civilisation mégalithique de Bouar: prospections et fouilles 1962-
           1966.   Firman-Didot Etudes, Paris.

NICHOLAS DAVID

Survival of Bird Populations Stranded on Land-Bridge Islands

Principal Investigator: Jared M. Diamond, University of California Medical Center, Los Angeles, California.

Grant No. 1357:   In support of a 1974 ornithological expedition to the Solomon Islands.

The purpose of the present expedition was to study bird distributions on one of three groups of land-bridge islands in the New Guinea region: the Kavieng group in the Bismarck Archipelago, the Samarai chain off southeast New Guinea, or the Choiseul-Ysabel group in the Solomon Archipelago. The last-named group proved most feasible and was selected. Generous cooperation of the people and government of the Solomon Islands made it possible to complete not only the proposed land-bridge studies but also three further major projects: an ornithological reexploration of nearly the whole Solomon Archipelago; a detailed analysis of flycatcher diets, as a basis for understanding why only certain combinations of flycatcher species can be "assembled" on an island; and studies of geographic variation in voice and habits, to complement knowledge of the geographic variations in the morphology of Solomon bird species that have become textbook examples of evolutionary processes through the work of Ernst Mayr.

On August 11, 1974, I flew from Los Angeles to Australia to attend the International Ornithological Congress and reached Honiara, capital of the British Solomon Islands, on August 18. Two sets of negotiations during my first week in Honiara sealed the success of the expedition. First, Alisasa Bisili, a retired government officer, was persuaded to join the expedition. Alisasa knew leading men in virtually every village we visited in the Solomons and proved a master of making local arrangements as well as of censusing birds. Second, the problem of ship travel, which offers the only possible means of reaching most Solomon islands and often proves an infinite source of exasperation to biological expeditions, was solved by charter of the government vessel *Telina* followed by arrangements for travel on the private yacht *Kathleen Gillette* belonging to Reg and Margaret Stephenson of Rabaul. As a result of both sets of negotiations, although the expedition program involved surveys of 41 islands, it was completed without a single delay or day lost.

The Solomon Archipelago consists of a northern and a southern chain of islands surrounding a sea called the Slot, with the additional large islands of Malaita and San Cristobal to the east (see map, fig. 1). All the islands in the northern chain from Buka and Bougainville to Shortland, Fauro, Choiseul, Ysabel, and Ngela (Florida) and possibly Guadalcanal are separated by shallow-water gaps and were consequently joined into a single huge island ("Greater Bukida") in the Pleistocene. Similarly, the present islands of the southern chain were formerly grouped into three larger islands, of which one ("Greater Rendipari") has now fragmented into Rendova and Tetipari, another ("Greater Vellonga") into Vella Lavella, Bagga, and Ganonga, and the third and largest ("Greater Gatumbangra") into Kulambangra, Wana Wana, New Georgia, Vangunu, and Gatukai. Islands that have not had a recent connection to another island include Simbo, Gizo, Savo, and Ugi, the more isolated Russell group, Borokua, and Mono, and the remote Rennell and Bellona. The predominant vegetation of all islands is tropical rain forest.

My itinerary was designed to permit comparisons among the present-day fragments of Greater Bukida, fragments of the smaller land-bridge islands in the southern chain, and the isolated islands. The itinerary fell into four parts: visits to Savo and the easternmost fragments of Greater Bukida (Guadalcanal, Buena Vista, Ngela) in late August; visits to the Russells, Borokua, and all the islands of the southern chain in September and early October; visits to Mono and the northern fragments of Greater Bukida (Choiseul, Fauro, Shortland; I had studied Bougainville in 1972) in mid-October; and visits to the eastern outliers San Cristobal and Ugi in late October.

On each island I spent the daylight hours observing, especially to detect interisland variation in songs, behavior, and ecology, and was usually able to observe 70 - 90 percent of the species known from an island. In the evenings I met with the older men of the village at which I was based that day, to ask them about bird habits and about species that I might have overlooked. Many people in the Solomons are walking encyclopedias of bird lore, and can describe rare species observed once, for example, in 1928 or vagrant species recorded in 1952 and never seen since, and can succinctly summarize niche differences among sibling species. With practice I learned how to describe each bird species of the Solomons, not as a western ornithologist recognizes it through binoculars or as a museum study skin, but as a villager recognizes it in silhouette at 200 yards. The information elicited in this way made it possible to assemble with confidence a virtually complete species list for each island, as well as a history of some recent immigrations and extinctions. In particular, a complete species list is necessary to assess whether an island is "supersaturated" with species or supports relict populations as a result of

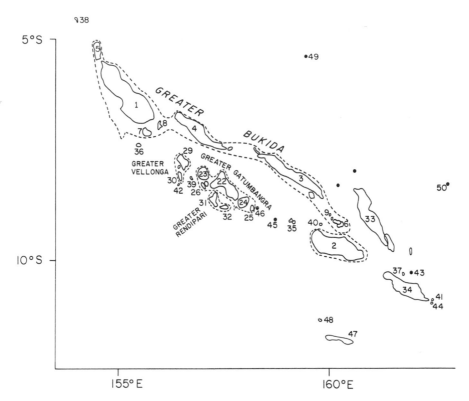

FIG. 1. The Solomon Archipelago. Dashed lines show the outlines of land during late-Pleistocene periods of lowered sea level, as deduced from present hydrographic depth contours. Names of the four expanded Pleistocene islands (Greater Bukida, etc.) are in capital letters. Numbers 1 through 50 identify islands. Islands that receive particular discussion in the text are: 1 = Bougainville, 2 = Guadalcanal, 4 = Choiseul, 6 = Ngela, 7 = Shortland, 23 = Kulambangra, 34 = San Cristobal, 40 = Savo, 45 = Borokua. Code numbers of other islands are identified in Diamond and Mayr (1976).

Pleistocene land bridges. In the 1920's the Whitney South Seas Expedition explored the avifauna of the Solomons exhaustively but often did not bother to note the presence or absence on each island of the numerous widespread tramp species of little taxonomic interest, so that the Whitney records cannot be used for quantitative analysis of second-order factors affecting species diversity.

The first series of island visits, to Savo and the Florida group (Buena Vista, Dalakalonga, Ngela Sule, Ngela Pile, and Nugu) on August 24 - 30, was made in the government ship *Telina*. Of interest on Savo were breeding grounds of the megapode *Megapodius freycinet,* which incubates its eggs not by body heat but by exogenous heat sources. Three such sources are used in the Solomons: heat of fermentation of rotting fallen logs of certain tree species; heat of volcanoes; and heat of the sun on sand beaches. Harvest of eggs from colonial laying grounds of megapodes on Savo's volcanic hotsprings and beaches is closely regulated by villagers; each person has egg rights to a section of beach marked off by poles, and searching for eggs is strictly forbidden during the evening hours when laying megapodes might be disturbed. Ngela, the largest island of the Florida group, yielded a striking example of the effects of seemingly insignificant barriers on tropical bird distributions. This island is divided into two topographically similar and not quite equal-sized halves, Ngela Sule and Ngela Pile, by a channel (Utuha Passage) 5 miles long and varying in width from 120 yards to 500 yards. A very large and noisy cuckoo, *Centropus milo,* was found to be present on Ngela Sule but absent on Ngela Pile. While this cuckoo is a weak flier, Ngela villagers relate that they have seen individuals cross Utuha Passage and that a cyclone blew numbers from Ngela Sule to Ngela Pile, but that the Ngela Pile colonists gradually disappeared. Evidently the finite but low colonization rates across this narrow water gap, combined with some average slight ecological difference between Ngela Sule and Ngela Pile, result in a stable distributional border. A more picturesque explanation is offered by Ngela villagers, who tell how the chief of devils, Mánemagútu, expelled the vuleváu (the local name for this cuckoo) from Ngela Pile because of its loud unpleasant calls and its ground-feeding habits ("it brooms rubbish from the ground").

On September 3 I set out again from Guadalcanal in the *Telina* to the Russells (Banika and Pavuvu visited), Borokua, and the southern chain of the Solomons (Kicha, Gatukai, Vangunu, Tetipari, Rendova, New Georgia, Wana Wana, Kulambangra, Gizo, Simbo, Ganonga, Vella Lavella, and various small islets visited; the summits of Gatukai, Vangunu, Rendova, and Kulumbangra climbed). We transferred on September 13 from the *Telina* to the *Kathleen Gillette,* which had set out from Rabaul and met us at Vangunu. The southern chain of the Solomons has become famous among evolutionary biologists for its examples of geographic variation and speciation across narrow water gaps, especially in the white-eye *Zosterops rendovae* and its relatives. The populations on islands such as Rendova, Tetipari, New Georgia, Gizo, and Vella, separated by gaps of only 1 - 4 miles, proved to differ as dramatically in voice and habits as in appearance. I found interisland variation in voice through the Solomons particularly marked in the whistler *Pachycephala pectoralis,* the cuckoo-shrike *Coracina tenuirostris,* the various *Zosterops* white-eyes, the kingfisher *Halcyon chloris,* and the flycatcher *Myiagra ferrocyanea.* For instance, the song of *Pachycephala pectoralis* on Kulambangra is a dazzlingly rapid, mellow, loud, crescendoing run often given as a male-female duet, the most breathtaking display of vocal virtuosity I have heard from any bird; on the Russells, a crescendoing series of equally spaced slurs; on Guadalcanal, a rapid series of alternating upslurs and downslurs; and on Choiseul, a much weaker series of upslurs and downslurs.

Resident villagers of the southern chain, as elsewhere in the Solomons, were able to provide for numerous bird populations historical accounts of colonizations and extinctions that maintain the species number on an island in a dynamic equilibrium. For instance, the cyclone of 1952 blew the Australian pelican *Pelecanus conspicillatus* and the cormorant *Phalacrocorax melanoleucos* all over the Solomons. The hornbill *Aceros plicatus,* formerly virtually confined to Malaita plus many fragments of Greater Bukida, successfully colonized every island of the southern chain except Simbo and Ganonga about 30 years ago, and more recently it colonized one small island of the Russell group, Savo, and the Florida group. The crested pigeon *Reinwardtoena crassirostris* was eliminated from Ngela by the 1972 cyclone. The ibis *Threskiornis molucca* reached Mono about 20 years ago and has persisted.

Two mountainous islands, Borokua and Kulambangra, provided spectacular scenery as well as intriguing avifaunas. Borokua is an isolated, small, high, very steep, extinct but still perfectly symmetrical volcanic cone, of which the south side has been blown out, leaving a small flat plain (the former crater floor) surrounded on three sides by walls rising at 45° to a height of 1,181 feet. The number of resident bird species (presently about 13) is lower than on any other Solomon island of comparable size. Particularly surprising is the fact that insectivorous bird species are absent from Borokua except for three individuals of a kite that takes large insects, plus a few individuals of a small flycatcher confined to the flat plain. At the other extreme, Kulambangra, a 5,800-foot volcanic cone where we made a mountain camp for several weeks, has the richest avifauna of the southern chain (80 species). Two species of birds that were discovered by the Whitney Expedition but whose habits had never been described are confined to the mountains of Kulambangra: the white-eye *Zosterops murphyi* and the warbler *Phylloscopus amoenus.* The white-eye proved the most abundant species in the mountains of Kulambangra and foraged in flocks of 100 birds or more. These flocks move up and down the mountain depending on the weather and the time of day. Equally conspicuous were flocks of a mountain pigeon confined to the Solomons, *Gymnophaps solomonensis.* Like its New Guinea relative *G. albertisii,* this pigeon displays by diving thousands of feet downhill over the forest canopy along a ridge crest, with wings closed, at high speed, and making a continuous rushing sound with its feathers as it dives.

The third phase of the expedition (October 13 - 21) consisted of visits to the northern fragments of Greater Bukida (Choiseul, Fauro, Shortland, and 10 smaller islands) plus the outlier Mono. Choiseul has received more than its share of ornithological attention because it is the island where the most distinctive and magnificent bird species of the Solomon Islands, the pigeon *Microgoura meeki*, was discovered in 1904 by Lord Rothchild's collector A. S. Meek. The Whitney Expedition and Shane Parker searched Choiseul without success for this species and concluded that it may have been exterminated by feral cats. At Sasamungga on Choiseul I quizzed local people and walked into the Kolombangara River basin, last reported stronghold of *Microgoura*, without obtaining evidence of its existence. I suspect that *Microgoura* is a land-bridge relict species of Greater Bukida, that it was formerly on other large fragments of Greater Bukida such as Ysabel, and that it survived until Meek's explorations of the Solomons only on Choiseul because this was the last major Bukida island to become regularly visited by Europeans (and hence to receive cats). Another ornithological problem of the northern Greater Bukida islands is posed by the closely related golden whistler *Pachycephala pectoralis* and the black-tailed whistler *P. melanura,* which the Whitney Expedition had found to hybridize on three small islets of the Shortland group in 1927. I found that *P. pectoralis* is confined to inland forest on the largest island of the Shortlands, while *P. melanura* and hybrids are apparently confined to the very smallest islands of the group, so small that they coexist with at most one other species of flycatcher. *P. melanura* and the flycatcher *Monarcha cinerascens* exemplify "supertramps," r-selected species that are widely distributed on small islands of the Bismarcks and Papuan region, on which the numerous, more sedentary, K-selected flycatcher species of larger islands cannot maintain stable populations. In the Solomons the few large-island flycatcher species are themselves sufficiently "trampy" (i.e., ready colonizers) for these two supertramps to have been displaced even from most of the small islets of the Solomons.

The final phase of the fieldwork took place in the eastern Solomons during the last week of October, on the islands of San Cristobal and Ugi. Extensive information was also obtained from residents of the neighboring islands of Santa Catalina and Santa Anna. As Ian Galbraith and Ernst Mayr have emphasized, this eastern group is interesting because of three related facts: some species widespread throughout the rest of the Solomons are absent from this group (e.g., the goshawk *Accipiter novaehollandiae,* the dove *Ptilinopus superbus,* the cockatoo *Cacatua ducorpsi,* the cuckoo-shrike *Coracina papuensis,* the mynah *Mino dumontii*); other species that have invaded the Solomons from the east have not reached beyond the San Cristobal group (e.g., the dove *Ptilinopus richardsii*, the triller *Lalage leucopyga*, the fantails *Rhipidura fuliginosa* and *R. tenebrosa*, and the honeyeater *Myzomela cardinalis*); and some widespread Solomon species are represented on San Cristobal by strikingly distinct subspecies or semispecies. I was interested to see whether these sets of phenomena were ecologically related to one another. It turned out that although the added eastern species do not replace the missing widespread species as simple one-to-one equivalents, ecological guilds are nevertheless reshuffled through selection of colonists, exclusion of invaders, and coevolution of established colonists, in complex but discernible ways. For example, the widespread sunbird *Nectarinia jugularis* has been squeezed out of San Cristobal by two honeyeaters, one of them the eastern invader *Myzomela cardinalis*. It appears from local information that the invasion may have taken place within this century and that *M. cardinalis* may have hybridized or may still be hybridizing with the previously established *Myzomela tristrami* as the invasion front expanded. The niche of the absent cuckoo-shrike *Coracina papuensis*, a consumer of large, soft-bodied insects at the forest edge, seems to have been divided among distinct local subspecies of the kingfisher *Halcyon chloris*, the cuckoo-shrike *Coracina lineata*, the flycatchers *Pachycephala pectoralis* and *Monarcha megarhyncha*, and the endemic honeyeater *Meliarchus sclateri*. Possibly the most interesting reshuffle involves the flycatcher guild, in which one widespread species is missing, two eastern invaders have been incorporated, and the five resident widespread species have coevolved drastically altered abundances, morphologies, and foraging behavior to reconstitute a stable guild.

The general conclusions derived from expedition results concerning bird distributions in the Solomons may be summarized under four headings: distributions of land-bridge relict species, species-area relation for the avifauna as a whole, area requirements of water-crossing species, and applications of these findings to conservation strategies:

1. *Distributions of land-bridge relict species.* Thirteen bird species endemic to the Solomon Islands are now confined to one or more of those islands that represent fragments of the former large Pleistocene land-bridge island, Greater Bukida. These species are evidently unable (in the case of one flightless species) or unwilling (in the case of the remaining 12 species, which fly) to cross water gaps. They must have been distributed over Greater Bukida when it was a single landmass. Their present distributions, as summarized in table 1, reflect the extent to which they have become extinct on the fragments of Greater Bukida in the ca. 10,000 years since rising sea level dissected Greater Bukida. Table 1 permits the following conclusions about extinction rates as a function of island area and of the properties of individual species:

TABLE 1.   Distribution of Land-Bridge Relict Bird Species on the Post-Pleistocene Fragments of Greater Bukida, Solomon Islands

Island[1]	Area (sq. mi.)	Halcyon leucopygia	Zosterops metcalfii	Corvus woodfordi	Nesoclopeus woodfordi	Pitta anerythra	Accipiter imitator	Nesasio solomonensis	Halcyon bougainvillei	Rhipidura drownei	Pachycephala implicata	Stresemannia bougainvillei	Melipbaga inexpectata	Microgoura meeki
Bougainville	3,317	√	√	√	√	√	√	√	√	√	√	√		
Guadalcanal	2,039	√		√	√				√	√	√		√	
Ysabel	1,497	√	√	√	√	√	√	√						
Choiseul	1,145	√	√	√	√	√	√	√	√					√
Buka	236		√	√										
Ngela	142	√	√											
Shortland	90		√	√										
Wagina	35			√										
Fauro	27	√												
Buena Vista	5.4	√												
Molakobi	2.96			√	√									
Fara	2.80	√												
Arnavon	2.18													
Bates	2.02				√									

[1] No relict bird species on the following islands (area in sq. mi.): Piru (1.14), Oema (1.10), Nusave (0.206), Bagora (0.126), Nugu (0.0577), Samarai (0.0351), New (0.0273), Dalakalonga (0.0257), Elo (0.0211), Kukuvulu (0.0156), Tapanu (0.0062), Kanasata (0.0035), Near New (0.0027).

(a)   No single island has retained all 13 of the relicts. Even the largest island, Bougainville (3,317 square miles), has lost 2 of the 13. The number of relict populations decreases steeply with decreasing island area (fig. 2). Islands of 100 - 250 square miles retain only two relicts. Not a single relict population has survived on any of the numerous ornithologically explored Greater Bukida fragments of less than 2 square miles.

(b)   Some species are more prone to extinction than others, even after we remove from consideration *Microgoura meeki* (whose apparent distribution may

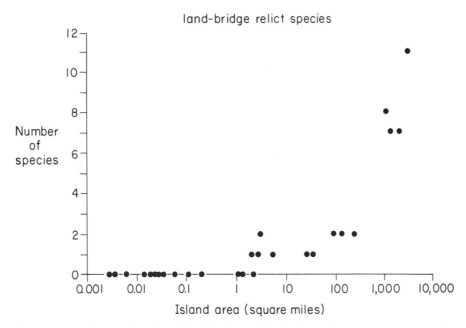

FIG. 2.   Ordinate: Number of land-bridge relict bird species present on each ornithologically explored island that represents a post-Pleistocene fragment of Greater
Bukida. Abscissa: Island area on a logarithmic scale. The total number of relict species is 13. Note that the number of relict populations surviving on an island increases with island area, and that no relicts at all have survived on islands smaller
than 2 square miles.

merely indicate what islands had few feral cats as of 1904) and the five montane species *Meliphaga inexpectata, Stresemannia bougainvillei, Pachycephala im-
plicata, Rhipidura drownei,* and *Halcyon bougainvillei* (now confined to either or
both of the two islands with the highest mountains, but possibly also formerly
on medium-high islands when Pleistocene cool climates lowered the altitudinal limits of montane vegetation). Of the remaining seven species, four *(Neso-
clopeus woodfordi, Pitta anerythra, Accipiter imitator, Nesasio solomonensis)* are now
confined to three or all four of the four islands with areas exceeding 1,000
square miles. Three species *(Halcyon leucopygia, Zosterops metcalfii, Corvus woodfordi)* have survived on eight islands each, including most islands with areas of
90 square miles or greater plus a few islands with areas of 2 - 35 square miles.
Two characteristics distinguish the former four species, which must be considered extinction-prone, from the three latter species, which are evidently
more resistant to extinction: (a) The extinction-prone species have consider-

ably lower population densities than the extinction-resistant species; (b) the extinction-prone species are probably confined to the interior of primary forest, whereas the extinction-resistant species occur in broken habitats and forest-edge situations as well as in forest.

We conclude that probabilities of extinction for isolated populations increase with decreasing area, differ greatly for different species, and are higher for species of low abundance or narrow habitat requirements than for species that are abundant or else tolerant of a range of habitats.

2. *Species-area relation for the whole avifauna.* Species-area relations (i.e., between the area of an island and the number of species it supports) often serve as a starting point for modern biogeographic theories. Much of the data against which these theories are usually tested suffers from the disadvantage that the data were not gathered specifically for this purpose. In particular, the collectors who have produced such data often did not bother to do thorough surveys of small islands (which tend to have few of the rare species that attract collectors) or to record presences of "uninteresting" tramp species on each large island. The data on Solomon bird distributions have the advantage of having been compiled specifically for the purpose of determining the species-area relation and of including thoroughly explored islands that range over six orders of magnitude in area. Analysis of these data yields the following conclusions:

(a) Mountainous islands harbor montane species absent at sea level. The higher and larger the island, the more montane species it supports. On the average, each 1,000 feet of elevation adds a number of montane species equal to 2.1 percent (standard deviation ±1.0 percent, 14 islands) of the species at sea level. This estimate is in reasonable agreement with the estimate of 2.7 percent per 1,000 feet that I previously obtained for islands of the whole Southwest Pacific (Diamond, 1972).

(b) If one confines attention to islands for which isolation effects on species number should be slight (i.e., the large islands of the northern and southern chains, and islands within 8 miles of these islands), the number of lowland bird species increases regularly with island area (fig. 3). Of interest is the fact that a double logarithmic plot of the species-area relation is not linear, as generally assumed, but is obviously curved, as my data for birds of the Bismarck Archipelago previously indicated less convincingly (Diamond, 1974). The curvature is in the direction predicted theoretically by Robert May, who considered the number of species expected if one samples different areas of a community with the usual biological characteristics of a lognormal species-abundance relation and population numbers proportional to area. The reason that this curvature was missed in earlier studies may have been the lack of ade-

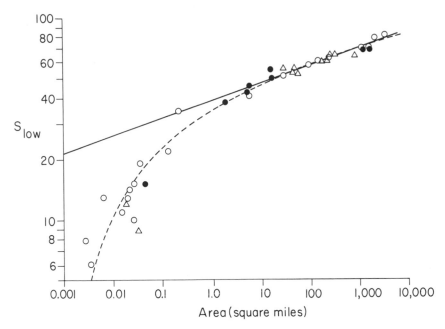

FIG. 3.   Species-area relation for central islands of the Solomons, plotted with double logarithmic scales. ○ = islands derived from Greater Bukida; △ = islands derived from Greater Gatumbangra, Greater Vellonga, or Greater Rendipari; ● =
other islands.   (From Diamond and Mayr, 1976.)

quately censused very small islands. The increased scatter in the values for
very small islands probably reflects statistical fluctuations in their very small
species numbers (6 - 20) and populations (island size comparable to bird territory sizes). If one follows the usual practice of fitting a straight line through
the points of figure 3 for areas greater than 1 square mile, one obtains a slope
of 0.085. This value is much lower than the values of 0.22 - 0.30 obtained for
most archipelagoes. From comparison with other Pacific archipelagoes, I interpret this to mean that immigration rates within the Solomons are relatively
high, because the isolation of the Solomons from New Guinea combined with
their small area requires most populations that reached and persisted in the
Solomons to be superior colonists.

     (c)   Isolated islands, defined as islands 8 - 400 miles distant from the
large islands of the northern and southern chains, have fewer bird species than
central islands of comparable size (fig. 4). A distance of about 100 miles reduces the species number by a factor of 1.1 to 8, the factor being greater for

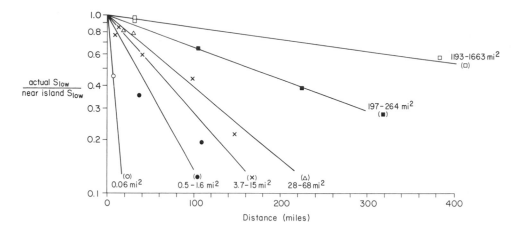

F<small>IG</small>. 4.   Effect of isolation on number of breeding lowland bird species in the Solomon Archipelago. Ordinate: Actual number of breeding lowland bird species S_{low}
on an isolated island, divided by the number on a central island of the same area.
Abscissa: Distance from nearest central island. Different symbols are used for islands of six different size classes, as coded on the figure. The lines are exponentials
fitted through the points for islands of each size class. Note that the ratio depicted
on the ordinate decreases with distance, and that the decrease is steeper for smaller
islands. That is, isolated islands have fewer species than central islands; the smaller
the island, the more severe is this effect of isolation   (From Diamond, Gilpin, and
Mayr, 1976).

smaller islands. In terms of the MacArthur-Wilson equilibrium theory of island biogeography, this effect is interpreted in terms of the decline in immigration rates with increasing distance.

(d)   The species number on Borokua, and to a lesser degree on Savo, may
be lower than expected from area or isolation. These islands also struck me as
having conspicuously low bird population densities, suggesting low resource
productivity. Correlated effects of productivity on abundance and on species
number have been documented previously for neotropical birds by John Terborgh, for desert rodents by James Brown, and for desert lizards by Eric
Pianka.

(e)   Figure 3 reveals no gross difference between species number on fragments of Greater Bukida and on other islands of comparable size, whereas
land-bridge islands of the New Guinea region (my work) and of the neotropics
(John Terborgh's work) show conspicuous "supersaturation" of species number. In more detail, however, the Greater Bukida fragments Choiseul and

Ysabel have three or four more species than the similar-sized "oceanic" islands Malaita and San Cristobal. The slightness of this supersaturation is consistent with the fact that only 11 percent (13 out of 116) of the species of Greater Bukida are unable or unwilling to cross water, whereas the comparable figure for Pleistocene New Guinea is about 70 percent. I suggest three reasons for the slightness of supersaturation effects on Greater Bukida compared to New Guinea: species had to be superior overwater colonists to reach the Solomons from New Guinea in the first place; Greater Bukida and its largest fragments have a much smaller area and hence higher extinction rates than Pleistocene New Guinea and its fragments, so that loss of water-crossing ability was a much more dangerous option for species of Greater Bukida; and Greater Bukida's smaller size also means that the initial "supersaturation ratio" was much closer to 1 for its fragments than for the New Guinea land-bridge islands.

3. *Area requirements of water-crossing species.* Table 1 shows that land-bridge relict species differ in the area of island required to maintain a stable population. This same conclusion applies to the much larger fraction of the Solomon avifauna that can and does cross water gaps. In surveying Solomon islands of different size, it soon became obvious to me that, for each species, there was a characteristic island area below which the species would certainly be absent, another characteristic area above which it would certainly or probably be present, and an intermediate range of areas over which its presence could be predicted with a probability increasing with increasing area from 0 toward 1. Previously, I expressed similar relations for the avifauna of the Bismarck Archipelago by constructing so-called incidence functions, which plot for each species the probability of occurrence against island species number. Similar functions can be constructed for the Solomon avifauna. Table 2 illustrates differences among Solomon water-crossing bird species in the minimum area of island on which the species is found to occur. There are two species (the cuckoo-shrikes *Coracina holopolia* and *C. caledonica*) that do not exist on Solomon islands smaller than 210 square miles, despite their ability to cross water. Numerous other species require areas of 2 - 47 square miles. At the other extreme, some species, such as the kingfisher *Halcyon saurophaga* and the starling *Aplonis cantoroides,* can live on tiny islets of 0.0035 square mile (2 acres). These differences can be interpreted in terms of the dispersal frequency, mean dispersal distance, extinction probability, and minimum territory requirement of each species.

4. *Applications of these findings to conservation strategies.* Tables 1 and 2 contain examples of the raw data required to predict how large a national park or forest reserve is required to reduce the probability of extinction of a particular species to a particular value. It appears that some bird species, including the

TABLE 2.   Minimum Island Area Required by Water-crossing Bird Species of the Solomon Islands

The table gives the area of the smallest island on which the species occurs. However, the fraction of all islands of this minimum size that the species actually occurs on is generally much less than 1.0.

Species	Minimum area (square miles)
Coracina holopolia	210
Coracina caledonica	210
Rhipidura cockerelli	47
Columba vitiensis	42
Cacomantis variolosus	15
Ceyx lepidus	14
Ceyx pusillus	9
Zosterops [*rendovae*]	9
Alcedo atthis	9
Aplonis grandis	5
Coracina lineata	3
Ninox jacquinoti	2
Hemiprocne mystacea	2
Pachycephala pectoralis	0.5
Mino dumontii	0.08
Eurystomus orientalis	0.08
Halcyon saurophaga	0.0035
Aplonis cantoroides	0.0035

most distinctive species of the Solomons, are unlikely to be able to survive except in forested areas of at least several hundred square miles. The other ingredient required to design a national-park system is knowledge of the distributions of localized endemic species. On the basis of this information plus feasibility considerations, a set of proposals for forest national parks has been submitted to the Forestry Review Commission of the British Solomon Islands. The main features of the proposals are: large, high-priority forest reserves on either Choiseul or Ysabel, large daughter islands of Greater Bukida with relatively small human populations, and on Guadalcanal and San Cristobal; smaller high-priority reserves on Kulambangra, Rennell, and in the mountains of Malaita; and additional reserves on New Georgia, Rendova, Tetipari, Ganonga, Gizo, Ugi, Santa Cruz, and Vanikoro.

REFERENCES

DIAMOND, JARED M.
 1972. Biogeographic kinetics: Estimation of relaxation times for avifaunas of Southwest Pacific islands. Proc. Nat. Acad. Sci., vol. 69, pp. 3199-3203.
 1974. Colonization of exploded volcanic islands by birds: The supertramp strategy. Science, vol. 184, pp. 803-806.
DIAMOND, JARED M.; GILPIN, MICHAEL E.; and MAYR, ERNST
 1976. Species-distance relation for birds of the Solomon Archipelago, and the paradox of the great speciators. Proc. Nat. Acad. Sci., vol. 73, pp. 2160-2164.
DIAMOND, JARED M., and MAYR, ERNST
 1976. Species-area relation for birds of the Solomon Archipelago. Proc. Nat. Acad. Sci., vol. 73, pp. 262-266.

JARED M. DIAMOND

Amphiboles from the Mantle Beneath Nunivak Island, Alaska

Principal Investigator: John S. Dickey, Jr., Massachusetts Institute of Technology, Cambridge, Massachusetts.

Grant No. 1327:   In support of sampling the earth's mantle from volcanoes on Nunivak Island.

Many crustal events, such as volcanic eruptions and earthquakes, are provoked and controlled by subcrustal phenomena, and many natural resources, such as precious metal deposits and geothermal sources, are born beneath the crust. This is why we want to learn more about the earth beneath the crust, especially the mantle, the spherical shell of dense silicates, oxides, and sulphides, which extends from the base of the crust, 40 kilometers down, to the core 2,900 kilometers below.

Samples of the mantle are difficult to obtain. Even in the ocean basins, where the crust thins to a few kilometers, no drill has penetrated the mantle. Nature occasionally brings pieces of mantle rock to the surface in the course of mountain building or as fragments entrained in rising rock melts. Fragments carried by melts are smaller but generally fresher than those included in mountain belts. The least altered of these so-called volcanic xenoliths are brought up by the fastest (and perhaps coolest) ascending melts, such as those that create diamond-bearing kimberlite pipes, maars or explosion craters, and other gas-rich explosive intrusions and eruptions. In these there is a high proportion of relatively undepleted, or fertile, xenoliths characterized by higher concentrations of low-melting constituents such as water and alkali metals.

Nunivak Island, near the west coast of Alaska (lat. 60°N., long. 166°W.), is a late Tertiary to Recent volcanic eruption center. The youngest eruptions were of xenolith-rich alkali olivine basalts some of which created large maars. In June and July 1974 we visited Nunivak to collect mantle xenoliths from the maars and other explosive vents. Several thousand xenoliths were collected and returned to the Massachusetts Institute of Technology for laboratory study.

Almost all the mantle xenoliths from Nunivak are spinel lherzolites, dense green rocks composed of olivine, pyroxenes, and spinel. The most interesting feature in these xenoliths was the presence of chromian amphibole. Amphiboles are complex silicates of the general formula $X_{2-3}Y_5Z_8O_{22}(OH)_2$

143

where X = Ca, Na, K, Mn; Y = Mg, Fe, Al, Ti, Mn, Cr, Li, Zn; and Z = Si and Al. The capacity of amphiboles for OH and alkali metals makes them particularly interesting constituents of mantle rocks. Of roughly 2,000 lherzolite xenoliths we found 10 that contained chromian amphibole. Furthermore, more than 50 percent of the entire collection showed signs of having contained amphibole before eruption.

The Nunivak amphiboles occur as small crystals lying among chromian spinel and diopside crystals. In many xenoliths the amphibole-spinel-diopside aggregates are accompanied by tiny droplets of glass, indicating that the xenoliths were beginning to melt during eruption. The amphiboles are quite uniform in composition and resemble mantle amphiboles found in lherzolite xenoliths elsewhere: 44.8 percent SiO_2, 0.4 percent TiO_2, 13.5 percent Al_2O_3, 2.3 percent Cr_2O_3, 3.7 percent Fe as FeO, 0.1 percent MnO, 18.1 percent MgO, 9.9 percent CaO, 3.8 percent Na_2O, 1.2 percent K_2O, 2.2 percent H_2O.

Our studies indicate that chromian amphibole is a common accessory mineral in the mantle beneath Nunivak Island. There is evidence that amphibole was present in many of the samples before eruption. We suspect that the survival of the amphibole in the 10 samples was due to high initial concentrations of the mineral and the unusually rapid rate of eruption. Textural evidence also suggests that the amphibole was not a primary mineral in the lherzolite but formed by chemical reactions between aluminous minerals, such as garnet or spinel, and an alkali-rich fluid. The nature of this fluid, its source and its relationship to the origins of some forms of explosive volcanism are important questions which are not yet answered.

REFERENCES

FRANCIS, DONALD M.
  1974.   Xenoliths and the nature of the upper mantle and lower crust, 237 pp.   Ph.D. thesis, Massachusetts Institute of Technology.
  1976a.   Amphibole pyroxenite xenoliths: Cumulate or replacement phenomena from the upper mantle, Nunivak Island, Alaska.   Contr. Min. Petrol., vol. 58, pp. 51-61.
  1976b.   The origin of amphibole in lherzolite xenoliths from Nunivak Island, Alaska.   Journ. Petrol., vol. 17, pp. 357-378.
  1978.   The implications of the compositional dependence of texture in spinel lherzolite xenoliths.   Journ. Geol., vol. 86, no. 4, pp. 473-485.
PETERSON, RONALD, and FRANCIS, DONALD M.
  1977.   The origin of sulfide inclusions in pyroxene megacrysts.   Amer. Min., vol. 62, pp. 1049-1051.

JOHN S. DICKEY, JR.
DONALD M. FRANCIS

Paleoecology of the Dinosaur-bearing Morrison Formation

Principal Investigators: Peter Dodson, University of Pennsylvania, Philadelphia, Pennsylvania; Robert T. Bakker, Johns Hopkins University, Baltimore, Maryland; A. K. Behrensmeyer, Yale University, New Haven, Connecticut; and John S. McIntosh, Wesleyan University, Middletown, Connecticut.

Grant Nos. 1295 and 1500.   In support of a study of the Morrison dinosaur fauna of the western United States.

The following is a report of the scientific results of the Morrison Formation Dinosaur Ecology Study Group, which was funded by separate grants from the National Geographic Society in 1974 and 1975. Investigators are Dr. Peter Dodson, University of Pennsylvania; Dr. Robert T. Bakker, Johns Hopkins University; Dr. A. K. Behrensmeyer, Yale University; and Dr. John S. McIntosh, Wesleyan University. Vicki Rowntree served as field assistant during the 1974 season. Field investigations were carried out during the summers of 1974 and 1975 at the localities described below. Comparative field-work in Europe was carried out in 1976 and 1978.

The Morrison Formation

The Upper Jurassic Morrison Formation, laid down in Portlandian times, some 140 million years ago, crops out over a huge area of the western United States, from Arizona and western Oklahoma in the south and west to southern Montana and western South Dakota in the north and east. Estimates of former areal extent range up to 500,000 square miles (Mook, 1916). Morrison sediments represent a phase of terrestrial sedimentation following the withdrawal of Oxfordian seas from much of the western interior of the United States. Thicknesses range from 300 meters or more at some places in western Colorado and Utah to 40 to 80 meters in southeastern and northern Wyoming. Throughout its range, the Morrison Formation has yielded an exceedingly rich and varied fauna. Two named members have general utility in Colorado and Utah (Stokes, 1944), the Salt Wash and the Brushy Basin members. The Salt Wash, transitional from underlying marine deposits, consists of sandstones, mudstones, and freshwater limestones. The Brushy Basin contains

145

much less sandstone and correspondingly more siltstone and mudstone, some drab gray, some bright variegated reds, maroons, and greens. In the thinner sections of Wyoming, the characteristic sandstones of the Salt Wash are uncommon. More applicable is a tripartite division into a lower unit that includes marly limestone, a middle unit of red and green variegated mudstone, and an upper unit of gray mudstone.

HISTORY OF COLLECTION

Throughout its range of exposures, the Morrison Formation has yielded an exceedingly rich and varied vertebrate fauna, particularly of dinosaurs. In 1877, the first major discoveries of dinosaurs were made at three separate localities in what subsequently came to be known as the Morrison Formation: at Morrison, Colorado, near Denver; at Canon City, Colorado, and at Como Bluff, Wyoming (Ostrom and McIntosh, 1966) (Table 1). Como Bluff, truly one of the world's richest fossil deposits, was worked continuously until 1889; superb collections were sent from there to both Yale University and the Smithsonian Institution. Como Bluff is the southern flank of an anticline capped by the resistant Dakota Sandstone. Fossil vertebrates are found in abundance along a linear outcrop extending for 9 miles (Ostrom and McIntosh, 1966). Though not as areally extensive as Como, the Canon City localities are scarcely less important. The Felch Quarry yielded a major fauna for Yale and the Smithsonian (Ostrom and McIntosh, 1966), while specimens from the Cope locality ended up at the American Museum of Natural History (Osborn and Mook, 1921).

In the final years of the 19th century, activity was renewed in the region to the north of Como Bluff. The American Museum of Natural History made a major discovery at Bone Cabin Quarry, 10 miles north of Como, in 1897 (Osborn, 1904) and also located single specimens of *Stegosaurus* and *Apatosaurus* nearby. Bone Cabin Quarry was worked from 1898 to 1904. At the same time the Carnegie Museum discovered rewarding accumulations at Sheep Creek and in the Freezeout Hills, 10 miles north and 10 miles west of Bone Cabin Quarry respectively. Attention was also turned to far-flung areas. Elmer Riggs of the Columbian Field Museum of Chicago made major finds in the Grand Junction-Fruita region of western Colorado in 1900 (Riggs, 1901 a and b, 1903, 1904). The next major find was made by Earl Douglass of the Carnegie Museum in 1909. Prospecting a few miles north of Jensen, Utah, he discovered an articulated series of sauropod caudal vertebrae in a steeply dipping sandstone body on the south flank of an anticline. The ensuing excavation revealed a fossil bed measuring more than 200 meters in length and 20 meters in breadth (Gilmore, 1936). This quarry was worked until 1923. After a lengthy hiatus, excavation and in situ exposure was resumed in 1953 and carried on to the present. The Cleveland-Lloyd Quarry of central Utah was discovered in 1927 (Stokes, 1944) and has been worked extensively by the University of Utah, particularly in the 1960's (Madsen, 1976). In 1931, J. W. Stovall began excavation in the vicinity of Kenton, Oklahoma, and over a period of several years removed 6,000 bones from a series of Morrison exposures (Stovall, 1938). In 1932, Barnum Brown discovered the Howe Quarry in the Bighorn Basin of northern Wyoming, and in 1934, the American Museum of Natural History excavated the entire quarry, removing some 4,000 bones (Brown, 1935). During the 1960's and 1970's, Jensen has collected actively and with great success in the Morrison of western Colorado and Utah. Thus, a century after the initial discoveries, new finds continue to be made in the Morrison Formation and new animals described.

PURPOSE OF INVESTIGATION

The Morrison dinosaurs constitute one of the best known terrestrial faunas from the whole of the Mesozoic from anywhere in the world. Yet there re-

TABLE 1.   Quarries Visited

Location	Discovery	Citation	Principal institution
Morrison, Colo.	1877	Ostrom and McIntosh, 1966	Yale
Felch Quarry, Canon City, Colo. (Garden Park)	1877	Ostrom and McIntosh, 1966	Yale, Smithsonian, Carnegie
Cope Quarry, Canon City, Colo. (Garden Park)	1877	Osborn and Mook, 1921	American Museum of Natural History
Como Bluff, Wyo.	1877	Ostrom and McIntosh, 1966	Yale, Smithsonian
Bone Cabin Quarry, Wyo.	1897	Osborn, 1904	American Museum of Natural History
Freezeout Hills	1898		Carnegie Museum
Sheep Creek	1898		Carnegie Museum
Grand Junction, Fruita	1900	Riggs, 1901	Columbian Field Museum
Dinosaur National Monument, Jensen, Utah	1909	Gilmore, 1936	Carnegie Museum
Cleveland-Lloyd Quarry, Cleveland, Utah	1927	Stokes, 1944; Madsen, 1976	University of Utah
Kenton, Okla.	1931	Stovall, 1938	University of Utah
Howe Quarry, Shell, Wyo.	1932	Brown, 1935	American Museum of Natural History

main fundamental gaps in our knowledge of the habits, distribution, and evolution of Morrison dinosaurs. For instance, were sauropod dinosaurs swamp-dwellers, as so often depicted (e.g., Colbert, 1961), perhaps even incapable of supporting themselves on land; or were they quite competent terrestrial animals (Bakker, 1971; Coombs, 1975)? The purpose of the present investigation is to review the faunal composition, diversity and demography, and geography of the Morrison dinosaurs in the light of sedimentary context, environmental reconstructions, and taphonomic characteristics. We were particularly interested in documenting the taphonomic character of the Jurassic-Cretaceous boundary, as the Cretaceous ushered in a totally new chronofauna, based on the ornithopods as dominant herbivores, replacing the sauropod-stegosaur-dominated community.

In collecting our data base, we visited most major dinosaur-producing sites in the Morrison Formation, locating quarries, measuring stratigraphic sections, recording sediment types and sedimentary features and searching for fossils in situ, particularly those of potential environmental sensitivity (e.g., remains of crocodiles, turtles, fishes, elements of the small herpetofauna, invertebrates, plant mega- and micro-fossils). In addition, we consulted published accounts of faunas and unpublished museum records and studied collections themselves at a variety of institutions. The complete data set is published elsewhere (Dodson, Behrensmeyer, Bakker, and McIntosh, 1980); only highlights will be presented here.

RESULTS

Morrison Environments.   Comprehensive studies of the Morrison Formation (e.g., Mook, 1916; Stokes, 1944) have differed considerably in interpretation of the environments represented. Mook (1916) visualized reasonably lush, mesic conditions, while Stokes (1944) cautioned, "The dinosaur fauna does not necessarily indicate lush vegetation and tropical conditions; and the paucity of plant remains is hard to explain if a well-watered terrain is postulated." He postulated desert conditions surrounding ephemeral lakes. A number of authors (e.g., Stokes, 1944; Moberly, 1960; Wahlstrom, 1966; Bilby et al., 1974) have emphasized volcanic components to the sediments.

We recognized four major lithotopes in the Morrison Formation: limestones, sandstones, drab mudstones, and variegated mudstones. Bedded limestones constitute prima facie evidence of standing water, in the form of either permanent or ephemeral lakes. Although not volumetrically abundant, limestones are locally common in the lower Morrison (Salt Wash). At some localities in the Uncompaghre Plateau of western Colorado such limestones attain a thickness of 1.5 meters! At Como Bluff, half-meter-thick limestones show algal laminae and biscuit-shaped stromatolytes. A few of the quarries are associated with limestones or marly sediments, notably Sheep Creek and Cleveland-Lloyd; neither fauna is of well-balanced high diversity.

Quite another matter is a 2-meter-thick limestone found at Dinosaur National Monument, 10 to 15 meters above the bone-producing horizon. This is an irregular cavernous deposit enclosing pebbles and granules, whose aspect is very suggestive of caliche, a soil formation of semi-arid regions with seasonally fluctuating water tables. Elsewhere in the upper Morrison, zones of carbonate nodules, and vitreous texture with slickensides in red mudstones indicate soil horizons.

Channel sandstones are locally important, particularly in the Salt Wash, but are volumetrically subordinate everywhere. At Dinosaur National Monument skeletons are preserved in a coarse, sometimes pebbly, sandstone that measures up to 3 meters thick. The sandbody can be traced laterally for more than a kilometer. At Canon City, the Marsh Quarry (Felch Quarry) is situated in fine sediments immediately above a 3-meter-thick cross-bedded sandstone. The general paucity of major channel systems in the Morrison is a conspicuous feature.

Volumetrically, the dominant sediment in the Morrison is drab gray or gray-green mudstone, sometimes well sorted and silty, more often poorly sorted; claystones are uncommon. The environmental significance of such sediments is not entirely clear. They almost never show lamination suggestive of lake deposits, although this could be explained away by floculation of clays or bioturbation (e.g., "dinoturbation"—trampling by dinosaurs). The comparatively poor sorting of such sediments is suggestive of wet overbank, shallow backswamp, and poorly drained emergent conditions. This lithotope is a dominant one for preservation of dinosaurs in the Morrison, including such major localities as Como Ridge, Morrison, and Howe Quarry.

Variegated red, maroon, purple, and green mudstones are highly characteristic of the upper half of the Morrison. Oxidation of iron (with local reduction) is suggestive of well-drained floodplain conditions, an interpretation reinforced by the presence of carbonate nodules and other features characteristic of soils. Important faunal associations with this lithotope include the Cope Quarry at Canon City and the *Apatosaurus* quarry at Fruita.

SMALL VERTEBRATES

In sharp contrast to Upper Cretaceous deposits of western North America (e.g., Estes, 1964; Dodson, 1971), the remains of small aquatic and terrestrial vertebrates are rare in the Morrison. Abundant remains of crocodiles, turtles, frogs, salamanders, lizards, and rhynchocephalians are found only at

Quarry 9, Como Bluff (Gilmore, 1928; Hecht and Estes, 1960) and, very recently, near Fruita. We located comparatively abundant crocodile and turtle remains in the Freezeouts. Crocodile skulls have been recovered from Como Ridge and from Dinosaur National Monument. Strangely, crocodile and turtle remains are presently completely unknown from two of our "wettest" sites, Cleveland-Lloyd and Sheep Creek. Studies at East Rudolf (Turkana) have shown that the ratio of crocodile-turtle remains to terrestrial mammals is greatest in lake margin sediments, intermediate in stream channel deposits and lowest in well-drained overbanks (Behrensmeyer, 1975). In the Morrison Formation, the distribution of large dinosaurs relative to crocodiles and turtles is analogous to that of terrestrial mammals at East Rudolf. In fact, the greatest number of genera of large herbivorous dinosaurs (Como Ridge being exceptional) is found in the over-all context of channels and well-drained overbank, an environmental category representing the least amount of permanent water.

PLANTS

The paucity of plant remains in the Morrison Formation has been widely commented upon. In sharp contrast to Cretaceous formations, there are no coals or even plant-rich mudstones. Silicified wood (cycad) is found locally, and careful search may turn up dispersed carbonized plant fragments in brown mudstones, as at Dinosaur National Monument. The over-all aspect of the Morrison Formation is a situation of either low productivity or of high oxidation of plant remains.

The search for pollen from the Morrison has been frustrating. Of several dozen samples analyzed, only specimens from Sheep Creek and Bone Cabin Draw *Stegosaurus* yielded significant quantities of pollen, chiefly conifer *(Spheripollenites, Inapperturopollenites, Araucariacites;* analysis by Allen Gottesfeld). Rare elements including bennetitales, filicales, gingkoales, and lycopsids suggest a Lower Purbeckian age for these two sites. Further details of the pollen analysis are given in Dodson, Behrensmeyer, and Bakker (1980).

Evolution Within Morrison Time

We found little biostratigraphic evidence for major generic level evolutionary change within the Morrison. Only one of the six genera of sauropods *(Brachiosaurus)* is restricted, as currently known, to the upper member; however, only two specimens are known. Among the common genera, *Apatosaurus, Camarasaurus,* and *Diplodocus,* the largest adult sizes, some 10 to 25 percent greater than other specimens, are found in individuals collected near the top of the formation. A long-limbed form of *Stegosaurus* seems to replace, at least in part, the short-limbed form characteristic of the lower and middle Morrison. At two locations, on the Red Fork of the Powder River and at Canon City, the form of *Diplodocus* seems to be more primitive than at all other sites; the two sites thus may be among the oldest. In general, however, the patterns of distribution of genera of large dinosaurs represent, in our opinion, ecological factors, not patterns of rapid evolution or extinction at generic level.

Distribution of Morrison Dinosaurs

The single most striking observation is that the large dinosaurian herbivores, *Camarasaurus, Apatosaurus, Diplodocus, Stegosaurus,* and to a lesser extent, *Camptosaurus,* occur throughout the entire range of fossil-bearing sedimentary environments in the Morrison, from lakes to poorly drained floodplains, from channels even to well-oxidized floodplains. This distribution strongly suggests that these animals did not limit their activities to the close proximity of lakes, ponds, and permanent water courses. For example, the presence of an adult specimen of *Apatosaurus* (weight about 30 tons) in well-oxidized overbank sediments indicates that the individual died very close to the location in which it was preserved, and that it was active on a dry floodplain immediately before its death. It seems extremely unlikely that such a huge carcass could be transported from a channel, across a levee, and then far out onto a floodplain, and subsequently be preserved in a highly articulated state.

Although sample sizes are still too small for statistical confidence, certain tentative inferences can be made about the habits of some of the Morrison dinosaurs. *Brachiosaurus* is the largest (and rarest) of the Morrison sauropods. Some workers have suggested that the long neck and the position of the nostrils high on the skull in front of the eyes are adaptations to life in deep water, although alternative explanations for these structures are available (Coombs, 1975). Only two specimens of *Brachiosaurus* are known from the Morrison despite intensive search for further remains. Both were found in the Grand Junction-Delta area of western Colorado. Here the Bushy Basin member is dominated by the well-drained floodplain facies with a notable absence of both lacustrine sediments and the remains of crocodiles and turtles. These occurrences suggest that in North America *Brachiosaurus* may not have lived in association with bodies of standing water. By contrast, at Tendaguru *Brachiosaurus* is abundant and evidently associated with water (Lull, 1915; Schuchert, 1918).

Haplocanthosaurus (structurally the most primitive Morrison sauropod) is common only at one locality, at Canon City, low in the Salt Wash member (this is the only major quarry in the Salt Wash). Since it is present, though rare, in the Upper Morrison of the Como region, it may be that ecological factors peculiar to the Salt Wash are responsible for its distribution.

Camarasaurus, Apatosaurus, and *Diplodocus* are present individually at 60 percent of quarries and collectively at more than 90 percent of the quarries. With *Stegosaurus,* they apparently represent a true community association. Of the three common sauropods, *Apatosaurus* is the least abundant and the most likely to be found as solitaires; it never dominates faunal assemblages. *Camarasaurus* and *Diplodocus* are never solitary. The outstanding observation about *Camarasaurus* is the tendency for large numbers of juveniles and subadults to occur, unlike *Apatosaurus* and *Diplodocus* from the same quarry. Juvenile specimens of *Camptosaurus* and *Stegosaurus* are also quite common (true also of *Kentrosaurus* from East Africa).

Ornithopods are common only at a single site, Quarry 13 at Como. At this quarry, *Camptosaurus* and *Stegosaurus* occur in subequal numbers, with *Camarasaurus* subordinate. Partial ecological segregation of *Camptosaurus* from sauropods is indicated.

As might be expected, the major carnivore, *Allosaurus,* is widely distributed both geographically and environmentally. James Madsen, State Paleontologist of Utah, has demonstrated that *Ceratosaurus* is neither a small nor a geographically restricted carnivore, but was widespread though never common in the environments preserved. Once known only from Canon City, it is now known from Como Bluff, Fruita, Dinosaur National Monument, Cleveland-Lloyd, and Kenton as well. James Jensen of Brigham Young University has discovered and is describing yet another genus of large carnivore that was present in western Colorado and at Como Bluff: *Torvosourus* (Galton and Jensen, 1979). Table 2 summarizes distributional data.

Jurassic-Cretaceous Transition

The Jurassic-Cretaceous transition marks a profound event in the evolutionary history of terrestrial faunas. At this boundary terminated a chronofauna based on sauropods and stegosaurs as dominant herbivores, and began a chronofauna based on progressive bipedal ornithopods, rare in the Morrison (Bakker, 1977). Sauropods survived throughout the Cretaceous, but were never again important. Stegosaurs became extinct, apparently replaced by ankylosaurs, their ecological vicars. Ornithopods were joined in the Late Cretaceous by the progressive quadrupedal ceratopsians. A second profound evolutionary event that occurred in mid Early Cretaceous was the origin and radiation of angiosperms (Doyle, 1977), which probably had much to do with the spectacular success of ornithischians in the Late Cretaceous.

Lower Cretaceous dinosaur faunas are much less known on a worldwide basis than are their Upper Jurassic or Upper Cretaceous counterparts. Several factors contribute to this. For one, such sediments are relatively scarce. For another, there was a fundamental change in taphonomic mode. In the Morrison Formation, mass accumulations of disarticulated or partially articulated materials are comparatively common. Consider these staggering figures. At Bone Cabin Quarry, Osborn (1904) estimates that the remains of 60 dinosaurs including 44 sauropods came from a mere 800-square-meter patch of ground. Brown (1935) supervised the removal of 4,000 bones from at least 20 individual dinosaurs from 200 square meters at Howe Quarry, an incredibly dense ac-

TABLE 2. Major Faunal Elements

Locality	Sauropods	Theropods	Ornithischians
Morrison	*Apatosaurus, Diplodocus, Camarasaurus*	*Allosaurus*	*Stegosaurus*
Felch Quarry	*Haplocanthosaurus, Apatosaurus, Diplodocus*	*Allosaurus, Ceratosaurus*	*Stegosaurus*
Cope Quarry	*Camarasaurus, Apatosaurus, Diplodocus*	*Allosaurus*	
Como (Main Ridge)	*Apatosaurus, Camarasaurus, Barosaurus, Diplodocus*	*Allosaurus, Ceratosaurus*	*Stegosaurus*
Como (Q 13)	*Camarasaurus*		*Stegosaurus Camptosaurus*
Bone Cabin Quarry	*Apatosaurus, Camarasaurus, Diplodocus*	*Allosaurus*	*Stegosaurus, Camptosaurus*
Freezeout Hills (NO)	*Haplocanthosaurus, Apatosaurus, Camarasaurus, Diplodocus*	*Allosaurus*	*Stegosaurus*
Sheep Creek	*Apatosaurus, Camarasaurus, Diplodocus*	*Allosaurus*	*Stegosaurus*
Grand Junction-Fruita	*Apatosaurus, Camarasaurus, Brachiosaurus*	*Allosaurus, Ceratosaurus*	
Dinosaur National Monument	*Apatosaurus, Barosaurus, Camarasaurus, Diplodocus*	*Allosaurus, Ceratosaurus*	*Stegosaurus Camptosaurus*
Cleveland-Lloyd Quarry	*Camarasaurus, Diplodocus*	*Allosaurus Ceratosaurus*	*Stegosaurus Camptosaurus*
Kenton	*Camarasaurus, Apatosaurus, Diplodocus*	*Allosaurus, Ceratosaurus*	*Stegosaurus, Camptosaurus*
Howe Quarry	*Camarasaurus, Diplodocus, Barosaurus*	*Allosaurus*	*Camptosaurus*

cumulation. Some 5,000 bones have come from Dinosaur National Monument (Gilmore, 1936), including more than 1,000 still in place (Lawton, 1977); at some 4,000 square meters, this is a comparatively large deposit. Madsen (1973; 1976) reports 10,000 bones from the Cleveland-Lloyd Quarry. Solitary specimens are vastly subordinate in terms of over-all provenance of Morrison fossils.

By contrast, the normal taphonomic mode in Upper Cretaceous is the occurrence of single specimens, often highly articulated (Dodson, 1971). The Lower Cretaceous Cloverly Formation clearly conforms to this mode (Ostrom, 1970). The major herbivores of the Cloverly are the ornithopod *Tenontosaurus* and the ankylosaur, *Sauropelta*. Two community associations are present in the Cloverly. *Tenontosaurus* occurs with remains of *Deinonychus,* a small predator, in a variety of facies, including dark mudstones with crocodile, turtle, and plant fragments. *Tenontosaurus* and *Sauropelta* do not tend to occur together. The latter tend to be disarticulated in variegated mudstones, with sauropod and large predator remains. The association of highly articulated tenontosaurs with plant-rich sediments of swampy aspect, suggests that these animals preferred wetter conditions than did comtemporaneous sauropods and ankylosaurs.

An increase in the quantity of plant matter in the sediments may indicate more mesic conditions of higher productivity in Cloverly times. On the other hand, the brightly colored variegated mudstones of the Cloverly lend an over-all aspect to the formation much more like that of the Morrison than of the succeeding drab Upper Cretaceous formations. The fact that the taphonomic mode of the Cloverly resembles the latter rather than the former apparently indicates that mode of preservation is more indicative of mode of life than of environmental conditions.

REFERENCES

BAKKER, ROBERT T.
    1971.   Ecology of the brontosaurs.   Nature, vol. 299, pp. 172-174.
    1977.   Cycles of diversity and extinction: a plate tectonic/topographic model.
             Pp. 431-478 *in* "Patterns of Evolution," A. Hallam, ed.   Elsevier,
             Amsterdam.
BEHRENSMEYER, ANNA K.
    1975.   Taphony and paleoecology of Plio-Pleistocene vertebrate assemblages of
             Lake Rudolf, Kenya.   Bull. Mus. Comp. Zool., vol. 146, pp. 473-
             578.
BILBEY, S. A.; KERNS, R. L., JR.; and BOWMAN, J. T.
    1974.   Petrology of the Morrison Formation, Dinosaur Quarry Quadrangle,
             Utah.   Utah Geological and Mineral Survey Special Studies, no. 48,
             pp. 1-15.

BROWN, BARNUM
  1935.   Sinclair dinosaur expedition, 1934.   Natural History, vol. 36, pp. 3-
           15.
COLBERT, EDWIN H.
  1961.   Dinosaurs, their discovery and their world, 300 pp.   Dutton, New
           York.
COOMBS, WALTER P., JR.
  1975.   Sauropod habits and habitats.   Palaeogeogr., Palaeoclimatol., Palaeo-
           ecol., vol. 17, pp. 1-33.
DODSON, PETER
  1971.   Sedimentology and taphonomy of the Oldman Formation (Campanian),
           Dinosaur Provincial Park, Alberta (Canada).   Palaeogeogr., Palaeocli-
           matol., Palaeoecol., vol. 10, pp. 21-74.
DODSON, PETER; BEHRENSMEYER, A. K.; and BAKKER, ROBERT T.
  1980.   Taphonomy of the Morrison Formation (Kimmeridgian-Portlandian)
           and Cloverly Formation (Aptian-Albian) of the western United States.
           Mém. Soc. Géol. France, new ser., no. 139, pp. 87-93.
DODSON, PETER; BEHRENSMEYER, A. K.; BAKKER, ROBERT T.; and McINTOSH,
     JOHN S.
  1980.   Taphonomy and paleoecology of the dinosaur beds of the Jurassic Morri-
           son Formation.   Paleobiol., vol. 6, no. 2 (spring), pp. 208-232.
DOYLE, JAMES A.
  1977.   Patterns of evolution in early angiosperms.   Pp. 501-546 *in* "Patterns
           of Evolution," A. Hallam, ed.   Elsevier, Amsterdam.
ESTES, RICHARD
  1964.   Fossil vertebrates from the Late Cretaceous Lance Formation, eastern
           Wyoming.   University of California Publ. in Geol. Sci., vol. 49, pp.
           1-180.
GALTON, PETER M., and JENSON, JAMES A.
  1979.   A new large theropod dinosaur from the Upper Jurassic of Colorado.
           Brigham Young Univ. Geol. Stud., vol. 28, pp. 1-12.
GILMORE, CHARLES W.
  1928.   Fossil lizards of North America.   Mem. Nat. Acd. Sci., vol. 22, pp. 1-
           201.
  1936.   Osteology of *Apatosaurus,* with special reference to specimens in the Car-
           negie Museum.   Mem. Carnegie Mus., vol. 11, pp. 175-300.
HECHT, MAX K., and ESTES, R.
  1960.   Fossil amphibians from Quarry Nine.   Postilla, no. 46, pp. 1-19.
LAWTON, REBECCA
  1977.   Taphonomy of the dinosaur quarry, Dinosaur National Monument.
           Contrib. Geol., University of Wyoming, vol. 15, pp. 119-126.
LULL, RICHARD S.
  1915.   Sauropoda and Stegosauria of the Morrison of North America compared
           with those of Europe and eastern Africa.   Bull. Geol. Soc. Amer., vol.
           26, pp. 323-334.
MADSEN, JAMES H., JR.
  1973.   On skinning a dinosaur.   Curator, vol. 16, pp. 225-266.
  1976.   *Allosaurus fragilis:* A revised osteology.   Utah Geol. and Mineralog.
           Sur. Bull. 109, pp. 1-163.

MOBERLY, RALPH, JR.
1960. Morrison, Cloverly and Sykes Mountain formations, northern Bighorn Basin, Wyoming and Montana. Bull. Geol. Soc. Amer., vol. 71, pp. 1137-1176.

MOOK, CHARLES CRAIG
1916. Study of the Morrison Formation. Ann. New York Acad. Sci., vol. 27, pp. 39-191.

OSBORN, HENRY FAIRFIELD
1904. Fossil wonders of the west—the dinosaurs of Bone Cabin Quarry. Century Illus. Monthly Mag., vol. 46, pp. 680-694.

OSBORN, HENRY FAIRFIELD, and MOOK, CHARLES CRAIG
1921. *Camarasaurus, Amphicoelias,* and other sauropods of Cope. Mem. Amer. Mus. Nat. Hist., vol. 3, pp. 249-387.

OSTROM, JOHN H.
1970. Stratigraphy and paleontology of the Cloverly Formation (Lower Cretaceous) of the Bighorn Basin area, Wyoming and Montana. Bull. Peabody Mus. Nat. Hist., vol. 35, pp. 1-234.

OSTROM, JOHN H., and MCINTOSH, JOHN S.
1966. Marsh's dinosaurs. The collections from Como Bluff, 388 pp. Yale University Press, New Haven.

RIGGS, ELMER S.
1901a. The dinosaur beds of the Grand River Valley of Colorado. Field Columbian Mus. Publ., Geol. Ser. vol. 1, pp. 267-274.
1901b. The foreleg and pectoral girdle of *Morosaurus.* Field Columbian Mus. Publ., Geol. Ser., vol. 1, pp. 275-281.
1903. Structure and relationships of opisthocoelian dinosaurs. Part I. *Apatosaurus* Marsh. Field Columbian Mus., Publ. Geol. Ser., vol. 2, pp. 165-196.
1904. Structure and relationships of opisthocoelian dinosaurs. Part II. The Brachiosauridae. Field Columbian Mus. Publ., Geol. Ser., vol. 2, pp. 229-247.

SCHUCHERT, CHARLES
1918. Age of the American Morrison and East African *Tendaguru* Formations. Bull. Geol. Soc. Amer., vol. 29, pp. 245-280.

STOKES, WILLIAM L.
1944. Morrison Formation and related deposits in and adjacent to the Colorado Plateau. Bull. Geol. Soc. Amer., vol. 55, pp. 951-992.

STOVALL, J. W.
1938. The Morrison Formation of Oklahoma and its dinosaurs. Journ. Geol., vol. 46, pp. 583-600.

WAHLSTROM, E. E.
1966. Geochemistry and petrology of the Morrison Formation, Dillon, Colorado. Bull. Geol. Soc. Amer., vol. 77, pp. 727-739.

PETER DODSON
ROBERT T. BAKKER
ANNA KAY BEHRENSMEYER

A Paleontologic Reconnaissance of Baja California, Mexico, 1974

Principal Investigators: Theodore Downs, Natural History Museum of Los Angeles County, Los Angeles, California; and William J. Morris, Natural History Museum of Los Angeles County, and Department of Geology, Occidental College, Los Angeles, California.

Grant No. 1361:   In support of vertebrate paleontologic reconnaissance of Baja California, Mexico.

During 1974 three expeditions were carried out in the peninsula of Baja California. The expeditions were sponsored by the National Geographic Society and organized as a cooperative effort between the Los Angeles County Natural History Museum and the Instituto de Geologia, Mexico City. The purpose was to accomplish a paleontologic reconnaissance of the peninsula with emphasis on collecting vertebrate fossils and noting localities that would yield vertebrate fossils. Approximately 10,000 miles were traversed. Although the newly opened and paved highway, Mexico Highway 1, was a significant improvement in reaching formerly inaccessible areas, the three expeditions covered in excess of 1,000 miles cross country.

In general, the first expedition proceeded the length of the peninsula to Cabo San Lucas then north along the eastern Gulf side of the peninsula of La Paz, northward across the Vizcaino Peninsula, and then northward on Mexico 1. The second expedition retraced the route to Cabo San Lucas then northward along the west, Pacific, margin of the peninsula to San Miguel Comonov and, after crossing to the eastern side, proceeding north on Mexico 1. The third expedition traveled extensively in the central and western sections of the Vizcaino Peninsula and revisited localities near Punta Prieta.

Theodore Downs, Natural History Museum of Los Angeles County, acted as project director. The first expedition was led by Ismael Ferrusquia, Instituto de Geologia, Mexico City, Mexico; and by Shelton Applegate, formerly Associate Curator of Vertebrate Paleontology, and William Morris, Research Associate in Vertebrate Paleontology, both of the Natural History Museum of Los Angeles County, Los Angeles, California. The second expedition was under the direction of Applegate, and the third under the direction of Morris.

The assistance of Ing. Diego Cordoba, Director of the Instituto de Geología, Universidad Nacional Autónoma de México, was invaluable; without his cooperation and interest the project would not have been successful.

In addition to the above, the following assisted in identifying specimens or in compiling geologic information: Lawrence G. Barnes, Natural History Museum of Los Angeles County, marine mammals; Robert Douglas, University of Southern California, microinvertebrates; Thomas Hill, University of California, Riverside, geologic sections at El Cien, and Santa Rosarito; George J. Jefferson, Natural History Museum of Los Angeles County, Pleistocene terrestrial mammals; and Edward Wilson, Natural History Museum of Los Angeles County, macroinvertebrates.

Fossil vertebrates ranging in age from Paleocene to Pleistocene were collected from 45 localities that were concentrated in Baja California del Sur. Attempts were made to collect in unfamiliar areas; therefore, the Cretaceous deposits near El Rosario, Baja California del Norte, were only briefly reexamined, as were possible localities near the international border and the area around San Felipe.

Geographic Setting

Baja California is a narrow peninsula extending southeast from the United States border for 1,200 kilometers. The widest part extends across the peninsula from the Gulf of Mexico across the Vizcaino Desert to the Pacific strand line, a distance of 170 kilometers. A line of mountains, divided into six ranges of high relief, extends along the peninsula to Cabo San Lucas. They are characterized by gentle western slopes and steep eastern slopes suggesting multiple fault scarps. The peninsula divide lies very close to the Gulf of California. Intermittent streams have dissected the western slopes so that steep canyons and numerous draws are common. These streams, during frequent flood stages, carry debris from the Sierra to be deposited on the mostly narrow alluvial plains, embayments, and continental margin along the western foothills. Except for minor changes in configuration of the strand line this general pattern of sedimentation persisted from the late Cretaceous in the northern part of the peninsula and, at least, back to the Oligocene in southern portions. The depositional history of the sedimentary strata, therefore, has largely resulted from uplift and erosion of the Peninsula Ranges.

Much of Baja California is characterized by an extreme desert type of climate and vegetation. Except for occasional oasis and irrigated flood and alluvial plains, only the southern one-third of the peninsula receives sufficient rainfall so that the lower elevations can maintain thick vegetative cover.

In 1974 a paved road, Mexico Highway 1, was extended from the United States Mexican border to Cabo San Lucas. Although this road now provides ready access to a narrow strip of territory along its length, prospecting to the east and west is still extremely hazardous and time consuming. For example, a side trip of 10 miles to examine the northern rim of Mesa de San Carlos, south of El Rosario, took one day. Not only is the extreme dissection of the land a hindrance but the dominance of cactus and yucca causes many areas to be inaccessible. Exploration of isolated desert areas, such as those of the Vizcaino Peninsula, still require experienced personnel in order to avoid jeopardy.

Paleogeography of Baja California

The location of marine and terrestrial vertebrate-producing sites in Baja California, as well as the relationship of the collected faunules to vertebrate assemblages reported from North America, the Pacific and Atlantic margins of the continent, and the Gulf of Mexico, is dependent upon the paleogeography of the area. Two geological characteristics are involved in the shifting paleogeographic patterns from the Cretaceous Period to the Pleistocene Epoch.

The first is the west and northward shift of the Baja California plate along the San Andreas Fault System and faults whose traces are to be found in the present Gulf of Mexico (Bischoff and Henyey, 1974). This movement opened a rift between Baja California and the mainland and resulted in the present geography of the region: an elongate peninsula of high relief separated from the mainland by a narrow but deep gulf. The west and northward rifting began first to the south in the Miocene Epoch and progressed northward where it is continuing at present (Atwater, 1970).

Superimposed upon the rifting of the Baja California plate is the palinspastic pattern of older epeiric marine incursions and local orogenic and epeirogenic uplift of nonmarine areas. The spatial arrangement of geographic elements are not well understood, owing to the lack of detailed geologic mapping, particularly south of Parallel 28. Only recently (Gastil, Phillips, and Allison, 1973), was a reconnaissance map of the northern part of the peninsula published. A summary of the paleogeography from Cretaceous through Pliocene has been presented by Durham and Allison (1960).

During the Early Cretaceous period, prior to late Cretaceous restrictions (Campanian), the Baja Peninsula existed as a submerged platform or as a segment of the submerged western margin of the Mexican continental plate. The Mexican Seaway covered the area, forming an unrestricted marine sea extending from the ancestral Atlantic to the Pacific. Conditions changed during the

FIG. 1. Panorama of the Miocene outcrops approximately 1 mile east of El Cien. The shark's teeth localities were collected from beds exposed in the large gully in the right center of the photograph. The measured section of figure 2 was started a few hundred yards beyond the right side of the photograph and ended at a conglomerate bed exposed at the top of the bluff in the left center of the photograph.

Late Cretaceous (Campanian-Maestrichtian) following a mid-Cretaceous orogenic episode. The sea regressed so that the Pacific strand line was approximately at its present position except for a major marine embayment occupying
the present Vizcaino Desert. A second maximum transgression followed, at
least in northwestern Baja California, extending south to Punta Canoas (Parallel 29), the southern limit of exposures of the Rosario Formation. By the Paleocene Epoch (and continuing into the Eocene) the Vizcaino Peninsula and
Cedros Island, Capo San Lucas to La Paz, small areas directly north of Coreto
and in the vicinity of Santa Rosalia, were islands. An area extending south of
the United States-Mexican border (Parallel 32) to approximately Parallel 28
was submerged only along the Pacific margin, the remainder being a region of
high relief marked today by the Sierra Juarez and Sierra San Pedro Martir.
This condition persisted until the Oligocene Epoch when, presumably, most
of Baja was emergent. Preliminary study of vertebrate fossils collected during
the summer of 1974 indicate a deeply subsiding basin in the vicinity of El
Cien between Loreto and La Paz. This new information may suggest that severe modification of the emergent episode is required. The Miocene paleogeo-
graphical situation was much like that of the Paleocene and Eocene except that
the two islands near Loreto and Santa Rosalia merged into one. By the Pliocene Epoch, Baja California had achieved almost its present configuration.
Except for minor coastal marine incursions the only significant geographic
feature was a marine channel cutting north to south across the peninsula in the
vicinity of La Paz. The connection between the Gulf of California and the Pacific was as it is today. Explorations of 1974 suggest that by Pleistocene time
the north-south La Paz channel had been reduced to a large lacustrine depositional basin in the vicinity of Rancho Carrizal.

Vertebrate specimens were collected from marine areas of deposition
ranging in age from Eocene-Oligocene to Pleistocene. In addition, on this as
well as related National Geographic projects, terrestrial vertebrates were collected from transitional, fluviatile, and lacustrine deposits of Cretaceous, Paleocene, and Pleistocene age. When related to the paleogeography, and when
study is completed, these collections should give us an excellent example of
paleozoogeographic work, and also should provide needed information in clar-
ifying the geologic history and development of Baja California. On a regional
scale the marine vertebrates, particularly from Miocene and Pliocene strata,
will serve as a link between those now recognized from the Pacific border and
those from the Gulf of Mexico and Atlantic Coastal Plain. The Cretaceous and
Paleocene terrestrial vertebrates will continue to provide links between those
of North America and of Asia. The Pleistocene terrestrial vertebrates will add
to our knowledge of development of Pleistocene faunas and will provide an in-

FIG. 2.   White Cliffs area. The beds are dipping away from the observer. The dark hill in the background contains layers correlative with the El Cien localities. The Eocene or Oligocene shark's teeth, White Cliffs, (NGB 29) were collected from the center foreground.

FIG. 3.   White Cliffs area, from about 10 miles away, looking north toward localities NGB 27 and 28.

FIG. 4. White Cliffs area looking north. NGB 27 is in the gully above the Talus cone.

FIG. 5.   Ysidro Formation at El Cien, NGB 6. Bioturbated interval near the base of the measured section exhibiting a heavily burrowed layer.

teresting example of faunal succession under insular conditions.

Although many more sites were investigated, 45 localities produced significant collections of marine vertebrates, terrestrial vertebrates, or invertebrates. Detailed information for each locality is on file at the Natural History Museum of Los Angeles County, Division of Earth Sciences. The fossils, by mutual agreement, belong to the Mexican Government and, therefore, have not been accessioned into the Museum collections. (The localities have been given the code NGB, National Geographic Baja, followed by a number indicating approximate order of discovery.)

Notes on Selected Localities

The purpose of this project was to extend our knowledge of the paleontology of Baja California by visiting as many promising localities as possible within the allotted time. Unless immediate results were obtained, those specimens present were collected and we moved on to sites which held greater promise. Many sites did not yield paleontological specimens and so were not

FIG. 6. Ysidro formation at El Cien, NGB 6. Concretionary and cross-bedded
sandstones near the base of the measured section.

listed in this report. Most of the sites yielded modest collections of vertebrates
or small collections of invertebrates. Such localities were listed on the locality
map, and in field books (by mileage), on file at the Natural History Museum
of Los Angeles County. A more complete geologic reconnaissance was attempted in those areas which yielded maximum results for the time spent in
prospecting. Information concerning these most productive localities is presented in this section. Localities NGB 15 (Punta Prieta) and NGB 44 (El
Rosario) are not reported despite their importance, as detailed information has
been furnished in earlier reports and publications.

The localities extend for 30 kilometers north of El Cien, a microwave station and general store, east and west of Mexico Highway 1. Exposures of the
stratigraphic section consist of brilliant white strata opening to considerable
badland terrains along even the minor drainages. Although the structure

FIG. 7.   Looking southeast toward NGB 6, El Cien. Shark-tooth fauna from two
resistant strata near top of hill.

FIG. 8.   "Salada" formation north of Loreto several miles south of NGB 2. The resistant layer is a pebbly siltstone containing a large mollusk fauna.

FIG. 9. "Salada" formation north of Loreto. The resistant bed at the top of the bluff is an oyster shell coquina (NGB 2).

seems to be homoclinal, dipping 5 degrees northeast, roadcuts along Highway 1 show open folds of small amplitude. Fossil evidence from localities NGB 6, 22, 23, 24, 25, 26, 27, and 28 indicate that the strata range in age from Oligocene to lower Miocene. According to Beal (1948), these strata were deposited in a basin extending from Punta Del Marques on the south to Punta San Juanico, a distance of approximately 480 kilometers.

Locality NGB 6 is 1.5 kilometers east of El Cien (figs. 1, 5, 6, 7, and 11). Figure 1 is a panorama of the region including NGB 6 looking southward.

NGB 26, 27, 28 (figs. 3 and 4) and 29 (fig. 2), are located approximately 16 kilometers north of El Cien and approximately 8 kilometers to the east of Highway 1. The section here is, at least, 35 meters thick. Figure 3 is a view of localities 27 and 28 from about 16 kilometers away, looking northward. Localities 26 and 29 are to the west and east of this photograph. Figure 4 is a closer view, looking north, of the area showing the location of NGB 27. The top of the section is lithologically identical to that exposed at El Cien (NGB 6). It contains the two shark-tooth-bearing beds followed by a sandy coquina and chert possible conglomerate. This conglomerate is overlain by ?Pliocene units that are lithologically similar to localities 23, 24, 25, and 41. There-

FIG. 10.   Close up of coquina bed shown in figure 11 (NGB 2). The large shells are oysters, although pectens are also abundant.

FIG. 11.   Concretionary sands at base of NGB 6, looking west.

FIG. 12. "Salada" formation at Santa Rosalia (NGB 1). Shark's teeth are abundant in the recessive weathering layer at the top of the cliff, seen in the top left portion of the photograph. The corkscrew burrows are in the more resistant beds below the shark-tooth beds.

fore, most of the strata at NGB 26, 27, 28, and 29 appear to be older than those exposed at NGB 6.

A third area is located 32 kilometers north of El Cien and 5 to 7 kilometers east of Highway 1. NGB 22, 23, 24, 25, and 41 are located here.

At locality NGB 25 the exposed interval consists of about 75 feet of light green to yellow shaley siltstone and claystone with a resistant caprock of calcareous, sparsely shelly, conglomeratic, sandstone and siltstone. Shark's teeth were collected from an orange, conglomeratic, argillaceous sandstone bed near the top of the exposed section, just below the resistant caprock.

SANTA ROSALIA AREA

This area contains locality NGB 1. The area was mapped in considerable detail by Wilson (1955). NGB 1 is located in the sandstone member of the Gloria Formation. This member occurs stratigraphically near the middle of the Gloria Formation (see figs. 8, 9, 10, 12, and 13). NGB 1 is located 4 kilo-

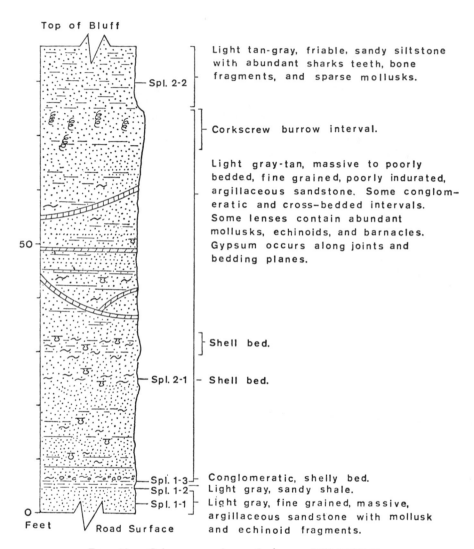

Top of Bluff

Spl. 2-2

Light tan-gray, friable, sandy siltstone with abundant sharks teeth, bone fragments, and sparse mollusks.

Corkscrew burrow interval.

Light gray-tan, massive to poorly bedded, fine grained, poorly indurated, argillaceous sandstone. Some conglomeratic and cross-bedded intervals. Some lenses contain abundant mollusks, echinoids, and barnacles. Gypsum occurs along joints and bedding planes.

50

Shell bed.

Spl. 2-1   Shell bed.

Spl. 1-3   Conglomeratic, shelly bed.
Spl. 1-2   Light gray, sandy shale.
Spl. 1-1   Light gray, fine grained, massive,
0   argillaceous sandstone with mollusk
Feet   Road Surface   and echinoid fragments.

FIG. 13.   Columnar section at Corkscrew Hill (NGB 1).

meters north of the city of Santa Rosalia on a sea cliff bordering the paved road. The rocks appear to be undeformed.

North of Santa Rosalia only reconnaissance mapping has been completed. Beal (1948) indicates a depositional basin approximately 8 kilometers wide and 15-24 kilometers long at Santa Rosalia. He called the Tertiary unit deposited in this basin the "Salada Formation." This is the Gloria Formation, in part, of Wilson (1955). Beal extended the name "Salada Formation" northward as far as NGB 2, north of Loreto (figs. 8, 9, 10). It is obvious, however, that such gross lithologic subdivisions are in need of revision.

Figure 12 is a columnar section measured at NGB 1, and shown in figure 13; a view looking southwest from the beach. The sediments are predominantly light gray-yellow brown, massive and poorly bedded, poorly indurated, argillaceous sandstones with a few thin intervals of siltstone. Near the top of the measured section corkscrew-shaped burrows are prominent. Shark teeth are abundant in the recessively weathering interval of argillaceous sandstone at the top of the outcrop.

RANCHO EL CARRIZAL

Rancho El Carrizal, NGB 3, 4, 17, 18, and 19 are located southwest of La Paz about 72 kilometers and is about 6-8 kilometers west of the main road. Pleistocene lacustrine and fluvial deposits are present in a broad flat plain east of an area of incised low foothills. The foothills are separated from the plain by a fault whose trace is very discernible on aerial photographs. A tentative hypothesis is that the Pleistocene alluvial and lacustrine deposition was initiated by subsidence or drainage interruption along the fault trace.

Approximately 10-20 feet of fossil-bearing strata are exposed in the gullies and these are apparently a mixture of fine-grained lacustrine deposits and coarser grained fluvial deposits. What are interpreted to be lacustrine deposits are light tan to light blue-green, massive to poorly bedded siltstones that contain, in addition to vertebrates, a prolific number of fresh-water gastropods, bivalves, and ostracods.

The lacustrine beds interfinger with coarser arkosic, conglomeratic and argillaceous sandstones that are probably stream and flood-plain deposits. The coarser deposits are massive to cross-bedded and contain lenses of conglomerate.

The fossil-bearing strata are exposed in a few deep gullies cut into the broad, flat plain.

Evaluation of Specific Aspects of the Reconnaissance

The possibilities of extending our knowledge of vertebrate paleontology, Cenozoic stratigraphy and biochronology, with continuing work in Baja California, are extensive. Several aspects, at this preliminary stage, seem worthy of special note. A short discussion of each follows, but this listing is not intended to be in order of priority.

Biochronology Based on Sections at El Cien and Santa Rosalita.   Although the sections between these two areas are interrupted by an extensive volcanic field, in the vicinity of Tres Virgines volcanoes, they appear to span an interval from the Eocene through the Pliocene, and, perhaps, Pleistocene. As noted in the faunal lists, localities within these areas are very fossiliferous, containing marine mammals, sharks and rays, macroinvertebrates, and microinvertebrates. In addition, as at NGB 6, rhyolitic tuffs are present, and may be amenable to K-Ar dating. A biochronological sequence is essential to further understanding of the stratigraphic relationships of the many scattered, often isolated, faunal localities found on this project and by previous workers. In most areas, aside perhaps from those at Rancho Carrizal, it appears that marine sequences grade laterally into transitional or nonmarine sequences. The biochronolgical key seems to be shark-tooth faunas. They are almost ubiquitous, even in those parts of specific sections where macro- and micro-invertebrates are absent. A biochronological sequence based on shark-tooth faunas keyed, where possible, into invertebrate biochronologies and K-Ar dates, would not only be valuable in Baja California, but would undoubtedly benefit the stratigraphic ordering of marine strata north along the Pacific Coast. Such a project would be an extensive one with many facets, but priority should be given to detailed geologic mapping and sedimentologic studies. This is needed to establish both horizontal and vertical control for collected faunal assemblages and to provide a context of environmental parameters. This latter aspect is not as important for the benthonic Foraminifera as it is for the shark-tooth assemblages.

As noted in the faunal lists, the shark assemblages differ and while most differences appear to be of a temporal nature there are others that may well be controlled by environmental parameters, such as bathymetry, or by pioneer-climax successions.

While the collecting of shark-tooth assemblages without adequate stratigraphic work, as outlined above, may add to more refined taxonomic arrangements and systematic understanding, it appears to be only a part of an over all more extensive, more informative project. This does not imply that smaller projects with a taxonomic or systematic theme are not justified, but only that they should be considered in light of biochronologic consideration.

Rancho Carrizal.   This Pleistocene series of localities presents a unique opportunity to study the effects of migration and isolation in a Rancholabrean fauna. Elements of the fauna necessarily dispersed southward at a time when the Baja Peninsula was isolated from the mainland, but a corridor remained open to the north. The presence of "giant" tortoise in a Rancholabrean assemblage from the southwestern part of the continent suggests a unique environ-

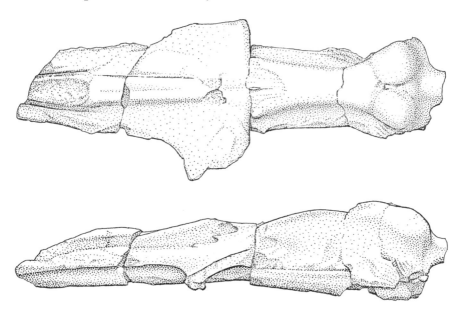

10 cm.

FIG. 14.   Skull of cf. *Mauricetus* sp., from El Cien, NGB 6.

mental context.

Undoubtedly, there are taxonomic novelties awaiting discovery, but it is of highest priority that collecting be accompanied by geologic mapping. As is common in Baja California, adequate stratigraphic control is lacking, and modern concepts of paleontologic study demand it.

Bahia Tortugas, Vizcaino Desert.   The association of macroinvertebrates with birds and marine mammals at several NGB localities discovered along the Pacific margin of the Vizcaino Peninsula near Turtle Bay gives, indirectly, the possibility of dating, for the first time, the significant Cedros Island verte-brate assemblage. Two Cenozoic units crop out of Cedros Island: the Pliocene Almejas Formation which overlies the middle Miocene Tortuga Formation. Birds and fragments of *Delphineus, Stenella,* and other Stenodelphininae from NGB localities near Turtle Bay correlate with the fauna obtained from the lower part of the Almeja Formation. On Cedros Island, however, marine mol-lusks are found only above the vertebrate-bearing horizon, while at the NGB localities these biochronological indicators occur with the vertebrates.

The El Cien Whale. At the very top of the section exposed at NGB 6 a partial cetacean skull was discovered. It is a *Mysticeti* belonging to the family Cetotheriidae. It is closely allied to *Mauicetus,* previously only known from New Zealand. Authorities differ as regards the age of the strata containing *Mauicetus* (fig. 14). It may be either lower Oligocene or lower Miocene.

Therefore, not only is the presence of cf. *Mauicetus* at El Cien a noteworthy systematic discovery, but it can be dated on the basis of both macro- and micro-invertebrates.

La Purisma Sirenians. Although late Tertiary sirenians are known from nearly complete skeletons, the occurrence of Dugongidae at locality NGB 32 are noteworthy for their abundance. Specimens were not collected but photographs and inspection indicates that along the La Purisma River the outcrop fairly bristles with bone from this group of sirenians.

REFERENCES

ATWATER, T.
  1970. Implications of plate tectonics for the Cenozoic tectonic evolution of western North America. Geol. Soc. Amer. Bull., vol. 81, no. 12, pp. 3513-3535.
BEAL, C. H.
  1948. Reconnaissance of the geology and oil possibilities of Baja California, Mexico. Geol. Soc. Amer. Mem. 31, pp. 1-138.
BISCHOFF, J. L., and HENYEY, T. L.
  1974. Tectonic elements of the central part of the Gulf of Mexico. Geol. Soc. Amer. Bull., vol. 85, no. 12, pp. 1893-1904.
DURHAM, J. W., and ALLISON, E. C.
  1960. The geologic history of Baja California (Mexico) and its marine fauna. Systematic Zool., vol. 9, no. 2, pp. 47-91.
GASTIL, R. G.; PHILLIPS, R. P.; and ALLISON, E. C.
  1973. Reconnaissance geological map of the State of Baja California. Geol. Soc. Amer. Mem. 140.
WILSON, I. F.
  1955. Geology and mineral deposits of the Beoleo Copper District, Baja California, Mexico. U. S. Geol. Survey Prof. Paper 273, pp. 1-134.

WILLIAM J. MORRIS

Andean Biogeography: Evolution of Distribution Patterns of Amphibians and Reptiles

Principal Investigator: William E. Duellman, Museum of Natural History and Department of Systematics and Ecology, University of Kansas, Lawrence, Kansas.

Grant No. 1304:   For a study of the evolution of distribution patterns of amphibians and reptiles in the Andean region.

From mid-June 1974 until mid-July 1975 I traveled throughout the Andes from Venezuela and northern Colombia to southern Argentina and Chile, accompanied by my wife (Linda Trueb), my daughter, and a research assistant (John E. Simmons). We traveled and lived in a truck-camper. The fieldwork had four primary goals: (1) to gather data on the patterns of distribution in the Andean herpetofauna, (2) to ascertain the ecological relationships of species of amphibians and reptiles within and between selected communities, (3) to determine the principal ecological and physiographic barriers to the distribution of species of amphibians and reptiles, and (4) to study the altitudinal distribution of species along selected transects.

Our major interests concerned the herpetofauna of the montane regions above tree line; thus, with the exception of southern Chile and Argentina and altitudinal transects, our study areas were mostly above 3,000 meters and reached 4,675 meters. In these high regions we sampled the herpetofauna at 66 localities, spending one to five days at each. At each locality maximum and minimum temperatures and amount of precipitation were recorded and the nature of the topography, soil, and physiognomy of the vegetation were noted.

At selected localities we made detailed quantitative samples; ten 10-by-10-meter quadrats were surveyed thoroughly at each site. The kinds of plants were determined and measured for height and percent of coverage; the amount of surface rock and water (if any) was measured. The quadrats then were collected systematically. For each animal found, the following data were taken: temperature of animal, substrate, and air, and relative humidity, time, proximity of water, structural habitat, and activity. Subsequently, size, weight, and volume were recorded for each individual before it was preserved. Data were obtained from 1,349 amphibians and reptiles from the quadrats. At the

175

University of Kansas, sex and reproductive condition of each specimen were recorded, and the stomach contents were subjected to analysis of the frequency of occurrence and comparative volume of prey items. These data were analyzed with respect to species diversity, niche breadth, and niche overlap (Péfaur and Duellman, 1980).

The distribution patterns of species of the Andean herpetofauna were analyzed on the basis of material that we collected, extant specimens in museum collections, and literature records. Tabulated according to their altitudinal distributions and habitats in 27 physiographic regions in the Andes were 727 species of amphibians and reptiles occurring at elevations of more than 1,000 meters. For purposes of analysis of patterns of distribution, these physiographic regions were placed in six major groups.

The results of these analyses were discussed in detail by Duellman (1979) and are briefly summarized here. Of the 32 species occurring in the Mérida Andes in Venezuela, only 7 are found in the larger fauna in the Cordillera Oriental in Colombia. In the isolated Sierra Nevada de Santa Marta, 16 of the 21 species in the cloud forests and páramos are endemic. Of the 415 species in the northern Andes (Colombia and Ecuador), 345 are endemic. Anurans with 262 species (225 endemic) are the most diverse group in the northern Andes, which have 7 endemic genera. The Huancabamba Depression in northern Perú is the major discontinuity of the principal chain of the Andes. Only 2 species of amphibians and reptiles occur in the Andes north and south of the depression. The central Andes in Perú and Bolivia have 159 species, of which 76 species and 2 genera are endemic. The herpetofauna of the southern Andes, including the Altiplano of Bolivia consists of 64 species, of which 36 are endemic.

A distributional analysis of all 727 species and of the 147 species restricted to elevations of more than 2,500 meters provides a basis for the recognition of eight ecophysiographic regions in the Andes. These regions are separated by physiographic or ecological barriers.

The Andean herpetofauna originated from separate invasions from the lowlands. A southern faunal assemblage is composed of groups derived from the ancient austral and more modern Patagonian faunas. The northern assemblage consists of groups derived from the tropical lowlands. The patterns of distribution and speciation in the herpetofauna of the high Andes are closely associated with the orogenic movements of the Plio-Pleistocene and climatic fluctuations in the Pleistocene.

These analyses reveal that although the herpetofauna of the high Andes (above tree line) is depauperate, the fauna of the forested slopes is rich and highly diverse. These montane forests are being destroyed by increased human disturbance. Thus, if the highly endemic herpetofauna in the cloud forests is to be preserved, it is urgent that natural preserves be established in the next few years.

REFERENCES

DUELLMAN, WILLIAM E.

1976.   Centrolenid frogs from Perú. Occas. Papers Mus. Nat. Hist. Univ. Kansas, no. 52, pp. 1-11.

1979.   The herpetofauna of the Andes: Patterns of distribution, origin, differentiation, and present communities. Pp. 371-459 *in* "The South American Herpetofauna: Its Origin, Evolution, and Dispersal." Monogr. Mus. Nat. Hist. Univ. Kansas, no. 7, 485 pp.

1980.   The identity of *Centrolenella grandisonae* Cochran and Goin (Anura: Centrolenidae). Trans. Kans. Acad. Sci., vol. 83, pp. 26-32.

1981.   Three new species of centrolenid frogs from the Pacific versant of Ecuador and Colombia. Occas. Papers Mus. Nat. Hist. Univ. Kansas, no. 88, pp. 1-9.

DUELLMAN, WILLIAM E., and SAVITZKY, ALAN H.

1976.   Aggressive behavior in a centrolenid frog, with comments on territoriality in anurans. Herpetologica, vol. 32, pp. 401-404.

DUELLMAN, WILLIAM E., and SIMMONS, JOHN E.

1977.   A new species of *Eleutherodactylus* (Anura: Leptodactylidae) from the Cordillera Oriental of Colombia. Proc. Biol. Soc. Washington, vol. 90, pp. 60-65.

DUELLMAN, WILLIAM E., and VELOSO M., ALBERTO

1977.   Phylogeny of *Pleurodema* (Anura: Leptodactylidae): A biogeographic model. Occas. Papers Mus. Nat. Hist. Univ. Kansas, no. 64, pp. 1-46.

LYNCH, JOHN D., and DUELLMAN, WILLIAM E.

1980.   The *Eleutherodactylus* of the Amazonian slopes of the Ecuadorian Andes (Anura: Leptodactylidae). Misc. Publ. Mus. Nat. Hist. Univ. Kansas, no. 69, pp. 1-86.

PÉFAUR, JAIME E., and DUELLMAN, WILLIAM E.

1980.   Community structure in high Andean herpetofaunas. Trans. Kansas Acad. Sci., vol. 83, pp. 45-65.

TRUEB, LINDA

1979.   Leptodactylid frogs of the genus *Telmatobius* in Ecuador with the description of a new species. Copeia, 1979, no. 4, pp. 714-733.

WILLIAM E. DUELLMAN

Behavior and Conservation of Hippotragine Antelopes in the Shimba Hills, Kenya

Principal Investigator: Richard Despard Estes, Academy of Natural Sciences of Philadelphia, Philadelphia, Pennsylvania.

Grant Nos. 1417 and   For East African antelope studies.
1517.

Introduction

Sable *(Hippotragus niger)* and roan *(H. equinus)* antelopes are the only living species of this genus. The blaaubok *(H. leucophaeus)* of the Cape Province of South Africa became extinct in the early nineteenth century (Harper, 1945). This report summarizes, as well as complements, previous publications on the sable and roan antelopes in Kenya, where both species are threatened with extinction (Sekulic, 1976a,b; 1978a,b,c,d; 1981; Sekulic and Estes, 1977; see also Estes and Estes, 1976). Elsewhere in Africa, the sable has been studied by Grobler (1974), Estes and Estes (1974), and Wilson and Hirst (1977), and the roan by Joubert (1970) and Wilson and Hirst (1977).

The sable has always had a restricted distribution in Kenya (Stewart and Stewart, 1963). The Shimba Hills National Reserve today appears to be the last refuge for this species. Sightings of sable in several widely separated locations of eastern Kenya were reported by Glover (1969) and Estes and Estes (1969) but subsequent habitat destruction makes it unlikely that any sable antelopes still survive in those areas (Sekulic, 1981). The congeneric roan antelopes were once plentiful in southwest Kenya and were also found in central Kenya (Stewart and Stewart, 1963). An estimated total for the whole country is now only about 300. In the early 1970's 38 roan antelopes were translocated into Shimba Hills from a site in central Kenya (Sekulic, 1978b). The present study concentrated on the indigenous sable but at the same time provided opportunity for a study of the introduced roan, its relationship with the sable, and the outlook for its survival in the new environment.

Study Area

The Shimba Hills National Reserve is situated in southeast Kenya, near the town of Kwale, at 4°5'S. and 39°29'E. The habitat consists of a mosaic of

179

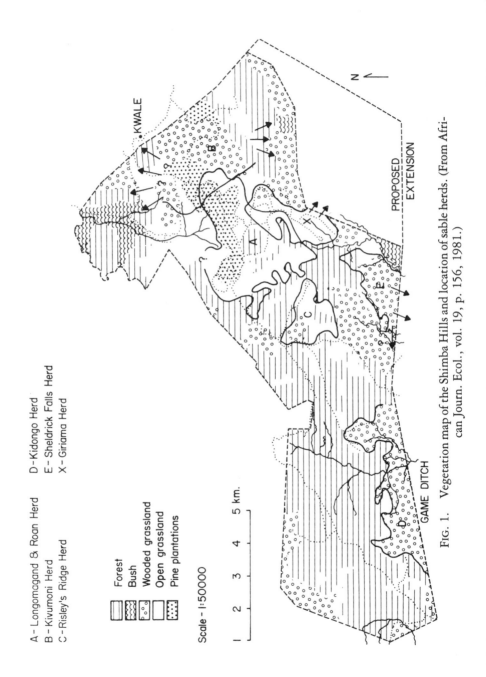

A - Longomagand & Roan Herd   D - Kidongo Herd
B - Kivumoni Herd   E - Sheldrick Falls Herd
C - Risley's Ridge Herd   X - Giriama Herd

Forest
Bush
Wooded grassland
Open grassland
Pine plantations

Scale - 1:50000

1   2   3   4   5 km.

FIG. 1.   Vegetation map of the Shimba Hills and location of sable herds. (From African Journ. Ecol., vol. 19, p. 156, 1981.)

forest and grassland. For a detailed description of climate, soils, and vegetation see Glover (1969). A part of Shimba Hills has been a forest reserve from the beginning of the century, and in 1968 180 square kilometers of it was gazetted as a National Reserve. However, the conflicting interests of the Forest Department continue to jeopardize the protection of the native flora and fauna, and planting of grassland with exotic softwoods has not ceased (Sekulic, 1978d, 1981).

Tabulated below are the larger mammals found at present in Shimba Hills; in addition, there is evidence that zebra, hartebeest, eland, and impala were formerly present:

PRIMATES
Galago crassicaudatus lasiotis	Bush baby
Colobus polykomos palliatus	Colobus monkey
Cercopithecus mitis kibonotensis	Sykes monkey
Papio cynocephalus cynocephalus	Yellow baboon

CARNIVORA
Mellivora capensis sagulata	Honey badger
Genetta genetta neumanni	Common genet
Herpestes sanguineus ibea	Black-tipped mongoose
Helogale undulata rufula	Dwarf mongoose
Ichneumia albicauda	White-tailed mongoose
Viverra civetta	African civet
Felis lybica taitae	Wild cat
Canis mesomelas elgonae	Black-backed jackal
Crocuta crocuta germinans	Spotted hyena
Panthera pardus pardus	Leopard
Panthera leo massaica	Lion ?

PROBOSCIDAE
Loxodonta africana	Elephant

ARTIODACTYLA
Potomaochoerus porcus daemonia	Bushpig
Phacochoerus aethiopicus aeliani	Warthog
Syncerus caffer caffer	Buffalo
Tragelaphus scriptus olivaceus	Bushbuck
Sylvicapra grimmia deserti	Grey duiker
Cephalophus monticola musculoides	Blue duiker
Cephalophus natalensis	Red duiker
Nesotragus moschatus deserticola	Suni
Madoqua kirkii nyikae	Dikdik
Kobus ellipsiprymnus kuru	Waterbuck
Redunca redunca tohi	Bohor reedbuck
Hippotragus niger roosevelti	Sable antelope
Hippotragus equinus langheldi	Roan antelope

FIG. 2. "Dot" female in 1968 (below) and 1973.

There are about 200 sable, about the same number of buffalo, and some 100 elephants. Buffalo, warthog, and the sable seem to be increasing, while elephants are on the decline, most probably because their migration outside the reserve has been nearly blocked by clearing and cultivation. Lions used to be numerous but were last reported in 1973.

My study concentrated on two sable herds (A and X, see fig. 1), which were habituated to vehicles and could be watched without apparent disturbance from a distance of 50 meters or less. Most of the surviving roan also frequented this area of about 34 square kilometers.

Methods

The study was conducted during several periods between June 1973 and July 1978, totaling about 1600 hours in the field. Most of the work was carried out from a Land Rover on loan from the Smithsonian Institution, Washington, D. C. Animals outside the main study area were located on foot. Reconnaissance flights over the Shimba Hills and surrounding areas were made with the East African Wild Life Society. Observations were made with the aid of 7x50 and 16x50 binoculars. The camera equipment consisted of a Nikon F camera with a 400-mm telephoto lens and a Nizo S-80 Super 8-mm movie camera. Study subjects were recognized by variations in horn structure, slits in ears or characteristic spots (figs. 2-3). Accurate estimation of ages was possible by comparison with known-age individuals (fig. 4).

Preferred Habitat

Sable in some areas spend considerable amounts of time in open woodland (Estes and Estes, 1976). Similar habitat is not available in the Shimba Hills. There the animals like to graze at the edges of termite mounds and its associated vegetation where the most tender species of grass grow. To define their preferences, a 1-square-kilometer grid was placed over the range of the largest herd A (see fig. 5), and divided into predominant vegetation and relief characteristics. Three factors were examined in defining preferred sable habitat: grass height, density of trees and bushes, and presence or absence of slopes (Sekulic, 1981). The sable avoided hills and wooded grassland, and showed strong preference for four quadrats where grass was frequently burnt or mown by the rangers. Little selectivity for grass species took place on these pastures but the sable rejected many mature grass species (table 1). Only 2.5 percent of the diet was composed of browse.

TABLE 1.   Most Common Grass Species in the Main Study Area and Their Utilization by the Sable Between September 1974 and January 1975

Key: 1, Species recorded by Glover (1969);
2, Species recorded by Estes and Estes (1969);
3, Observed visually;
4, Direct observation suggests greater consumption.

1	2	3	4	Grass species	Percent of diet [a]
				LOCALLY DOMINANT	
x	x			*Andropogon dummeri*	17.5
	x			*Andropogon shirensis*	9.25
	x			*Ctenium somalense*	11.5
x				*Cymbopogon excavatus*	3.25
x	x			*Hyparrhenia filipendula*	8.75
x	x			*Hyperthelia dissoluta*	8
	x			*Setaria sphacelata*	
x	x			*Setaria trinervia*	3.5
				Trachypogon spicatus	
				LOCALLY COMMON	
				Aristida sp.	
x	x			*Brachiaria brizantha*	4.5
		x		*Chloris gayana*	
				Chloris pycnothrix	
				Digitaria argyrotricha	
				Digitaria diagonalis	1.25
x	x		x	*Digitaria milanjiana*	3
x			x	*Digitaria mombasana*	
x	x			*Diheteropogon amplectens*	
	x			*Eragrostis perbella*	
x				*Eragrostis racemosa*	1.25
				Eragrostis tenuifolia	1.5
				Heteropogon contortus	1.25
	x			*Hylebates chlorochloe*	
		x		*Imperata cylindrica*	
x				*Panicum infestum*	3.75
x	x			*Panicum maximum*	
x	x		x	*Panicum trichocladum*	0.25
	x			*Paspalum orbiculare*	2.0
	x			*Pennisetum polystachion*	2.0
				Perotis hildebrantii	
				Perotis patens	
				Rhynchelytrum repens	
x	x			*Sporobolus pyramidalis*	2.25
				Dicots	2.5
		x		*Cyperus* sp	

[a] Average percent of the fecal samples

FIG. 3.   A three-year-old male (note the white dot on the neck) one month prior to eviction from the herd, performing *Laufschlag* display on an adult female.

Like the sable, the roan were usually found in open grassland. The aggressive interactions between the sable and the roan observed in the Shimba Hills (Sekulic, 1978a) may result from absence of the open woodland habitat, preferred by the sable (Estes and Estes, 1976), which offers ecological separation for the two species in other parts of Africa.

Daytime Activity Patterns

Between July and September 1975, whenever a group was observed intensively, activities were recorded at five-minute intervals. The records were made usually for several hours at a time but were discontinued during tourist

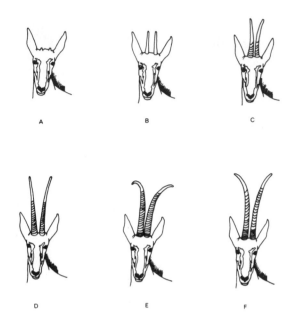

FIG. 4.   Aging of the Shimba Hills sable: A, Calf at 2 months; B, ~ 10 months; C,
~ 16 months; D, ~ 2½ years; E, 5-6 years; F, ~ 10 years. Yearling males can be
distinguished by their thicker horns. Note that the number of rings increases with
age, and that in individuals at age 5 and older the lower rings thicken to the point
of closing.

disturbance and heavy rain. During rain, the majority of the animals stopped
their previous activity and stood with their backs turned toward the direction
from which the wind was coming.

    Activity of each visible member of the herd was categorized as lying,
standing, grooming, interacting, walking, and grazing. Most ruminating
was done while lying down, usually in tall grass where few animals were clearly visible. Therefore ruminating was not recorded separately but, as expected,
it followed periods of intensive grazing.

    The observations for every five-minute period were pooled, four at a time,
to give a mean activity for every twenty minutes (see fig. 6). The mean activity patterns are much more regular over time in the sable than in the roan; this
reflects differences in the total number of animals observed.

    In general, the sable, which have a regular predawn resting period, got up
one by one between 0700 and 0800 hours and had a morning peak in grazing
between 0830 and 0930 hours. The roan most often did not get up until 0900

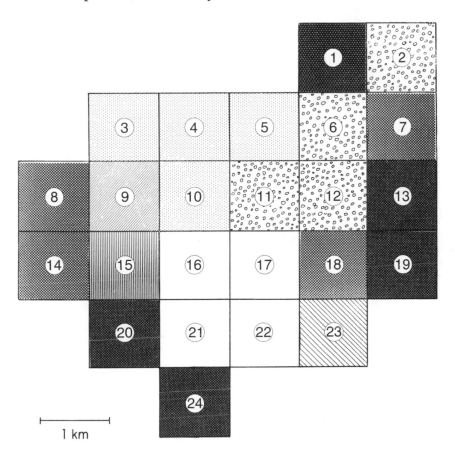

FIG. 5. Habitat types in the range of sable herd A.

and had the most intensive grazing period between 1000 and 1100 hours. The sable had a marked resting period between 1200 and 1300 hours, while that of the roan was between 1400 and 1500. Afternoon activities included bouts of lying and grazing for both species, but the roan spent more time lying than

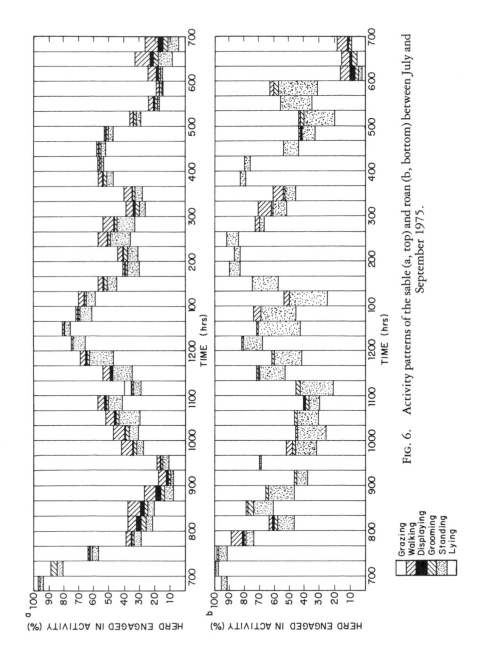

FIG. 6.   Activity patterns of the sable (a, top) and roan (b, bottom) between July and September 1975.

TABLE 2.   Daytime Activity Patterns of Sable and Roan

| | Percent of time | |
Activity	Sable	Roan
Grazing	51.3	37.3
Walking	3.7	2.0
Interacting	1.5	0.2
Auto-grooming	1.4	0.9
Standing	5.9	10.5
Lying	36.2	49.1

the sable. Toward late afternoon, both species grazed intensively. Other activities were difficult to compare because of their low frequency, but the roan appeared to spend more time throughout the day standing than did the sable.

The above observations do not consider possible differences between the two species in the total time spent in the various activities. Table 2 shows the activities converted into percentages for the whole period of observations. The Wilcoxon matched-pairs signed-ranks test was used to test the null hypothesis that the observed differences in hourly activity patterns were due to chance alone. The test is highly significant ($p < 0.001$) so the null hypothesis is rejected (Wilcoxon $N = 24$, $z = -3.82 \rightarrow -37.7$).

Unless the nocturnal activity pattern compensates for the differences observed during the day, there is a marked difference in the activity of the Shimba Hills sable and roan. The larger roan spend significantly more time inactive, and significantly less time in grazing, walking, interacting, and auto-grooming. Observations of roan in their natural habitat are needed to determine whether these differences reflect real differences between the two species or whether the activity of the roan has been influenced by their particular situation in the Shimba Hills.

Social Structure of the Sable

In all gregarious bovids three social groups are present: nursery herds of females and young, bachelor herds of juvenile to adult males, and single adult males (Estes, 1974; Leuthold, 1977). The sable adult males are territorial, while female home ranges cover territories of one or more males (Grobler, 1974, Estes and Estes, 1976; Sekulic, 1981). Bachelor herds are relatively unimportant in this species (Estes and Estes, 1976) and were not observed in the Shimba Hills.

TABLE 3.   Classification of Herd A and its Subdivision X in 1969, 1973-1978

	Herd A									Herd X								
	Total	Adult	2-yr		1-yr		Calf			Total	Adult	2-yr		1-yr		Calf		
		♀	♀	♂	♀	♂	♀	♂	?		♀	♀	♂	♀	♂	♀	♂	?
1969ᵃ	45	15	2	2	4	6	10	6	—	—	—	—	—	—	—	—	—	—
1973	57	18	3	6	7	5	9	6	19	10	5	—	—	—	—	2	3	—
1974ᵇ	64	27	4	6	5	6	9	7	2	14	5	—	—	2	3	—	4	1
1975	70	29	5	5	9	6	9	7	–	15	3	2	3	3	1	—	2	1
1976	84	28	8	6	6	7	6	8	15ᶜ	14	5	3	—	2	1	—	1	2
1977ᵈ (Mar.)	63	29	2	9	4	5	8	5	1	—	—	—	—	—	—	—	—	—
1977 (Dec.)	78	27	2	8	9	15	8	8	1	18	9	1	1	3	1	—	—	3
1978ᵈ	52	18	3	8	5	9	4	3	2	15	10	1	1	—	1	—	—	2

ᵃ From Estes and Estes (1969); includes subdivision x.
ᵇ Herd A includes 8 adult females and 3 young calves that joined from herd B.
ᶜ Newborn calves.
ᵈ Probably incomplete; 1978, Estes (pers. comm.).

RELATIONS BETWEEN HERDS AND SUBGROUPS

The Shimba Hills sable population has been expanding, with an increase of about 80 percent in six years. About 200 sable are divided into six herds, each inhabiting a well-defined home range of 10-24 square kilometers (Sekulic, 1981). Herd ranges are usually separated by patches of forest, and areas of range overlap, if present, are relatively small. For example, less than 20 percent of the 24 square kilometers of herd A overlapped with ranges of the neighboring herds B and X.

Herd A was studied most intensively, while few observations could be made on herd B because it remained shy. During 1974 herd X became habituated to vehicles and, unlike herd A, all individuals in it could be recognized. In other herds it was not possible to distinguish young animals except in a few cases. Nine females in herd A and all five females in herd B were known individually.

The classification of herd A in 1969 and in four consecutive summers between 1973 and 1976 and in December 1977 is shown in Table 3. The total number increased from 45 in 1969 to 96-98 in 1976-77. The percentage of young decreased from 76 in 1969 to between 56 and 66 in 1973-77 (1973 = 66; 1974 = 56; 1976 = 66; 1977 = 63). Some of these changes can be accounted for by the different timing of the reproductive cycle.

Herd X was a closed social unit the members of which stayed together except when a female was isolated for a few days to give birth. The much larger herd A, on the other hand, was usually divided into at least two groups, the composition of which changed almost daily. No consistency in the formation of subgroups was discerned. Such subgroups, however, may result in formation of new herds, since herd X was formed by subdivision from herd A between 1969 and 1973 (Sekulic, 1981).

Groups were classified each day and more than once a day when the composition changed during the course of the day. The sizes of groups observed between June 25 and September 10 in 1975 and 1976 were significantly different (fig. 7a and b; $X^2 = 24.64$, d.f. = 5, p < 0.001). During 1976 almost half the groups (females and young) recorded numbered 1-5 animals (total 192 groups). In 1975 about half the observations were of 1-15 animals (total 79 groups). Not only did sable form smaller groups in 1976 but the groups were also more dispersed (fig. 8): in 1976, for example, 90 percent of the animals were observed in 10 square kilometers, while in 1975, 90 percent of the sightings were made in only 7 square kilometers. The differences reflect at least partly stage differences in reproductive cycle. In summer 1975 most of

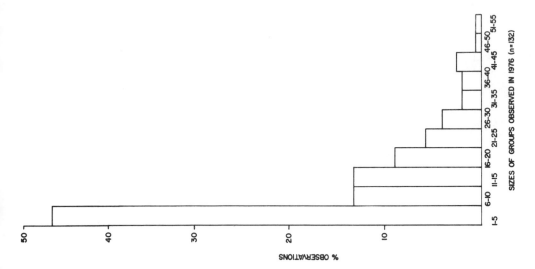

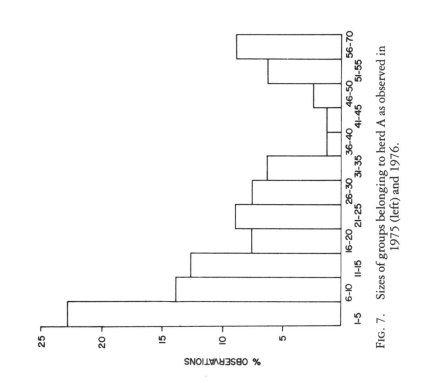

FIG. 7.   Sizes of groups belonging to herd A as observed in 1975 (left) and 1976.

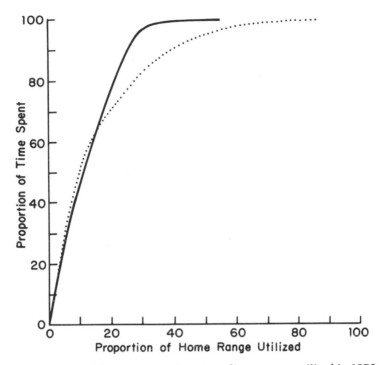

FIG. 8.   Proportion of time spent as a function of home range utilized in 1975 (solid line), and 1976 (dotted line).

the females were in later stages of pregnancy, while summer 1976 covered the peak calving season (Sekulic, 1978c).

FEMALE-FEMALE RELATIONS

Generally, disputes between females were settled after a laterial display, gentle interaction of horns or rubbing of the forehead against the other's shoulder, neck, or rump. Occasionally one female would chase another for a distance of over 30 meters. Rarely, the subordinate animal would lie down on the ground and bellow, or enter a bush to escape the aggressor.

Rank in a sable herd is manifested by dominance in such encounters as well as in leadership of the herd. It appears that a linear hierarchy based on seniority exists among the cows. Promotions in rank with age have been verified by observing females in herd A, known by Estes and Estes in 1968-69.

Observations on the behavior of the most dominant female were made on a cow (Granti) in herd X. When present, she was the only animal that ever succeeded in determining the direction in which the herd was moving. Herd

X usually rested close together, the distance between individual animals being less than 4 meters, but Granti most of the time would stand at a distance of 20 or more meters from the nearest animal. She seldom lay down, possibly because of the presence of the vehicle. Displays between her and the other two females were frequent. Granti also often intervened between animals that were fighting.

A female that was observed to lead a part of herd B to the herd A range was never seen to lose an encounter with another female for the four months that she was seen there. When she returned to herd B, after having become habituated to cars, she appeared to have a calming effect on the herd and I was able to approach it more closely than ever before.

A most interesting behavior by a herd A female was noted: this one, the oldest-looking female in the herd, detected the presence of a stalking leopard, which thereupon hid on the forest edge; the female then got the attention of the herd by snorting loudly, and having done so, led the animals away from the leopard. There was a noticeable difference in the degree of alertness that the older and younger females showed in these situations.

MALE-MALE RELATIONS

Unlike all young animals and adult females, which are brown, adult males are black. Even while still with the herd, subadult males associate with each other most of the time. Between three and four years of age, when they start turning black, they are evicted by a territorial bull. The bull chases the younger male until he stops trying to rejoin the herd and runs into cover. The adult male may repeatedly chase a younger male for short distances several months prior to final eviction, but the three observed hard chases of the young males who took refuge in the forest were final—none was ever again seen to rejoin the herd in the presence of the bull.

Five subadult males were excluded from herd A between July 1974 and September 1975. Two bulls who were evicted from the herd in July 1975 (Cheeky and Blacky) were regularly seen with a part of the herd, whenever an adult male was absent, until the study ended in September.

Particularly interesting was the case of a naturally marked male (Whitedot, fig. 3), known since July 1973. He was evicted from the herd in August 1974, when he was at most three years old. Until November, he was seen regularly in the range of herd A, once for a period of two weeks with an unknown four-year-old male that was never seen again. By June 1975 he had turned almost completely black. Between June and September, he joined a part of herd A on four different occasions when the territorial bull was not present and stayed with it for a period of up to two days. Cheeky and Blacky joined him for several weeks after they were evicted, but in September, during an aerial survey, White-dot was sighted alone in the valley north of herd A's range. Cheeky and Blacky were at that time in the southern part of herd A's range, either together or alone, and were also seen with herd X.

On two occasions when the three young bulls were seen joining a part of herd A, the following behavior was observed: the males took half an hour to approach the herd from a distance of about 100 meters; they apparently were watching alertly for the presence of the territorial male. When they finally joined the herd, they started to display to each other and fight. White-dot, being about a year older than the other two, attempted unsuccessfully to exclude Cheeky and Blacky from the herd.

Males occupied territories of 4-9 square kilometers throughout the year (fig. 9). Males in territories 2, 4, and 5, known since July 1973, still occupied the same areas in September 1975. Males in territories 1 and 3 were not seen in 1973, but in 1974 both were estimated to be older than seven years, so it is likely that they had been present in the same territories but previously overlooked. However, since none of these five males was known to Estes and Estes, they were not in their respective territories prior to 1969.

Only one change in territory has been observed prior to 1976. Male 1, the oldest of the five bulls, was replaced by a five- or six-year-old bull between February and June 1975. The ousted male was not resighted until September 1975, two weeks prior to termination of the study, when he was regularly seen about two kilometers from the border of his former range. He replaced another male (no. 2) and still occupied this territory in December (D. Pine, pers. comm.) but a different male was found there in June 1976.

Territorial changes are illustrated in Figure 10. Altogether, four males obtained territories in the period December 1975 through January 1976. In the case of Territory 4, another male took over half of the 8-square-kilometer territory following fierce fighting with the territory owner (D. Pine, pers. comm.). This male was observed in October 1974 in the range of herd A as a 4-year old subadult. Subdivision of Territory 3 took place in August 1976. All four subdivided territories remained unaltered, although new owners were later observed in territories 3A and 4A. Because no females were seen in the area, the territorial bull was not located in 3B in Dec. 1977/Jan. 1978 but the known owner was resighted in June 1978 so he probably remained in the territory throughout the period. Assuming that all the territorial changes that took place were recorded, the eight males that had lost their territories by the end of the study had occupied them between two and four or more years, for an average of about 2.8 years (excluded from this calculation is the male from territory 1, during his brief occupancy of territory 2).

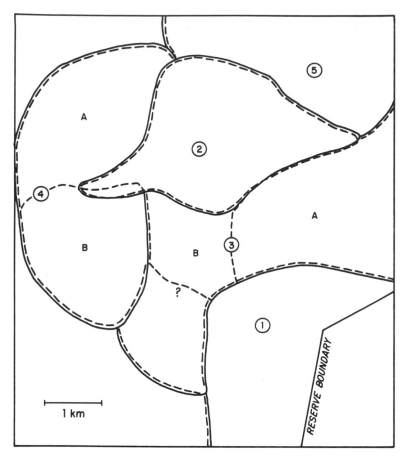

FIG. 9.   Spatial distribution of male territories in 1974, 1975 (solid line) and 1976-
1978 (dotted line). As indicated in Figure 10, territories 3 and 4 were subdivided.

Although adult males spend considerable time away from the nursery
herds, on only one occasion was one territorial male (bull 2) seen in the territory of another (bull 3). In that instance he walked toward the herd and started
displaying to females but was promptly chased out of the territory by bull 3,
who had been lying unnoticed behind a bush.

MALE-FEMALE RELATIONS

Subadult males spent a lot of time following and displaying to females,
even in the presence of the territorial male. Females often reacted very aggres-

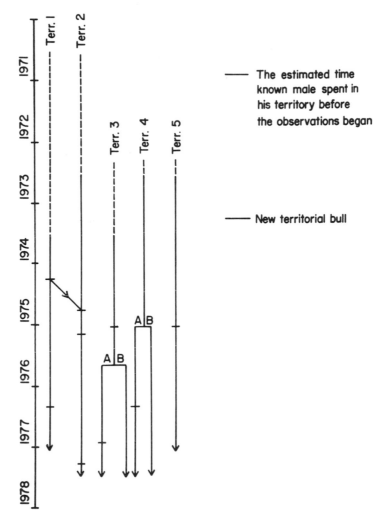

FIG. 10.   Temporal reconstruction of territory ownership during the five-year period 1973-1978.

sively to such attentions and the most serious fights I saw were between subadult and adult females and subadult males. Young males showed different degrees of attention to females. White-dot (fig. 3) and Cheeky were considerably more persistent than Blacky.

Territorial bulls, when present in the herd, were the most dominant animals and could usually direct the movement of the herd with a sweep of their head or by other dominance displays. Granti, the leading female of herd X, often resisted directions of the bull. He would then concentrate on chasing her in the desired direction, whereupon the rest of the animals followed her. Generally, however, bulls only herded animals when one of the females was in heat.

Estes and Estes (1969) describe the display patterns of *Laufschlag* (front leg kick), *Flehmen* and *Paarungskreisen* (circling) associated with courtship. Buechner et al. (1974) made observations in captivity and described intense aggression of an adult sable male toward females, but this has not been observed in Shimba Hills. On the contrary, females when pestered by young males sometimes lay next to a territorial bull, which usually did not pay any attention. The most intense display to females that was observed was by a non-territorial adult bull (the replaced male in territory 5). He once performed continuous *Paarungskreisen* with several females for a period of twenty minutes, and continued displaying less intensely for another half hour until darkness fell and the observations ended.

Social Structure of the Roan

The translocation of the roan antelope appeared to have had a profound influence on their behavior (Sekulic, 1978b).

In 1973 and 1974, the roan were found to be very shy. When disturbed, they tended to split and run toward the open, unlike the sable which usually sought cover. By 1975 the roan appeared habituated to vehicles.

Of the six adult females found in 1973, five shared the same home range of about 15 square kilometers, and were frequently seen together. The sixth female stayed in a separate area, but was seen near the other roan on several occasions and eventually joined them.

The roan herd was remarkably constant in composition at certain seasons, while at other times the animals scattered. They tended to stay together when very young calves were present but dispersed as soon as the calves were weaned. The two yearling females, born in 1973, spent about three months away from adults, either together or alone, despite the presence of adults in the vicinity. The low cohesion of the herd was also evident during resting periods. The average individual distance between the lying roan was 6.9 meters, as compared to 3.4 meters in the smallest sable herd.

The rank order among females remained constant, although they went through extended dominance displays and even fights after each prolonged absence (usually after calving isolation). One fight resulted in a broken horn.

The leader of the group, who was also the most dominant female, appeared to be the oldest, while the most subordinate was the youngest.

There may be two notable differences between the sable and the roan courtship. Post-coital smelling of a cow's vulva, which does not seem to occur in the sable, has been observed in the Shimba Hills roan (see also Joubert, 1970). From my limited observations of the roan, *Paarungskreisen* seems to be considerably longer and more pronounced than in the sable.

As only two roan bulls were present in the reserve, little information on the social structure could be obtained. The bulls were always in separate locations, and their marking behavior resembled that of the sable. I was under the impression that at higher densities they would have been a part of a territorial network. The only behavioral difference that I observed was that the roan bulls, unlike the sable, were twice seen to "kneel" down and "horn" soil.

Conclusions

1. The Shimba Hills can be considered as an ecological island for larger mammals whose migration routes outside the reserve have been nearly blocked by clearing and cultivations. About 40 square kilometers of open grassland remain, a habitat preferred by the sable and the roan. The Forest Department, however, continues to utilize the grassland for pine plantations.

2. The activity patterns of the introduced roan were significantly different from those of the indigenous sable. The larger roan spent less time grazing than the sable. Larger species should spend more time feeding than smaller ones, according to Clutton-Brock and Harvey (1977), so this finding is unexpected. Comparison of roan activities in their natural habitat are needed to determine whether the observed pattern has been influenced by the translocation.

3. Sable are found in herds whose members show antagonism toward nonmembers. Since most young females probably remain in the herd and range wherein they were born, these herds appear to be extended families. Each maintains more or less exclusive range, which may be traditional, learnt from generation to generation (Eisenberg, 1977). It is likely that occasional exchanges of animals occur, which would mitigate the effects of inbreeding. Since the range of each herd covers territory of more than one male, opportunities for mating with different bulls occur.

4. Grobler (1974) describes fighting as frequent among adult bulls in Rhodes Matopos National Park, Rhodesia, whereas I have observed no fights in 1,200 hours of observation, including one case of flagrant trespassing. Al-

though the density of males appears to be slightly higher in Rhodes Matopos, the observed difference may be correlated with climatic factors. In Rhodesia over 90 percent of the rain falls during a three-month period, while in Kenya some rain falls every month. In Rhodesia it is of advantage to females to drop calves during the rainy season when grasses are most nutritious, whereas in Kenya calves are born at all times during the year. Consequently, mating occurs during a short rutting season in Rhodesia but takes place year-round in Kenya. In Rhodesia males increase their reproductive success much more by holding territories during the rut than do the Kenya males during a comparable period. Therefore, in Rhodes Matopos males fight vigorously during the rut and as a result occupy territories for as little as four months.

5. In territorial ungulates, where only a small proportion of males breed, the degree of inbreeding should be dependent on the rate of male turnover. The effects of inbreeding have recently been reviewed by Wright (1977) for domestic animals, and by Ralls et al. (1979) for captive ungulates. Inbred lines show consistently lower numbers of young produced and greater mortality compared to controls. The time of territory tenure for the Shimba Hills sable falls just short of the time required for daughters to mature, the effect of which is prevention of a high degree of inbreeding.

6. Of the 38 roan introduced into the Shimba Hills, only 8 remained two years after the translocation. The numbers gradually increased to about 25 in 1978. This included only one mature bull and the second-generation young are the result of father-daughter matings. The amount of inbreeding must be considered in management of small ungulate populations (Ralls et al., 1979). Unless new bulls are introduced in the near future, a high degree of inbreeding may be the single most important factor that will jeopardize survival of the Shimba Hills roan.

Acknowledgments

The study was made possible through grants from the National Geographic Society, East African Wild Life Society and the Sigma Xi (the Scientific Research Society of North America). The research was sponsored by the Biology Department, Harvard University. The Smithsonian Institution, Washington, D. C., made a vehicle available during a part of the study. I am grateful to Dr. Richard Estes for his support and guidance throughout this study, and to Drs. B. Hölldobler, E. O. Wilson, and M. L. Reaka for their advice. S. Bruch prepared the illustrations.

REFERENCES

BUECHNER, H. K.; STROMAN, H. R.; and XANTEN, W. A.
   1974.   Breeding behavior of sable antelope in captivity.   Intern. Zoo Yearb., vol. 14, pp. 133-136.
CLUTTON-BROCK, T. H., and HARVEY, P. H.
   1977.   Species differences in feeding and ranging behaviour in primates.   Pp. 557-584 *in* "Primate Ecology," T. H. Clutton-Brock, ed.   Academic Press, New York
EISENBERG, J. F.
   1977.   The evolution of the reproductive unit in the class Mammalia.   Pp. 39-71 *in* "Reproductive Behavior and Evolution," J. S. Rosenblatt and B. R. Komisaruk, eds.   Plenum Publishing Corp., New York.
ESTES, R. D.
   1974.   Social organization of the African bovidae.   Pp. 166-205 *in* "The Behavior of Ungulates and its Relation to Management," V. Geist and F. Walther, eds.   IUCN Publ., new series no. 24, Morges, Switzerland.
ESTES, R. D., and ESTES, R. K.
   1969.   The Shimba Hills sable population.   Progress report to the National Geographic Society, 34 pp. (Mimeo).
   1974.   The biology and conservation of the giant sable antelope *(Hippotragus niger variani,* Thomas, 1916).   Proc. Acad. Nat. Sci. Phila., vol. 126, no. 7, pp. 73-104.
   1976.   Behavior and ecology of the giant sable.   National Geographic Society Research Reports, 1968 projects, pp. 115-129.
GLOVER, P. E.
   1969.   Report on an ecological survey of the proposed Shimba Hills National Reserve.   East African Wild Life Society, 148 pp.
GROBLER, T. H.
   1974.   Aspects of the biology, population ecology and behavior of the sable *Hippotragus niger niger* (Harris, 1838) in the Rhodes Matopos National Park, Rhodesia.   Arnoldia, vol. 7, no. 6, pp. 1-36.
HARPER, F.
   1945.   Extinct and vanishing mammals of the Old World.   American Committee for International Wildlife Protection, New York, Spec. Publ. no. 12, 850 pp.
JOUBERT, S.C.J.
   1970.   A study of the social behaviour of the roan antelope, *Hippotragus equinus equinus* (Desmosert, 1804) in the Kruger National Park.   Unpubl. M.Sc. Thesis, Univ. of Pretoria, 205 pp.
LEUTHOLD, W.
   1977.   African ungulates.   Zoophysiology and Ecology 8, 307 pp. Springer-Verlag, Berlin.
RALLS, K.; BRUGGER, K.; and BALLOU, J.
   1979.   Inbreeding and juvenile mortality in small populations of ungulates.   Science, vol. 206, pp. 1101-1103.

SEKULIC, R.
  1976a.   The Shimba Hills sable.   African Wildlife Leadership Foundation
           News, vol. 11, no. 3, pp. 12-16.
  1976b.   A case of adoption in the roan antelope in Kenya.   Saugetierkundliche
           Mitteilungen, vol. 24, no. 3, pp. 235-238.
  1978a.   A note on interactions between the sable and the roan antelopes in Ke-
           nya.   Journ. Mammal., vol. 59, no. 2, pp. 444-446.
  1978b.   Roan translocation in Kenya.   Oryx, vol. 14, no. 3, pp. 213-217.
  1978c.   Seasonality of reproduction in the sable antelope.   East African Wild
           Life Journ., vol. 16, pp. 177-182.
  1978d.   Reserved for what? A shrinking sanctuary for the roan.   Africana, vol.
           6, no. 9, pp. 27-30.
  1981.   Conservation of the sable antelope *Hippotragus niger roosevelti* in the
           Shimba Hills, Kenya.   African Journ. Ecology, vol. 19, pp. 153-165.
SEKULIC, R., and ESTES. R. D.
  1977.   A note on bone chewing in the sable antelope in Kenya.   Mammalia,
           vol. 41, no. 4, pp. 56-58.
STEWART, D.R.M., and STEWART, M.
  1963.   Past and present distribution of some East African mammals. East Africa
           and Uganda.   Nat. Hist. Soc. Journ., vol. 24, no. 3, pp. 1-48.
WILSON, E. E., and HIRST, S. M.
  1977.   Ecology and factors limiting roan and sable antelope populations in
           South Africa.   Wildl. Monogr. 154, 111 pp.
WRIGHT, S.
  1977.   Inbreeding in animals: differentiation and depression.   Pp. 44-96 *in*
           "Evolution and Genetics of Populations, vol. 3, Experimental Results
           and Evolutionary Deductions," S. Wright, ed.   University of Chicago
           Press.

RANKA SEKULIC

Maritime Culture Contact of the Maya: Underwater Surveys and Test Excavations in Quintana Roo, Mexico, May-July 1975[1]

Principal Investigator: Nancy M. Farriss, University of Pennsylvania, Philadelphia, Pennsylvania.

Grant Nos. 1404 and 1464. For a study of maritime culture contact of the Maya through underwater surveys and test excavations.

During the Postclassic period of pre-Columbian history, the east coast of Yucatán held a key position in a maritime network of interregional contact in Mesoamerica. Documentary and pictorial sources, as well as archeological evidence from land sites, suggest that by the time of the Spanish Conquest the east coast had become a flourishing center of long-distance trade and religious pilgrimage and had experienced at least several phases of foreign political influence through either colonization or conquest. Archeological material preserved under water along the east coast could provide further information on the nature, origin, and chronology of this maritime contact, and the purpose of our surveys has been to locate such material for eventual recovery and study.

Participants in the project were: Dr. Nancy M. Farriss, of the University of Pennsylvania; Dr. Harold E. Edgerton, of the Massachusetts Institute of Technology; Dr. Arthur G. Miller, of the Dumbarton Oaks Center for Pre-Columbian Studies; Pilar Luna, graduate student in archeology at the National School of Anthropology and History of Mexico; and John Gifford, doctoral candidate in marine geology and archeology at the University of Minnesota.

The surveys were conducted at three sites selected during a preliminary survey conducted during December 1974 and January 1975: Chunyaxché, a fresh-water lake connected to the sea by a series of lagoons and navigable channels; the broad, reef-protected bay of Tancah; and the well-sheltered inlet of Xelha. The survey was carried out in three roughly chronological phases. The first phase was aerial and shore reconnaissance of these sites in order to determine more precisely where to concentrate our searches. The second phase was

---

[1] For a similar version of this report see Farriss and Miller, 1977.

the preparation of bottom and subbottom profiles of the areas, using an E.G.&G. 5-KHZ sonar, operated from a 14-foot 6-inch Avon rubber boat propelled by outboard motor. Roughly parallel sweeps were made over areas where we believed archeological remains would most likely be buried, buoys were placed over targets recorded by the sonar, and bearings were taken to shore features. The third phase was under-water investigation of the sonar targets. Divers first carried out visual surveys using metal rods to probe the sediment and then test excavations were made of the most promising targets. In addition, sediment samples were collected from various test pits, and these will be analyzed by Mr. Gifford for information on the recent marine geology of the sites to enhance our understanding of the archeological evidence. Final conclusions about the results of the survey must also await analysis of the recovered artifacts by Dr. Miller.

Chunyaxché

We began our survey at Lake Chunyaxché, which we believed to be the most promising site on the east coast for the recovery of an intact pre-Columbian vessel. Chunyaxché is the innermost link in a complex inland water route between the Caribbean coast and the largest—though possibly least studied—Maya site in this region, Muyil. A short, perfectly straight artificial canal, which was reopened by chicle gatherers in 1924 but believed to be pre-Columbian in origin, connects Chunyaxché to a middle lake (for which neither maps nor the local inhabitants can furnish any name); and a much longer, winding channel connects the middle lake to the coastal lagoon of Ca'apechen. From Ca'apechen a series of smaller lagoons and channels extends south behind a narrow sand strip to the Bay of Asención.

Until recently fishermen from a settlement on the north shore of Asención Bay reached the territory's main highway, which runs past Muyil, by navigating these lagoons into Lake Chunyaxché, a journey of approximately 30 kilometers. It is likely that this, their safest and fastest supply route until the opening of a bridge across Boca Paila in January 1975, was also the route used by pre-Hispanic traders to Muyil, rather than the narrow and treacherous opening from Ca'apechen to the sea at Boca Paila.

The entire waterway is surrounded by low, marshy ground, most of it seasonally inundated, except for the site of Muyil. Muyil is built on the only high, well-drained land in the region, obviously chosen for that reason. Yet, although unsuitable for habitation, the shores and islets of this waterway contain a number of Postclassic structures easily accessible only by water, which attest to the importance of this route in pre-Columbian times.

Lake Chunyaxché was chosen for our survey because its central basin—termed a "drowned" *cenote* by Mr. Gifford—is the deepest part of the waterway. Both inland lakes become very treacherous in the stiff breezes that can spring up suddenly in the area, but Chunyaxché's central basin, dropping sharply from 11 to 25 meters, is the only area too deep for contemporary salvage of a vessel that had capsized or been swamped.

Our investigations confirmed earlier hints that the lake-bed sediment would be an excellent medium for preserving a wooden vessel and other perishable artifacts. The fine calcilutite silt overlying the bedrock is very deep, increasing from 2.7 meters at the extreme edge of the lake to an undetermined depth in the central basin, where we would expect vessels and cargoes to have been lost. We do not yet know the rate of sedimentation, but since most objects—including divers—sink rapidly into this soft, almost soupy silt, it is likely that any artifacts would be well buried in a short time—and once buried, well preserved. A shallow-water excavation that we made using a cofferdam device of two 55-gallon oil drums welded together produced a considerable quantity of waterlogged but otherwise perfectly preserved organic material, such as leaves and reeds. However, although the preservation of ancient archeological remains is also highly probable, we were disappointed to learn that, contrary to expectations, they cannot be located by sonar.

We obtained detailed bottom profiles on our various sweeps across the lake, but, instead of the clear subbottom profiles we had expected, we got only multiple echoes from the sediment's surface. The sediment's poor acoustical qualities are probably due to a high gas content that reflects the sound waves at the surface instead of permitting their penetration to reveal buried objects of greater density. Vegetation on the lake bed is scanty, but during our shallow-water test excavation we found deposits of decomposing calcareous algae mixed with the silt, which could produce enough gas bubbles, though barely visible, to interfere with the sonar.

We then turned to the side-scan sonar to detect surface features on the lake bed.[2] It seemed unlikely that anything of archeological interest would have remained exposed above the soft, deep silt, but we could not afford to assume so. The side-scan sonar—including an auxiliary device developed by Dr. Edgerton, called a rotary side scan, which is operated from the anchored boat to fix locations of surface anomalies more exactly—provides a rapid survey of a large area that would otherwise require many hours of diving time. The side-scan proved a very sensitive instrument, but, as feared, test dives revealed

---

[2] For an explanation of the application of side-scan sonar to underwater archeology, see Edgerton, Linder, and Klein, 1974.

the anomalies to be only natural irregularities: small bumps and ridges of silt on the basin's otherwise smooth slopes—possibly formed by geostrophic currents flowing slowly through the lake toward sea level—with no solid objects either on or within probe-length of the surface.

The technical problems interfering with the location of artifacts in Lake Chunyaxché were especially frustrating in view of the site's otherwise promising nature. It has long been assumed that the nearby site of Muyil was the terminus of the ancient water route leading from the sea.[3] But Muyil's impressive main structures are located well inland from the lake, and without any previously known direct connection to it. During shore explorations to establish a sighting line for the sonar sweeps from the canal's entrance toward Muyil's main plaza—hidden from the lake by tall forest—a heavily overgrown *sacbe,* or stone causeway, was discovered. The causeway, approximately 375 meters long, leads directly from the plaza's major temple through two small mounds straddling the causeway down to a larger structure, Postclassic in style, that stands right at the edge of the ancient lake bed. This ancient shoreline, now roughly 300 meters inland, is a clearly defined line between shrub and forest land, on the one hand, and, on the other, a low, marshy savannah filled with tall rushes and saw grass, which have gradually colonized the lake's edge. North of the Postclassic structure, along the same ancient lake shore, small rubble mounds were found together with other causeways, also leading back toward the main site and, finally, a series of worked stones leading in a straight line in the opposite direction into the savannah. Whether part of a foundation, a breakwater, or a smaller causeway, these stones and the other ancient remains clearly point to an association between the important site of Muyil and the lake and, ultimately, the sea.

It is most probable that pre-Columbian vessels and cargoes were occasionally lost without recovery and then preserved in this lake bed. But whether they can be located by techniques currently known to underwater archeology is open to question. The 3-kilometer-wide lake is too large and too deep for spot excavations on an extended grid system. Two other surface-operated search techniques are being considered: One is a magnetometer survey that would reveal only artifacts in sufficient concentration of a higher magnetic field than the sediment, and the other is trenching along the canal-causeway axis with a large, raft-mounted prop wash. Either or both could be pursued in conjunction with excavation at a more promising site in the area—Xelha— where we have already located underwater archeological remains.

---

[3] See Mason, 1927, for earliest published report on Muyil and the lake-sea route.

Tancah

Survey results at the other two sites, Tancah bay and the Xelha inlet, demonstrate the effectiveness of the bottom-penetrating sonar given suitable types of sediment—shelly sand at Tancah and closely packed fine marl, grading to sand, at Xelha, with little or no decomposing organic matter. In both areas the sediment covers a highly uneven coral or limestone base, with occasional outcrops, so that it is impossible to tell from the sonar record alone whether anomalies are archeological or geological in nature. However, the subbottom profiles narrow the search in the large expanse of almost featureless sea floor by providing a map of the only areas in which artifacts are likely to collect: in sand pockets or deep depressions in the underlying coral or limestone bedrock. The only other alternative to random excavation would be prohibitively time-consuming diver surveys with metal probes.

Even with the sonar we had to narrow our search at Tancah to a small portion of the long bay that stretches for over 12 kilometers in front of the pre-Columbian sites of Tancah and Tulum. The most hazardous areas for shipping would have been—and still are—near the natural openings in the barrier reef that allow access to the bay and which both marine biologists and marine geologists agree are likely to have been extremely stable over the centuries. Documentary evidence suggests that the opening we chose for the survey—in front of present-day Rancho Tancah—was the principal entrance to the entire bay at least as far back as early colonial times. (See "Relaciones. . . ," vol. 13.) Shallow-draft vessels that missed the entrance and hit the barrier reef to either side would be thrown by breakers over the reef crest to spill into the calmer, deeper water inside the bay. We therefore concentrated our sonar sweeps on a kilometer-wide area in front of and to each side of the opening. This area also has the deepest accumulation of sand, which should protect artifacts from being pulverized by the frequent hurricanes to which the region is subject. The other sizable reef entrance, in front of Tulum, has only a thin layer of sand over the dead coral that shelves gradually toward the shore.

The barrier reef affords only relative protection from the prevailing winds. Even in fairly calm weather the shallow bay, with a maximum depth of only 10 meters, is choppy, and heavy swells agitate the bottom. In these conditions we would not expect to find either the wooden vessels themselves or any orderly stratification of artifacts (except possibly by weight) but rather an accumulation in the sand pockets of nonperishable portions of cargoes, such as ceramic containers or stone implements. The sonar revealed not only sand pockets but also a number of denser anomalies within them, which were buoyed and their position fixed by triangulation both from boat to landmarks on shore and later from the landmarks to our buoys, in case either storms or local fishermen should dislodge them.

Neither the limits of our official permit—which was confined for this phase of the research to the sonar survey and controlled test excavations—nor the type of equipment we had available enabled us to carry out the extensive excavations required to verify the sonar readings. The one test excavation we were able to make, using a small airlift and an oil-drum coffer dam, proved mainly that such a technique is unsuited to the heavy swells in Tancah Bay. The only feasible approach is to excavate each sand pocket *in toto,* using the more efficient prop wash. This is an ideal tool when slower, more controlled methods are both difficult and unnecessary for the preservation of highly fragile artifacts or chronological stratigraphy. As with Chunyaxché, further work at Tancah, though much less of a needle-in-a-haystack search because of the smaller area and the sonar record, would be worth pursuing not as a purely independent operation but as an ancillary one to excavation at the third site, Xelha.

Xelha

The last of our three surveys, at Xelha, 10 kilometers north of Tancah, was by far the most successful. We were able to obtain very clear subbottom profiles and to recover a good sample of well-preserved archeological material during subsequent test excavations.

The deeply indented, Y-shaped *caleta* (inlet) of Xelha is perhaps the finest harbor for shallow-draft vessels on the east coast, similar to the *caletas* at Xcaret and Yalku but considerably larger and deeper. Prior to our work there in the summer of 1975, we had already encountered indications that the inlet had served as a port for the large pre-Columbian site bearing the same name (and possibly for a wider area). During a preliminary survey we located a previously unrecorded stone causeway that may have been the ancient city's main artery. This *sacbe* leads from the central peninsula that divides the *caleta*'s two arms inland through the main site to a temple complex (also previously unrecorded) bearing late Postclassic murals that show highland Mexican influence. (Farriss, Miller, and Chase, 1975). It is believed that these and earlier highland influences arrived on the east coast via extensive maritime contact. And the role of the Xelha inlet as the local terminus for this contact is further suggested by the concentration of mounds and surface sherds we found on the peninsula, the large defensive wall bisecting it, and several likely landing areas along its edge.

Most of our underwater test excavations were made off the north and south shores of this central peninsula, partly because of indications that the peninsula was the focal point of pre-Columbian activity in the port and partly because conditions there were found to be the most suitable both for our equipment and for the controlled testing required for the survey. Because of the coarser and more loosely packed sediment in the outer, seaward portion of the inlet, we found that cave-ins interfered with our test-pitting, since our oil-drum coffer dams were not permitted in the *caleta*. In other promising areas we found the water too shallow (less than 2.5 meters) for efficient use of the airlift we had devised in place of the more versatile water dredge, which had gone astray in transit and arrived too late.

Four of the six test excavations successfully completed in the vicinity of the peninsula, in water 2.5 to 4 meters deep, yielded heavy concentrations of archeological material. The test holes were all excavated down to bedrock and varied in depth from 50 centimeters to 2.3 meters, with the archeological material being found under a tightly packed fine marl sediment at depths of 20 to 70 centimeters down to bedrock. The rough subbottom configuration seems to account largely for these variations, with artifacts more concentrated in the deeper pockets.

The terms of the permit and the time available allowed us only to verify the existence of archeological material. It was clear that our 1/2- to 1-meter test holes by no means exhausted the deposits but rather yielded only a sample of the material in each area. Most of the material recovered was ceramic. Details on styles and origins await laboratory analysis by Dr. Miller, but a preliminary study indicates that most if not all of the pottery dates from the Postclassic period, including such types as Tulum Red, Puuc Slate, and Peto Black-on-Cream. No stone implements were recovered, but several ceramic fishing sinkers appeared; and one of the test holes produced a number of stones of the type that were used in construction as rubble fill and which were fire-blackened, suggesting the destruction of a building on the nearby peninsula. Perhaps the most exciting discoveries were the items of well-preserved organic material. Along with seeds and leaves were a piece of charred timber in the same area as the blackened stones—and which may have been part of the same shore structure—and a small piece of carved wood from another test hole. Neither sample was large enough, nor could their contexts be fully enough excavated, to provide much information on their functions. Their primary interest lies in their excellent condition and their apparently undisturbed contexts.

On the basis of our survey, extensive and systematic excavation of the Xelha *caleta* appears to be both feasible and potentially rewarding. The site is an unusual combination of a maritime context with conditions—more like inland *cenotes* than offshore areas—most favorable for the preservation of both undisturbed stratigraphy and artifacts of organic material. The favorable environment created under water at Xelha by the protective, densely packed sediment on much of the bottom, combined with the water's low salinity and the absence of wave/storm action, could very well enable us to supplement the scanty record from land excavations of baskets, textiles, wooden implements, and other highly perishable objects that formed such a large proportion of Maya material culture. It is impossible to say which, if any, of this type of artifact may eventually be recovered from Xelha. We would not expect any intact pre-Columbian trading canoe with unsalvaged cargo, because the *caleta* is so well sheltered and the water so shallow (the maximum depth of 7 meters is well within the limits of free diving), although we cannot entirely rule out the possibility that an ancient vessel or vessels may have been abandoned as unserviceable and preserved beneath the sediment. However, on the basis of samples already recovered, it is very unlikely that any organic material deposited here would be recovered in excellent condition.

The type of archeological remains we believe most prevalent at Xelha is "port refuse"—the material lost and discarded from boats that tends to accumulate in any busy harbor. We would also expect to find, again on the basis of our sample, objects from the nearby shores and even from parts of structures.

Such material would provide a valuable record of Maya maritime activities, including seaborne contact with neighboring areas. The grotto shrine on the south shore of the *caleta,* which unfortunately has been fairly thoroughly looted by now, indicates that the area had religious significance for seafarers and may have been one of the east-coast centers of pilgrimage. The peninsula's defensive wall, together with the charred timber and fire-blackened rubble recovered from our test excavation, suggest that the area may also have been the target of less peaceful visitors, perhaps seagoing raiders like those depicted in mural paintings in the Temple of the Warriors at Chichén Itzá (Miller, 1977). It is hoped that more extensive underwater excavations at Xelha will reveal more about this little-known turbulent aspect of east coast history.

Xelha offers ideal working conditions for underwater archeology. Its sheltered location and clear, relatively shallow water would enable large-scale excavation of the *caleta* to be carried out without major additions either to the equipment or personnel already used in the survey and test excavations. The main extra requirements would be local laboratory space, chemicals, and the services of a conservator for the preservation of artifacts of organic material after recovery.

At the same time, the equipment and personnel assembled to work at Xelha, with suitable permits and the availability of a large prop wash, could be devoted part of the time to excavation at Tancah and the location of material at Chunyaxché.

REFERENCES

EDGERTON, HAROLD E.; LINDA, ELISHA; and KLEIN, MARTIN
    1974.   Sonar search at Ashdod, Israel. Nat. Geogr. Soc. Res. Rpts., 1967 Projects, pp. 71-82, illus.

FARRISS, NANCY M., and MILLER, ARTHUR G.
    1977.   Maritime cultural contact of the Maya: Underwater surveys and test excavations in Quintana Roo, Mexico. Int. Journ. Naut. Archaeol. and Underwater Expl., vol. 6, no. 2, pp. 141-151, illus.

FARRISS, NANCY M.; MILLER, ARTHUR G.; and CHASE, ARLEN F.
    1975.   Late Maya mural paintings from Quintana Roo, Mexico. Journ. Field Archaeol, vol. 2, nos. 1/2, pp. 5-10.

MASON, GREGORY
    1927.   Silver cities of Yucatan, 340 pp., illus. G. P. Putnam's Sons, New York.

MILLER, ARTHUR G.
    1977.   The Maya and the sea: Trade and cult in Tancah and Tulum, Quintana Roo, Mexico. Pp. 97-140 *in* "The Sea in the Pre-Columbian World." Dumbarton Oaks Research Library and Collections, Trustees for Harvard University, Washington, D. C.

RELACIONES. . . .
    1898-1900. Relaciones de Yucatan. Vols. 11 and 13 of "Colección de documentos inéditos relativos al descubrimiento, conquista y organización de las antiquas posesiones españoles de Ultramer. Madrid. (Report on Çama in vol. 13.)

NANCY M. FARRISS

Maori Acculturation

Principal Investigator: William N. Fenton, State University of New York at Albany.

Grant No. 1414: In support of a study of differential acculturation of the Maori of New Zealand.

The Maori, a Polynesian people, preceded Europeans in discovering and settling the North Island and South Island of New Zealand by several centuries before Captain Cook's famous voyage late in the 18th century. Since then they have made a remarkable accommodation to the dominant British civilization while yet retaining their ethnic identity. Indeed the Kiwis or *Pakehas*, as the Maori call the Europeans, have themselves taken on a number of Maori ways that give their otherwise predominantly Scotch-English civilization a distinctive flair. A myth of racial equality prevails in public statements which is not upheld where the two races come into competition in crowded urban areas and in situations where upwardly mobile Maori abandon rural pursuits and take on professional roles. In these respects they offer interesting parallels and marked contrasts with American Indians, particularly the Iroquois of New York and Canada, who also assert a separate identity in a plural society. Each of these people has left a mark on his respective country.

Inasmuch as I have had long personal experience with the Iroquois, and since studies of "boundary maintenance" are much to the fore in modern social anthropology, I wanted to examine the Maori situation myself. I had first met this remarkable people and their culture in the seminars of Sir Peter H. Buck (Te Rangi Hiroa) at Yale University in the 1930's (see Buck, 1949).

With the aid of a Fulbright-Hays travel grant, besides National Geographic Society support of fieldwork, I was enabled to spend $3\frac{1}{2}$ months, from February 1 until May 13, 1975, in New Zealand. Residence at Dunedin on the South Island is not the most strategic location for fieldwork because the South Island has virtually no Maori settlements in contrast with the North Island where the Maoris are concentrated. But there were advantages in being accredited to the University of Otago, which has a great tradition in medicine and the sciences, in being received by colleagues in the anthropology faculty, and in being accorded the status of visiting fellow at Knox College to enjoy the perquisites of the high table and the Common Room. Since Knox draws

213

its residents from every corner of the two islands and from all ranks of New Zealand society, I found myself plugged into a network of relationships for understanding Pakeha society and for contrasting life in my own university. Special thanks are due J. S. Somerville, Master of Knox College, for this privilege and for other courtesies during my stay. Professor Charles Higham, Chairman, and Professor Peter Wilson of the anthropology faculty provided me with an office in the Anthropology Department's Cumberland Street house, opposite the Otago Museum, and adjacent to the University Library. Here at hand were advice, Maori collections—both artifacts and books—and facilities for planning research.

Since much of the more recent Maori literature is not readily available in the United States, the first month passed in Dunedin reading the latest anthropological books and monographs on the Maori, historical works on Maori displacement, biographies, and the poetry and social criticism of the young Maori writers. New Zealand has its own publishers, as well as its own Maori and Pakeha writers, and the excellent bookstores of Dunedin and Wellington attest to a highly literate public. The beautiful prose of Witi Ihimaera and the poetry of Hone Tuwhare convey the imagery of the old Maori chants, and as protest literature parallels that of recent American Indian writers, notably Vine Deloria. If anything, the Maori protest is more subtle and less bitter.

As an exchange of amenities at Dunedin, I advised a historian on colonial America, gave a seminar on the history of anthropology, delivered a Faculty of Arts Open Lecture on "The Lore of the Iroquois Longhouse," and, at the end, summarized my research for the Anthropological Society of Otago. In retrospect, these offerings, which attracted both Maori and Pakeha audiences, should have come earlier in the term, since they brought offerings of assistance too late for the research. Indeed, as in American Indian fieldwork, the first trip is a throwaway, an effort to discover the problem and establish rapport, which pays off in a return visit.

By the second month I was ready to take to the field and talk to some Maoris. This meant going to the North Island (in flight time comparable to from Washington to Chicago) and consulting with colleagues at Victoria University in Wellington, and with personnel in Maori Affairs. I also called at the Cultural Affairs Office at the United States Embassy. These arrangements were made for me by L. A. Cox, Executive Secretary of the New Zealand-United States Educational Foundation. They included a visit to the New Zealand Council for Educational Research, which has sponsored important work on Maori linguistics.

The best advice suggested following my own hunch to go up to the Taranaki district near New Plymouth and visit Te Rangi Hiroa's people at Urenui while making a pilgrimage to his grave at Okoki Pa. Professor Joan Metge (1967) put me in touch with Marjorie Rau at New Plymouth, a relative of my former teacher, and herself the daughter of a former Taranaki chief. Although everyone agreed that the Maori living around and about Taranaki are among the more acculturated representatives of their people, I felt that they might afford me the best chance of success in the brief time at my disposal.

At New Plymouth, I was greeted Maori style by Marjorie and Pepi Rau, a Maori and Tongan couple, who took me into their home, introduced me to other Maori leaders, and remained my point of contact during two short visits among the kindred of Te Rangi Hiroa. Pepi had known him in Tonga, Marjorie kept discovering his relatives, and saw to it that I was properly introduced. They were most interested to discover whether I might be related to some Maori Fentons, including an Anglican priest, and produced one "Tui" Fenton who took me to meet Billy Bertrand, an octogenarian cousin of Peter Buck (Te Rangi Hiroa), who had known him from boyhood and served in the Maori Battalion as his bat boy in France during the Great War. Indeed this was the first of a series of interviews that would produce material for an article on Sir Peter Buck, supplementing Condliffe (1971), the existing biography of the Maori physician, statesman, and self-made anthropologist.

The first visit to New Plymouth for fieldwork among the Ati Awa and Ngati Matunga Maori coincided with the biennial meeting of the New Zealand Association of Galleries and Museums. By then I had seen the collections at Otago (Dunedin), Wellington, and at Taranaki (New Plymouth), which became my letter drop for later fieldwork. One heard the familiar topics of accreditation and support being discussed. In general the collections from the Maori are superb, there seems to be money for acquisitions, but the storage problem and the urgent need for conservation of objects are national concerns that museum personnel have not succeeded in communicating to their boards of trustees or to the national funding agencies. Ethnological research on and with the collections appears minimal, and, save in archeology, contact between museum curators and anthropologists in university faculties is no better developed than in the United States.

The Maori people, however, are much interested and active in restoring their ancient crafts, and unlike American Indian militants who demand repatriation of ethnological collections from museums, the Maori elders deposit their precious objects in museums and borrow them for great occasions. This aspect of Maori-Pakeha relations is worthy of emulation. The push to use the ethnographic collections will come from the Maoris and not from the anthropologists, who are committed to social anthropology and seem uninterested in material culture studies.

Of the 3 months and 12 days in New Zealand, only 16 days can be counted properly as fieldwork among the Maori. Although the range of observations was somewhat broader, actual fieldwork counted 4 days at New
Plymouth, Urenui, and Okoki Pa, when I was welcomed on the *marae* (sacred
platform) and visited sacred sites with museum people; and a second trip of 11
days in April of more intensive work, alone. There was also a day at Waikato
University in Hamilton as the guest of Professors James Ritchie and Jane Ritchie, when I observed the Maori Chancellor preside over a meeting of faculty
to grant tenure and promotion, interviewed two Maori professors, and met a
class in anthropology.

It may be useful to sketch research accomplished, comment on problems
encountered, and then venture a paradigm of Maori and Iroquois comparisons. My principal accomplishment in the field is the material collected as Sir
Peter Buck's student from his relatives at Urenui and Waitara on his family
background and his return visits to his native *marae*. Several long interviews
were taped. They only represent a sample of what might have been accomplished given more time in the field. As in my American Indian experience,
results begin to emerge at the end of the visit that only pay off in a return visit,
which in itself is symbolic of serious interest. I regard my work as only the
briefest glimpse at a problem that would require at least a year to do it justice.
Although the connection with the University of Otago was useful in preparing for the field and in becoming acquainted with New Zealand society from
the Pakeha side, residence in Dunedin on the South Island posed logistic
problems of travel which meant that I spent too little time on North Island
and accomplished little of what I had set for myself. I really do not have a body
of solid data from which to make general statements; my impressions of the
nature of Maori acculturation enable me to advance some hypotheses that
would enable one to write a better design for comparative research.

In my experience the Maori are more friendly to strangers, easier to get
acquainted with, much less defensive than most American Indians, and they
are more communicative. Indeed their hospitality is somewhat overwhelm-
ing. Less withdrawn than American Indians, their humor is no less subtile but
more open. Should a return visit become possible to accomplish the tasks I set
for myself and which I only skimmed, I should plan to settle on the North Island and make excursions to the South Island, where I am at home in the local
culture. I would make the Maoris my home base and the Pakehas secondary.

A common paradigm of cultural identity and boundary maintenance, as
between Maori and Iroquois, arises from a similar historical experience but
different cultural roots. As Professor William Morrell of Otago pointed out in
his Hocken Lecture, and in conversations, the British North American experi-

ence with Red Indians disposed the Colonial Office in London to advise the New Zealand Company on colonization. As in North America, Christian missionaries followed on the heels of traders and whalers. New tools and new diseases were introduced, but a century or more elapsed between Captain Cook's discovery in 1769 and the first ethnological observations of Elsdon Best, late in the 19th century. In the New Zealand experience there was even wider discrepancy between theory and practice—between Parliamentary policy, Colonial Office advice, and the conduct of affairs in the colony. In North America the British had learned that trade and peace were one thing, they recognized that Indians had sovereign rights, and there ensued a series of treaties in the name of the Crown over land cessions. Distance to the antipodes prevented closer scrutiny of traders, whalers, and land sharks. Although the Waitangi Treaty followed the American model, it could not head off the Land Wars of the 1860's any more than the model had prevented the Colonial Wars in America. To be certain there were men of integrity on both sides in both places; but as one reads the record of the Maori Wars and the attendant land deprivation, the behavior of the Taranaki Constabulary would make the VIIth Cavalry in the next decade on the Plains look like polite actors (Sinclair, 1957, 1961). The Americanist sees a natural parallel between the messianic movements among deprived Indians on the frontier at the close of the 18th century, particularly that of Handsome Lake, the Seneca prophet (Wallace, 1970), and the peace movement of Te Whiti, the Maori prophet of Parihaka (Scott, 1975). Just as we know certain native institutions among the Iroquois from 19th-century anthropologists (Morgan, 1851; Hale, 1883), likewise the extremes of culture change among the Maori meant that only the oral literature and myths were recorded systematically, while much of the culture escaped the record, despite English writers like Best and Williams and Maori scholars such as Buck and Ngata.

At that the Maori have fared better than other colonial peoples, in the view of one eminent New Zealand scholar (Morrell, 1975) who hands the Pakehas little credit for Maori survival. He attributes the phenomenon to cultural qualities of the Maori themselves. This raises the question: what then were the qualities that enabled the Maori to maintain the boundaries of their culture and to retain their identity as a people? My own experience as an ethnohistorian of American Indians suggests that if these qualities could be discovered and identified they could be read back into the history of Maori-Pakeha relations to illuminate it in a meaningful way. I shall suggest a few of these for future research.

The institutions that survived were those that required constant repetition and depended on a vigorous oral tradition. Paralleling the great Iroquois origin myths that periodize their history and charter their institutions (Fenton, 1962, 1971, 1975), the Maori recall genealogies of the canoes from Hawaiki, which establish the ranking of chiefly families, and are identified with particular landing places. The Maori feeling for family (Whanau) (Witi Ihimaera, 1974) receives ritual support from the *Tangi* (funeral rite) and the return from the cities to the Marae for family reunions. Like the Iroquois the Maori have a strong sense of proper procedure. They also have strong feelings for place, as evidenced by their reverence for the sites of old *Pa's* (village sites), battlegrounds, and cemeteries. Indeed Maori place-names prevail on both islands and Pakehas proudly interpret them for visitors. Other outward symbols of Maori identity are the constant reference to *Maori tanga,* which reflects an inner feeling hard to define, and may be recent, but in general means "Maori ways"; the efforts to maintain the language, which is now learned as a first language by fewer people; the constant reference to *Kai* (one's food); and the movement to preserve the native arts and crafts—mat weaving, carving, and painting. Traditional Maori hospitality as symbolized by the *Hangi,* the earth oven feast, is now shared by both cultures. The Hangi is to Maori what the Kettle is to Iroquois. More subtile is the concept of *Aroha* (love), which suggests that Iroquois preoccupation with luck and health. "Indian time," an hour after an event is scheduled, had prepared me for "Maori time." Both cultures place enormous stress on speech, song, and the dance. They both respect elders who know everything.

Points of tension between Maori and Pakeha cultures come out in ethnic jokes on both sides, the reference to an overloaded, decorated, much used car as a "Maori Mustang"; and the expression from the other side, "To hell with the Pakehas anyhow. They're a bunch of bloody foreigners!" Having read David Ausubel's controversial study of New Zealand National Character, Social Attitudes, and Race Relations (1960, 1965), I chanced to discuss his findings with two native teachers of Maori language and culture at a northern university. Both men thought he was right, that his statements needed to be said, and that events have transpired as he predicted. One of them was a member of a Maori team that visited the American Southwest. As Maoris they were shocked that the Hopi would not receive them. Given the diversity of American Indian situations, a comparison with Maori-Pakeha relations to them seemed unfeasible. As university professors they symbolized the shift in Maori-Pakeha relations. They expected affairs to worsen. One said: "Formerly when 70% of the Maoris were rural it was possible for Pakehas to avoid meeting Maoris. Now, when 70% of Maoris are urban . . . , the Pakehas must learn to cope with Maori ways. It is no longer a matter of Maoris becoming Europeanized, but of the Pakehas internalizing New Zealand ways that are

Maori. . . ." His reasons were that the level of Maori education and expectancies have risen. "There are not now just a few great leaders as in the days of the Te Aute graduates—Buck, Ngata, Carroll, etc." The era of that phenomenon has passed. Today, when an educated Maori speaks out, when he addresses a letter to the editor on a public issue affecting his people—say the flooding out of a *marae,* its cemetery, and a Pa of 400 Maoris—and performs a characteristically New Zealand act, he finds himself attacked, threatened with libel suits, and if he is an academician, he may be called by his Vice-Chancellor for rocking the boat. It infuriates the established interests to have to realize that predatory deals involving Maori land are no longer possible without some reasoned protest in the press. As in America, one encounters militants, but this investigator did not find them unreasonable or uncommunicative; however, this well may reflect the privileged position of the outsider.

REFERENCES

AUSUBEL, DAVID P.
    1960, 1965.   The fern and the tiki.   Holt, Reinhart and Winston, New York.
BUCK, SIR PETER H. (TE RANGI HIROA)
    1949.   The coming of the Maori.   Maori Purposes Fund Board, Wellington.
CONDLIFFE, J. B.
    1971.   Te Rangi Hiroa: The life of Sir Peter Buck.   Whitcomb and Tombs, Christchurch.
FENTON, W. N.
    1962.   This island, the world on the turtle's back.   Journ. of American Folklore, vol. 75, no. 298, pp. 283-300.
    1971.   The Iroquois in history.   Pp. 129-168 *in* "North American Indians in Historical Perspective," Eleanor Burke Leacock and Nancy Oestreich Lurie, eds.   Random House, New York.
    1975.   The lore of the longhouse: Myth, ritual and red power.   Anthrop. Quart., vol. 48, no. 3, pp. 131-147.
HALE, HORATIO E.
    1883.   The Iroquois book of rites.   D. G. Brinton's Library of Aboriginal Literature, II, Philadelphia. (Reprinted with an Introduction by William N. Fenton. University of Toronto Press, 1963.)
IHIMAERA, WITI
    1972.   Pounamu Pounamu.   William Heinemann, Auckland.
    1973.   Tangi.   Heinemann, Auckland.
    1974.   Whanau.   Heinemann, Auckland.
METGE, JOAN
    1967.   The Maoris of New Zealand.   Routledge and Kegan Paul, London.
MORGAN, L. H.
    1851.   The League of the Ho-de-no-sau-nee, or Iroquois.   Sage, Rochester.
MORRELL, WILLIAM P.
    1975.   Maori and Pakeha relations in the light of history.   The Hocken Lecture, April 22, 1975.   Dunedin (unpublished).

SCHWIMMER, ERIK, ed.
  1968, 1972.   The Maori people in the nineteen-sixties: A symposium.   Long-
                man Paul, Auckland.
SCOTT, DICK
  1975.   Ask that mountain: The story of Parihaka.   Heinemann/Southern
           Cross, Auckland.
SINCLAIR, KEITH
  1957, 1961.   The origins of the Maori wars.   Auckland University Press; Ox-
                ford University Press.
TUWHARE, HONE
  1970, 1974.   Come rain hail.   Caveman Press, University of Otago, Dunedin.
WALLACE, A. F. C.
  1970.   The death and rebirth of the Seneca.   Knopf, New York.

WILLIAM N. FENTON

Search for Other Planetary Systems in the Universe

Principal Investigators: Tom Gehrels, Krzysztof Serkowski,[1] and Robert S. McMillan, Lunar and Planetary Laboratory, University of Arizona, Tucson, Arizona.

Grant Nos. 1405, 1544, 1683, 1846, 1968, 2218.   For a search for other planetary systems in the universe.

The University of Arizona Radial Velocity Spectrometer (RVS) is being developed to detect the presence of planets orbiting solar-type stars by measuring the reflex orbital velocities of the stars. The Sun moves about the center of mass of the Sun and Jupiter with a velocity of about 12 meters per second. Therefore, the accuracy required to detect Jupiter-like planets exceeds that attainable with conventional spectrographs by at least an order of magnitude; our instrument is being developed for that capability.

The first result of our planetary detection program will probably be the discovery of faint stars of comparatively small mass orbiting solar-type stars. This discovery will have scientific merit of its own because the distribution of such faint stars as a function of mass is poorly known. Theories of the formation of binary star systems could be improved if this distribution were better determined. As more data are accumulated, companions of smaller mass will be detected and the transition between stars and planets will be crossed. This transition is expected to be at a mass of roughly ten times the mass of Jupiter, but whether there is a continuous distribution or a gap in this region is unknown. If there is a gap, then binary star systems and planetary systems may form by entirely different processes. If there is a continuum of masses, then a similar process may control the formation of both types, according to the initial conditions of the nebulae from which the stars form. Our understanding of the formation of the solar system will be greatly improved by this investigation, because with just one example of a solar system, one cannot tell which characteristics of our solar system are general properties of all such systems.

Speculation about planets around other stars has pervaded philosophical literature for at least two thousand years. Discovery of planets around stars would provide a strong impetus to intensify a search for signals from other

---

[1] Professor Serkowski died October 7, 1981, after a long illness.

221

civilizations. Learning which types of stars have planets would greatly increase the efficiency of such a search.

The scientific and philosophical importance of the question of the existence of extra-solar planetary systems can hardly be overstated. In the Preface to the published proceedings of the Workshop on Ground-based Techniques for Detecting Other Planetary Systems the editors (Black and Brunk, 1980) summarize their perception of the situation as follows:

> The advances in scientific understanding on a variety of fronts which would result from this program are immense. The results of the search itself, be they positive or negative, will have an impact on man's perception both of himself and of his relationship to his environment that will persist well beyond the foreseeable future.

When the radial velocity spectrometer was first used to observe stars in July through December of 1977, the detector was a Digicon, a photoelectron-counting image tube with a linear array of 105 pixels. The image scrambler was a rotating reversion prism. Six bright G- and K-type stars were observed on a total of ten clear nights in 1977. The mean deviation of radial velocity for a single night from an average over 4 or 5 nights was about ±70 m/sec. In 1978 the RVS had been improved, providing ±27 m/sec mean deviation of a single observation of Arcturus.

Various scientific results were obtained with the Digicon version of the RVS (Serkowski et al., 1980). Observations of Eta Cas did not indicate the variation of radial velocity of ±2 km/sec over a 9.2-day period that was suspected by Abt and Levy (1976). During May 1978 the RVS was used to confirm the retrograde rotation of Venus' stratosphere. An equatorial zonal wind velocity of 39 ±6 m/sec was inferred (Serkowski et al., 1979), which appeared to be in substantial agreement with results obtained by other methods (see above paper for references). The RVS, modified somewhat to serve as a high resolution polarimeter, also was used to map the distribution of polarization on Venus' surface (Gehrels, Gradie, and Howes, 1979), and to detect changes in polarization along the H Beta line profile in Be stars, with 0.5 A (Ångstroms) resolution (McLean et al., 1979).

After these observations the sensitivity of the Digicon, which had been decreasing gradually for poorly understood reasons, had dropped to such a low value that it had to be replaced. An Intensified Charge Injection Device (ICID) was selected. The large number of pixels in a 342 x 42 format allows seven echelle orders, covering about 225 A, to be observed simultaneously. This was considered to be a great improvement over the 105 pixels covering 26 A provided by the Digicon.

In 1979 the rotating reversion prism image scrambler also was replaced by a single optical fiber of fused silica about 10 meters long. The efficient and

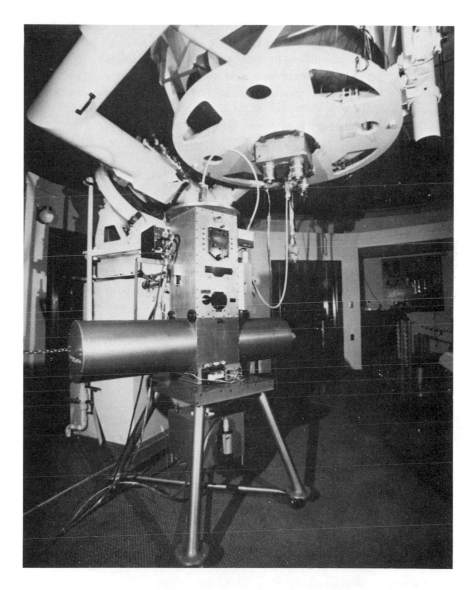

FIG. 1.   The University of Arizona radial velocity spectrometer.

stable image scrambling by the fiber ensures invariant illumination of the spectrograph optics irrespective of seeing effects and guiding errors, an essential feature if we are to obtain the required accuracy of radial velocity measurements. (With the reversion prism as an image scrambler, the quality of image scrambling depended strongly on the stability of the axis of rotation of the prism. This stability could not be readily verified.) In addition to its superior image scrambling, the optical fiber acts as a remote coupler, allowing the spectrometer body to be mechanically isolated from the telescope, thereby increasing its stability.

The combined advantages of the large spectral range provided by the ICID and the superior stability and image scrambling of the optical fiber were expected to allow stars fainter than those accessible to the Digicon RVS to be observed, and to provide measurements of radial velocity considerably more accurate than the ± 27 m/sec performance of the Digicon RVS.

After the installation of the optical fiber coupler, Arcturus (Alpha Boo) was reobserved in February and April 1980. The results were disappointing, in that the standard deviation of the observations was ± 45 m/sec and that stars fainter than blue magnitude 3.0 would be too faint to observe, because of readout noise. The "poor" radial velocity accuracy was thought to be due to two effects: an oversimplification of a numerical algorithm in the stellar reduction program, and the presence of a slight wedge angle between the Fabry-Perot etalon plates. (In March 1981 it was realized that a third defect was really the main reason for the low accuracy. This is the inadequate separation of the Fabry-Perot transmission maxima, discussed below.)

Following the March 1980 observing run the Fabry-Perot etalon was studied in the laboratory. When the reflecting surfaces of the Fabry-Perot etalon are separated by optically contacted spacers, they are usually not exactly plane parallel, but form a wedge amounting to a small fraction of an arcsecond. During the summer of 1980 we measured this wedge to be a 20th of a wavelength across a 32-mm baseline, i.e. 0.14 arcsecs. During scanning of an emission line from a hollow cathode lamp, the area of the etalon transmitting most of the light moves on its surface when we change the etalon tilt. Therefore, if the spectrum is not very sharply focused on the detector, an image of the emission line would shift on the detector when the etalon tilt is changed. Similar shifts occur also for stellar absorption lines. They may cause serious systematic errors in radial velocities which may be difficult to eliminate. Such errors are caused not only by imperfect focusing of the spectrum on the detector, but also by astigmatism in the echelle spectrograph. An astigmatic circle of least confusion formed on the detector is, in the absence of other aberrations, a mirror image of the etalon. We are eliminating this possible source of error by removing residual astigmatism with a tilted plano-convex lens placed just below the entrance slit of the echelle spectrograph; nevertheless we decided that imperfect focusing would have been sufficient to degrade the accuracy of radial velocity measurements, once it became clear that a wedge was present in the etalon.

The disappointing sensitivity of the instrument in February-April 1980 was attributed at that time to a degradation of the reflectivities of the mirrors in the spectrometer, to the inferior quality of the optical fiber terminations, and to the high readout noise of the ICID detector system.

During the summer of 1981 Frecker investigated the merits of reading the signal charge on the charge-injection device (CID) detector array nondestructively. With this type of readout circuit, the signal charge on each pixel would not be destroyed when read; multiple readings would allow the signal charge to be measured more accurately. However, Frecker found that the video circuit provided by the manufacturer for sampling the waveforms from the CID would have to be improved considerably before any benefit could be obtained from nondestructive readout. Furthermore, the GE TN2201 CID does not have good intrinsic characteristics for nondestructive readout. At about the time these facts were learned, pressure was applied on Frecker to develop a Charge Coupled Device (CCD) detector system for the Spacewatch Camera project. Since the CCD ultimately would be a better detector for RVS as well, plans to modify the circuitry of the CID were abandoned in favor of concentrating all of Frecker's time on CCD's.

From April through September 1980 the mirrors were resurfaced, coated, and aligned; a coupler for the 10-meter optical fiber was prepared, and attempts were made to diminish the wedge angle of the etalon. The last effort was first attempted by an optical engineer at the University of Arizona Optical Sciences Center by polishing a few strokes on one or more of the pads and then reassembling the etalon so that the wedge angle could be remeasured. After some two months of such iterations, it was feared that instead of further improvement in the parallelism of the plates, the separator pads were becoming rounded off by the polishing tool and might no longer be making good optical contact with the etalon plates. Therefore, this iterative method of eliminating the wedge was abandoned and the manufacturer of the etalon (Continental Optical Co.) was commissioned to fabricate two new sets of 4 pads each; within each set any 3 pads could be used in the etalon. The first combination of 3 pads we tried showed once again a wedge corresponding to $\lambda/20$ across a 32-mm baseline. However, there are 48 different permutations of the above 8 pads taken 3 at a time (it is not permitted to mix the two sets) and perhaps a better arrangement can be found. Alternatively, we have found it is possible to apply pressure over one or two of the pads to eliminate the wedge angle. To explore the latter possibility we first secured the services of Dr. Earl Pearson, a consultant in optical engineering, to theoretically analyze by means of a finite-element computer model the effects of various amounts of spring tension applied over the pads. We were especially interested in whether there would be serious higher-order distortions in the plate surfaces if too much force were applied. Dr. Pearson's analysis shows that no such significant higher-order distortions should occur from forces corresponding to a differential compression of $\lambda/20$, *provided* that the pads are flat. His computer model is not able to simulate the effect of a "cup" or "potato chip" shape in a separator pad.

After the optical resurfacing and the construction of a new optical fiber coupler in September 1980, the instrument was again tested for sensitivity to stars in October. The sensitivity was only half that in February 1980. Subsequent laboratory tests showed that the light losses were occurring in the optical fiber termination assemblies. The efficiency with which off-axis rays are transmitted through an optical fiber depends on the ratio of the refractive indices of the fused silica fiber and the soft plastic cladding. The manufacturer chooses a cladding with the appropriate refractive index, and the intensity of transmitted light drops only a factor of 2 per *kilometer* through a clad fiber. However, in 1980 the terminations of our optical fibers had been prepared by stripping the cladding off the last few centimeters of fiber and cementing the bare portions into steel ferrules with a cement judiciously chosen to have a refractive index smaller than that of the core. However, since our lab tests showed that skew rays were not being transmitted efficiently through the fiber, we concluded that the light was escaping from the fiber into the cement because the refractive index of the cement was too high, or that the fiber was not uniformly coated with cement, causing the fiber to come into contact with bare metal.

During this time Dr. Heacox resigned, so during the preceding months he and Mr. Merline put a lot of effort into the documentation of the computer programs. The duties of Dr. Heacox were taken over by Dr. Robert McMillan and Mr. Peter Smith, each working half time on this project. Mr. Smith has a Master's degree in optics and many years of experience with optical spectrographs and advanced computer programming. Graduate student William Merline, electronic engineer Jack Frecker, and mechanical engineer Edward Roland continued on the project. This new crew decided to postpone telescopic observations in favor of more thorough laboratory testing, so that the factors responsible for radial velocity errors and light loss could be identified, quantified, corrected, and verified in the lab.

In December 1980, duties were assigned as follows: Roland and Smith began checking the focus and alignment of every optical component from the collimator preceding the Fabry-Perot to the image intensifier; McMillan began preparing an optical fiber with the manufacturer's cladding left on the fiber to within 1 mm of the end, and Merline continued the data reduction. At the end of February 1981, Roland and Smith had completed the following: refocused the collimator lens; stabilized the grism (grating-prism) camera mirror, focused and aligned the grism camera mirror, replaced the field stop at the grism camera focus, aligned and focused the echelle collimator and camera, focused the collimator lenses in front of the calibration lamps, aligned the flat mirrors that fold the beams from the lamps, and positioned the iris diaphragms in the beams from the lamps. McMillan finished the assembly and polishing of the new optical fiber and this was installed on the reassembled radial velocity meter in early March 1981. The new fiber was found to have better transmission than the old one; quantitative measurements are in progress.

With the RVS reassembled with all components except the etalon, Smith and Merline measured dark count and counts from an emission line as functions of integration time, source brightness, intensifier gain, and offset voltage in the A/D circuit. The parameters of saturation of the ICID are now well known, a fact that will allow more judicious choices of gain and integration time for the various laboratory light sources. These tests also showed that reciprocity failure (failure of the inverse relationship of source signal and integration time) and blooming (enlargement of the image of an emission line after saturation) are only minor effects.

With the optical transmission, focus and collimation improved and the photometric properties of the detector better understood, a concentrated effort was made in March to find to what extent image quality might be affecting the accuracy of radial velocity measurements. The spectral resolution elements in the RVS are defined by the width and order number of the maxima of transmission through the Fabry-Perot etalon rather than by the wavelength scale in A/pixel. Therefore, the spectral resolution, wavelength scale, and radial velocity accuracy should be relatively insensitive to the size and shape of the image of a transmission maximum, *as long as the images of successive maxima are sufficiently widely separated on the detector that they do not significantly contaminate each other.* The amount of this contamination with a continuum light source can be calculated from the convolution of the profile of transmission through the etalon with the instrumental profile of the image of a monochromatic source. The amount of contamination also can be judged by looking at the measured raw intensity of continuum light vs. pixel number. The contrast, or ratio of intensities of continuum light at maxima and minima of transmission through the etalon, is a good diagnostic of how distinct the etalon maxima are from each other. Data taken with the Digicon detector in the RVS had a contrast ratio of 3.0 while data taken with the ICID version of the RVS has a contrast ratio of 2.0. The image quality is probably being degraded by the limited spacial resolution of the microchannel plate intensifier. To verify this, Smith and Merline made laboratory measurements in March of the instrumental profiles of an emission line from the hollow cathode lamp. They found an instrumental full width at half maximum of 3.5 to 4.0 pixels, both parallel and perpendicular to the echelle dispersion, while the separation between the neighboring Fabry-Perot transmission maxima was 6.0 pixels in both these directions. This instrumental profile, when convolved in *two dimensions* with the etalon transmission profile, is sufficiently wide to explain fully the poor contrast observed in continuum lamp data. More specifically, each minimum of etalon transmission is affected by light from not only the adjacent etalon maxima at shorter and longer wavelengths, but also from those in the two neighboring ("above" and "below") echelle spectral orders.

In summary, the accuracy of radial velocities is being degraded by inadequate separation of the images of maximum transmission of continuum light through the Fabry-Perot etalon. Our planned solutions to this are to obtain a cross-dispersion grism with twice the dispersion of the present one, thus increasing the separation of the echelle orders by this factor, and to replace the intensifier by one with twice the image size, allowing us to image the echelle spectra at twice the present scale. This magnification will be achieved by simply eliminating the focal reduction lens presently used in front of the intensifier. These plans for image magnification will be supported by our planned conversion to the RCA CCD detector array, which has a larger image format and much lower readout noise than the presently used CID.

In April 1981, Smith, Roland, and Merline investigated the other optical phenomenon thought to contribute to the errors of radial velocity measurements, namely the wedge angle between the Fabry-Perot etalon plates. They assembled a test facility that allows measurement of the separation of the etalon plates as a function of position on the etalon. The Fabry-Perot housing is placed on a horizontal piece of ground glass which is illuminated from below by a single-isotope mercury lamp filtered to transmit only the 4358 A line. A small telescope is focused at infinity and mounted vertically to look down at the illuminated screen through a small aperture stop above the etalon. The aperture stop is offset from the center of the etalon and can be translated to map out the plate separation as a function of position on the etalon. The view through the telescope is a series of concentric rings corresponding to successive orders of constructive interference of light transmitted through the etalon at various angles from the vertical. In principle, the variation of separation between the etalon plates could be measured from the changes in radius of the interference rings as the telescope is translated across the etalon. However,

Smith and Merline set up a null-measurement technique which allows the plate separation to be measured to an accuracy of better than $\pm\lambda/100$ without requiring measurement of the radii or spacing of the rings. They vary the *effective* plate spacing by controlling the pressure of nitrogen gas, which is proportional to the refractivity of the N_2 gas, in the whole etalon chamber with the adsorption vacuum pump, a valve, and a pressure gauge. At one location of the telescope aperture they select a pressure such that the intensity of the central interference maximum is most sensitive to changes in pressure. Then as the telescope and aperture are rotated about the center of the etalon, the pressure in the chamber can be adjusted to compensate for slight variations of the optical spacing of the plates. The variation in pressure needed to keep the same relative intensity of the central order can be converted into a variation of plate spacing from knowledge of the pressure variation needed to scan through one full fringe. This test configuration allows many tests at various temperatures and combinations of spring tensions on the etalon plates to be made in a very straightforward way. One combination of tensions in the three springs compressing the plates onto the separator pads has been found to reduce the total variation of plate spacing over the etalon to less than $\lambda/60$ over a baseline of 38 mm. Thus the problem of the wedge angle between the etalon plates is now under control and is near a solution.

The instrument is currently operational and was used in February and October 1980 to obtain trial observations of Arcturus and other bright stars. These observations indicate that with the present throughput the detector readout noise does not allow observing stars fainter than B=3.0 magnitude, and the precision of radial velocities, about ±150 m/sec on solar-type stars (±45 m/sec on Arcturus), is not satisfactory. Therefore, our present efforts are concentrated on detailed laboratory tests of the instrument aimed at optimizing its performance.

After extensive laboratory tests, the reasons for the current limitations of the Radial Velocity Spectrometer have been identified. The present goal is to increase the limiting magnitude to B=6.0 mag. and to bring down the mean error of a single differential radial velocity observation to ±15 m/sec. The needed improvements, on which we are working, are:

1. Replace the presently used grism by one giving twice greater cross-dispersion, so as to reduce the contamination of each echelle order by the neighboring orders. This contamination is quite serious, considerably reducing the contrast in the spectrum and hence the precision of radial velocities. Increasing the cross-dispersion will also allow us to combine more pixels perpendicular to the echelle dispersion, which will reduce our sensitivity to a wedge angle between the etalon plates.

2. Replace the intensifier by one having a photocathode of higher quantum efficiency and larger size, on which a spectrum of twice the present size can be imaged. The larger scale will be obtained by eliminating a doublet lens which is presently used in front of the intensifier. After this magnification of the spectrum formed on the intensifier cathode, the consecutive Fabry-Perot transmission maxima along the echelle dispersion will be well resolved, preventing the observed contamination of each transmission maximum by the light of the neighboring ones.

3. Replace the CID detector by an RCA SID 53601 512x320 CCD array. This CCD detector, which recently became commercially available, has considerably lower readout noise than the CID array, considerably reducing the photometric errors. Also, the larger size of the CCD detector, accompanied by a 2:1 focal reduction from the intensifier output, will allow observing about 15 echelle orders simultaneously, increasing the wavelength range to about 500 A. (On the CID detector only three or four echelle orders will be imaged after the higher-dispersion grism is installed.)

4. A new method of mounting the ends of the optical fiber is being developed which may increase the transmittance of the fiber assembly several times.

5. A new mounting is needed to allow the grism camera mirror to be run reproducibly through focus and reproducibly tilted. The present mount does not allow focus and tilt to be done independently or reproducibly, which handicaps laboratory tests.

6. A force of a few pounds will be applied by springs at three points around the edge of the top plate of the Fabry-Perot interferometer. The force exerted by these springs will be adjusted to eliminate the residual wedge between the interferometer plates, which is presently a source of systematic errors in wavelength calibration.

7. An effort is needed to correct various imperfections in the software and to adjust this software to the proposed new CCD detector.

8. Optics must be built to feed an f/13.5 beam of integrated-disk sunlight into the RVS laboratory room. The ability to observe the sun without going to a telescope will avoid the delays associated with transporting and setting up the RVS.

The tests of the instrument on the telescope will be resumed as soon as the laboratory tests indicate that the expected precision of radial velocities is sufficiently good to make the telescopic observations worthwhile. We should keep in mind that even in April and May of 1978, the prototype Radial Velocity Spectrometer, which theoretically should have given considerably *lower* precision than the present version of the instrument, was repeatedly measuring the radial velocity of Arcturus with a mean error of about ±27 m/sec for a single one-hour observation. This corresponded to ±90 m/sec on a solar-type star of the same brightness. We have no doubts that with the modifications described above our instrument will achieve significantly better accuracy.

REFERENCES

ABT, H. A., and LEVY, S. G.
    1976.   Multiplicity among solar-type stars.   Astrophysical Journ., Suppl. 30, no. 3, p. 273.

BLACK, D. C., and BRUNK, W. E., eds.
    1980.   An assessment of ground-based techniques for detecting other planetary systems.   NASA Conference Publication No. 2124.

GEHRELS, T.; GRADIE, J. C.; HOWES, M. L.; and VRBA, F. J.
    1979.   Wavelength dependence of polarization. XXXIV. Observations of Venus.   Astron. Journ., vol. 84, p. 671.

McLEAN, I. S.; COYNE, G. V.; FRECKER, J. E.; and SERKOWSKI, K.
    1979.   High resolution polarization structure of Hβ in Be-shell stars with a new Digicon spectropolarimeter.   Astrophysical Journ., vol. 228, p. 802.

SERKOWSKI, K.; FRECKER, J. E.; HEACOX, W. D.; KENKNIGHT, C. E.; and ROLAND, E. H.
    1979.   Retrograde rotation of the stratosphere of Venus measured with a Fabry-Perot radial velocity spectrometer.   Astrophysical Journ., vol. 228, pp. 630-634.

SERKOWSKI, K.; FRECKER, J. E.; HEACOX, W. D.; and ROLAND, E. H.
    1980.   The University of Arizona radial velocity spectrometer. Pp. 175-196 *in* vol. 2 of "An Assessment of Ground-based Techniques for Detecting Other Planetary Systems," D. C. Black and W. E. Brunk, eds.   NASA Conference Publication No. 2124.

KRZYSZTOF SERKOWSKI
ROBERT S. MCMILLAN

A Biological Exploration of Cerro Tacarcuna

Principal Investigator: Alwyn H. Gentry, Missouri Botanical Garden, St. Louis, Missouri.

Grant No. 1400:   For a biological exploration of Cerro Tacarcuna, Panama-Colombia.

Cerro Tacarcuna, the sacred mountain of the Cuna Indians, is just over 1,900 meters in altitude and straddles the border between Panama and Colombia. It is the highest peak in the stretch of some 600 kilometers of lowlands that separates the Andes from the Central American mountain systems. Prior to our explorations Cerro Tacarcuna was in large part biologically unexplored and generally acknowledged to be potentially the most exciting botanical collecting locality in Panama. As a result of an expedition of just over a month, a team consisting of four scientists—myself, Charles W. Myers (herpetologist from the American Museum of Natural History), Rudolfo Hinds (ornithologist from the Gorgas Memorial Laboratory, Panama), and Scott Mori (botanist, then curator of the Summit Herbarium, Canal Zone)—was able to reach the summit area of the mountain and make rather extensive biological collections.

Cerro Tacarcuna harbors an isolated montane forest on its upper slopes (above 1,400-1,500 meters). This forest may be considered a relict from Pleistocene times. The dominant tree species is an oak, *Quercus humboldtii,* previously known only from the Andes of northern South America and the only species of its north temperate genus to reach that continent. Associated with the oaks were other tree species previously known only from the Andes or the Central American mountain systems. Above the oak forest, on the highest ridges of the Tacarcuna massif, occurs an elfin forest with *Drimys* and *Clusia,* the two most prevalent tree species. This forest is restricted to the steepest ridge tops and, where best developed, has a low 5-to-6-meter-high canopy formed by gnarled, twisted, intertwined trees. Everything is covered by thick growths of moss and leafy liverworts. On the extreme top of the highest peak, somewhat isolated from the main ridge system, is a very different kind of vegetation of slender, erect trees crowded rather closely together and almost unbranched. Most of these trees are about 8 meters tall and 3 to 4 inches in diameter, and only five tree species occurred on the almost parklike summit. Interestingly, one of these five is a new species of *Freziera,* which may have the

233

most asymmetric leaf bases of any angiosperm and has a population size of three! The summit is a short, sharp, north-south running ridge. Our three altimeters gave readings of 1,780 meters, 1,850 meters, and 6,600 feet. Corrected by calibration against their respective readings at a similar known altitude in Bogotá, all three of these readings are very close to 1,900 meters for the summit altitude.

As might have been predicted, the summit vegetation of Cerro Tacarcuna (i.e., above 1,400 meters) is extremely rich in endemic species, previously undescribed. About 20 percent of its plant species are new to science (46 out of 239 species analyzed to date). Obviously, the discovery of all these species will be of great interest in biogeographic, taxonomic, and evolutionary studies.

Perhaps more interesting are the distributional patterns shown by nonendemic strictly montane species: 21 of these were previously considered endemic to Costa Rica and adjacent Chiriquí Province of Panama; 12 were previously known only from the Andes; an additional 10 were known from both Costa Rica-Chiriquí and the Andes; while 13 are widespread montane species mostly ranging from southern Mexico to Peru or Bolivia. Several especially spectacular range disjunctions include *Grammitis randallii* (Jamaica and Cerro Tacarcuna), *Podocarpus magnifolia* (Guayana highlands, Bolivia, and Cerro Tacarcuna), and *Chrysochlamys clusiaefolia* (Guayana highlands, Venezuelan Coastal Range, Cerro Tacarcuna). Six species were previously known only from other Panamanian mountain tops—3 from Cerro Jefe, 2 from Cerro Campana, and 1 from Cerro Pirre. Of special interest are the shared Andean/Tacarcuna and Costa Rica/Tacarcuna species. All but one (*Anthericum macrophyllum* Baker) of the species shared by Costa Rica/Chiriquí and Tacarcuna are derived from South American groups. The species limited to Tacarcuna and the Andes include groups of both North and South American derivation. These patterns suggest that some floristic exchange between Tacarcuna and the Andes has occurred subsequent to the isolation of Tacarcuna from Costa Rica/Chiriquí but that at some earlier time Tacarcuna and Costa Rica/Chiriquí must have undergone floristic interchange while mutually isolated from an Andean source area. Moreover, the presence of montane oak forest at 1,500 meters on Cerro Tacarcuna (1,400 meters on Cerro Mali with one tree at 1,200 meters on the spur ridge south of the Pucuro) provides strong evidence for an "isthmian effect" of altitudinally depressed vegetation zones in the Panamanian isthmus, since the lower limit of similar oak forest in the Colombian Andes is at 2,300-2,500 meters. Extrapolated back to the Pleistocene such an "isthmian effect" would have made the Panamanian isthmus a much more effective land bridge for montane organisms than has been previously suspected.

Analysis of the Tacarcuna plant collections is still proceeding. Descriptions of many of the new species have been published and others are now in press. An over-all account of the vegetation of the region is in manuscript form, and the floristic data base was used in an overview of regional phytogeographic patterns. It will be significantly more time before all the potentially new species have been analyzed, verified, and described.

A popularized version of the account of this expedition appeared in the *Explorers Journal* for March 1977.

REFERENCES

GENTRY, ALWYN H.
  1977. Botanical exploration of Cerro Tacarcuna. Explorers Journ., vol. 55, no. 1, pp. 40-45, illus.
  1978. A new *Freziera* (Theacae) from the Panama/Colombia border. Ann. Missouri Bot. Gard., vol. 65, pp. 773-774.
  1981. Phytogeographic patterns as evidence for a Chocó refugium. Pp. 112-136 *in* "The Biological Model of Diversification in the Tropics," G. Prance, ed.

ALWYN H. GENTRY

Exchange Systems among the Chambri of Papua New Guinea

Principal Investigator: Deborah Gewertz, Amherst College, Amherst, Massachusetts.

Grant No. 1303:   In partial support of a study of the integrative potentials of dispersed networks of exchange in New Guinea.

I originally journeyed to the lowlands of Papua New Guinea to investigate the integrative potential of discrete networks of exchange. I expected to find ceremonial exchange networks comparable to those which have been discovered in the highlands of New Guinea—the Te and Moka systems of the Western and Eastern Highlands, respectively (see Meggitt, 1974, and Strathern, 1971). These networks of ceremonial exchange link discrete groups of subsistence horticulturalists, living in relatively homogeneous environments, into wider socio-political systems. I wished to discover whether comparable networks existed among the economically interdependent groups of hunter-gatherers living in the Middle Sepik. I hypothesized that I would find these networks of ceremonial exchange, but my data did not bear out this supposition. The rest of this research report will consist, therefore, of a description and tentative explanation of two of the types of exchange I did find in the Middle Sepik.

The Chambri and the Fish-for-Sago Marketing System

I worked primarily among the 1,300 Chambri people of the East Sepik Province (see fig. 1). The Chambri live in three villages, Indingai, Kilimbit, and Wombun, all of which are situated on the shore of a loaf-shaped mountain, about 500 feet in height. Surrounding the mountain are the waters of Chambri Lake. During the wet season, from January through March, Chambri Lake is a vast expanse of water. During the dry season, however, from July through September, the lake recedes to a small fraction of its former size.

The waters of Chambri Lake are full of fish; and, wet season or dry, Chambri women are able to acquire more than enough to feed their families. Once a week they take their surplus fish to barter markets in the Sepik Hills where they exchange them for chunks of sago, each about the size of a grapefruit. Sago is a starch prepared from the pith of the sago palm, *Metroxylum rumphii*.

Between the Sepik Hills are valleys completely covered with sago palm vegetation, and Sepik Hills women prepare the carbohydrate for both subsistence and barter. Neither they nor the Chambri are horticulturalists. The Chambri have little land suitable for horticulture, and what land they do have is frequently inundated for over half the year. Fish and sago, therefore, comprise the bulk of the Chambri diet, and barter markets at which the Chambri acquire sago are critical to their subsistence.

The interaction at these barter markets is ritualized. The sago-supplying women walk among the seated fish-suppliers offering their product in an obsequious manner (see fig. 2). Chambri women, who are actually quite anxious to acquire sago at these markets, nevertheless accept a chunk condescendingly, as if they were doing the Sepik Hills women a favor by trading with them. Thus, although the exchange of foodstuffs is equitable, the interaction at the fish-for-sago barter markets is complementary, with the fish-supplying women assuming a dominant and aggressive role.

I could not at first understand why the necessary exchange of foodstuffs would be ritualized as complementary interaction. It seemed to me that equality in demeanor should characterize equitable exchange relationships. I recognize now, however, that as Gregory Bateson points out,

> Cases in which group A sometimes sell sago to group B and the latter sometimes sell the same commodity to A, may be regarded as reciprocal; but, if group A habitually sell sago to B while the latter habitually sell fish to A, we must, I think, regard the pattern as complementary (1972, p. 69).

In effect, then, the ecological heterogeneity of the Middle Sepik has produced a system of marketing in which women exchange locally produced foodstuffs. These barter markets can be seen as elaborations on the theme of complementarity—fish is exchanged for sago and fish-supplying women dominate their sago-suppliers. I will return to this point later, but first it is necessary to describe another complementary relationship, this time on the intra-village level between wife-givers and wife-takers.

The Affinal Exchange System

The Chambri divide themselves into 34 exogamous patriclans. Each patriclan is thought of as potentially equal to all others, except where two clans are linked by marriage, in which case wife-givers become superior to wife-takers. Their superiority is institutionalized in asymmetrical affinal exchange, with valuables moving from wife-takers to wife-givers during rites of passage celebrated for sisters' sons.

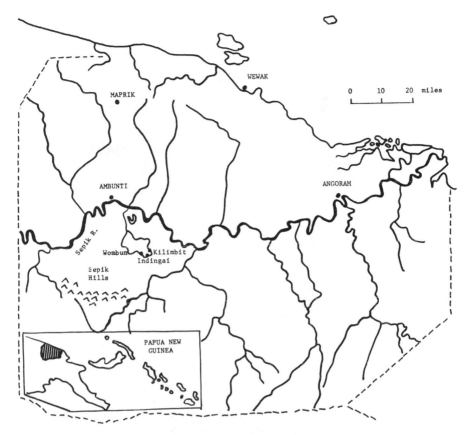

FIG. 1.   East Sepik Province.

Although there is no explicit rule of village endogamy, most Chambri marriages are made between village members (see Table 1). Intertribal marriages, between Chambri and Sepik Hills people, are rare indeed, and the Chambri do not contract marriages to establish or solidify intervillage relations as do the people of the New Guinea Highlands.

Highlands people play the status game by rules which are also very different from those followed by the Chambri. In the Highlands of New Guinea status differentials between individuals and groups are established and maintained through competitive equal exchange. One individual gives a number of goods to his trading partner who reciprocates with more goods, forcing the first donor to give even more goods. Certain individuals and groups will be in-

Fig. 2.   Sago-supplying women walk among the seated fish-suppliers. Interaction at these Chambri markets is ritualized.

TABLE 1.   The Frequency of Endogamous Marriage at Chambri in 1974

Source: Figures were collected by the author. They are calculated from the male perspective to avoid double-counting and include the marriages of migrant laborers.

Origin of spouse	Number of marriages					Percent of endogamy	
	Chambri village				Sub-non-Chambri		
	Indingai	Kilimbit	Wombun	Total		By village	All Chambri
CHAMBRI VILLAGE							
Indingai	64	11	6	81	7	73	92
Kilimbit	13	94	2	109	11	78	92
Wombun	6	1	86	93	11	83	90
Totals	83	106	94	283	29	78	91

debted to other individuals and groups at any one point in time, "and it is possible to analyze the political system of the society at least partly in terms of these groups and their interrelations" (Strathern, 1971, p. 220). Ceremonial exchange systems, therefore,

> can . . . be seen as a mechanism creating status divisions within the society. But this mechanism (and the big-men who emerge through it) has to be placed in the context of group transactions . . . [It is] a system of total presentations . . . [that are] made between groups who are in an unstable state of alliance with each other: the only way they can maintain their alliance is by continuing positive ceremonial exchanges of valuables . . . [The system] is one in which reciprocative transactions prevail and the relationship between partners is relatively egalitarian (ibid. pp. 214-215).

Among the Chambri, too, clans are potentially equal, but the Chambri do not engage in competitive equal exchange. Instead, enterprising big-men achieve status and power on behalf of their patriclans by assisting unrelated clans to meet their affinal debts. When an individual and his clan co-members cannot amass sufficient valuables to compensate their wife-givers, they will seek assistance from an unrelated clan. The unrelated clan, by giving assistance, gains power over its clients; thus status differentials are established and maintained (see Gewertz, 1977a).

Take, for example, the somewhat simplified case of Wundan. He took Nandi as his wife after she had been abandoned by Minjim, but he could not repay her bride price to Minjim's clan. He requested and received assistance from Tanameri, who conjoined sufficient valuables to repay Minjim on behalf of Wundan. Tanameri also presented Nandi's father with a large gift of valuables, thereby bettering the bride price that had initially been paid for her by Minjim and his clan co-members. Through his manipulation of the affinal exchange system, Tanameri gained power over Wundan, who effectively became his client. More significantly, Tanameri proved himself Minjim's superior by adding to the initial bride price. Tanameri and Minjim had been competing for prominence within Indingai for some time, and I believe Tanameri decided to assist Wundan because he knew he would thereby gain an opportunity to better Minjim. Neither Minjim nor Tanameri confronted the other directly; their competition for status and power took place exclusively through their influence on the affinal exchange relationships of others.

It is important to note that the frequently complex politicking of Chambri males has no effect upon their wives' barter relations. During the many months it took to straighten the antagonisms between Wundan and Minjim, for example, Nandi acquired sago at barter markets as she always had done.

De Facto Dominance and the Stability of Complementarity

In the Middle Sepik, competition can only occur between equals, and, according to Forge—

> to be equal and to stay equal is an extremely onerous task requiring continual vigilance and effort. Keeping up with the Joneses may be hard work, but keeping up with all other adult males of a community is incomparably harder (1972, pp. 533-534).

Inter-clan equality must be continually verified and reestablished, for, as in the case of Wundan, Minjim, and Tanameri, it is possible for certain individuals and groups to become temporarily "more equal" than those with whom they are competing.

When, on the other hand, individuals and groups are de facto unequal, when fish-suppliers, for example, are de facto dominant to their sago-producers, competition between them is impossible for "their exchanges [are of] different things, [and] cannot be subjected to an exact accounting or comparison" (Forge, 1972, p. 537).

If the sago-producers were defined as equal to their fish-suppliers the marketing system could no longer operate. It is for this reason that the barter relationship between Chambri and Sepik Hills women must be complementary, with both fish-suppliers and sago-producers acknowledging publicly the dominance of the former. A bartering system which is noncompetitive and stable allows for the equitable and regular exchange of necessary foodstuffs.

In an area of such ecological diversity, where exchange of foodstuffs is necessary to survival, competitive interaction at barter markets would be highly mal-adaptive.

Conclusion: Symmetry and Complementarity as Organizing Principles

To give a wife is to gain dominance over the wife-taker. To take a wife is to become submissive to the wife-giver. Since all Chambri men both give and take wives, their dominance and submission cancel out each other, leaving all Chambri men equal transactors of women.

If Chambri men are the equal transactors of women within the affinal exchange system, Chambri women are merely items of exchange used to verify male equality. Within the bartering system, quite to the contrary, Chambri women are the active transactors, and, through their alternation of interactional mode, they delimit one system from the other. Let me elaborate.

At the barter markets Chambri women act dominantly, and thus represent the aggressive supremacy of the fish-suppliers. Chambri men, who prefer to stay away from barter markets, are accustomed to think of their wives and sisters as no more than items of transaction. Yet, they are aware of the ambience at barter markets, and acknowledge that Chambri women represent the Chambri tribe in relation to the passive and weak sago-suppliers, both men and women alike. Thus, from the male perspective it would be inconceivable to marry a Sepik Hills woman, for even Chambri women—mere items of exchange themselves—dominate these sago-producers. To marry a woman from the Sepik Hills would necessitate the payment of bride price, and thus the public acknowledgment of a Sepik Hills father-in-law as dominant. Few women are worth the ridicule that would accompany such an acknowledgment, or at least that is how the Chambri seem to feel.

Thus, Chambri men do not marry their sago-producers, and competitive interaction does not adhere to the bartering system. All Chambri women have uninterrupted access to all sago markets, regardless of the politicking of their husbands, brothers, and fathers.

REFERENCES

BATESON, GREGORY
    1972.   Steps to an ecology of mind, 517 pp.   Ballantine, New York.
FORGE, ANTHONY
    1972.   The golden fleece.   Man, vol. 7, pp. 527-540.
GEWERTZ, DEBORAH
    1977a.   The politics of affinal exchange: Chambri as a client   Ethnol., vol. 16,
        pp. 285-298.

GEWERTZ, DEBORAH—continued
  1977b. From sago suppliers to entrepreneurs: Marketing and migration in the
          Middle Sepik.   Oceania, vol. 48, pp. 126-140.
  1977c. On whom depends the action of the elements: Debating among the
          Chambri people of Papua New Guinea.   Journ. of Polynesian Society,
          vol. 86, pp. 339-353.
  1978.   Tit for tat: Barter markets in the Middle Sepik.   Anthrop. Quart., vol.
          51, pp. 36-44.
  1981.   An historical reconsideration of female dominance among the Tcham-
          buli of Papua New Guinea.   Ethnology, vol. 8, pp. 94-108.
MEGGITT, MERVYN
  1974.   Pigs are our hearts.   Oceania, vol. 44, pp. 165-203.
STRATHERN, ANDREW
  1971.   The rope of Moka, 254 pp., illus.   Cambridge University Press, Cam-
          bridge, England.

                                                    DEBORAH GEWERTZ

Highly Accurate Extinction Measurements for Sensitive Assessment of Air Quality

Principal Investigators: John S. Hall and Louise A. Riley, Lowell Observatory, Flagstaff, Arizona.

Grant Nos. 1319, To make highly accurate extinction measurements for sensi-
1752. tive assessment of air quality.

Background

The prime objective of this program was to determine very accurate extinction coefficients at Flagstaff, Arizona, and in other areas of different elevation in which clear air is most likely to be found, in order to establish baseline data which can be used as a reference at some future time when anthropogenic sources of contamination are suspected to be present.

The only comparable long-path data are those obtained many years ago in Pasadena by Baum and Dunkelman (1955) and near Chesapeake Bay by Knestrick et al. (1962). Elterman (1968) used these results in compiling a table of "representative" aerosol extinction coefficients for different wavelengths at low elevations. For higher elevations he derived his tabular values from data obtained in the "free" air by a variety of methods involving balloons, airplanes, and searchlights.

The results summarized here are based on photoelectric measures made at eight different sites ranging in elevation from near sea level to 2.4 km and over horizontal paths of 1 to 20 km. These measures were made in nine or more spectral bands in the visual and the ultraviolet, within the wavelength span bounded by ozone and water vapor absorption (0.32 to 0.66 μm).

The data refer only to the extinction (βp) due to particulate matter, the extinction caused by Rayleigh scattering (βr) having been previously subtracted. The procedure involved the use of a carefully controlled quartz-halogen light source measured consecutively at two positions—one near the photometric equipment (zero absorption) and the other several kilometers away. (An alternative method involved the use of two optical flats placed at near and far positions.) The measures were usually made in the early hours of darkness. Details regarding the instrumental equipment, observational procedures, and data obtained have been published elsewhere by Hall and Riley (1979).

245

Indirect methods of measuring atmospheric absorption at one point, day or night, have been developed by others (Weiss et al., 1979; Heisler et al., 1980, vol. 2, pp. 323-325). These measures, when combined with scattering measures made with a nephelometer, give the extinction coefficient at the point of observation. At several sites we were invited to help calibrate other data-gathering methods with our long-path transmissometer observations. The measures made at a point site under stable conditions agreed reasonably well with our more labor-intensive long-path data.

The air quality at a given site should, of course, be evaluated by measures made over a long period of time, in different seasons of the year, and at different times of day. However, one can observe during normal weather conditions for a short period at a given site and in this way obtain a good general idea of the probable long-term air quality at that site.

Observations at High Elevations

At Flagstaff, Arizona (population 31,000, elevation 2.2 km, in October of 1973, we made measures over a 3.3-km differential path well above a sparsely settled area which showed virtually no aerosol extinction on two nights when the air movement was gentle and down-slope from the nearby San Francisco Mountains. The absence of aerosols, however, was indicated on only 2 nights out of a total of 25. Our data include some nights in which the aerosol extinction was nearly constant with wavelength, suggesting absorption by particles which were predominantly large, and other nights in which relatively strong ultraviolet extinction indicated pronounced selective scattering by very small particles.

A site of comparable elevation, 2.3 km, was near the top of Mount Hopkins. Measures were made on eight nights at this site, 55 km south-southeast of Tucson. The data for those periods that were free of aerosols brought in by strong winds show mean extinction coefficients in the visual which are somewhat greater than those obtained in Flagstaff. In the far-ultraviolet the mean extinction at Mount Hopkins was found to be less than at Flagstaff, presumably because of the absence of auto traffic and wood fires in the general vicinity of Mount Hopkins.

Observations were also made at an elevation of 2.3 km at the airport just west of the entrance to Bryce Canyon, in southeastern Utah. Data obtained here in the off-tourist season indicated that this region had clearer air than any we had found elsewhere. On three of the nine nights on which we observed, the aerosol density was below our limit of detection.

Observations at Intermediate Elevations

Observations were made across Lake Powell and the Grand Canyon at an elevation of 1.2 km, over a 6.6-km path on two nights in the off-tourist season. These data showed no significant departure from Rayleigh scattering throughout the entire spectral range. Under favorable wind conditions, this area, which has only desert vegetation, can be remarkably clear. (The Navajo Power Plant was about three miles east and downwind from our light path.)

We measured air quality on seven consecutive nights within the White Sands National Monument, at a site which has an elevation of 1.23 km and which is surrounded immediately on the north, west, and south by desert. Alamagordo (population 22,000) is 25 km to the east, Las Cruces (43,000) is 80 km to the southwest, and El Paso (370,000) lies 110 km to the south. The prevailing winds are from the west and southwest. The data show small extinction with only a slight increase toward the ultraviolet.

Observations at Low Elevations

The most significant set of measures made at low elevation (0.5 km) was that made on 10 consecutive nights within the Organ Pipe Cactus National Monument. This desert area has sufficient vegetation to inhibit the frequent development of dust devils. It is roughly 500 km east-southeast of San Diego and is bordered on the west by a government proving ground and on the south by grazing lands in Sonora, Mexico. The Gulf of California and Baja California lie to the west and southwest.

With the exception of the runs made on two successive nights when strong winds associated with a frontal passage were present, the air quality was excellent, showing a very low particle count. On about half the nights the smoothed wavelength-extinction curves were virtually straight and horizontal lines. On other nights they sloped upward slightly in the ultraviolet, indicating more small particles.

Observations at low elevation (0.2 km) were carried out also in grazing country near Gila Bend, Arizona, on one clear night, and in farming country near Richland, Washington, on two nights.

Observations under Special Conditions

Consistent measures were made near Gila Bend during a severe dust storm which covered several hundred square kilometers. The aerosol extinction was found to be constant with wavelength and 12 times larger than that found under clean air conditions on the following night.

We detected no particulate matter in the air immediately after rainy periods on Puget Island, Washington, in March 1977. Puget Island, a few meters above the Columbia River and about 50 km from its mouth, was the only site where observations were made under very humid conditions. On one occasion, the extinction increased rapidly as the night progressed, particularly in the ultraviolet. At sunrise, a heavy fog covered the island from the surface to a height of perhaps 50 meters.

Summary

Mean extinction coefficients due to aerosols (βp), found at eight different sites in two spectral regions centered at 0.35 μm and 0.55 μm, are given in Table 1. Although the table shows the results for only these two spectral regions, the conclusions drawn here would apply equally well in a figurative sense to the observations made in the other spectral regions. The most surprising characteristic shown by these data is their similarity—even though the sites were widely separated and differed drastically in elevation.

TABLE 1.   Mean Extinction Coefficients Observed at Different Sites

Site	β_p (Km^{-1})		Elevation (km)	Path (km)	Dates	No. of nights
	0.35 (μm)	0.55 (μm)				
Flagstaff	0.042	0.020	2.2	1.0-20.3	1973-1976	25
Mount Hopkins	0.028	0.025	2.3	2.0	Nov 1976, Apr 1976	8
Bryce Canyon	0.018	0.009	2.3	2.7-3.5	Oct 1977, Nov 1977	9
White Sands	0.032	0.027	1.2	4.0	May 1978	5
Organ Pipe	0.032	0.022	0.5	6.3	Apr 1978	10
Lake Powell	0.005	0.000	1.2	6.6	Apr 1975	2
Richland	0.039	0.024	0.2	4.7	Sep 1976	2
Gila Bend	0.044	0.032	0.3	1.4	Mar 1975	1

Extinction and Elevation

Three sites, Flagstaff, Mount Hopkins, and Bryce Canyon, are at similarly high elevations. The coefficients observed at Bryce Canyon were considerably lower than those found at the other two sites in both the visual and the ultraviolet. Of the two sites at intermediate elevation (1.2 km), White Sands and Lake Powell, the latter showed little evidence of particulates on two nights when the power station plume was downwind. The data for White Sands were similar to those found for other sites which are closer to vehicular traffic and other anthropogenic particle sources. For sites at low elevation, the coefficients observed at Organ Pipe Cactus National Monument were some-what smaller than those found at Richland and Gila Bend, where there was more human activity.

Near the western seacoast one would expect to find even fewer solid par-ticulates because of on-shore sea breezes; however, the presence of moist air, fog, and salt particles introduces complications. Data which we secured on Puget Island showed such wide variations that they are not included in Table 1.

Our results show no clear-cut relationship between elevation and extinc-tion. Evidently, factors other than elevation also are important in influencing the measures made in these areas.

Suggested Future Sites

Although the observations reported here are not as numerous as we would have liked and are limited in the number of areas explored, they have the mer-it of being fundamental in nature and therefore can be used as a basis for com-parison at any future time. We suggest two areas at which future comparisons might have special significance: one at high elevation and one at low elevation.

It is significant that the cleanest air was found at two sites about 80 km apart in the general area of the Grand Canyon where anthropogenic effects should be minimal. If the Lake Powell and Bryce Canyon data are combined, we derive a weighted mean value of 0.007 (km^{-1}) for the mean extinction coef-ficient at 0.55 μm and 0.016 (km^{-1}) for the mean ultraviolet coefficient at 0.35 μm. These coefficients are about 0.8 and 0.3 of their respective Rayleigh values. Although there are doubtless many other regions in the vicinity of the Grand Canyon where, under conditions free from obvious anthropogenic con-tamination, equally clean air can be found, we hope that further fundamental measures will be carried on by others in the Bryce Canyon area. Aside from the fact that representatives from several institutions have made air quality mea-surements there, the site near the airport is readily accessible and close to ade-quate living accommodations which, under normal weather conditions, are downwind.

We also suggest that further observations be made near Lukeville at Organ Pipe Cactus National Monument. At this site the mean coefficient was about double the Rayleigh value at 0.55 μm and four-tenths the Rayleigh coefficient at 0.35 μm. Another site at low elevation with air of comparable clarity may be difficult to find in the southwest.

Acknowledgments

The active cooperation and advice of Alan Waggoner and Ray Weiss have been most helpful.

REFERENCES

BAUM, WILLIAM A., and DUNKELMAN, LAWRENCE
1955.   Horizontal attenuation of ultraviolet light by the lower atmosphere. Journ. Optical Soc. America, vol. 45, pp. 166-197.
ELTERMAN, L.
1968.   Ultraviolet, visible and infrared attenuation for altitudes to 50 kilometers.   Environmental Research Papers, no. 285, Air Force Cambridge Research Laboratories, L. G. Hanscomb Field, Bedford, Massachusetts.
HALL, JOHN S., and RILEY, LOUISE A.
1979.   Spectrophotometric measures of extinction.   Pp. 270-277 *in* "Proceedings: Carbonaceous Particles in the Atmosphere," T. Novakov, ed.   University of California, Lawrence Berkeley Laboratory 9037, Berkeley.
HEISLER, S. L.; HENRY, R. C.; WATSON, J. G.; and HIDY, G. M.
1980.   Final report: The 1978 Denver haze study. Environmental Research and Technology, Inc., Westlake Village, Calif.   Document no. P-5417-1.
KNESTRICK, G. L.; COSDEN, T. H.; and CURCIO, J. A.
1962.   Atmospheric scattering coefficients in the visible and infrared region. Journ. Optical Soc. America, vol. 52, pp. 1010-1016.
WEISS, R. E.; WAGGONER, A. P.; CHARLSON, R.; THORSELL, D. L.; HALL, J. S.; and RILEY, L. A.
1979.   Studies of the optical, physical and chemical properties of light-absorbing particles.   Pp. 257-262 *in* "Proceedings Carbonaceous Particles in the Atmosphere," T. Novakov, ed.   University of California, Lawrence Berkeley Laboratory 9037, Berkeley.

JOHN S. HALL

The Gilgil Baboon Project

Principal Investigator: Robert S. O. Harding, University of Pennsylvania, Philadelphia, Pennsylvania.

Grant No. 1401: In support of a study of the ecology and behavior of olive baboons in Gilgil, Kenya.[1]

In 1970, a long-term study of a troop of olive baboons *(Papio anubis)* was initiated on an 18,000-hectare cattle ranch near the village of Gilgil in the central Rift Valley of Kenya, some 115 kilometers to the northwest of Nairobi and midway between the larger towns of Naivasha and Nakuru. The central part of Kekopey Ranch, an area of about 4,500 hectares, consists of a series of parallel grassy valleys divided by rocky cliffs, and it is here that PHG, the baboon troop under study (so-called "Pumphouse Gang"), has its home range.

When the study began, Kekopey had been in the hands of the Cole family, Kenyan citizens of English descent, since the early part of this century. The Coles had managed Kekopey as range for livestock: sheep in the earlier years and, more recently, cattle. The natural environment of the ranch was slightly modified to improve conditions for stock raising: large predators had been controlled or (in the case of lions) all but eliminated; water, piped to open troughs throughout the ranch, was available for local wildlife as well as cattle; and finally, many large expanses of leleshwa *(Tarchonanthus camphoratus)* thicket had been converted into grassland during the previous decade. These changes, aided by the Coles' generally benevolent attitude toward wildlife, provided excellent conditions for a rich variety of animal life. In addition to at least seven troops of baboons, healthy populations of zebra and antelope such as eland, waterbuck, impala, mountain and Bohor reedbuck, Thomson's gazelle, klipspringer, steenbok, and dikdik flourished in Kekopey's central region.

[1] In addition to the Society's grant, financial support from the National Science Foundation, the National Institute of Mental Health, the L. S. B. Leakey Foundation, the University of Pennsylvania, and the University of California, San Diego, is gratefully acknowledged. We thank the Government of Kenya for authorization to conduct research, the Cole family for permission to begin it, and GEMA for permission to continue it.

251

TABLE 1. Gilgil Baboon Project Research Topics

Year	Researcher	Topic	Publications
1970-71	R. S. O. Harding	Range utilization; adult male behavior; predatory behavior.	1973a, b, 1974, 1975, 1976, 1977; 1976 (with Strum).
1971-1972	W. A. Malmi	Aspects of the evolution of language	
1973-1974	S. C. Strum	Social organization; predatory behavior	1975a, b, 1976a, b, 1976 (with Harding).
1973	M. D. Rose	Positional behavior	1976, 1977, 1978
1973-1974	L. Muckenfuss	Troop fission	
1975	S. C. Strum	Social organization	
1975-1976	H. A. Gilmore	Social communication	n.d., n.d., 1979 (with Hausfater)
1975-1976	P. Gilmore	Social development of juveniles	n.d.
1976	R. S. O. Harding	Routine activity rhythms—I	
1976-1977	L. M. Scott	Adolescent female kinship	n.d.
1976-1977	M. W. Demment	Feeding ecology	
1976-1977	S. C. Strum	Adolescent male development	
1976-	D. L. Manzolillo	Population structure	In progress
1977-	N. Nicolson	Weaning conflict	In progess
1977-	B. Smuts	Female reproductive strategies	In progress
1978	R. S. O. Harding	Routine activity rhythms—II	In progress

In some sense, then, Kekopey could be considered an "unnatural" environment in which to study a free-ranging group of animals. In other ways, however, it proved to be almost ideal. With the exception of the national parks, where baboons are undeniably affected by the presence of increasing numbers of tourists, there are few if any areas left in East Africa where baboons have not been trapped for export to scientific labs overseas or harassed by nearby agriculturists. The maintenance of a large piece of land by one family for a long period of time provided a haven for many species of animals, baboons included. Scientists from all over the world have been able to take advantage of these conditions to study everything from warthog reproduction to impala digestion, and we were fortunate to be allowed to establish our long-term study at Kekopey.

Once the PHG baboons had become accustomed to an observer's presence, the first year was devoted to a study of range utilization (Harding, 1973, 1976). When this was completed, a second individual assumed the observer's role, and since that time, with but one hiatus, the PHG baboons have been under continuous observation by a series of observers (table 1). Our objective has been to collect data on a variety of specific topics over as long a period as possible, while allowing each individual observer to pursue specialized research topics in some depth.

The long-term data fall into three broad categories: behavioral, ecological, and demographic. On the behavioral side, we have recorded changes in social structure and relative status of individual animals, female sexual cycles, consort relationships, encounters with other troops, and predatory behavior. Ecological data include range-utilization patterns, identification of plant and animal food items, and monitoring of changing meteorological conditions. Finally, we have routinely kept track of changes in the local population structure, including births, deaths, emigrations, immigrations, and maturational phases.

Between 1970 and 1978 PHG more than doubled in size, but individual identification of every animal transmitted from each observer to the next made possible the accumulation of detailed data on family relationships and provided insight into the development of a number of interesting behavior patterns. The growth and spread of predation by the PHG baboons have been observed and documented (e.g., Harding, 1975; Strum, 1976a). On a larger scale, it has become apparent that male baboons spend at least part of their adult lives in a troop other than the one in which they were born, whereas females are much less mobile, passing from infancy to maturity to old age in their natal troop. The relative stability of female relationships results in a troop organization that differs from that which is usually postulated.

The transience of male hierarchical relationships accords well with the behavior of yellow baboons at Amboseli described by Glenn Hausfater (1975). The Gilgil Baboon Project has also been able to provide valuable comparative data for other aspects of the Amboseli work, particularly studies of maturation and reproductive parameters (Altmann et al., 1977).

While generally supportive of the Gilgil Project for many years, a grant from the National Geographic Society was of special value in assisting Hugh Gilmore to take up the resident observer's position from March 1975 until

May 1976. In addition to routine data collection for the Project's long-term records, Gilmore's individual interest was a study of the nature of social communication in the PHG baboons.

The initial stages of Gilmore's tenure in the field were spent in routine tasks such as learning to distinguish individual animals, becoming familiar with their home range, and refining data collection procedures. By June he was ready to begin work on his own project. After establishing an ethogram (a catalogue of the baboons' behavior patterns), Gilmore kept extensive records of social interactions, including the identity of each baboon involved as well as their behavior before, during, and after every observed interaction. The data accumulated in this way have enabled Gilmore to analyze the individual elements, or signals, used by the PHG baboons. Gilmore's doctoral dissertation (in preparation) concentrates on a message analysis of one such signal, a low-frequency grunting vocalization that the baboons emit in a variety of circumstances which superficially appear to be unrelated. Similar analyses of additional signals in the baboons' repertoire are currently being undertaken.

During the course of his year at Gilgil, Gilmore also collaborated with his wife, Perry, on a study of the protocol used by baboons when visiting mothers with newly born infants, while Perry Gilmore conducted her own study for 8 months on social development in juvenile baboons.

Late in 1976, Kekopey Ranch was sold by the Cole family to GEMA, a large cooperative organization made up of members of the Kikuyu, Emba, and Meru tribes. GEMA, in turn, is in the process of converting most of the ranch into small farming plots. Small-scale agriculture and free-ranging baboons are obviously incompatible over the long run, and although a part of PHG's home range is being kept free for cattle raising, unless something unforeseen intervenes the days of the Gilgil Baboon Project are probably numbered. The data already collected, however, will serve as a rich source of original analysis and comparative studies for many years to come.

REFERENCES

ALTMANN, JEANNE; ALTMANN, STUART; HAUSFATER, GLENN; and McCUSKEY, SUE ANN
    1977.   Life cycle of yellow baboons: Infant mortality, physical development, and reproductive parameters.   Primates, vol. 18, pp. 315-330.
GAULIN, STEVEN J. C., and KURLAND, JEFFREY A.
    1976.   Primate predation and bioenergetics.   Science, vol. 191, pp. 314-315.

GILMORE, HUGH A.
_____. The evolution of agonistic buffering in baboons and macaques. Paper read at 46th annual meeting of American Association of Physical Anthropologists, Seattle, 1977. (Unpublished MS.)
_____. Interpreting a baboon vocalization. Paper read at 47th annual meeting of American Association of Physical Anthropologists, Toronto, 1978. (Unpublished MS.)

GILMORE, PERRY
_____. Retrievals of baboon infants. M.Sc. thesis, Temple University, 1976. (Unpublished MS.)

HARDING, ROBERT S. O.
1973a. Range utilization by a troop of olive baboons *(Papio anubis),* 179 pp. Ph.D. thesis, University of California, Berkeley.
1973b. Predation by a troop of olive baboons *(Papio anubis).* Amer. Journ. Phys. Anthrop., vol. 38; pp. 587-592.
1974. The predatory baboon. Expedition, vol. 16, pp. 30-39, illus.
1975. Meat-eating and hunting in baboons. Pp. 245-258 *in* "Socioecology and Psychology of Primates," 474 pp., R. H. Tuttle, ed. Mouton, The Hague.
1976. Ranging patterns of a troop of baboons *(Papio anubis)* in Kenya. Folia Primat., vol. 25, pp. 143-185.
1977. Patterns of movement in open country baboons. Amer. Journ. Phys. Anthrop., vol. 47, pp. 349-354.

HARDING, ROBERT S. O., and STRUM, S. C.
1976. The predatory baboons of Kekopey. Natural History, vol. 85, no. 3, pp. 46-53, illus.

HAUSFATER, GLENN
1975. Dominance and reproduction in baboons *(Papio cynocephalus).* Contrib. Primat., vol. 7, pp. 1-150, illus.

HAUSFATER, GLENN, and GILMORE, HUGH A.
1979. Age-related changes in the neutral tail carriage of anubis baboons *(Papio anubis).* Mammalia, vol. 43, no. 4, pp. 465-472.

ROSE, MICHAEL D.
1976. Bipedal behavior of olive baboons *(Papio anubis)* and its relevance to an understanding of the evolution of human bipedalism. Amer. Journ. Phys. Anthrop., vol. 44, pp. 247-262.
1977. Positional behavior of olive baboons *(Papio anubis)* and its relationship to maintenance and social activities. Primates, vol. 18, pp. 59-116.
1978. The roots of primate predatory behavior. Journ. Human Evol., vol. 7, pp. 179-189.

SCOTT, LINDA M.
_____. Mate choice by adolescent female baboons. Paper read at 47th annual meeting of American Association of Physical Anthropologists, Toronto, 1978. (Unpublished MS.)

STRUM, SHIRLEY C.

    1975a.   Life with the "Pumphouse Gang": New insights into baboon behavior. Nat. Geogr. Mag., vol. 147, no. 5, pp. 672-691, illus.

    1975b.   Primate predation: Interim report on the development of a tradition in a troop of olive baboons.   Science, vol. 187, pp. 755-757.

    1976a.   Predatory behavior of olive baboons *(Papio anubis)* at Gilgil, Kenya, 287 pp.   Ph.D. thesis, University of California, Berkeley.

    1976b.   [Reply to Gaulin and Kurland, 1976.]   Science, vol. 191, pp. 315-317.

ROBERT S. O. HARDING

HUGH A. GILMORE

Quaternary Studies, Western Desert,
Egypt and Sudan, 1975-1978

Principal Investigator: C. Vance Haynes, Departments of Anthropology and Geosciences, University of Arizona, Tucson, Arizona.

Grant Nos. 1371,   For Quaternary studies in the Western Desert of Egypt and
1538, 1647, 1804.   Sudan.

Introduction

The Western Desert is that part of the Sahara bounded by the Nile on the east, the Eocene limestone plateau on the north, the international boundaries of Libya and Sudan on the west, and the Wadi Howar on the south (fig. 1). Rainfall over much of this vast area is too slight to measure (less than 5 millimeters per year), thus the climate of the area is hyperarid with generally northerly winds. Hot southerly winds occur a few times each year and commonly create sand or dust storms.

The Cretaceous Nubia Formation, one of the great aquifers of the world, underlies the Libyan Desert and supplies the oases with water where deflation has lowered the surface to the zone of saturation. The only population of the area today is confined to the oases of Dakhla and Kharga.

In recent years explorations in the Western Desert have turned from geographical studies conducted mainly by the British before World War II to archeological and geological studies. For eight years The Combined Prehistoric Expeditions of Fred Wendorf, Southern Methodist University, and Romuald Schild, Polish Academy of Sciences, investigated the prehistory of the Nile Valley, but because of the wartime status of the populated regions we have for the past four years (1972-75) concentrated on unraveling the prehistory of the Western Desert. This has resulted in some important discoveries indicating that man and central African animals lived at various times during the Pleistocene in what is now essentially a rainless desert. The miniature oases of Bir Tarfawi and Bir Tarfawi West (see fig. 1) are today the only places for hundreds of kilometers around where water can be reached at shallow depth by digging at the base of tamarisk mounds in wind-scoured basins that held small spring-fed lakes at various times, tens to hundreds of thousands of years ago (Schild and Wendorf, 1975).

257

Each spring the Expedition, with the support of the Egyptian Geological Survey, maintains in this remote desert a remarkably well organized and efficient field camp (fig. 2), including a dozen or more scientific personnel from several nations and several dozen Bedouin and Arab mechanics, drivers, guides, cooks, and workers. Transportation is by rugged, Soviet-made, 4-wheel-drive vehicles including large lorries and tankers to carry water and gasoline. This did not provide an efficient means of exploring farther afield for archeological sites and sites of geological or paleoecological interest. It was, therefore, my desire to revive the techniques of Bagnold (1935) and operate self-sufficiently with three fuel-efficient vehicles.

1975 Fieldwork

In 1975, supported by the National Geographic Society, I obtained three Volkswagen Type 181, lightweight, air-cooled vehicles from Mexico, where they are engineered for operation with low-octane fuel such as was available in Egypt at the time. These were brought to Tucson, Arizona, and were outfitted with "cold" type sparkplugs, larger fuel-metering jets, extra fuel cells, air compressors, independent rear-wheel hand brakes, spare-tire racks, and wide rear tires for operation in loose sand.

After testing these desert-adapted vehicles in Arizona, they were driven to Houston, Texas, shipped to Egypt, and then driven to our camp at Gebel el Nabta in the desert 100 miles west of the Nile from Abu Simbel. With these vehicles, we were able to accomplish several objectives that could not otherwise have been reached without a larger scale operation.

In the vicinity of Gebel el Nabta we were able to complete geological mapping of Pleistocene deposits, including Nabta Playa with its associated archeology. The shores of this ancient and hitherto unrecognized lake were occupied by the latest Paleolithic people approximately 9,000 to 10,000 years ago. After drying up, the shores were occupied again in two subsequent lake phases by early Neolithic peoples 6,000 to 9,000 years ago. Literally thousands of artifacts litter deflated sand dunes that bordered the ancient lake, and several buried wells reveal the drop in the water table that occurred between two lake phases.

Other more ancient lake deposits were mapped, but aside from their possible association with Acheulean and Mousterian artifacts, their age is unknown.

The highlight of the season's work was a 2400-kilometer reconnaissance trip, with Fred Wendorf, Romauld Schild, and Rushdi Saïd, to the Gilf el Kebir plateau in the remote southwestern part of Egypt. During a side trip to

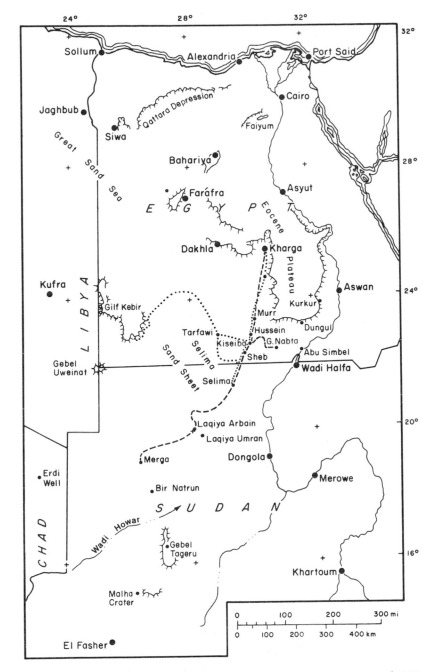

FIG. 1.   Map of the Western Desert, Egypt and Sudan, showing routes of 1975 reconnaissance trips to the Gilf Kebir (dotted line), and 1976 trip to Bir Kiseiba, Selima, Laqiya Arba'in, and Merga lake (dashed line).

FIG. 2.   Camp of the Combined Prehistoric Expedition on Nabta playa from the top of an active barchan dune. The field vehicles are modified Type 181 Volkswagens.

Selima Oasis in north-central Sudan in anticipation of future work in that area, I found lacustrine sediments and tufa deposits that made a return visit very desirable.

The Gilf Kebir trip was where the modified type 181 Volkswagens received their real desert test. They performed quite well over very rocky terrain and in all types of sand except so-called "liquid sand" in which any vehicle would get stuck and would have to be extracted with the help of iron sand channels under the drive wheels. Fuel consumption was half that of the Soviet "jeeps."

Brief scientific reconnaissance trips have been made to the Gilf Kebir by Egyptian Prince Kemal el Dine (1928), and by the British before World War II (Bagnold, 1931, 1939; Almásy, 1936; Clayton, 1936; Penderel, 1934; Shaw, 1936); and archeological sites of both early Paleolithic and Neolithic aspects were reported in what is now one of the most remote and waterless regions of the world (Myers, 1939). We were able to examine Myers's late Acheulean site at the base of the eastern cliff of the Gilf Kebir and note that it lies in the uppermost stratum of an ancient alluvial fan deposit.

Near the head of Wadi el Bakht, a Neolithic site occurs in association with ancient playa deposits formed when sand dunes blocked the wadi and im-

FIG. 3. Playa deposits of Wadi Bakht in the Gilf Kebir as seen from the top of an ancient dune that blocked the wadi. Giant ripple dunes appear in the foreground and figures standing on the playa (middle ground) provide scale.

pounded water at a time of greater rainfall than today (Peel, 1939). Headward erosion of the playa deposits was apparently caused by spillover which breached the natural dam. It is incredible that there has been insufficient run off in the ensuing six millennia to entrench the deposit any more than a few tens of feet (fig. 3). Fortunately, ostrich eggshell fragments from a Neolithic site were found in the uppermost playa sediment. They yielded a radiocarbon date of 6980±80 B.P. (SMU 273) for the final stage of the playa.

The return journey to our El Nabta camp was via Bir Tarfawi and Bir Kiseiba. After descending the Kiseiba escarpment, one encounters for several miles to the east, very soft silts that are expanded by evaporitic salts. This is a most difficult type of terrain to negotiate by motor vehicle.

These puffed up silts also occur in the depressions at Dakhla and Kharga Oases and in a shallow trough extending from Bir Nakhlai to Dunqul Oasis. This, plus anomalous features visible on ERTS photographs of the region within the 200-meter closed contour, suggests that many areas between the Kiseiba escarpment and the central Eocene Plateau may have held lakes at one or more times in the Quaternary. The former existence of a large lake would have had profound effect on the prehistory and paleoecology of this part of the

FIG. 4.   Semi-playa yardangs north of Gebel es Shams, Kharga Oasis, contain historic artifacts and stratigraphically overlie Neolithic playa deposits.

Western Desert. A major effort of our future geologic work in Egypt will be to test these hypotheses, and to map and date the playa deposits.

In summary, the accomplishments of the season's research include the mapping and radiocarbon dating of Nabta playa sediments and sites, the discovery of lacustrine sediments and tufa at Selima, the radiocarbon dating of Wadi Bakht playa, Gilf Kebir, and the recognition of many more playa basins in the Kiseiba-Dunqul depression than hitherto realized.

1976 Fieldwork

Our 1976 field season occurred in February and March and had as objectives: 1, the geochronological investigation of ancient spring deposits and associated archeology, in the area of Kharga Oasis; 2, the examination of the area between Bir Sheb and Kharga Oasis for evidence of playa lakes with associated archeology; and 3, the paleoecological and geochronological survey of the depressions of Selima, Laqiya, and Merga in northwest Sudan in search of evidence of former lakes.

The base of operations was the camp of the Combined Prehistoric Expedition, made up of an archeological contingent under the direction of Fred Wendorf and a geological contingent of the Egyptian Geological Survey directed by Rushdi Said. The field camp was located a few kilometers east of the airport at Kharga.

INVESTIGATIONS IN THE KHARGA AREA

Kharga Oasis, known in ancient time as "the Great Oasis" (Beadnell, 1909, p. 13), lies in a 30- by 150-kilometer deflational basin over 300 meters below the general level of the Eocene plateau which forms the eastern and northern borders (see fig. 1). The oasis actually consists of over a dozen villages with numerous wells, many of which were artesian but most of which now require pumping to maintain the agricultural population. East of the town of Kharga, the seat of the local government, there are numerous inactive and deflated spring deposits with abundant archeological evidence of intermittent human occupation of the area from late lower Paleolithic times to the present (Caton-Thompson, 1952).

In addition to the spring deposits there are Holocene deposits in ancient depressions that are considered by some to be lacustrine deposits (Beadnell, 1909, p. 110) and by others to be of eolian and spring origin (Caton-Thompson, 1952). Many of these deposits have historic (Persian, Greek, and Roman) artifacts associated with them, and, as discussed later, it appears that both origins are in part valid. In the field we referred to them as playa deposits, and Embabi (1972) has called them semi-playa deposits.

Archeological work this season was started in the same area worked by Caton-Thompson and Gardner in the 1930's. The excavation of new sites discovered this year provided a useful cultural sequence within detailed but discontinuous stratigraphy, and associated samples were collected for radiocarbon dating and pollen analysis. Both terminal Paleolithic and Neolithic sites were discovered by Wendorf and crew in playa deposits, some of which are correlatable to artesian discharge of some of the extinct springs.

Terminal Paleolithic artifacts appear to be in consolidated dune deposits stained with hydrated iron oxides, indicating subsequent saturation of the dunes. This occupation may have accompanied a pluvial phase as did the Terminal Paleolithic occupation at Nabta playa 350 kilometers to the southeast (Wendorf, Schild, et al., 1976), where lake bottom clays eventually buried both Terminal Paleolithic and Neolithic horizons.

In the Kharga depression Neolithic sites appear to be at the base of a sequence of interbedded brown sands and clayey silts (fig. 4) which contain abundant historical sites mostly of Greco-Roman age throughout their thickness of 10 meters or more. The sands which make up most of this thickness show predominantly planar-type cross stratification in beds up to a meter thick. These may be separated by thinner beds, commonly less than 10 centimeters, of laminated sands, but in some areas massive to weakly laminated calcareous, clayey silts, and fine sand occur within the current bedded coarser sands. This finer grained lithology becomes dominant in the upper part of the section, as does the quantity of potsherds, horse and cattle bones, and fire hearths, one of which provided charcoal that dated 2890±70 B.P. (SMU-377) by radiocarbon. Here also occur lenses of silty clays with numerous snail shells of the species *Malanoides tuberculata,* indicating shallow ponds or marshes. If this surface water was due to contemporary rain, the carbonate in the shells should be approximately the same age as the radiocarbon-dated fire hearth, but if ground water via springs or wells were the source, the shell carbonate would yield an erroneous age older than the charcoal. The apparent age of 18,800±170 B.P. (SMU-383) indicates that ancient ground water was being exploited.

Most of these beds are exposed as deflational remnants, or yardangs (see fig. 4), elongated north-south parallel to the prevailing wind direction. From these exposures and our trench excavations it is apparent that they unconformably overlie an earlier deflational landscape composed of consolidated dunes, lagged fluvial gravels from the limestone plateau, playa muds, and ancient spring deposits, some of which stand up as irregular mounds on the present landscape.

The stratigraphy of the spring mounds is complex and varied, as Caton-Thompson recognized, and contains late Acheulean, Mousterian, Aterian, and Neolithic artifacts but seldom on clearly defined activity floors (Schild and Wendorf, 1975). It is apparent that some springs have been sites of discontinuous artesian discharge since late Acheulean times, and maximum human presence has pretty much coincided with the times of discharge. In historic times (since 3000 B.C.), there is abundant stratigraphic evidence of wells having been dug in and around sites of former artesian discharge, indicating that such natural discharge may have been declining. The development of artesian wells would further reduce the static head and eventually require more wells to sustain the agricultural population of historic times. Thus, man has been ever requiring more sophisticated technology to sustain himself in the Kharga depression.

The abundant evidence of historic wells suggests that they may have played a significant role in the origin of the interbedded sands and clayey silts containing the abundant remains of Greco-Roman occupation. As stated earlier, the origin of the Holocene sediments is controversial. Beadnell (1909), the first to recognize and map them, considered them to be lake deposits and offered two hypotheses to explain the lake. The first involved artesian water from uncontrolled wells, the second involved deflation through the imperme-

Fig. 5.   A solitary yardang approximately one kilometer north of Bir Kiseiba displays laminated lacustrine beds below more massive playa mud.

able shales over the sandstone aquifer. A third hypothesis, that of a pluvial lake in the internally drained basin, is not mentioned.

The second is untenable for the Holocene lake, because we now know that artesian discharge in the Kharga area is at least as old as the Acheulean springs on the floor of the depression (Caton-Thompson, 1952). Such an origin for these earliest springs is quite possible, however, and deserves further consideration, because both Caton-Thompson and ourselves observed in some Acheulean spring vents a chaotic stratigraphy that suggests violent discharge or eruption.

Beadnell's first explanation is more tenable, especially so today because paleoclimatic records of North Africa indicate that the time of the lake, estimated to be sometime between 500 B.C. and A.D. 100, was one of dry climate and low lake levels (Butzer, 1971, p. 333) thus precluding a pluvial origin, the third hypothesis for the water.

Caton-Thompson (1952, p. 10), on the other hand, does not consider the clayey sands and silts to be lacustrine, and ascribes their origin to eolian deposition and well discharge, but in both cases she invokes some degree of water action. From our observations of the stratigraphy and aquatic gastropods it is

FIG. 6.   Chalcedony nodules armor a matrix of maroon mudstone near Gebel
Wagif.

clear that intermittent shallow bodies of water existed in the Kharga depression contemporaneously with eolian activity such that calcareous playalike clayey silts are interbedded with cross-bedded eolian sands. Similar observations were made by Embabi (1972), who called these sediments semi-playa deposits because of their mixed character.

Similar depositional environments can be observed locally today where shallow pools of irrigation water or marshy fields are being encroached upon by sand dunes and much of the surrounding ground is covered with an efflorescent crust of salts. The remote desert salt lake of Merga in northwestern Sudan is a natural example of the same phenomenon that will be discussed in detail later on.

Hellstrom (1940) has presented calculations showing, if correct, that under present climatic conditions and evaporation rates on the order of 5.5 millimeters per day (2 meters per year) no open body of water of 2000-square-kilometer size suggested by Beadnell could possibly exist at Kharga. Because the sediments we observed do show evidence of former saturation and shallow ponds the main problem is probably that instead of a single body of water as envisioned by Beadnell there were many intermittent shallow bodies of water alternating with saturated marshy ground with parts of the area being overrid-

FIG. 7. The ground-water supported lake at Merga Oasis, northwest Sudan is extremely salty due to high evaporation rates and very little rain. Submerged dunes form semi-playa deposits.

den from time to time by sand dunes. The fact remains that these sediments formed extensive deposits in the depression up to the early part of the Christian era.

Caton-Thompson's observation that these sediments are invariably associated with ancient wells supports an artificial rather than climatic cause for them, but Embabi (1972) was the first to point out that there are two sets of playalike deposits separated by an erosional contact. We have found the lower deposit to be of Neolithic age and lithologically similar to Neolithic playas elsewhere in the Western Desert (Wendorf et al., 1976). I will apply Embabi's term semi-playa deposits to the upper sediments of early historic age and retain playa for the lower deposits.

John Ball (1927) defined a scientific model of the ground-water hydrology of the Libyan Desert that has proved to be a basis for later studies (Hellstrom, 1940; Murray, 1952; Attia, 1954). Permeable sandstone in the Nubia Formation is the regional aquifer and was believed by Ball to receive its recharge from the eastern flanks of the Ennedi and Erdi Mountains in Chad. The aquifer slopes gently (1 to 2,000) to the north and east and extends throughout Egypt and northern Sudan. All of the major oases of the Western Desert occur where deflational basins have intersected this water table, in some cases assisted by geologic structures.

In the Kharga area there are several aquifers within the Nubia Formation, but the shallow one ("Shallow water sandstone") was exploited by historic peoples and is now essentially dry (Beadnell, 1909). Faulting has influenced the location of some artesian springs near the floor of the depression, but deflation has played a major role in bringing the floor closer to the shallow aquifer and within reach of ancient technology.

A state of quasi-equilibrium may be established between discharge and deflation. Disturbance of this state would occur if the recharge areas in the highland received more precipitation and thus increased the hydrostatic head throughout the aquifer. The unknown factor here is the time it would take for this increase in recharge in the Erdi-Ennedi area to be felt in the Kharga area in the form of increased discharge. Using Hellstrom's (1940) figures the actual subterranean flow would take between 40,000 and 400,000 years to reach Kharga. Subsequent isotopic studies have supported the lower figure (Knetsch and others, 1962). The increase in hydrostatic pressure would occur simultaneously, but it is conceivable that spring discharge could occur at Kharga several thousand years after the dry part of a climatic cycle, i.e., completely out of phase with pluvial cycles. On the other hand, Knetsch et al. (1962) suggest that recharge may have been directly to the oases depressions.

It is at present impossible to evaluate this possibility for the Roman age discharge in the Kharga depression without better knowledge of the chronology of wells, microfacies relationships to the clayey silts and sands, and variations of discharge. Some such knowledge could be obtained, however, by: 1, search of historic records; 2, more detailed stratigraphic-geochronological studies of ancient wells and spring mounds in conjunction with archeological investigations; and 3, more investigation of aquifer flow parameters, using isotopic techniques. To test the hypothesis that recharge may have been directly to the aquifer through the oases depressions during the Neolithic pluvial and not from the highlands in Chad, we hope to make isotopic age determinations on shallow ground waters at desert wells.

Another question that begs further inquiry is the reason for the extensive desiccation and deflation of the historic age semi-playa deposits. The remnants of these clayey silts and sands represent only a small fraction of what once covered most of the depression below approximately 70 meters elevation; thus, vast areas of agricultural soils and sediments, up to 20 meters thick in places, have been blown away in the last two millennia. Was this the result of: 1, depletion of the available ground water by over-exploitation and/or drier climate; 2, poisoning of agricultural soils by evaporite accumulation; or 3, greater eolian activity?

The abundance of extinct wells of Persian, Greek, and Roman age, as well as the prevalence of salts in the playa sediments and the incredible efforts to mine water from under the northern escarpment and transport it southward into the basin via subterranean aqueducts (Beadnell, 1909), all together suggest that ground-water depletion by over-exploitation under hyperarid conditions like those of today, and the loss by deflation of most of the agricultural soils since then, led to the population decline of the Great Oasis after Roman time. Thus, Kharga may be an ancient example of man destroying the vital qualities of his environment already weakened by the climatic change from pluvial to hyperarid.

Today the oasis is enjoying a new era of relative prosperity because of modern techniques of exploiting the deeper aquifers and irrigating the desert (Ezzat, 1974). Even though these aquifers have a much greater capacity than the shallow one, they too have a limited life unless pluvial conditions return, because water is not being recharged today at the rate it is being removed (Münnich and Vogel, 1962).

Playa Deposits of the Kiseiba Escarpment

The former existence of pluvial lakes in the Western Desert is known from Holocene deposits of playa clays and silts in several areas south of Kharga and the Eocene Plateau (Peel, 1939; Issawi, 1968 and 1971), and detailed archeological investigations of Nabta playa 100 kilometers west of Abu Simbel have shown a Terminal Paleolithic occupation between 7000 and 8000 B.C. and several Neolithic occupations between 6250 and 5200 B.C. to be related to the playa deposits (Wendorf et al., 1976, 1977; Haynes et al., 1977). Other playa deposits were recognized in the El Nabta area and none appears to be related to ground water discharge. They, being derived from runoff, are truly pluvial in origin.

The surprising abundance of playa deposits prompted us to look elsewhere within the 200-meter closed contour (British War Office, Division of Military Survey, 1961) for evidence of other lake deposits and to consider the possibility of a single large body of water during the Holocene. After these preliminary investigations of the playa deposits of the Kharga depression we surveyed the area between there and Bir Sheb for evidences of former lakes and associated archeology. South of Maks, the most southerly of the villages in the depression, the ground rises to a higher, relatively level plain known as the Atmur El Kibeish. Farther south this plain is bordered by the impressive Kiseiba escarpment (fig. 7) trending north-northeast to south-southwest. Several desert watering places known as birs occur along the ancient caravan route (Darb el Arba'in) that more or less follows the Kiseiba escarpment. Near Bir Murr a number of yardangs of yellowish brown laminated clayey silt mark the site of a deflated playa, and farther south a more extensive playa was mapped by Issawi (1971). We found lake deposits to extend southwesterly along the shallow depression at the foot of the Kiseiba escarpment from Issawi's outcrops in the north to Bir Sheb in the south, a distance of at least 70 kilometers. South of Bir Kiseiba remnants of what may be a shoreline terrace can be seen along the escarpment, and a yardang of yellowish brown laminated playa silts (fig. 5) occurs a kilometer north of the bir.

Along the Darb el Arba'in for over 30 kilometers, in the vicinity of Gebel Waqif and Gebel Shirshir, the ground is armored by white nodular chalcedony up to 15 centimeters in diameter (Issawi, 1971). Test excavations (fig. 6) revealed that these are lagged from an underlying reddish brown mudstone that forms low hills and ridges. Similar deposits in the El Nabta area are believed to be playa or lake deposits topographically inverted by the formation of a protective armor of the chalcedony nodules during deflation of the surrounding mudstone. Their age is uncertain but they appear to predate Acheulean artifacts in the El Nabta area.

Silica-rich saline lake waters are known in central Africa and nodular chalcedony occurs in lacustrine deposits of Olduvai Gorge (Hay, 1968). The source of silica in the Western Desert is not known. It is not common in the ground water. A pedogenic source is one possibility and dissolution of sand in saline waters is another. In either case the occurrence of these inverted, chalcedony-armored playas suggests a much earlier generation of lakes.

Eastward from the Kiseiba escarpment the ground rises gently and the extent of the lacustrine deposits is masked by a sand sheet. This relatively level surface is broken in places by low outcrops of bedrock, some of which are protected from further deflation by accumulation of a shinglelike armor of silicified, ferruginous sandstone forming a lag concentrate. Extensive areas of this type of ground, referred to as lag hamada occur between the Kiseiba escarpment and the Nile. Between Bir Kiseiba and Bir Nakhlai the sand sheet and lag hamada are underlain in places by soft powdery clays expanded by salts. Such ground is treacherous to vehicles.

LACUSTRINE FEATURES OF THE SUDANESE OASES

South of Bir Sheb there are four oases occupying deflational basins in Sudan. By using specially equipped Volkswagen (Type 181) Safaries, Peter Mehringer, Sayed El Zaghloul, and I, with Bedouin guides Ayed and Shater Marief Salimm, were able to visit three of these in a single journey from a temporary camp at Bir Kiseiba by establishing a fuel dump on the Egyptian-Sudanese border (Haynes et al., 1979).

Selima Oasis, 120 kilometers south-southwest of Sheb, lies in a depression at the base of a south-facing 80-meter cliff. The floor rises southward from the foot of the cliff where excellent water may be had at a meter depth. Remnants of laminated, lacustrine, olive-green clays and white marls occur around the lower part of the basin near the well and at least one cut terrace occurs against the bedrock cliff. In addition, gray masses of porous tufa with abundant plant casts occur on knolls of Nubian sandstone and have protected them from deflation. From the evidence seen in this brief visit it is clear that the Quaternary history of Selima Oasis includes at least one phase of relatively deep water and one of spring-fed marshes.

Laqiya depression, 200 kilometers southwest of Selima, extends for over 50 kilometers in a general northwesterly direction below an impressive escarpment on the north that is in excess of 100 meters high in some places. Several large reentrants cut back into the cliffs and are floored with reddish brown playa silt-clays. Yardangs of these deposits stand as much as 4 meters above the deflated floor and two strandlines are apparent near the base of the cliffs. These were observed only at a distance, but their horizontal extent was clearly in contrast to the gentle dips of the bedrock.

In the westerly part of the Laqiya depression we also observed areas of fluvial gravels overlying consolidated red sands. Exact stratigraphic relationships could not be worked out in the time available, but our impression is that these deposits underlie the playa deposits of probable Neolithic age and have been exposed by deflation.

The vegetation, in addition to date palms around the well at Laqiya Arbain, consists of clumps of acacia scattered along the foot of the escarpment.

Approximately 200 kilometers southwest of Laqiya a more shallow basin holds the salt lake of Merga (Nukheila in Sudan). Visited by less than a half dozen foreign expeditions since its discovery in 1925 (Ball, 1927) the lake, measuring approximately 50 by 100 kilometers, is an incredible sight for such an arid environment (fig. 7). It is the result of exposed ground water being trapped by dunes, and may have existed there during part of the Pleistocene. Our main effort was to collect cores from the lake bottom for pollen and radiocarbon analyses. Two 1-meter cores of black, organic, pyritic sand were recovered and found to overlie compact sand that could not be penetrated with the equipment available.

The lake itself is highly saline and efflorescent crusts forming in a marshy area at the west end appear to be a hydrated sodium carbonate, e.g., natron, trona or a mixture thereof. At the east end an active dune is moving into the lake and may be a modern analog of the historic age deposits of Kharga discussed earlier.

Some of the bedrock hills around the Merga depression show a marked strandline that clearly truncates earlier alluvial features, and low outcrops of Nubian sandstone near the lake have been softened and made friable by salt weathering.

CONCLUSIONS

From these observations of the oases depressions it is abundantly clear that significant bodies of water partially filled them at one time or another. Some are obviously due to pluvial conditions but others as at Kharga and Merga may have been partially the result of ground water discharge. Further investigations of stratigraphy in conjunction with archeology and radiocarbon dating should help answer some of these questions and tell us if the indicated pluvial periods were synchronous over the Western Desert or of a more local nature.

1977 Fieldwork

The 1977 field season, during February and March, included investigations in the Gebel Nabta area and the Bir Kiseiba area with reconnaissance trips (see fig. 8) to the Abu Ballas area, Bir Nakhlai, Bir Safsaf, Bir Tarfawi, and the Roman ruins of Um Dabadib. The base camp was that of the Combined Prehistoric Expedition at Nabta playa where the final season of archeological excavations was being conducted (Wendorf, Schild, et al., 1976; and Wendorf, Close, et al., 1977).

KHARGA-UM DABADIB

From Asyut, Dr. Rushdi Said, director of the Geological Survey of Egypt, and I drove to Kharga Oasis via the ancient Darb el Arba'in caravan route across the Eocene limestone plateau. On both the eastern and western escarpments we observed terra rosa filling solution cavities in the limestone. The evidence for two contrasting climates was manifested by (1) the terra rosa and solution features requiring much greater rainfall than today and (2) the erosion of the limestone into fluted yardangs by eolian processes under a hyperarid climate like that of today. As a reasonable working hypothesis I believe the plateau surface may be a truncated karst.

One of my objectives this season was to begin systematic sampling of shallow ground water for radiometric age determinations to determine the extent to which it had been recharged during the Neolithic pluvial 9000 to 5000 B.P. Sampling was begun in Kharga Oasis a week earlier by Herbert

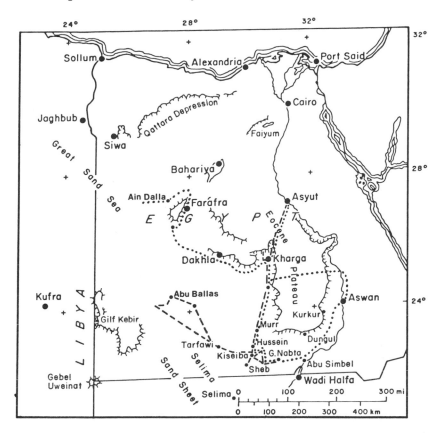

FIG. 8.   Routes of 1977 (dashed line) and 1978 (dotted line) reconnaissance trips
through the Western Desert of Egypt.

Haas who sampled some of the deeper aquifers as a comparative test to the radiocarbon dating of others (Knetch et al., 1962). While in Kharga we were
fortunate in meeting Eberhart Klitzsch and a scientific team from The Free
University of Berlin who were also making isotopic investigations of the deep
ground water.

At Um Dabadib near the mud brick ruins and gallery wells of Greco-Roman age we observed the Quaternary features reported by Caton-Thompson
(1952) and measured what appear to be pre-Holocene playa deposits on bedrock benches at least 5 meters above the playa muds attributable to the Neolithic pluvial.

Stream beds draining the plateau scarp at Um Dabadib are extinct, as indicated by the extremely wind abraded and fluted tops of boulders making up

the bed load. These appear to be overlain by the Holocene playa muds downstream.

GEBEL NABTA AREA

Following the Darb el Arba'in (road of forty) on the way to Nabta Playa we observed chalcedony-bearing mudstones (see fig. 6) over 45 kilometers of the route and playa deposits extending over 16 kilometers near Bir Murr.

In and around Nabta playa, soil test pits were excavated on various surfaces and sampled. An outcrop of chalcedony-armoured mudstone within Nabta playa was sampled in detail because it is a likely candidate for being a much older Quaternary lacustrine deposit and an obvious source of the clays in the muds of Nabta playa.

The most important observations of this field season were of strand lines and beach benches associated with Beid and Kurtein playas to the north of Nabta playa, where such features were not observed after several seasons of searching. After doubts expressed by some of my colleagues, the lacustrine origin of the features was convincingly demonstrated by stratigraphic trenches exposing rounded beach gravels and interstitial salts.

Another significant observation, in a large unnamed playa east of Beid playa, was the interfingering of coarse pebble to cobble alluvial gravels with Holocene playa muds and their extension over the highest playa deposits. This suggests more flashy discharge at the end of the Holocene pluvial.

BIR NAKHLAI, BIR TAKHLIS, AND BIR SAFSAF

Reconnaissance trips were made to Bir Nakhlai and Bir Takhlis in the company of botanist Nabil Hadidi, from the University of Cairo, who was pleased to discover that some plants around the wells and forming phytogenic mounds are apparently remnants of a relict Sudanese flora. Two stone blockhouses overlooking the wells at Bir Nakhlai are relics of the Dervish War (fig. 9). Manned by Anglo-Egyptian forces they controlled access to this remote watering place and thus inhibited raids on the main oases of Kharga and Dakhla farther north. A more detailed vegetation study of these and other remote wells is planned for the next two years.

En route to Bir Safsaf from Bir Kiseiba we crossed the Atmur el Kibeish, a flat expanse covered for the most part by sand sheet. The presence of shallow ground water is indicated by several phytogenic mounds of eolian sand held by the vegetation (fig. 10). It is thought that as trees, either *Acacia erhenbergia* or *Tamarix amplexicanlis* die, new ones germinate at the leeward end leaving the oldest dead wood windward. Radiocarbon dating will shed light on the rates of this process.

FIG. 9. One of two abandoned stone blockhouses overlooking the wells at Bir Nakhlai that stand as silent reminders of the importance of the remote desert wells during the Dervish War.

At Bir Safsaf, named for the reeds *Phragmites australis* that surround the small clump of date and dom palms (fig. 11), we collected plant samples and salts formed by evaporation from the shallow ground water.

My introduction to Bir Safsaf was in 1973 by Bahay Issawi of the Geological Survey of Egypt. At that time we collected several kilograms of ripe dates but have not found any more there since that time. On the present trip we were without guides and navigated successfully by dead reckoning and continue to do so.

BIR TARFAWI, ABU BALLAS

In 1972 a concentration of tarfa (*Tamarix* sp.) mounds in a depression 11 kilometers west of Bir Tarfawi was mistakenly called Bir Sahara by the Combined Prehistoric Expedition (Wendorf, Schild, et al., 1976; Wendorf, Close, et al., 1977). We subsequently learned that the actual Bir Sahara is a 17.5-meter deep hand-dug well reportedly 20 kilometers farther to the southwest (Beadnell, 1931). Our reconnaissance in 1977 failed to locate this well, but I will refer to the westerly depression as Tarfawi West.

Here we collected shallow ground water from the hand-dug well of the 1973-74 field season and precipitated the bicarbonate ions for radiocarbon analysis.

En route to Abu Ballas (Pottery Hill) we examined a hill marked on the 1:500,000 scale map (British War Office, Division of Military Survey, 1960) as having a dike on the southwest side and found instead an irregular alignment or wall of boulders that is clearly man-made. It is, perhaps, a relict of the Neolithic occupation of the region.

Southeast of Abu Ballas about 50 kilometers we examined playa yardangs in a depression below a prominent scarp on the north side but found little archeological evidence other than a few scattered pieces of worked flint, all highly wind abraded.

Abu Ballas is an isolated pair of conical sandstone hills (fig. 12) surrounded by a sand sheet. The name derives from the many large pottery jars that were discovered at the base of the northerly hill in 1918 by Dr. John Ball while on a military topographic survey with a Lieutenant Moore, using Model T Fords (Ball, 1919). The date of discovery is often given as 1916 or 1917 but the entry for February 15, 1918, in Ball's field book, now in the Geological Museum in Cairo, states, "Halted till 4:25, then on over level sand, rather soft in places but all right if taken at full speed by light cars, to (4:50 p.m.) pair of SS hills, of which the N one marks site of a quantity of large earthenware jars, all more or less broken and sand worn. No inscriptions or other remains." The site did not receive scientific recognition until 1923 when Ball guided Prince Kemal el Dine (1927) to it; there, upon excavation, hundreds of jars were found "set in regular order in the sand and obviously forming a water-dump" (Ball, 1927, p. 122). The source of the jars is still a mystery although an archeologist has informed R. A. Bagnold (pers. comm.) that they appear to be late New Kingdom in age (ca. 1500 B.C.).

In comparing my photographs of the hill with some of those shown by Ball (1927) I find a remarkable lack of correspondence in those taken at a distance (figs. 12 and 13); so much so that I question the identity of those in Ball's paper. On the other hand the close-up photographs are identical and show little change in the colluvial slope in 54 years (fig. 14).

Southwest of Abu Ballas we were surprised to see vehicles in this remote part of the world moving westerly. They turned out to be a scientific team from The Free University of Berlin. The scientists, including geologist H.-J. Pachur and archeologist B. Gabriel, were equally as surprised at seeing us.

Thirty kilometers farther southwest we examined more playa yardangs in a depression at the base of an impressive scarp. We continued westward on a sand sheet leeward of the depression and finally turned southeasterly on a

FIG. 10. Phytogenic mound on Atmur el Kibeish. The tree, *Acacia ehrenbergiana*, is supported by shallow ground water and holds a mound of wind-blown sand.

FIG. 11. View westward of Bir Safsaf. Lieutenant Comyn (1911) may have planted the date palms in 1906.

Pottery Hill, possible site of " Zerzura," from the south-west

FIG. 12.   Top, 1923 photograph reportedly of Abu Ballas published by Ball (1927) and Prince Kemal el Dine (1927) does not compare with my photograph (below) taken in 1977.

Pottery Hill from the south: at foot, petrol and water supplies of Prince Kemal el Din's Expedition of 1923

FIG. 13. Top, 1923 photograph of the south end of Abu Ballas does not match the contemporary photograph (below) taken in 1977.

heading for Bir Tarfawi and then easterly to Bir Kiseiba, stopping on a sand sheet of the Atmur to make a test pit. This revealed laminated coarse to medium eolian sand with moderate prismatic soil structure (late Holocene?) over a truncated paleosol (mid-Holocene?) in which sedimentary structure had been obliterated by pedoturbation (fig. 15).

KISEIBA SCARP AREA

The shoreline terrace observed in 1976 (fig. 16) about 112 kilometers southwest of Bir Kiseiba was trenched to reveal subrounded beach gravels and salts grading easterly to finer grained facies.

Two prominent outliers (fig. 17) of Nubian sandstone approximately 2 kilometers northeast of Bir Kiseiba show a prominent beach terrace cut into the bedrock and a recessional strandline cut into pale olive lacustrine clayey silt (fig. 18). Test excavations in the beach terrace at what we call Two Hills playa revealed rounded sandstone gravel in a silty matrix charged with salts and overlain by a shinglelike armor of shaley colluvium. Terminal Paleolithic and Neolithic archeological remains are relatively abundant in this area and some charcoal-bearing rock hearths have provided radiocarbon dates clustering around 8790 and 6850 B.P., indicating two periods of human occupation.

More archeological sites were observed all the way to Bir Kurayim and Bir Sheb. One, 12 kilometers south of Bir Kiseiba, provided radiocarbon dates clustering around 5800 B.P., and above the escarpment several small shallow depressions contain deflated playa silts and archeological remains.

The evidence for a standing body of open water along 70 kilometers of the Kiseiba escarpment is not indicated, and a series of separate, shallow playas seems more likely.

1978 Fieldwork

ORGANIZATION

Co-investigators Robert Giegengack, Donald L. Johnson and Peter J. Mehringer, Jr., and I arrived in Cairo on January 30 and found accommodations awaiting us as planned. This, however, was about all that went as planned for the rest of the season. It took us four days of incredible bureaucratic negotiations to clear my shipment of parts and supplies through customs. In the meantime, permission to conduct our research in Sudan had not been received by their embassy, who would not grant visas to fly to Khartoum, even for the purpose of coordinating with the Geological Department there. While in Cairo we coordinated with Galal Mustafa, new director of the

FIG. 14. Top, 1923 photograph at the north end of Abu Ballas shows the ancient water jars. Below, little change can be detected in the colluvium after 54 years (1977).

Geological Survey of Egypt; Dr. Bahay Issawi, senior geologist; Dr. Paul Walker, director of the American Research Center; Dr. Adison Richmond, science attaché, U. S. Embassy; Dr. Harold Hoogstraal, entomologist, NAMRU-3; Dr. Nabil Hadidi, herbarium, Cairo University; and the Continental Delta Oil Company, Maadi.

DAKHLA-AIN DALLA AREAS

On February 8 we went by bus to Kharga Oasis where the VW-181 field vehicles were stored and spent two days getting them ready for the desert. On February 12 with geologist Sayed El Zaghloul and driver-mechanic Abdu Zedan we examined deposits at Deir El Hagar playa, about 5 kilometers southeast of Gebel Edmonstone, Dakhla depression. These have been mapped by Zaghloul and contain Neolithic artifacts in place in the lower of two stratified playa beds (fig. 19). The younger bed appears to be of Roman age and related to an ancient system of wells and irrigation canals. Several radiocarbon samples were collected from this sequence.

February 13 and 14 were devoted to examining the Abu Mungar and Faråfra depressions. Both contain surface scatters of Neolithic artifacts, and playa deposits about 15 kilometers north-northwest of Faråfra village have been mapped by Zaghloul. Two radiocarbon samples were collected enroute to Ain Dalla, a large spring mound about 70 kilometers northwest. This was a major watering place for the Long Range Desert Group in World War II, and it was being used this year by Geosource Company seismic crews exploring for petroleum for Conoco. Back-dirt from well excavations on the mound indicates that it is stratified and contains artifacts as early as Mousterian. Several basins from Ain Dalla to Faråfra contain playa sediment, some of which crop out as rather typical clusters of yardangs.

Because we could not work in Sudan as planned, we decided to take advantage of the Geosource base camp west of Ain Dalla as a means of getting to the northern Gilf Kebir and the silica glass area, and of looking for playa deposits between ridges of the Sand Sea. In our attempt to reach the base camp, one of the VW's broke a connecting rod about 70 kilometers east of it. Fortunately on February 15 one of their six-axle trucks towed me to Faråfra where we left the inoperative vehicle to be picked up later by Geological Survey personnel. While our entry into the Sand Sea was brief, we did manage to observe playa deposits there that may, with closer study, enable us to date the dunes.

KHARGA DEPRESSION

After returning to Kharga and reorganizing, we examined and recorded playa deposits and soils between Qasr El Gyb and Qasr Lebukha in the north-

FIG. 15. Soil test pit in the sand sheet of the Atmur el Kibeish, between Bir Tarfawi and Bir Kiseiba, shows weak to moderate soil structure in the late Holocene laminated eolian sand that disconformably overlies a middle Holocene(?) paleosol, in which sedimentary structure has been obliterated by pedogenesis.

ern part of the Kharga depression. Qasr El Gyb, a Roman fort on the ancient caravan route (Darb el Arba'in) to central Africa, stands as an impressive, mud-brick ruin isolated on a hill and surrounded by depressions that hold remnants of playa deposits and underground aqueducts (fig. 20). In one of these depressions, 5 kilometers south of Qasr El Gyb, we found spoil piles from aqueduct cleanout shafts overlying playa deposits. At least 2 meters of deflation had occurred since abandonment, and the roof of one of the underground tunnels had collapsed. Entering one of these north of Qasr El Gyb, we found water about 2.5 meters below the present surface, on which several small patches of irrigated ground occurred. According to our guide from the village of Moharik, his relatives had farmed these a few years earlier. Apparently the exhausted "shallow water" aquifer can still yield small amounts of water periodically if allowed to recover sufficiently. We hope to collect here next season.

Farther to the south we discovered collapsed, sand-blasted wells and vast quantities of pottery at what is clearly a Roman ruin that is not on our maps.

About 13 kilometers south-southwest of Qasr El Gyb we crossed more playa deposits before reaching Qasr Lebukha, another ancient Roman garrison where stands of tamarisk are being cut for wood today. On a hill (ca. 170-180 meters elev.) below the western scarp and about 5 kilometers southwest of Qasr El Gyb we examined a large deposit of quartz-chalcedony nodules similar to those I had studied in previous years in the area of Gebel Nabta and Gebel Wagif. They occur as chalcedony armored hills within depressions. The nodules occur in salty maroon mudstones that are either Pleistocene lacustrine sediments or Cretaceous shales possibly modified by Pleistocene saline lakes.

In Kharga village we examined soils maps at the Soil Department and found that three of their map units for the most favorable agricultural soils correspond to Quaternary playa deposits. These, unfortunately, are among the most deflatable deposits and are being destroyed. At the Irrigation Department we examined 1:10,000 British topographic maps of 1933 with 10-meter contour intervals. The contours appear to be somewhat generalized but the maps would be very useful for elevation control to within 5 meters. They are not available, however, and may be examined only at the office.

On our way to Bir Kiseiba on February 24 we excavated a 1-meter deep pit in the quartz-chalcedony deposits (ca. 140-180 m elev.) near Gebel Wagif, described the mudstone and sampled it and the nodules (see fig. 6). Between there and Bir Abu El Husein we met three small camel caravans heading for a rendezvous at Bir Kiseiba from which they would proceed as a single caravan for 700 kilometers to the natron deposits near Merga in Sudan.

BIR KISEIBA-GEBEL NABTA AREA

Six days (February 25-March 2) were spent in the vicinity of Bir Kiseiba differential leveling beaches and deposits along the base of the Kiseiba escarpment. A prominent beach bench 17 kilometers southwest of the bir appears to be at 194.4 meters elevation (fig. 16), a Neolithic site 4 kilometers east of the beach is at 192 meters, Bir Kiseiba is at 178 meters, and a prominent beach bench at the two hills (Two Hills playa, fig. 18), 6 kilometers northeast of Bir Kiseiba is at 179.5 meters. Datum is a Desert Development Department bench mark 1 kilometer northeast of Bir Kiseiba, said by the Geological Survey to be 176.7 meters. From these data it is apparent that there is a complicated history of pluvial lakes and human occupation of the Kiseiba depression during late Quaternary time.

Several radiocarbon samples were collected from hearths which predate pedogenic jointing of the sand sheets and several archeological sites were recorded. Two days were devoted to digging a new well at Bir Kiseiba and collecting water for radiocarbon and stable isotope analyses from this and the main well.

FIG. 16. A pebble beach line is well displayed along the base of the escarpment south of Bir Kiseiba. The scatter of artifacts in the foreground is typical of Neolithic sites at playas.

The north end of the Kiseiba depression was examined north of Bir Ayed, where more water was collected. The playa there had received rain since my visit the previous year as evidenced by fresh runnels into the playa and several areas of mud crack curls that had not yet blown away. Most of the runoff had disappeared into desiccation cracks instead of ponding. Heading southward toward Bir Nakhlai we encountered a patch of a dozen or so low-spreading plants (fig. 21) that were probably germinated in response to the same rain that fell at the playa. In collecting these plants which were in flower we noticed several types of insects on and around them.

At Bir Nakhlai, on March 3, we collected water from an old cribbed well located between two Dervish-war block houses. Between there and Gebel Nabta we crossed a flat area with a nodular calcic horizon similar to the one underlying the Atmura El Kibeish above the Kiseiba escarpment and possibly a remnant of the same relict paleosol.

West of Gebel Nabta about 8 kilometers we found two more patches of plants some of which were kharit (cf. *Salsola baryosma*), the plant I have been testing for atomic age radiocarbon with the hope of learning if the rains that caused germination were random or part of a general period of widespread

FIG. 17.   Descending the Kiseiba escarpment. Neolithic-age playa deposits and
beach deposits occur on the far (southeastern) sides of the two hills.

rains. The new plants will allow me to test the time of germination against the
[14]C atomic production curve because checking with NOAA (National Oceanographic and Atmospheric Administration) revealed that a major storm front
crossed this part of the Western Desert on December 17, 1977.

KHOR TUSHKA PROJECT

By the time we reached Nabta playa we were too far behind schedule to do
any differential leveling of the sites and deposits, so on March 3 we headed for
the Nile Valley via the Tushka arm of Lake Nasser to see if any playa deposits
extended into the arm. Upon arriving there late that afternoon we discovered
the excavation of a canal in progress that is designed to carry overflow of Lake
Nasser water into the Kiseiba-Dungul depression. This, the Sadat Canal, is to
follow a low area, below 190 meters, extending northwest from the Tushka
arm. The lowest areas are shallow closed depressions containing playa deposits
and numerous Neolithic sites are exposed on the surface.

Contour maps produced in Yugoslavia, at a scale of 1:100,000 with a
contour interval of 10 meters, were displayed at the construction site. These
revealed that the highest closed contour of the Kiseiba-Dungul depression is

FIG. 18. The pebble beach line of Two Hills playa is clearly visible at the foot of the most northerly of the two hills. Lower strand is recessional. Archeologist Mottamza (left) and geologist el Hennawi (right).

the 180-meter contour which apparently does not close off the Kharga depression. Furthermore, if our leveling of the Pluvial Lake Kiseiba beach is correct the water would have filled all of the depressions of the Western Desert south of the Egyptian plateau. Such a body of water could not exist today above the 183-meters sill elevation in the Tushka arm. If it existed in the past it would have had to be before 9300 B.P. when Terminal Paleolithic peoples occupied many playas on the floor of the depression (Wendorf, Schild, et al., 1976). By 8700 B.P., Two Hills playa in the Kiseiba depression was occupied by prehistoric peoples who became widespread and occupied numerous playas throughout the area between then and 6000 B.P. after which hyperaridity became the dominant climatic regime.

If such a large lake did exist there at 10,000 B.P., for example, it would correlate with the Holocene high lake stands in Chad and East Africa, and archeological sites of this age should be on the periphery. On the other hand, we must also consider the possibility that the high Kiseiba beach was due to a smaller, more isolated playa that has had the eastern half of its basin walls removed by wind scour and deflation, the dominant processes of the hyperarid

Fig. 19.   Yardang on Dier el Hagar playa, Dakhla Oasis show early historic semi-playa deposits over Holocene playa deposits with polygonal jointing and Neolithic artifacts on the contact dating to 5300 B.P. Geologist S. el Zaghloul examines outcrops.

intervals (Haynes, 1980). If this was the case then the beach could be much older and possibly of Mousterian-Aterian age, however the pedogenic development is relatively weak and, therefore, incompatible with such an age. To more clearly define the maximum extent of Holocene lakes more mapping and elevational control on shore features is needed.

Did the Nile ever flood the Kiseiba-Dungul depression? is another question that should be asked. In late Holocene time it would have had to rise at least 60 meters to top the present hill, a most unlikely event. But bore-hole logs displayed at the construction site revealed at least 25 meters of what are probably Quaternary age sediments in the subsurface of the Tushka Valley, and bedrock is below 155 meters.

The engineers of the Khor Tushka project living at Abu Simbel were most cooperative in allowing us to examine the excavation, which had gone to a depth of only 1.5 meters, and to collect samples. Johnson and I extended our stay in Egypt in order to fly back to Abu Simbel and spend two more days collecting soil and radiocarbon samples. Permission was granted by Eng. Ahmed Hassanein, High Dam Authority, for us to return to the Project next year in

FIG. 20.   The mud brick ruins of Qasr el Gyb lie on the ancient Darb el Araba'in caravan route and overlook flats of Holocene playa deposits farmed by irrigation agriculture during Greco-Roman times.

order to continue our investigations. The history of sedimentation in the Tushka arm may be critical to understanding the origin and geochronology of the depressions of the Western Desert.

RETURN TO KHARGA AND THE EGYPTIAN PLATEAU

After leaving Wadi Tushka we followed the Darb el Galaba camel caravan route to Aswan and then proceeded along the Nile to Isna. On February 7 we followed a reasonably good road across the Egyptian Plateau from Armant to Ain Gaga in the Kharga depression. On the way we observed playa deposits and strand lines in small basins on the limestone plateau and collected both plants and radiocarbon samples from these.

The last day in the Kharga area was spent differential leveling to playa sediments at the top of a bedrock hill south of Bulaq. These deposits were first recognized by Beadnell (1909) as being in part lacustrine. We found muds and sands of Greco-Roman age unconformably over playa muds of Neolithic age. From these data at least 30 meters of deflation has occurred since Greco-Roman times.

FIG. 21.   Living plants (*Fagonia arabica L.*), March 3, 1978, on sand sheet 15 kilometers west of Gebel Nabta (right background) apparently germinated in response to a storm that a NOAA satellite photographed over the region December 17, 1977. These are the first living plants we have observed in this area in five years of observation. Egyptian Geological Survey personnel have been working in this area since 1968 and have not observed living plants.

On the return trip to Cairo we inspected quarry exposures of the plateau limestone and observed relict terra rosa soil in solution pipes and cavities (fig. 22). These confirm my earlier suggestion (Haynes, in press) that the plateau surface is an ancient karst partly obliterated by eolian erosion. The relict soil is probably of Plio-Pleistocene age and may correlate with a red paleosol observed on the Gilf Kibir plateau.

Acknowledgments

This research was supported by the National Geographic Society and by the Smithsonian Institution, Office of Fellowships and Grants, with the cooperation of the Geological Survey of Egypt. People who have participated or who, in one way or another, helped include:

FIG. 22. Terra rosa filling solution cavities in a limestone quarry on the Eocene plateau southwest of Asyut.

Robert F. Giegengack	Donald L. Johnson	Rushdi Said
Herbert Haas	Ayed Marif Salimm	Romauld Schild
Nabil Hadidi	Shater Marief Salimm	Paul Walker
Ahmed Hassanein	Peter J. Mehringer, Jr.	Fred Wendorf
Mohammed Hinnawi	Galal Moustafa	Abdu Zedan
Harold Hoogstraal	Adison Richmond	Salah Zedan
Bahay Issawi	Sayed El Zaghloul	

REFERENCES

ALMÁSY, COUNT L. F. DE
    1936. Recentes explorations dans le désert Libyque 1932-1936, 201 pp. Publication Special, Société Royale de Géographie d'Egypte, Cairo.
ATTIA, M. I.
    1954. Ground water in Egypt. Desert Institute, Egypt, Bull. 4, no. 1, pp. 198-213.

BAGNOLD, R. A.
   1931.   Journey in the Libyan desert, 1929-30.   Geographical Journ., vol. 78, pp. 13-39 and 524-535.
   1935.   Libyan sands: Travel in a dead world, 351 pp.   Hodder and Stoughton, London.
   1939.   An expedition to the Gilf Kebir and Uweinat.   Geographical Journ., vol. 93, pp. 291-313.
BALL, JOHN
   1919.   Recent determinations of geographical positions in the Libyan desert. Survey Department Paper 34, Cairo, 15 pp.
   1927.   Problems of the Libyan desert.   Geographical Journ., vol. 70, pp. 21-38, 105-128, and 209-224.
BEADNELL, H. J. L.
   1909.   An Egyptian oasis, 262 pp.   John Murray, London.
   1931.   Zerzura.   Geographical Journ., vol. 77, pp. 245-250.
BUTZER, K. W.
   1971.   Environment and archaeology, 524 pp.   Aldine Press.
CATON-THOMPSON, G.
   1952.   Kharga oasis in prehistory, 213 pp.   Athlone Press, London.
CLAYTON, P. A.
   1936.   The South-Western Desert Survey Expedition.   Bull. Soc. Roy. Géogr. D'Egypte, vol. 19, pp. 245-265.
COMYN, D.
   1911.   Service and sport in the Sudan, pp. 289-316.   John Lane, London.
EMBABI, N. W.
   1972.   The semi-playa deposits of Kharga depression, the Western Desert, Egypt.   Bull. Soc. Géogr. d'Egypte, vol. 41-42, pp. 73-87.
EZZAT, MOHAMED ALY
   1974.   Ground Water Series in the Arab Republic of Egypt. Exploitation of Ground Water in El-Wadi El-Gedid Project Area, Part 1, Regional Hydrogeologic Conditions, 121 pp.   Ministry of Agriculture and Land Reclamation, Cairo.
HAY, R. L.
   1968.   Chert and its sodium-silicate precursors in sodium-carbonate lakes in East Africa.   Contr. Mineral Petrol., vol. 17, pp. 255-274.
HAYNES, C. VANCE
   1980.   Geological evidence of pluvial climates in the El Nabta area, Libyan Desert, Egypt.   Pp. 353-371 *in* "Prehistory of the Eastern Sahara," F. Wendorf and R. Schild, eds.   Academic Press, N.Y.
HAYNES, C. VANCE; MEHRINGER, P. J., JR.; and ZAGHLOUL, S. A.
   1979.   Pluvial lakes of Northwestern Sudan.   Geogr. Journ., vol. 145, pp. 437-445.
HAYNES, C. VANCE; SAID, R.; and EL HENNAWI, M.
   1977.   Quaternary lakes of the Nubian Desert. Paper presented to the Tenth Congress.   INQUA, Birmingham.

HELLSTROM, B.
  1940.   The subterranean water in the Libyan desert.   Särtryck ur Geografiska
          Annaler, nos. 3-4.   Stockholm.
ISSAWI, B.
  1968.   The geology of Kurkur Dungul area.   Geological Survey of Egypt, Pap.
          no. 46, 102 pp.
  1971.   Geology of Darb el Arbain, Western Desert, Egypt.   Annals Geol. Sur-
          vey Egypt., vol. 1, pp. 53-92.
KEMAL EL DINE, HUSSEIN
  1927.   Les depots de jarres du Desert de Libie.   Revue Scientifique, pp. 596-
          598.
  1928.   L'exploration du Desert Libyque.   La Géographie, vol. 50, pp. 171-
          183 and 320-336.
KNETSCH, VAN G.; SHATA, A.; DEGENS, E.; MÜNNICH, K. O.; VOGEL, J. C.;
          and SHAZLY, M. M.
  1962.   Untersuchungen an Gründwassern der Ost-Sahara.   Geol. Rundschau,
          vol. 52, pp. 587-611.
MUNNICH, K. O., and VOGEL, J. C.
  1962.   Untersuchungen an Pluvian Wässern der ost Sahara.   Geol. Rund-
          schau., vol. 52, pp.611-624.
MURRAY, G. W.
  1951.   Water beneath the Egyptian Western Desert.   Geographical Journ.,
          vol. 118, pp. 443-452.
MYERS, O. H.
  1939.   The Sir Robert Mond Expedition of the Egypt Exploration Society.
          Geographical Journ., vol. 93, pp. 287-291.
PEEL, R.
  1939.   The Gilf Kebir.   Geographical Journ., vol. 93, pp. 295-307.
PENDÉREL, H. W. G. J.
  1934.   The Gilf Kebir.   Geographical Journ., vol. 83, pp. 449-456.
SCHILD, R. and WENDORF, FRED
  1975.   New explorations in the Egyptian Sahara.   Pp. 65-112 *in* "Problems in
          Prehistory: North Africa and the Levant," F. Wendorf and A. E. Marks,
          eds.   Southern Methodist University Press.
SHAW, W. B. K.
  1936.   An expedition in the southern Libyan Desert.   Geographical Journ.,
          vol. 87, pp. 193-221.
WENDORF, FRED; CLOSE, A.; SCHILD, R.; SAID, R.; HAYNES, C. V.; GAUTIER, A.;
          and HADIDI, N.
  1977.   Late Pleistocene and Recent climatic changes in the Egyptian Sahara.
          Geographic Journ., vol. 143, pp. 211-234.
WENDORF, FRED; SCHILD, R.; SAID, R.; HAYNES, C. V.; GAUTIER, A.; and
          KOBUSIEWICZ, M.
  1976.   The prehistory of the Egyptian Sahara.   Science, vol. 193, pp. 103-
          114.

                                               C. VANCE HAYNES

Saltpeter Conversion and the Origin of Cave Nitrates

Principal Investigator: Carol A. Hill, Albuquerque, New Mexico.

Grant No. 1358:   For a study of saltpeter conversion and the origin of cave nitrates.

During the War of 1812 cave earth was mined from Mammoth Cave, Kentucky, and converted into saltpeter, a component of gunpowder. The objectives of the present project were to duplicate the conversion process, using both actual and reconstructed saltpeter relics; to investigate how cave nitrates relate to different types of guano (bat, rat, beetle, cricket) and the microorganismal activity on these guanos, and to surface drainage and amount of nitrates in overlying bedrock; and to study the regeneration rates and the mineralogy of cave nitrates. The project thus was interdisciplinary, involving historical, archeological, microbiological, chemical, and geologic aspects. The participating researchers were Carol A. Hill, mineralogist; P. Gary Eller, chemist; Carl B. Fliermans, microbiologist; and the late Peter M. Hauer, saltpeter artifact expert.

The "action history" saltpeter conversion experiment was carried out during the week of June 30-July 7, 1974. It included the construction of a saltpeter hopper, the removal of saltpeter dirt from Mammoth Cave, the leaching of the saltpeter dirt, and the subsequent crystallization of saltpeter, KNO_3. The studies on the origin of nitrates and microbiological regeneration were begun concurrently with the "action history" experiment.

Replication of Artifacts

We first tried a small-scale replication of a saltpeter vat (using sawn boards and nails) at Lobelia Saltpeter Cave, Pocahontas County, West Virginia, in order to iron out possible construction difficulties.

The first step in making the Mammoth Cave hopper was to construct the framework of the vat. A variety of wood, including yellow locust and birch, was used for this purpose. The corner posts were axed to length and the tops trimmed to pegs with a small broad hatchet and finished with a pocket knife. The peg holes were drilled with an antique wood auger. A wooden mallet was used to pound the framework into place, and then the vat was lined along the sides with slabs of white oak. The bottom drain trough of the hopper was also

FIG. 1.   The finished vat loaded with wheat straw and saltpeter dirt.

constructed of white oak. A log was cut to length with a hand ax, hewed out
with a broad hatchet and foot-adz, and then finished with a chisel and mallet.
The shorter catch trough, which received the "mother liquor" from the drain
trough, was cut of white oak and was hewn with the same tools as before.
When finished, the vat was lined with wheat straw and loaded with saltpeter
dirt (fig. 1). The loaded vat seemed quite stable. The straw, combined with
the wet saltpeter dirt, sealed the sideboards so that there was very little leakage along the sides of the vat. No nails of any kind were needed in the construction of the vat. In keeping with the handmade tools of the original

saltpeter miners, the mother liquor was ladled from the trough to kettle with a gourd.

Saltpeter Conversion

Before the actual full-scale Mammoth Cave saltpeter conversion experiment was begun, both a laboratory run and a field run were tried. The laboratory bench run with a 500-gram sample (2.4 percent nitrate) from Kingston Saltpeter Cave (Bartow County, Georgia) yielded 8 grams of high-purity saltpeter and reconfirmed the practicality of the conversion process. A field run at Lobelia Saltpeter Cave, Pocahontas County, West Virginia, served to identify difficulties inherent in the saltpeter conversion process.

Just preceding the "action history" experiment at Mammoth Cave a number of cave dirt samples were analyzed for percent nitrates and phosphates. It was found that large local variations of nitrate concentration (between 0-2 percent) and phosphate concentration (0-2 percent) occur. A site in Audubon Avenue, Mammoth Cave, was finally chosen for the "action history" test area because (1) the dirt at this site gave a strong nitrate test (0.55 percent nitrate), (2) the site was far away from any visitor contamination, and (3) the site was within an area that was mined in 1812 for saltpeter dirt. Approximately one bushel (103 kilograms) of niter earth was dug with an antique mattock and hewn saltpeter paddles (fig. 2). Period costume (homespun shirts) and authentic lighting (lard-oil lamps) were used during the mining operation. The niter earth was then carried out of the cave in gunny sacks and placed in the leaching vat. The vat was lined with straw to prevent leakage, and water (25 gallons) was allowed to percolate slowly through the niter earth. The leach water, or "mother liquor," was collected in the drain trough and then recycled through the vat for further concentration of nitrates. Concentrated potash lye liquor (5.4 percent potassium), prepared by leaching oak and hickory hardwood ashes, was added to the leach water until further addition produced no further turbidity. This particular step, the only chemical transformation in the whole saltpeter conversion process, serves two functions: the precipitation of undesired calcium and magnesium as insoluble hydroxides, and the addition of potassium ions to give (ultimately) the nonhygroscopic KNO_3. The gelatinous precipitates were removed by straining through cheesecloth, and the liquor was concentrated in an iron apple-butter kettle (approximately $\frac{1}{2}$ meter in diameter). At a volume of about 1 liter, the first product separated as tabular crystals of arcanite (K_2SO_4). At 600 milliliters a thin surface layer of "grease and foam" (which old published accounts mention) was successfully removed by adsorption onto turnip chunks. Concentration to 300 milliliters

FIG. 2. Digging niter dirt in Mammoth Cave with an antique mattock and hewn saltpeter paddles. A lard-oil lamp is being used for lighting. The rocks (shown in the background) were piled against the cave wall by Negro saltpeter miners during the War of 1812.

gave a mixture of arcanite crystals and schoenite ($K_2SO_4 \cdot MgSO_4 \cdot 6H_2O$) crystals. At 100 milliliters additional arcanite and needle crystals of niter (KNO_3) formed. Further concentration yielded almost exclusively niter crystals. Crystalline products were identified by physical and chemical properties, by elemental analysis, and by X-ray diffraction patterns. Quantities obtained were: schoenite (116 grams), arcanite (12 grams), and niter (44 grams). The once-leached niter earth was again leached with 25 gallons of fresh water and the above conversion and evaporation process was repeated. Again, only three crystalline forms were observed; schoenite (22 grams), arcanite (30 grams), and niter (54 grams). The saltpeter was readily refined by fractional crystallization from water to give white needles of approximately 85 percent purity (based on potassium analysis) (see fig. 3). The total quantity of saltpeter obtained (98 grams, or 11 percent recovery of the total nitrate in the niter earth) indicates that the leaching process is very inefficient and certainly does not approach the 2-6 pounds per bushel sometimes claimed in the old literature. The poor yield, however, could reflect our inexperience with the leaching and conversion process.

The sulphate minerals that crystallized undoubtedly derive from dissolution and conversion of soluble sulphate minerals commonly present in Mammoth Cave sediments (primarily gypsum, epsomite, and mirabilite). The solubility curves in figure 4 vividly illustrate the reason the fractional crystallization serves so well to isolate pure saltpeter. The solubility curves of the most common impurities are relatively flat with respect to temperature, whereas the solubility of saltpeter increases markedly with temperature. In contrast to old accounts of the crystallization process, no sea salt (KCl and NaCl) crystals were observed. Once the vat was constructed and the niter earth collected, the saltpeter conversion was easily performed on a small scale (such as was done during the July expedition) by one individual in two days.

Microbial Studies

Before leaching, microbiology fieldwork was done prior to the "action history" experiment in order to determine *Nitrobacter* (both *N. winogradskyi* and *N. agilis*) population densities, nitrate-nitrite levels in soils in different parts of Mammoth Cave, and microbial environmental influences (pH, moisture, and nutrients) on *Nitrobacter's* metabolic activities. The environment for microbial growth in Mammoth Cave is both constant and extreme in that bacteria experience no light (in the nonvisitor areas of the cave), constant temperature, a well-buffered habitat, and low nutrient levels. Respiration,

FIG. 3.   Saltpeter crystals obtained as a result of the "action history" saltpeter conversion experiment.

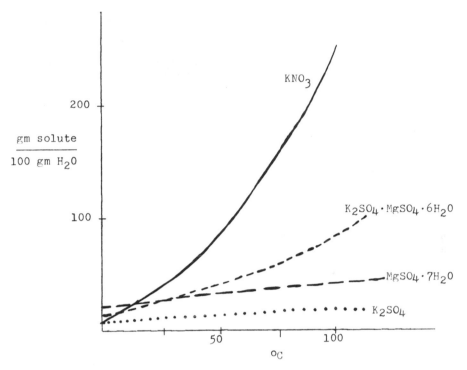

FIG. 4.   Solubility curves for niter (KNO$_3$), schoenite (K$_2$SO$_4$ • MgSO$_4$ • 6H$_2$O),
epsomite (MgSO$_4$ • 7H$_2$O), and arcanite (K$_2$SO$_4$).

biomass, and culture studies were performed during and after leaching, and
washout rates and reestablishment populations of *Nitrobacter* were measured.

MATERIALS AND METHODS

All culturing maintenance techniques were those described in Fliermans
et al., 1974. New isolates were obtained from cave sediment through a series
of enrichments, and final isolates were picked from streak plates. We routinely and rigorously checked all cultures using five different media for purity.
Since *Nitrobacter* is a strict chemoautotroph and unable to grow on organic
compounds, a variety of organic media were employed. The absence of *Nitrobacter* growth in these five media was confirmation of cultural purity.

Over 280 sediment samples were aseptically taken with either an alcohol
flamed spatula or soil corer and immediately placed in sterile Whirl Pak bags
(NASCO) and returned to the laboratory for processing.

Each sediment sample was measured for pH, percent moisture, and nitrite and nitrate levels. Moisture determinations were made by placing cave

sediments into tared metal containers, which were sealed after collection. The sediment was then dried at 110° C. for 24 hours, cooled, and stored in a desiccator for temperature equilibration and weighed. The percent moisture was then calculated gravimetrically. Sediment pH values were obtained by preparing a 1:1 w/v slurry with distilled water, stirred until the slurry became homogeneous, and the pH was measured with an Orion pH meter with a combination electrode.

Qualitative spot tests for nitrate and/or nitrite were taken extensively throughout the cave with diphonolamine in concentrated sulphuric acid. We extracted sediment samples with distilled water, filtered using a swinnex and a 0.45μ Millipore filter. Several drops of the filtrate were placed in white porcelain plates and equal amounts of reagent added. A complex between the diphenolamine and the nitrate or nitrite results in a deep blue color. This simple spot test enables one to take samples for more detailed studies from areas either high or low in nitrates.

Nitrites and nitrates were measured colorimetrically by the procedure of Shinn (1941). Sediments were extracted by placing 50 grams of sediment in a large-mouth bottle with 250 milliliters of distilled water and 0.5 grams of $CaSO_4$ added. The sample was shaken on a mechanical shaker for 10 minutes and the suspension allowed to settle. The supernatant was decanted and filtered through a Whatman No. 42 filter until clear and nitrite levels determined. Nitrate analyses were performed by passing the extracted liquid through a cadmium reduction column. Nitrate was reduced to nitrite at the 93-97 percent efficiency level and the nitrate concentration was calculated by difference.

Densities of *Nitrobacter* populations were accessed by means of species specific fluorescent antibodies. Sediment samples were diluted 1:10 on a weight/volume basis with distilled water and placed in a Waring blender. The suspension was homogeneously mixed for 2 minutes and flocculent (2 parts $Ca(OH)_2$:5 parts $MgCO_3$) 1.5 g/10g sediment was added. The suspension was allowed to settle and an aliquot of the supernatant containing the extracted bacteria was pulled onto black Millipore filters (Millipore HABGO 2500). The filters were treated with a gelatin-rhdamine conjugate and the specific fluorescent antibody was applied. Samples were viewed by vertical illumination fluorescence microscopy.

LOCATION OF SAMPLING SITES

Samples were collected in areas where public influence was deemed negligible, or when collected in visited areas samples were taken from ceilings, walls, and crevasses. Sampling was concentrated in the Rotunda and Booth's

Amphitheater areas since archeological evidence indicates that extensive salt-peter mining took place there.

Before-Leaching Experiments

Nitrite levels were generally less than 0.2 ppm NO_2^- but did occur as high as 19.5 ppm. On the other hand, nitrate levels were high, ranging from 1 to 660 ppm NO_3^- with a mean 223 ppm. Samples of water coming into the cave were always low in NO_3^-, having less than 5 ppm, while soil samples above the cave were generally less than 50 ppm. Such levels above the cave are consistent with nitrate levels found in agricultural soils where nitrification is an active process.

Values for pH ranged from 5.95 to 8.99 with a mean of 7.94. This is as expected since the cave is formed in a limestone region where the buffering capacity would be high.

Moisture content of the sampled sediments was rather dry except for samples taken where water is actively moving into the cave, such as at Side Saddle Pit and Richardson's Spring. Sediment moisture levels ranged from 1.1 to 28.6 percent with a mean of 8.2 percent. The highest moisture levels occurred in the deepest part of the cave nearest the ground water, while lower moisture levels were observed in the upper regions.

Bacterial respiration produces CO_2, which can be measured and used as an index of bacterial activity. In Mammoth Cave sediments bacterial respiration is very low but is stimulated nearly 300 percent by the addition of water. The addition of nutrients, i.e., glucose, acetate, or a series of amino acids, does not increase the rate of respiration appreciably over that of water. Thus, it appears that the limiting factor for the bacterial population in the sediments is water rather than nutrients.

Population densities of *Nitrobacter* as measured by specific fluorescent antibodies were quite high—6 x 10^5/gram of cave sediment. Soil samples taken above Mammoth Cave had less than 10^3 *Nitrobacter*/gram of soil. Such *Nitrobacter* populations above the cave are characteristic of those found in agricultural soils. Since the prepared fluorescent antibodies were species specific, the distribution of *Nitrobacter agilis* and *N. winogradskyi* could be determined. Of the total *Nitrobacter* population sampled in Mammoth Cave, over 85 percent of the *Nitrobacter* is *N. agilis.* Pure cultures obtained from agricultural soils demonstrate that *N. winogradskyi* is the only species isolated. If the two species of *Nitrobacter* are grown together, i.e., a mixed culture situation, *N. winogradskyi* quickly becomes dominant and outcompetes *N. agilis.* Thus there appears to be some unusual characteristic of the Mammoth Cave environment that allows *N. agilis* to dominate.

TABLE 1. Presence of *Nitrobacter* in Eastern Saltpeter Caves

Cave	Location	Nitrobacter
Dan Boone Hut Cave	Bath County, Kentucky	-
Breathing Cave	Bath County, Virginia	+
Minor Saltpeter Cave	Lee County, Virginia	+
Perry Saltpeter Cave	Botetourt County, Virginia	+
Lawson Saltpeter Cave	Scott County, Virginia	+
Big Boone Cave	Van Buren County, Tennessee	+
Petre Cave	Polaski County, Kentucky	+
Crawford Cave	Randolph County, West Virginia	+
Ellison's Cave	Walker County, Georgia	+
Faust Saltpeter Cave	Wise County, Virginia	+
John Rogers Cave	Jackson County, Kentucky	+
Wind Cave	Wayne County, Kentucky	+
John Friends Saltpeter Cave	Garrett County, Maryland	+
Me Bane Saltpeter Cave	Pulaski County, Virginia	+
Saltpeter Cave	Buffalo River State Park, Arkansas	+
Greenville Saltpeter Cave	Logan County, West Virginia	+
Madison Cave	Madison County, Virginia	-
Cave Mountain Cave	Grant County, West Virginia	+
Henshaw's Cave	Warren County, Tennessee	+
Carter Caves	Carter County, Kentucky	+
Dyers' Cave	Hardy County, West Virginia	+
Saltpeter Cave	Mineral County, West Virginia	+
Lobelia Saltpeter Cave	Greenbrier County, West Virginia	+

No strong correlation exists between the population densities of *Nitrobacter* and the parameters of moisture and amount of nitrate/gram of sediment. Population densities were especially low in the Side Saddle Pit and Richardson's Spring areas. This correlates with the observations of Faust (1968): In areas where vadose water is active nitrate concentrations are low.

DURING-LEACHING EXPERIMENTS

Sediment samples of 1 gram each were homogeneously mixed and textural analysis made hydrometrically. The pooled sample contained 64 percent sand, 19.8 percent silt, and 16.2 percent clay, which classifies the sample as a sandy loam. The sediment was then leached with distilled water and the eluent collected and monitored for nitrates, *Nitrobacter*, and total bacterial numbers. The flow rate through the sediment was 1 ml/min. Total bacterial populations before leaching were 7.2×10^6/gram of sediment, while after 400 milliliters had been leached through the column the population had decreased by 50 percent. On the other hand, *Nitrobacter* populations were 4.8 x 10^4/gram of sediment and increased or showed no significant change to 5.2 x 10^4/gram. Thus it appears that leaching of the sediments seems to selectively remove the nonnitrifying population, yet have very little effect on the *Nitrobacter* themselves. Nitrification was measured qualitatively both before and after the leaching experiments. Prior to leaching only 10 percent of the NO_2^- added was converted, whereas 24 hours after leaching the excess NO_3^- from the system, 98 percent of the added NO_2^- was converted to NO_3^-. Within 48 hours the conversion was 100 percent, and the total *Nitrobacter* population had increased to 3.6 x 10^6. This study has relevance to the regeneration of nitrates phenomenon where sediment was replaced in the cave and mined again in 3 to 5 years. Such recovery was probably due to the stimulation of nitrate production by (1) removal of excess and inhibiting NO_3 , (2) the addition of water to a system whose biological activity was water limited, and (3) the selective retention of the nitrifying population within the soil while other organisms such as *Bacillus* sp. were removed from the system.

AFTER-LEACHING EXPERIMENTS

After leaching the dirt was put back into Mammoth Cave at the test site in Audubon Avenue and control dialysis bags were set up at the site. Unfortunately, the cellulose dialysis bags were partially destroyed either by cave rats or by cellulose decomposing bacteria. Nondegradable chambers have since been made and will be used in future experiments.

NITROBACTER IN OTHER SOUTHEASTERN CAVES

In order to determine if the presence of *Nitrobacter* in Mammoth Cave was a widespread phenomenon in other saltpeter caves, grab samples were taken from 24 different saltpeter caves in the Southeastern United States. All but two of the caves had *Nitrobacter* present in their sediments as measured by immunofluorescence.

Microscopic Detection of Bat-derived Excreta

Cave dirt samples from the Rotunda, Wright's Rotunda, side passage of Wright's Rotunda, and Audubon Avenue, Mammoth Cave, were examined to determine the possible presence of insect exoskeletal remains characteristic of the guano of insectivorous bats. Each sample was examined under low magnification to find intact or partly decomposed guano pellets of insectivorous bats. The samples were then examined under magnification of up to 250 pow-

FIG. 5.   An original 1812 Mammoth Cave boiling kettle. Notice the beveled sides. This was the middle of three kettles used at Mammoth Cave during the War of 1812. The owner of the kettle, Walter Davis, is shown in the picture.

er, and subsamples of each were sent to the Royal Ontario Museum for scanning, electron microscope examination, and comparison with reference insectivorous-bat guano samples. A sample of guano from New Cave, Carlsbad Caverns National Park, was prepared and examined in a way similar to that for the cave dirt samples from Mammoth Cave and was used for comparison with them.

Gross microscopic examination of the samples of cave dirt revealed intact insectivorous-bat guano pellets and isolated pieces of insect exoskeleton in the Mammoth Cave samples labeled Wright's Rotunda and Audubon Avenue. The condition of these guano pellets and exoskeleton fragments suggested they were of recent origin and had not been exposed to moisture. The isolated exoskeletal pieces were very similar to pieces in intact guano pellets and were probably derived from mechanical fragmentation of guano pellets. The guano pellets and isolated exoskeletal pieces accounted for less than 0.5 percent of the mass of the samples. Examination of the samples under higher magnification, including the scanning electron microscope, revealed the remainder of the samples contained no fragments that could be identified as insect exoskeletal remains. However, other particles present in all the cave dirt samples in Mammoth Cave were nearly identical to particles that make up the guano deposit in New Cave, Carlsbad Caverns National Park. The guano deposit in New Cave is several thousand years old and has been buried beneath a flowstone cap. It has lost all resemblance to fresh insectivorous-bat guano and, perhaps because it has been exposed to moisture, resembles red soil.

The composition of the particles in the soils of Mammoth Cave and New Cave was not chemically checked. The similarity in structure of these particles in the two caves suggests that particles found in the cave dirt samples probably are derived from insectivorous-bat guano. Since insect exoskeleton, and thus the bulk of insectivorous bat guano, is composed of chitin (a nitrogen-containing polysaccharide), this would be a source of nitrogen in the cave dirt for nitrogen-using bacteria. The 0.5 percent intact guano pellets are of insignificant quantity to realistically be the source of nitrogen for the large *Nitrobacter* populations in Mammoth Cave. They probably represent isolated pellets derived from scattered, small, present-day bat populations in Mammoth Cave. Future chemical analysis will determine if the majority of other particles in the dirt samples are composed of a nitrogen containing polysaccharide-like chitin.

History and Archeology

The following important historical and archeological discoveries were made by the saltpeter research team:

(1) An authentic 1812 Mammoth Cave boiling kettle (weighing some 900 pounds) was found in a cornfield near Brownsville, Kentucky (fig. 5). This kettle is beveled on two sides and was especially cast for the Mammoth Cave boiling chimneys. Two other end kettles (each beveled on only one side) sat up against this middle kettle inside one of the two chimneys just outside the entrance of Mammoth Cave.

(2) Previously undocumented remains of saltpeter vats were identified in two other caves within Mammoth Cave National Park. Other saltpeter artifacts such as saltpeter paddles and poles were also found in these caves.

(3) The foundations of the two original boiler chimneys were located at the entrance to Mammoth Cave.

(4) Cartographic surveys and "old timer" descriptions of the condition of the pumps in the early 1900's indicate that the "mother liquor" was probably

pumped out of Mammoth Cave in the war years (1812-1814) with the help of Negro slave labor rather than by a gravity-flow system as has heretofore been thought.

Photography

All stages of the "action history" experiment were photographically recorded by Pete Lindsley, cave photographer. An excellent file of color photographs now exists that documents all facets of the "action history" experiment, associated chemical and microbiological experiments, saltpeter artifacts, boiling kettles, local historical personalities, and subjects of geographical interest in the Mammoth Cave area.

Conclusions

A handmade saltpeter vat was a practical reservoir in which wood ashes and niter earth were leached for lye and saltpeter. It is probable that this type of "V" vat was used extensively by homesteaders for making soap and gunpowder during the 1700's and early 1800's in the United States.

The practicality of the saltpeter conversion process was demonstrated for the first time in over 100 years. The "lost art" of making saltpeter is now known in scientific detail, the exact chemical steps and mineral precipitates being determined by the "action history" experiment.

Nitrate levels are high in Mammoth Cave soils (223 ppm average) and are much higher than nitrate levels in the surface soils above Mammoth Cave (on the average less than 50 ppm). *Nitrobacter* population densities in the soils of Mammoth Cave are high (6 x 10^5/g of cave sediment) whereas in the above surface soils there is only about 10^3 *Nitrobacter*/g of soil. The predominant species of *Nitrobacter* in Mammoth Cave is *N. agilis* and not *N. winogradskyi*, which is always the *Nitrobacter* species of surface agricultural soils. Moisture levels of Mammoth Cave sediments are low and bacterial respiration is very low as measured by CO_2 levels. Leaching of the cave soil removes the nonnitrifying bacterial populations, yet it has little effect on *Nitrobacter* populations. Regeneration of nitrates (mentioned by old reports to have taken place within 3-5 years after leaching) is probably stimulated by (a) removal of excess and inhibitory NO_3^-, (b) addition of water to a moisture limited bacterial population, and (c) selective removal of competing bacteria during the leaching process.

Insect exoskeletal chitin fragments and bat-guano pellets were not present in significant quantities in Mammoth Cave soils. The soil samples were instead characterized by particles that are probably altered remains of once whole insectivorous bat-guano pellets.

Important historical and archeological artifacts were discovered during the course of the expedition.

Results of geological and mineralogical investigations as to the origin of saltpeter can be found in the three articles by Hill (1981a, b, c) listed in the References, below.

REFERENCES

FAUST, BURTON
    1968.   Notes on the subterranean accumulation of saltpeter.   Journ. Spelean Hist., vol. 1, no. 1, pp. 3-9.
FLIERMANS, CARL B.; BOHLOOL, B. B.; and SCHMIDT, EDWIN L.
    1974.   Autecological study of the chemoautotroph *Nitrobacter* by immunofluorescence.   Appl. Microbiol., vol. 27, pp. 124-129.
HILL, CAROL A.
    1981a.   Mineralogy of cave nitrates.   Nat. Speleol. Soc. Bull., vol. 43, no. 4, pp. 127-132.
    1981b.   Origin of cave saltpeter.   Nat. Speleol. Soc. Bull., vol. 43, no. 4, pp. 110-126.
    1981c.   Origin of cave saltpeter.   Journ. Geol., vol. 89, pp. 252-259.
HILL, CAROL A.; ELLER, P. GARY; FLIERMANS, CARL B.; and HAUER, PETER M.
    1974.   Saltpeter conversion and the origin of nitrates in caves.   Cave Res. Foundation Ann. Rpt. 1974, pp. 34-38. Yellow Springs, Ohio.
SHINN, M. B.
    1941.   Test for nitrate nitrogen.   Ind. and Anal. Chem., Analytical Edition, vol. 13, pp. 33-35.

CAROL A. HILL
P. GARY ELLER
CARL B. FLIERMANS
PETER M. HAUER

Pollinating Bats and Plant Communities

Principal Investigator: Donna J. Howell, Purdue University, West Lafayette, Indiana.

Grant No. 1373:   For a study of the effects of pollinating bats on plant communities.[1]

Ecology texts, while dwelling on competition and predator-prey dynamics, dismiss mutualism as a fascinating biological topic but one whose "importance in populations in general is small" (Williamson, 1972). However, evidence is growing that such interactions might generate and maintain certain aspects of community structure. For example, pollinators may strongly influence the diversity and composition of plant communities. Investigations of symbioses have important points of interest: (1) Confrontation between the natural history of mutualistic systems and current theoretical ideas about their dynamics is likely to improve modeling and suggest which field data are important. (2) Major hardwoods and other economically important plants are animal pollinated, and so results of these investigations may be useful in management. Future control of such resources requires knowledge of pollinator and plant behavior and the components necessary for stability.

Owing to the stigma attached to animals that work the night shift, live in the netherworld, and star in horror films, as much as to the impracticability or lack of creativity associated with the study of nocturnal organisms, bats have received less than their share of biological attention. This is especially true in view of the fact that they are the second most common order of mammals and likely the most diversified.

---

[1] Grateful acknowledgment is made to the following, who contributed to this study: Herbert G. Baker, University of California, Berkeley, for constructive criticism; Andrew Baird, Princeton University, Stephen Humphrey, Florida State Museum, and Tim McCarthy, Peace Corps Belize, who helped with photography and fieldwork; Morris Levy, Mike Overmeyer, and John Bednarczyk, Purdue University, who assisted in gathering allelochemical information or helped with the flock model; the Auditory Research Laboratories, Princeton University, and the Department of Physiology, Indiana University, for providing equipment and space. The Mexican and Guatemalan governments were most gracious; special thanks go to Dr. Luis Lujan, Instituto de Antropología. The diurnal staff of the American Museum of Natural History Field Station, Portal, Arizona, offered help, hospitality, and tolerance of nocturnal organisms of several sorts.

Morphological aspects of the bat-plant association have been elucidated by Van der Pijl (1936), Vogel (1969), Meeuse (1961), Baker (1961), and others. My previous work (see *References* under Howell) has shown physiological and further morphological co-adaptation between "nectar-feeding" bats and chiropterophilous plants. Bat-adapted flowers produce copious pollen with a full complement of essential amino acids and an abundance of 2 amino acids of special importance to bats. Bat-plant pollens are twice as high in protein as congeneric pollen dispersed by wind or insects. Some of the pollen is, of course, transferred to subsequent flowers but much is ingested by the bats as their only reliable nitrogen source. The bats have modified hairs that gather pollen efficiently and special digestive mechanisms for extracting nutritious cellular contents from within the resistant exine.

This report describes a pilot study of interactions between pollinating bats and host-plant populations. The aims of the study were: (1) to describe aspects of the sociality of bats and plants that might be co-evolved; (2) to determine ways that sympatric chiropterophilous plant species blooming in the same season might maximize appropriate pollination and minimize competition for pollinators; and (3) to investigate those buffers against perturbations in mutualistic interactions that might provide the steady state conditions necessary to maintain equilibrium.

Bat Spacing

The nectar-feeding bat studied most extensively was *Leptonycteris sanborni*. These beasts are in many senses mammalian hummingbirds. Their small size and accompanying high metabolism create energy demands of particular interest to investigators and of long-range importance to their host plants. It seemed possible that their foraging could be similar to that of hummingbirds as well; they might defend plants against conspecifics. One nagging question accompanies this view, however. What would motivate a territorial bat to move between plants and accomplish the required pollen transfer for these plants that are primarily outcrossers? Bat plants often have many flowers with copious nectar, more than enough to fill an individual bat's energy demand.

By use of chemoluminescent bulbs (American Cyanamid) and Reflexite (Rowland Corporation) attached to the bats, we discovered that they forage in flocks when working many species of plants. We looked diligently for the social structure of these flocks but found none. Reflective tape colors allowed individual recognition in our field-tagged bats and in groups later brought into a large enclosure. All bats within a group ingested similar amounts of nectar with no significant variation due to sex, age, or original weight. Bats circled

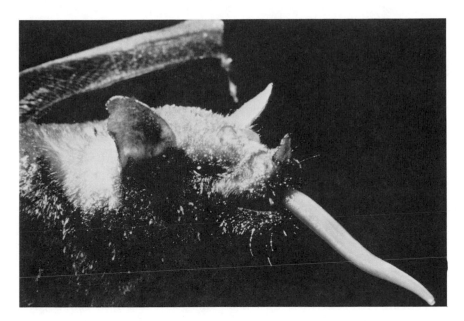

FIG. 1. *Leptonycteris sanborni* extending tongue. (Photo courtesy of Oxford Scientific Films.)

plants in orderly formation at about 16 KPH, (kilometers per hour) individually taking turns (x = 0.3 second) at inflorescences.

After a feeding bout in which each bat ingests about 4 grams of nectar, all bats stop feeding and within 30 seconds have moved as a group to a nearby tree or rock surface to roost. They hang in a tight cluster and groom pollen from their own fur and that of cluster mates. The ingestion of pollen is important, but this extensive allogrooming may have a conciliatory function in the cluster as well. These intermittent roosting periods seem to be the solution to the bats' problem of having expensive engines but small fuel tanks. Four grams of nectar is a full load, but since "bat-nectars" range from 11-20 percent sugar, the energy is in diluted form. During roosting bouts, the bats absorb and excrete the watery portion of their diet. After 20-30 minutes roosting, bats become restless and engage in much wing-stretching and grooming. At this time a peculiar behavior is seen: bats extend their tongues up to 50 millimeters and hold them extended for a second or more (fig. 1). This may be "limbering up" or it may be related in some way to olfactory testing in view of the well-developed vomeronasal organ in nectar bats.

As soon as one bat flies out from the cluster, all follow. The stimulus promoting flock cohesion is problematic. Tunable ultrasonic detectors tied to the plants indicate no acoustic communication during feeding or in switching from one plant to another. In fact, only the first bat to reach a plant echolocates at all, and then only weakly. Followers are silent. It may be that vision and/or olfaction is the chief modality in flock maintenance and both are likely important in locating plants as well.

The success of coevolved systems depends in part on an energetic balance between symbionts. The quantity and distribution of rewards a plant offers interact with the pollinator's energetics to determine foraging techniques.

The standard metabolism of *Leptonycteris* is 1.6 ml O_2 gm^{-1}hr^{-1} or 0.14 kcal/bat hr (Carpenter and Graham, 1967). I used Thomas's (1975) formula for power, $P=58.4m^{-0.21}$, to predict flight metabolism. Minimal power for flying *Leptonycteris* is 2.34 watts or 2.01 kcal/bat hr. At a flight velocity of 16 KPH, cost of transport is 7.39 kcal kgm^{-1}km^{-1} or 0.13 kcal/bat km. Therefore flight metabolism is at least 14 times standard metabolism. The daily time-energy budget for nonreproductive months is estimated as follows: 3 hours flying (x 2.01 kcal/bat hr), 7 hours engaged in miscellaneous activities such as grooming, looking around, etc., at an estimated 1.7 x SMR (standard metabolism rate) (7 x 0.24), 14 hours at resting metabolism (14 x 0.14) = 9.67 kcal for a 24-hour period. The high cost of flying is seen in the fact that *Leptonycteris* expends 63 percent of its energy output in 13 percent of its time. Intuitively it would seem such an organism would seek to save energy in any possible way. In order for a bat just to break even (no energy stored, no reproduction) it must ingest at least 9.67 kcal each day.

During the work supported by this grant we had no way of assessing flock numbers. As tagging each bat required several minutes and the lifespan of the luminescent compound is limited, only 12-25 bats were tagged each night. Understanding more of the behavior and energetics of the bats, we have now devised a simple model of maximum flock size. The foraging efficiency of any one bat depends not only on his own physiological demands and on characteristics of the plants, it is also a function of how many bats are in the flock. An individual in a feeding group does not get a turn each time he circles the plant; another bat may be feeding when the first bat is in position for a turn. The more bats in the flock, the more times a given bat will have to circle before conditions allow it to feed. At some point the calories expended in circling will exceed the calories gained from nectar during a turn. If natural selection moves to optimize animal energy budgets, bats should not find themselves in such a situation.

A simplified model of the factors which may interact to influence energy budget and hence flock size has been established (Howell, 1979). Inserting field data for the bat/*Agave* association in the Chiricahuas we arrived at a maximum flock size of 123 bats. This will be tested, but we expect smaller numbers since available habitat (caves or mines), plant distribution and abundance, etc., will also work to limit the maximum flock size. Such general calculations should, however, be useful for comparative analysis of data from other geographic areas. For instance, when the bats work a plant species with richer nectar or one that affords better extraction, flock size may expand.

But why feed in flocks if immediate foraging efficiency may be reduced by the presence of other bats? If feeding were an individual undertaking, a bat could "get a turn" whenever it wanted, rather than having to circle in formation. A variety of views on flocking is put forth in the ethological and ecological literature. In the current study the most robust advantage to flocking is increasing the long-term efficiency of searching for and harvesting food resources. Many chiropterophilous plants are spatially and temporally patchy and such resources are more readily located by groups, which move as though they had momentum over a straighter search path than would individuals. The broad search front is comprised of many sensory monitors; by remaining aware of each other's behavior, all members of the flock benefit. Such considerations may apply to the frugivorous flocking bats (Heithaus et al., 1975) as well as to nectar-bats.

We allowed a dozen tagged bats to find one plant that we had loaded to the brim with natural nectar. We recaptured the flock and released them again with 10 inexperienced bats. The entire flock moved without hesitation to the loaded inflorescence. When a plant becomes depleted of nectar, one bat in the flock makes the decision to move on to the next plant; all the flock members follow it without bothering to circle and confirm the decision. Depending on flower characteristics and plant spacing, such imitation can save individual bats 30-50 calories each time it is performed. Field tagging showed that bats seldom revisit plants visited earlier in the evening.

Not only is search more efficiently performed by groups, harvesting is as well. A swath of plants is worked so thoroughly by a group that a clear distinction is created between used and nonused flowers, thus maximizing nectar-intake on the return trip to the roost. These considerations wherein the flock enhances the local predictability of the food resources depend on flock cohesiveness. By knowing where your friends are, you can be assured that the next larder hasn't been raided.

A second advantage of social foraging is that it allows social roosting between feeding bouts. Most intermittent roosts are on trees or rock faces; the cool nights may be below 15°C. The insulating effect of bats on one another decreases the energy required for active thermoregulation in these homeothermic animals. This allows more energy allotment for rapid and efficient digestion. At 10°C., clustered bats assimilated nectar sugars with an efficiency of 98.5 percent; only 0.36 percent sucrose remained in the excreta. Single bats' efficiency was only 91.75 percent, with 1.38 percent sucrose in the excreta. These differences were highly significant at the $p < 0.001$ level. At 20°C. the differences were somewhat less, but clustered bats were still more efficient at the $p < 0.05$ level. The average weight of excreta from clustered bats after 1/2 hour was 0.51 gm/bat, for singles 0.25 gm/bat. These data indicate that absorption and/or urine formation proceeds at a higher rate in grouped bats.

Plant Spacing

Such a social foraging system as seen in *Leptonycteris* would be likely to persist only if the resource(s) "cooperate(s)" by being clumped, and plentiful enough within clumps to serve all the flock members. Looking at the bats' sociality and energetics helped us form ideas on how the host plants might be distributed. Plants using bats as pollinators enjoy the benefits of highly mobile, homeothermic, fairly constant or predictable gamete carriers. But the expensive tastes of the pollinator could affect plant spacing (see Levin and Kerster, 1969). In the tropics where phytophagy and interspecific competition is strong, hyperdispersal might be an adaptive strategy (Janzen, 1970), but the adoption of such spacing by plants poses two problems in regard to their pollinators: Plants must be good advertisers to promote localization by pollinators over long distances; so costs of odor and color production, morphological positioning for visibility, etc., rise. Secondly, members of the plant population would have to build very rich nectar to support the flight of the bat to the next plant. We employed infrared photography, aerial photography, and range finders to study plant dispersion. The majority of New World chiropterophilous plants exist in habitats that are poor to medium in species diversity (thorn-woodland, deciduous seasonal or semi-evergreen forests). For instance, sites designated by Holdridge et al. (1971) as "tropical dry" may have 13-18 percent of the vegetation represented by bat-pollinated forms. These are often among the five most important trees. Wetter sites show 6-10 percent chiropterophiles; wet montane areas have very few, 0-2 percent. We find their spacing patterns range from highly clumped with canopies often touching (Hymenaea) to moderately clumped with interplant distances a fraction of a kilometer (*Bombacopsis, Marcgravia, Mucuna, Luehea, Crescentia*). Some bat-pollinated species owe their proximity to riparian situations (*Inga* spp., *Pachira aquatica*) or flood-plain habitats (*Ceiba, Crescentia*). Local preservation by natives of *Crescentia, Ceiba, Parmentiera,* and other chiropterophilous trees has enhanced their distribution in patches as well. Many genera *(Bauhinia, Bombacopsis, Ceiba, Cordia, Calliandra, Eugenia, Inga, Luehea, Mucuna, Ochroma)* are common secondary vegetation or disturbance plants and as such exist in poorer soils where species density is likely to be heightened (Yoda et al., 1963). It is not uncommon to find several bat-pollinated species in association exhibiting similar phenologies, the effect of which is to present a dense clump of potential food to the pollinating bat. In such situations, plants can pool advertising. The manner in which each associated chiropterophile maximizes appropriate pollen transfer between its own individuals is discussed hereinafter.

It is easy to assume now that aspects of the bats' gregariousness and phytosociality are coadapted, but how did such specializations come about?

Discussions of the evolution of coadaption are readily subject to circularity and often rely on a priori existence of one partner in order to derive the other. It is probable that nectar-feeding bats or their fruit- or insect-eating ancestors were social before the existence of chiropterophily and that many proto- or pre-chiropterophilous plants were as well.

Most Chiroptera are gregarious. Their small size imposes stringent and specific physiological needs that are met in limited roosting sites and within group-created microenvironments. Eisenberg (1966) states that low reproductive potential (most bats bear one young annually) could also favor groups as a "convenience for reproductive efficiency." He documents sleeping, nursing, and hibernating associations but indicates that the groups are not cohesive when animals forage. It is probable in this case that group feeding came about as nectar-feeding bats began to exploit clumped and patchy prey. Independent bats would exploit such resources in a more haphazard fashion, reducing the nectar in such a way that a good spot would be increasingly hard to locate. As Cody (1971) states, "flocking is a response to selective pressure to maintain as much of the feeding area as possible untouched or to glean an area very thoroughly."

Now, however, we must find advantages to or reasons for clumping and patchy disperal in many chiropterophilous plants, independent of their pollinators. Some species *(Agave,* columnar cactus) tend to pioneer hot, rocky hillsides and cliffs. Survival of seedlings is promoted by this habit which prevents grazers from gaining access to the general area or from reaching seedlings amid the talus. The predilection for such sites results in fragmented, island-like distributions. Yoda et al. (1963) indicate a tendency for plant species on poorer substrates to have greater seedling survival and hence denser distributions.

TABLE 1.   Families Containing Chiropterophiles and Specific Chiropterophiles with
Known Allelopathic Chemicals

Compounds from listings by [B-S] Bate-Smith (1962), [Cl] Claus et al. (1970), [Y] Youngken (1943), [R] Rice (1974), [P] Pallares (1960, 1961).

Family	Characteristic of family	Compounds	Specific member reported	Reference
Bignoneaceae		Caffeic acid	*Crescentia* spp.	B-S
Bombacaceae		Caffeic acid	*Ceiba pentandra*	B-S
Boraginaceae		Quercitin	*Cordia alliodora*	B-S
		Caffeic acid		
Cactaceae	Alkaloids			P, B-S
Capparidaceae	Mustard oils			B-S
		Ellagic acid	*Cleome* spp.	B-S
		Quercitin		
Convolvulaceae	Caffeic acid			B-S
		Ergot alkaloids	*Ipomoea*	Cl
Legume Complex				
Caesalpinoidea	Tannins			B-S
Papilionatae	Coumarins			
	Rotenoids			B-S
		Quercetin	*Bauhinia*	B-S
		Alkaloids	*Mucuna*	Y
		Isoquinoline Alkaloids	*Erythrina*	
		Rotenone	*Lonchocarpus*	
Mimosoidea	Catechins			B-S
Lythraceae	Alkaloids			Y
Malvaceae		Free amino acids	*Abutilon*	R
		p-Coumaric acid		B-S
Myrtaceae	Volatile oils			Y
		Quercitin	*Eugenia*	B-S
		p-Coumaric acid		
		Ellagic acid	*Eucalyptus*	B-S
		Quercitin		
		Volatile terpines		
		Ellagic acid	*Melaleuca*	B-S
Polemoniaceae		Quercitin	*Cobaea scandens*	B-S
Proteaceae		Quercitin	*Grevillea*	
Solanaceae	Scopoletin			B-S
Sterculaceae	Catechins			
		Quercitin		
		Caffeic acid	*Dombeya*	B-S
		Caffeic acid	*Theobroma*	B-S

FIG. 2.   A bat-flower *(Mucuna urens)* with explosive pollen delivery to posterior region of bat.

Concentration of toxic substances leading to decreased intraspecies competition would be another potential advantage to aggregation. Such effect has been demonstrated for a number of herbaceous and woody species by authors cited in Rice (1974).

Some bat-pollinated species or their families have characteristic compounds which, although they have not been demonstrated to inhibit other plants, offer protection against insects which might eat various plant parts. The agaves, for instance, have steroidal sapogenins (Claus et al., 1970). These insecticidal chemicals may free their bearers from the high phytophagy that often accompanies monocropping. Table 1 is a partial list of chiropterophiles containing phenolics, alkaloids, and other compounds that are cited by various authors as allelopathic.

Once incipient pollinators evolve sociality, however loose, and once potential host plants are patchily distributed and clumped, however loosely, cooperative ventures can reinforce and tighten gregariousness on both parts. The

FIG. 3.   A bat-flower *(Crescentia alata)* with pollen delivery to middorsum of bat.

advantage of cohesiveness for the bats has been the major thrust of this paper. The following examples show how tighter grouping is beneficial to the plants. Outlying individual plants would tend to be ignored by pollinators; it would be to the bats' energetic advantage to visit adjacent plants; hence clumping is promoted. Likewise, with a generalist pollinator, it is of evolutionary concern to the plant to minimize pollen transfer to other species. Monocropping should accomplish this. Levin and Anderson (1970) discuss the beneficial effect of patchiness in retarding the decline of a minority species in an area with a plurality of simultaneously blooming plants utilizing the same pollinator. They say that "larger patches of regular shape are most effective in reducing the competitive differential," and Levin and Kerster (1969) write, "plants serve as pollen and gene traps"; as such, the more trees per area the shorter the mean dispersal distance. Group distribution can pool the plants' olfactory and visual advertising. Levin and Kerster discuss the evolutionary flexibility of plants with "high density display" and explain that high density affords great-

FIG. 4.   A bat-flower *(Inga marginata)* with pollen delivery to head and shoulders of bat.

er ability to respond to and exploit local environmental heterogeneity and fluctuation. This should give competitive superiority to clumped plants, *all other things being equal*.

Maximizing Appropriate Pollen Transfer and Minimizing Competition for Pollinators

In the dry months of January through March there is especial profusion of chiropterophiles in flower (see Frankie et al., 1974; Fleming et al., 1972). These authors list only trees and shrubs; if bat-pollinated vines such as *Marcgravia, Mucuna, Couepia, Cobaea, Eperua,* etc., or epiphytes such as *Pitcairnea* or *Vriesia* were added, the number of coblooming species would increase.

It appears, superficially at least, that these flowering species compete for the services of pollinating bats. Good seed set would depend not only on the number of visits a plant received but also on the number of those visits that

TABLE 2.   Chiropterophilous Plants Suspected of Being Hypodispersed

Locality	x̄ Spacing	Range
Santa Rosa, Costa Rica		
Pseudobombax quinata	0.5 km	0.05-2 km
Inga sp.	0.5 km	0.1-3 km
Luehea speciosa	0.3 km	3 m-1.3 km
Columnar cactus	0.3 km	1 m-1.2 km
Bombacopsis quinata	0.7 km	0.5-2 km
*Hymenaea courbaril	0.1 km	1 m-0.2 km
*Crescentia alata	15 m	5 m-0.02 km
Cerro del Muerte, Costa Rica		
Pitcairnea	0.1 km	0.1 m-0.2 km
Monte Verde, Costa Rica		
*Mucuna urens	3 m	0.3 m-0.1 km
Marcgravia		
Tikal, Guatemala	0.1 km	0.1 m-0.1 km
Bombax ellipticum	0.08 km	0.03-0.6 km
Bauhinia cf. *jenningsi*	0.5 km	Dense young trees-1 km
Central farm, British Honduras		
*Ipomoea cf. cathartica	0.01 km	1m-1 km
Various localities		
Parmentiera edulis		Groups on river banks or
Pachira aquatica		around *aguadas*
Capparis sp.		

*Obvious clumps-interclump distance not measured.

brought conspecific pollen. It would seem in the plant's best interest that the pollinator be faithful to that species. Previous pollen analysis of bat guts and feces (Alvarez and González Q., 1970; Howell, 1972) show quite the opposite. For instance, in one month in Michoacán, Mexico, *Glossophaga soricina* samples indicated mixed diets of cactus *(Ceiba, Roupala, Calliandra, Agave)* and legumes. Even the more committed nectarivores like *Leptonycteris sanborni* showed *Ipomoea, Bombax, Ceiba,* and *Agave.*

Levin and Anderson (1970) point out that under such apparent pollinator promiscuity, a minority plant species should be at a strong disadvantage since it would receive fewer pollinator visits per night, and of those visits, a higher percentage would bring inappropriate pollen.

Hypothetically, minority species should decline rapidly and oligotypy should prevail. Since the plant communities including bat-plants persist in being polytypic, we can assume they haven't heard of this dilemma. Levin and Anderson (1970) suggest solutions to this problem which would relieve competitive pressures:

FIG. 5. *Leptonycteris* on a flower of *Lemaireocereus thurberi,* the organ-pipe cactus.

A. Patchiness
    (1) clumping as discussed above
    (2) specific differences in microhabitat preference
B. A shift in flowering period or time of nectar and pollen presentation
C. A shift to selfing or apomixis

We investigated the above and suggest an additional escape (body-partitioning) as discussed below.

A. A preliminary list of chiropterophiles that appear to be less widely scattered than most tropical species appears in table 2. The starred plants are those obviously existing in clumps, in closely spaced orchardlike distributions *(Crescentia),* or in linear groups due to riparian or roadside (pathside) habitat preferences. Heithaus et al. (1975) mention several of these as clumped also. *Pachira aquatica, Parmentiera edulis,* and *Inga* sp. often cluster along river banks or around aguadas as do some *Capparis* species (cf. *lundelli, tuerckheimii).*

One of the advantages the plants may gain from this close spacing are spatial separation from competitors and increased chance of visiting pollinators bearing conspecific pollen.

Still we are left with a number of cobloomers within the same site without the above mechanisms. For instance, in Holdridge site 1A in the chiroptero-

TABLE 3.   Plants Exhibiting Autogamy with Some Seed Set or Other Apomixis

Mechanism unknown or unstated	Anther-stigma contact	Adjacent floral contact	Vegetative or vivipary	Reference
			Pachira aquatica	Fryxell, 1957
		Ceiba pentandra		Purseglove, 1968
				Fryxell, 1957
Theobroma cacao				Purseglove, 1968
Cordia sp.				Bawa, in Bowman, 1966
	Cobaea scandens			Knuth, 1902
			Agave*	Fryxell, 1957
Capparis sp.				′′
	Ipomoea sp.			′′
	Marcgravia			′′
Eugenia sp.				′′
Grevillea banksii				′′
Nicotiana rustica				′′
N. tabacum				′′
			Sonneratia	′′
Bauhinia ungulata				Bawa, 1974
Luehea speciosa				′′
Ochroma pyramidale				′′

*Fryxell lists 17 *Euagave* with 13 having autogamous or apomictic potential.

phile-rich tropical dry habitat, *Bauhinia ungulata, Bombocopsis quinata, Ceiba pentandra, Luehea speciosa, Ochroma lagoprus,* and *Pseudobombax septenatum* may be blooming within 3,000 square meters.

B. The possibility of relieving competition by escape in time had been previously overlooked both by bat and plant workers. Our investigations supported by this grant showed that the chance of inappropriate pollination is minimized because nectar and pollen are available at different times on different flower species (Howell, 1977).

Solution C, selfing, will be discussed below, but before leaving the problem of pollinator competition we suggest another potential solution, that plants partition the bat itself. Near Monte Verde, Costa Rica, for example, several popular bat plants appear to do this. The "spring-loaded" anthers of *Mucuna urens* (fig. 2) explosively deposit pollen on the belly or rump of the bat as it leaves the flower, *Crescentia* (fig. 3) daubs pollen on the bat's mid dorsum and bombacaceous species and *Inga* sp. (fig. 4) coat the face and neck. Essentially the plants are using three different, and highly constant pollinators.

All these investigated "escapes" still do not relieve us of the fact that many sites in Costa Rica have five or more bat-plants in apparent readiness (no microtemporal data on nectar flow) at the same time all using "head and shoulder" bats. Much more work is needed before we can say how these species coexist.

"Slop" and Stability

The most dramatic, visible facts of mutualistic interactions are the precise correlations that exist between partners. These coadapted characteristics make neat stories in the short run for scientific publications and for children's books. In broader view, however, questions arise as to the wisdom of partners becoming too dependent on each other.

Intuitively, we see mutualistic systems becoming a shambles if the population of one or the other partners fluctuated. May (1973), reading the symbioses papers in the narrow (but forgivable) way they tend to be written, concluded that such one-to-one relationships would tend to be destabilizing and speculated stability considerations may account for the apparent scarcity of symbiotic relations compared to predator-prey or competitive relations. This same thinking may have led Williamson (1972) to discount mutualism as having little importance in populations in general.

However, if one puts effort into literature search, one can come up with "escape" mechanisms for both partners in most plant-animal symbioses. Pollinators may be generalists in terms of plant species or more totally omnivorous, moving to different foods (fruit, insects) during times of flower scarcity. This is certainly true for the "nectar-feeding" bats (Alvárez and González Q., 1970; Fleming et al., 1972; Howell, 1974a).

For many chiropterophiles, longevity can be considered a safety factor; if pollinators are scarce one season, perennials have many more chances for good seed set in subsequent seasons. Likewise, no bat-plants are visited solely by bats; early-rising bees, hummingbirds, and butterflies scavenge nectar "left-overs" and may be large enough to effect some pollination.

Many bat plants tend to be straggling bloomers with one tree or trees within a habitat in bloom for months; this allows overlap between species with consecutive phenologies. Such is a safety mechanism for the bat and for the plants too, in that long blooming brackets the time when migratory nectar bats might be expected. The bats' relative promiscuity works with the consecutive blooming of a host of plant species to preclude obligatory relationships. *Ipomoea, Crescentia, Inga, Luehea, Eugenia, Parmentiera,* and *Pachira* as well as fruits and insects "take care" of the bats in the wet season (see Baker, Cruden, and Baker, 1971).

Although most bat-adapted flowers are strongly allogamous, many exhibit accessory mechanisms whereby the genetic stock may be maintained if pollinators decline (table 3). Fryxell (1957) warns against assumptions of allogamy based on floral structure: "While structural considerations frequently may be indicative of functional behavior, the only case where one may obtain assurance is in a dioecious species which must be cross-pollinated and even then one must retain a reservation in favor of . . . apomixis." He cites several species with variances in the percent of natural outcrossing and indicates such conditions (selfing or apomixis) might be encountered "where there is a dearth of pollinators or where plants are spaced at such wide intervals that cross-pollination is restricted." The ease with which a plant could effect a shift in pollination systems, e.g., a one-gene mutation effecting anther position, is discussed by Rick (1966).

Having become aware of such "slop" in many mutualistic systems, which may promote their stability, May (1976) has modified his thinking and suggests that mutualism receive the same sort of attention that modelers have given to predator-prey and competition. Rather than agreeing with Williamson on the irrelevance of mutualism to community dynamics, May points out that interactions such as plant/pollinator or plant/disperser are central to the understanding of plant communities. Whittaker (1975) suggests more realistic models to describe mutualistic relations which he feels, too, merit further attention.

It is excusable that past authors have dwelt on the neatness of symbioses, but one hopes future works will tell a more comprehensive story, one that will enable theoreticians to "allow" the existence of mutualism in natural communities.

REFERENCES

ALVÁREZ, T., and GONZÁLEZ Q., L.
    1970.   Análisis polinico del contenido gástrico de murciélago Glossophaginae de México.   Anal. Esc. Nac. Cienc. Biol., vol. 18, pp. 1-77.

BAKER, HERBERT G.
    1961.   The adaptation of flowering plants to nocturnal and crepuscular pollina-
             tors.   Quart. Rev. Biol., vol. 36, pp. 64-73, illus.
BAKER, HERBERT G.; CRUDEN, ROBERT W.; and BAKER, I.
    1971.   Minor parasitism in pollination biology and its community function:
             The case of *Ceiba acuminata*.   Biol. Sci., vol. 21, pp. 1127-1129.
BATE-SMITH, E. C.
    1962.   The phenolic constituents of plants and their taxonomic significance.
             Journ. Linn. Soc. Bot., vol. 58, pp. 95-173.
BAWA, K. S.
    1974.   Breeding systems of tree species in a lowland tropical community.
             Evolution, vol. 28, pp. 85-92.
BOWMAN, ROBERT I.
    1966.   The Galápagos, 318 pp., illus.   University of California Press, Berke-
             ley and Los Angeles.
CARPENTER, ROGER E., and GRAHAM, JEFFREY B.
    1967.   Physiological responses to temperature in the long-nosed bat, *Lepto-
             nycteris sanborni*.   Comp. Biochem. and Physiol., vol. 22, pp. 709-722,
             illus.
CLAUS, E. P.; TYLER, VERRO E.; and BRADY, LYNN R.
    1970.   Pharmacognosy, 518 pp.   Lea & Febiger, Philadelphia.
CODY, M.
    1971.   Finch flocks in the Mohave Desert.   Theoret. Pop. Biol., vol. 2, pp.
             142-158.
EISENBERG, JOHN F.
    1966.   The social organization of mammals.   Handbuch der Zoologie, vol.
             10, pp. 1-92.
FLEMING, THEODORE H.; HOOPER, EMMET T.; and WILSON, D. E.
    1972.   Three Central American bat communities: Structure, reproductive
             cycles and movement patterns.   Evolution, vol. 53, pp. 555-569.
FRANKIE, G. W.; BAKER, HERBERT G.; and OPLER, P. A.
    1974.   Comparative phenological studies of trees in tropical wet and dry forests
             in the low lands of Costa Rica.   Journ. Ecol., vol. 62, pp. 881-919.
FRYXELL, PAUL A.
    1957.   Mode of reproduction in higher plants.   Bot. Rev., vol. 23, pp. 135-
             233.
HEITHAUS, E. E.; FLEMING, THEODORE H.; and OPLER, P. A.
    1975.   Foraging patterns and resource utilization in seven species of bats in a
             seasonal tropical forest. Ecology, vol. 56, pp. 841-859.
HOLDRIDGE, LESLIE R.; GRENKE, W. C.; HATHEWAY, WILLIAM H.; LIANG, T.;
        and TOSI, JOSEPH A., JR.
    1971.   Forest environments in tropical life zones, 747 pp.   Pergamon Press,
             New York.
HOWELL, DONNA J.
    1972.   Physiological adaptations in the syndrome of chiropterophily with em-
             phasis on the bat *Leptonycteris* Lydekker, 217 pp.   Ph.D. dissertation,
             University of Arizona.

HOWELL, DONNA J. (continued)
1974a.   Bats and pollen: Physiological aspects of the syndrome of chirop-
          terophily.   Comp. Biochem. and Physiol., vol. 48, pp. 263-276.
1974b.   Feeding and acoustic behavior in glossophagine bats.   Journ. Mam.n.,
          vol. 55, pp. 263-276.
1976a.   Weight loss and temperature regulation in clustered versus individual
          Glossophaga soricina.   Comp. Biochem. and Physiol., vol. 53, pp. 197-
          199.
1976b.   Bat-loving plants, plant-loving bats.   Nat. Hist., vol. 85, no. 2, pp.
          52-59, illus.
1977.   Time sharing and body partitioning in bat-plant pollination systems.
          Nature, vol. 270, pp. 509-510.
1979.   Flock foraging in nectar-feeding bats: Advantages to the bats and to the
          host plants.   Amer. Nat., vol. 114, pp. 23-29.
JANZEN, DANIEL H.
1970.   Herbivores and the number of tree species in tropical forests.   Amer.
          Nat., vol. 104, pp. 501-528.
KNUTH, P.
1902.   Handbook of flower pollination, 330 pp.   Oxford University Press.
LEVIN, D. A., and ANDERSON, W. W.
1970.   Competition for pollinators between simultaneously flowering species.
          Amer. Nat., vol. 104, pp. 455-467.
LEVIN, D. A., and KERSTER, H. W.
1969.   The dependence of bee-mediated pollen and gene dispersal upon plant
          identity.   Evolution, vol. 23, pp. 550-571.
MAY, ROBERT M.
1973.   Stability and complexity in model ecosystems, 231 pp.   Princeton
          University Press.
1974.   General introduction.   Pp. 1-14 *in* "Ecological Stability," 191 pp.,
          M. B. Usher and M. H. Williamson, eds.   Halsted Press, New York.
1976.   Theoretical ecology, 317 pp.   W. B. Saunders Co., Philadelphia.
MEEUSE, BASTIAAN J. D.
1961.   The story of pollination, 243 pp.   Ronald Press, New York.
POLLARES, E.
1960.   Alcaloides de las cactaceas.   Cactos y Suculentes de México, vol. 5, pp.
          35-43.
1961.   Sugestión para un nuevo agropamiento de las plantas.   Cactos y. Sucu-
          lentes de México, vol. 6, pp. 12-15.
PURSEGLOVE, J. W.
1968.   Tropical crops, 2 vols., 719 pp.   John Wiley & Sons, Philadelphia.
RICE, ELROY L.
1974.   Allelopathy, 353 pp.   Academic Press, New York.
RICK, CHARLES M.
1966.   Some plant-animal relations in the Galápagos Islands.   Pp. 215-232 *in*
          "The Galápagos," R. I. Bowman, ed.   University of California Press,
          Berkeley and Los Angeles.

THOMAS, STEPHEN P.
   1975.   Metabolism during flight in 2 species of bats, *Phyllostomus hastatus* and *Pteropus gouldii*.   Journ. Exp. Biol., vol. 63, pp. 273-293, illus.
VAN DER PIJL, L. VON
   1936.   Fledermaus und Blumen.   Flora, vol. 131, pp. 1-40.
VOGEL, S.
   1969.   Chiropterophile in der neotropischen Flora.   Flora, vol. 158, pp. 289-323.
WHITTAKER, ROBERT H.
   1975.   Communities and ecosystems, ed. 2, 206 pp.   Macmillan Co., New York.
WILLIAMSON, M.
   1972.   The analyses of biological populations, 180 pp. London.
YODA, K.; KIRA, H.; OGAWA, H.; and HOZUMI, K.
   1963.   Self-thinning in overcrowded pure stands under cultivated and natural conditions.   Journ. Biol. Osaka City Univ., vol. 14, pp. 102-129.
YOUNGKEN, H. W.
   1943.   Textbook of pharmacognosy, 743 pp.   Blakiston Co., Philadelphia.

DONNA J. HOWELL

Early Cretaceous Mammals from the Cloverly Formation, Montana

Principal Investigators: Farish A. Jenkins, Jr., and Alfred W. Crompton, Museum of Comparative Zoology and Department of Biology, Harvard University, Cambridge, Massachusetts.

Grant Nos. 1294, 1309, 1472. To collect and study rare Early Cretaceous mammals in south-central Montana.

The Mesozoic history of mammals spans 120 million years from the late Triassic to the latest Cretaceous. However, the fossil record of mammals during this time is poorly known in comparison to that of other Mesozoic vertebrate groups. Major advances in our understanding of the origin and diversification of mammalian lineages, and especially the differentiation of therians and nontherians, are dependent to a large extent on the discovery of new fossil material that documents stages in the long pre-Tertiary history of the class.

The Cloverly mammal project, which was supported by National Geographic Society research grants 1294 and 1309 in 1974 and 1472 in 1975, resulted from the discovery by Arnold D. Lewis (at that time chief preparator at the Museum of Comparative Zoology and currently on the staff of the National Museum of Natural History) of a mammal-bearing site in the Early Cretaceous Cloverly Formation near Bridger, Montana. This find, made in 1973, culminated two years of intensive prospecting in the Cloverly Formation by parties led by Charles R. Schaff (curatorial associate in vertebrate paleontology, Museum of Comparative Zoology). Prior to this time, Prof. John H. Ostrom of the Peabody Museum of Natural History at Yale University had undertaken a major stratigraphical and paleontological study of the Cloverly Formation (Ostrom, 1970). Ostrom described an extensive early Cretaceous fauna from the Cloverly, principally comprised of dinosaurs (representatives of four families of theropod saurischians, a sauropodomorph, an iguanodontid, and an acanthopholid ankylosaur) as well as crocodilians, chelonians, and fishes. Despite the fact that Ostrom undertook an extensive washing and screening program, no mammalian or other microfaunal remains were recovered as a result of his work.

Fieldwork by Museum of Comparative Zoology (MCZ) field parties during the summers of 1974 and 1975 concentrated on quarrying operations at the Lewis site and to a lesser extent on prospecting for other mammal-bearing localities in the Cloverly Formation. The field parties were directed by F. A. Jenkins, Jr., with the assistance of C. R. Schaff, W. W. Amaral, and A. W. Crompton; student assistants were J. Langdon, J. Schweitzer, C. Janis, S. Orzack, C. Moseley, P. O'Connell, and T. Steinbock.

Intensive excavation at the Lewis Quarry produced more than 20 mammalian specimens as well as other small vertebrates (reptiles, amphibians, and fishes) not previously known in the Cloverly fauna. Most of the mammalian fossils are skulls and/or jaws, and all these represent triconodontines (closely related to, if not identical with, *Astroconodon*). One specimen is associated with a nearly complete postcranial axial skeleton, as well as appendicular elements; other postcranial elements were also recovered, but not in direct association with dental or cranial remains. The Lewis Quarry was intensively and thoroughly worked with small hand tools, and all matrix removed from the site was washed and wet-screened. In comparison to the few other Mesozoic mammal localities known that have yielded abundant material, the Lewis Quarry is peculiar in its restricted mammalian fauna: only triconodontines were recovered.

The triconodontine material is particularly important because it represents the most complete cranial remains of post-Triassic triconodonts known in the world. The excellent preservation yields detailed information on almost all aspects of the skull, including the braincase, as well as the postcranial skeleton.

The interpretation of the structure of the braincase in early mammals has been regarded as crucial evidence in determining the interrelationships of therian and nontherian mammals. In nontherians (e.g., monotremes and multituberculates) the side wall of the braincase is formed in part by a large anterior extension of the periotic (the "anterior lamina") and only to a limited extent by the alisphenoid. Therian mammals, in contrast, possess a greatly expanded alisphenoid, and the "anterior lamina" of the periotic is absent. The point of contention is whether such a fundamental structural difference is the result of an extremely early phylogenetic divergence (among different groups of therapsid reptiles) or whether the braincases typical of therians and nontherians were derived from a common therapsid ancestor at or near the reptile-mammal transition. The recovery of triconodontine skulls from the early Cretaceous Cloverly Formation permitted re-examination of this question, and a preliminary account of this study is given by Crompton and Jenkins (1979). Structural details of the side wall of the braincase appear to support the taxonomic distinction between nontherians and therians, and at the same time confirm the view that the Rhaeto-Liassic mammal *Eozostrodon* as well as triconodontines should be included among nontherians. However, it is now clear that the therian braincase can also be derived from that of cynodont therapsids. The comparative anatomy of this region does not support the view that early therians and nontherians are distantly related or that they arose from different therapsid stocks. On the contrary, the structure of the braincase supports other evidence, derived from studies of the dentition, that both nontherian and therian mammals arose from a middle or late Triassic cynodont.

Three mammalian scapulae were also recovered from the Lewis Quarry. These specimens cannot be identified positively as those of triconodontines because they were not associated directly with dental remains. However, no evidence of any other mammalian taxon was recovered during the extensive quarry operation; the evidence is thus circumstantial that these elements pertain to a triconodontine. The unexpected finding is that the scapulae are clearly therian in nature, each with a well-formed supraspinous fossa and a much reduced, beaklike coracoid process. Until recently it was believed that nontherian mammals never developed a therian pectoral girdle pattern, and thus multituberculates and recent monotremes shared with the nontherian *Eozostrodon* a fundamentally different adaptation in shoulder structure. The circumstantial association of a therian type of scapula with the Cloverly triconodontines does not positively refute this long-standing supposition, but it does open the possibility that the pectoral girdle in some nontherian lineages may have undergone parallel evolution and achieved an essentially therian grade of organization.

Detailed accounts of the Cloverly triconodontine materials are being prepared for publication by A. W. Crompton and F. A. Jenkins, Jr.

In addition to the Lewis Quarry excavation, MCZ field parties prospected known exposures of the Cloverly Formation as well as other outcrops that had not been examined previously. As a result of this reconnaissance, two additional Mesozoic mammals were recovered. Both specimens are well-preserved partial skeletons, including jaws, teeth, skull fragments, and various postcranial elements (some of which are complete), and appear to represent a new taxon of amphilestine triconodont. With proportions on the order of a modern Virginia opossum, this amphilestine attained unusually large size for a Mesozoic mammal. The dentition has several unusual features. The mesial incisors of the mandible are large and procumbent, and possess roots that extend back into the body to a point below the second premolar alveolus. Radiographs clearly demonstrate that the molariform teeth were replaced in a front-to-back sequence. Previously, amphilestines were accorded familial or subfamilial status with the Triconodonta, but a recent review of occlusal patterns in triconodonts (Jenkins and Crompton, 1979) reopens the question of their taxonomic affinity. Among other unusual postcranial features, the scapula clearly shows evidence of a supraspinous fossa, and therefore it was of a therian pattern. Both the calcaneus and astragalus have major structural differences from the basic therian pattern. A deep fossa occurs between the lesser trochanter and shaft on the dorsal aspect of the femur, a feature as yet unknown in any other mammal. A spurlike ?tarsal (or carpal) element is reminiscent of the tarsal spur in modern monotremes. Taken together, the structure of the Cloverly amphilestine is sufficiently different from that expected on the basis of current knowledge of Mesozoic mammal phylogeny to open the possibility for reinterpreting traditional taxonomic boundaries between therian and nontherian mammals. A preliminary reconstruction of this form by J. H. Matternes has been published by Ostrom (1976).

The dentition of the Cloverly amphilestine is very similar to that of *"Gobiconodon borissiaki"* (Beliajeva, Trofimov, and Reshetov, 1974) represented by eleven specimens recovered from Lower Cretaceous deposits in the Mongolian People's Republic (Khoboor, Ubur-Khangai region). F. A. Jenkins, Jr., has been able to examine the Mongolian specimens through the courtesy of Drs. Trofimov and Reshetov; the dentitions are uniformly about half the size of those of the Cloverly amphilestine but are otherwise sufficiently similar to be congeneric. Beliajeva et al. did not provide a formal description with their use of the name *"Gobiconodon borissiaki,"* which is thus a *nomen nudum*.[1] At the present time, the amphilestines are the only mammalian relatives shared by the Cloverly and Khoboor faunas; although the Khoboor fauna is quite diverse (including multituberculates, symmetrodonts, and therians), no evidence of triconodontines has been recovered to date.

A complete description of the Cloverly amphilestine is being prepared for publication by F. A. Jenkins, Jr., and C. R. Schaff.

---

[1] EDITOR'S NOTE: Subsequent to the writing of this report a publication by Boris Trofimov on *Gobiconodon borissiaki* has removed this name from a *nomen nudum* status.

REFERENCES

BELIAJEVA, E. I.; TROFIMOV, B. A.; and RESHETOV, V. J.
   1974.   General stages in evolution of Late Mesozoic and Early Tertiary mamma-
           lian fauna in Central Asia [In Russian].   Pp. 19-45 *in* "Mesozoic and
           Cenozoic Faunas and Biostratigraphy of Mongolia," 380 pp., N. N.
           Kramarenko (editor-in-chief).   Transactions of the Joint Soviet-Mon-
           golian Paleontological Expedition, vol. 1.   Moscow.
CROMPTON, A. W., and JENKINS, FARISH A., JR.
   1979.   Origin of mammals.   Pp. 59-73 *in* "Mesozoic Mammals—the First
           Two-thirds of Mammalian History," J. A. Lillegraven, Z. Kielen-
           Jaworowska, and W. A. Clemens, eds.   University of California Press,
           Berkeley.
JENKINS, FARISH A., JR., and CROMPTON, A. W.
   1979.   Triconodonta.   Pp. 74-90 *in* "Mesozoic Mammals—the First Two-
           thirds of Mammalian History," J. A. Lillegraven, Z. Kielen-Jawor-
           owska, and W. A. Clemens, eds.   University of California Press,
           Berkeley.
OSTROM, JOHN H.
   1970.   Stratigraphy and paleontology of the Cloverly Formation (Lower Creta-
           ceous) of the Bighorn Basin area, Wyoming and Montana.   Peabody
           Mus. Nat. Hist. Bull. 35, 234 pp.
   1976.   The triumph of mammals.   Pp. 119-140 *in* "Our Continent: A Natural
           History of North America," 398 pp., illus.   National Geographic Soci-
           ety, Washington, D. C.

FARISH A. JENKINS, JR.
A. W. CROMPTON

Head-body Temperature Control and Behavioral Thermoregulation in the American Alligator

Principal Investigator: Clifford R. Johnson, University of California, Berkeley, California.

Grant No. 1321:   For study of thermoregulation in the American alligator *(Alligator mississippiensis)*.

Head-body temperature gradients of up to 4.2°C. and 2.5°C. were found during artificial heating (radiant heat source: 250-watt infrared heat lamp) and solar heating, respectively. Differences of 1°C. to 2°C. were more often the case during both types of heating. Head temperature exceeded body temperature during heating, while subcutaneous temperature remained below head temperature but above that of the body during solar heating. Temperature tended to equilibrate after movement to shade.

A 3.4-kilogram female alligator was artificially heated after six thermocouple and thermistor leads had been implanted. Head temperature remained 3°C. to 4°C. above the other temperatures during heating. Heart and stomach temperatures remained close during heating. Ventral subcutaneous temperatures approximated deep cloacal temperatures during heating but during cooling followed those of the heart more closely. Tail temperature rose abruptly after movement to shade, possibly indicating a movement of warm blood into the tail region.

Calculated grouped data for head and body mean preferred temperature were 31.8°C. (range 28.9°C.-35.9°C.) and 32.0°C. (range 29.9°C.-35.6°C.), respectively, and the differences were not significant. Slight significant differences were found between mean head and body preferred temperature in the majority of the animals tested, and in three individuals mean head preferred temperature was found to be higher than mean body preferred temperature. A comparison of thermal preferenda for different sized individuals of *Alligator mississippiensis* showed a direct relationship between size and mean preferred temperatures. Mean voluntary maxima for the head and body were 34.4°C. and 33.7°C., respectively.

The most effective method of reducing head and body temperature was that of seeking shade. Head temperature was lowered immediately when the head was immersed in water, but enough water for complete submersion was

337

not available to the test animals. Raising of the head above the substrate lowered head temperature slightly, probably by eliminating heat conductance from the substrate, as raising of the head above the substrate by crocodilians does not appreciably reduce the absorptive area exposed to the heat source as it does in saurians, ophidians, and chelonians. Gaping was observed several times during the study but appeared to have little effect on head temperature.

A 49.9-kilogram alligator was heated and cooled in constant-temperature water baths at 15°C. and 35°C. The alligator heated to within 1°C. of the 35°C. water bath in 239.2 minutes. It took 616.1 minutes to cool within 1°C. of the 15°C. water bath. The warming-time constant was 68.9 minutes and the cooling-time constant was 188.7 minutes. The rates at the midtemperature (25°C.) were 0.145 and 0.053°C./min., during warming and cooling respectively. The ratio of tw/tc was 0.365 and is a measure of the alligator's ability physiologically to alter its rate of heat exchange. Thus this large alligator was able to heat in less than half the time it required for cooling. In addition it is predicted that metabolic heat would aid significantly the thermal homeostasis by reducing cooling rate and enhancing the rate of warming.

REFERENCES

JOHNSON, CLIFFORD R.; VOIGT, W. G.; and SMITH, E. N.
    1978.   Thermoregulation in crocodilians, III: Thermal preferenda, voluntary
             maxima, and heating and cooling rates in the American alligator, *Alligator mississippiensis*.   Journ. Linn. Soc. (Zool.), vol. 62, pp. 179-188.
SMITH, E. N.; JOHNSON, CLIFFORD R.; and VOIGT, W. G.
    1976.   Leech infestation of the American alligator.   Copeia, 1976, no. 4,
             p. 842.

CLIFFORD R. JOHNSON

Quaternary History of the Río General Valley, Costa Rica

Principal Investigator: Richard H. Kesel, Louisiana State University, Baton Rouge, Louisiana.

Grant Nos. 1375   In support of a study to establish the Quaternary history of
and 1747.   the Río General Valley, Costa Rica.

Although there is abundant literature concerned with the Quaternary history of North and South America, little has been done to determine the events of the Quaternary and their effects on the Central American isthmus. From previous fieldwork in Central America, I selected the Río General Valley in Costa Rica as an area to initiate such a study.

The Río General Valley is located in southwestern Costa Rica and is the northern portion of a structural depression that continues into Panama (fig. 1). The Valley is situated between two parallel mountain ranges, the Cordillera de Talamanca along the northeastern margin and the Fila Cortena (Coast Range) along the southeast. The Valley provides a unique opportunity to study the Quaternary history of this part of the Central American isthmus because it contains a complete sedimentary record since the emergence of this portion of the isthmus from the ocean in the late Tertiary. The Río General Valley has acted as a sediment trap during the Quaternary Period and provides a record of the climatic, botanical, tectonic-volcanic, and erosional history for this period.

Fieldwork was carried out, under the initial grant from the National Geographic Society, from December 1974 to January 1975, and from May to August 1975. Further fieldwork during 1977 and 1978 was made possible by a continuation grant from the Society. During the course of the research a number of persons made valuable contributions to the project, either in the field or in the laboratory, and include the following participants: Dr. Donald Lowe and Dr. W. van den Bold, Department of Geology, Louisiana State University; Mr. Bradley Spicer, Soil Conservation Service, Baton Rouge, Louisiana; Dr. William Haag and Dr. Fred Wiseman, Department of Geography and Anthropology, Louisiana State University; and Dr. Harold Vokes, Department of Geology, Tulane University.

339

Methods

Fieldwork included mapping the geomorphological surfaces, the soils developed on these surfaces, and the bedrock and surficial geology. Stratigraphic units were defined and their thicknesses determined. Samples were collected from all stratigraphic units and soil horizons. Stratigraphic samples were analyzed by mechanical analyses and thin section to determine their mode of transport and deposition. In addition, the source and direction of sediments were determined by measuring imbrication of gravel deposits and by comparing the results of heavy mineral analyses. Soil samples were analyzed according to the procedures outlined by the Soil Conservation Service in order to establish soil types. Samples were also collected for pollen analysis.

Chronology for the area was established by radiocarbon dating of vegetal material, K-Ar dating of volcanic rocks, and an examination of micro and macro fossils. Dating of samples was carried out by Geochron Laboratories, Cambridge, Massachusetts. Several areas also were examined to establish the presence or absence of possible pre-Columbian human occupation sites.

Geology and Geomorphology

The Cordillera de Talamanca is an uplifted inactive segment of the Central American Magmatic Arc. It is composed largely of upper Eocene, Oligocene, and lower Miocene marine strata with interstratified basaltic and andesitic volcanic rocks (Weyl, 1957, 1971). The Coast Range is made up of middle Eocene to upper Miocene sedimentary rocks striking northwest, parallel to the range, and dipping northeast toward and beneath the Río General Valley (Henningsen, 1966). The bulk of the strata is marine and is composed of coarse-grained volcaniclastic sandstone, shale, and minor carbonate.

The structural trough in which the Río General Valley is located was formed by differential uplift of the bounding Cretaceous basement and the Talamanca block. Dengo (1962) suggested that this uplift occurred from late Pliocene to Holocene. The Río General Valley, formed during this uplift, is floored largely by alluvial fan sediments derived from the Talamanca; these alluvial fan sediments are interfingered with valley-bottom lacustrine sediments. Henningsen (1966) included these sediments in the Paso Real Formation, a unit defined by Dengo (1962) and composed largely of volcanic rocks. Dengo (1962) suggested that the Paso Real Formation is Miocene to Pliocene in age while Henningsen (1966) tentatively dates it as Pliocene. Within the Valley, little or none of the sedimentary activity has been assigned to the Quaternary Period.

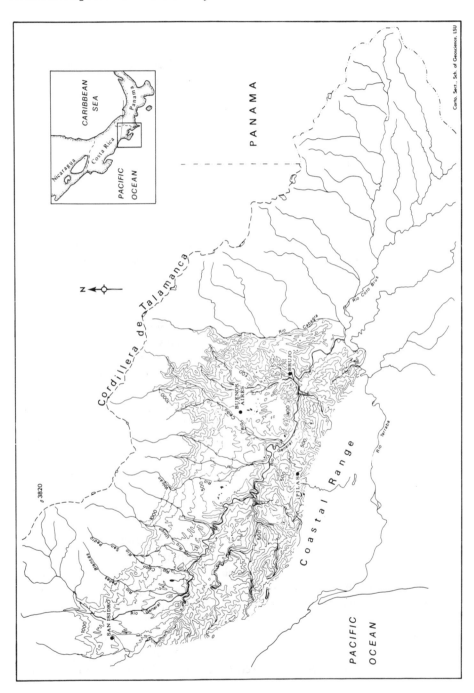

Fɪɢ. 1.   Location and contour map of Río General Valley.

As the result of this study, it is possible to revise the stratigraphic divisions and their ages and to give a more detailed account of the Quaternary events within the Valley (fig. 2). Previously, submergence of the area beneath the ocean extended only into the Miocene based on the youngest marine sediments in the Valley, the Gatun Formation (Miocene). In several areas (see fig. 4) a massive, brownish gray weathering claystone was found overlying the Gatun Formation and was lithologically distinctive from it. Microfauna found within the claystone included *Globigernoides ruber* (lower Pliocene–Recent), *Globognadrina altispira* (lower Miocene–middle Pliocene), and *Pulleniatina primalis* (Pliocene) (van den Bold, pers. comm.). The type of microfauna and the sediment characteristics indicate a marine environment extending well into the Pliocene. During the initial study, the claystone was found only in one location; during the continuation portion of the study, however, several other outcrops were found. The distribution indicates that these marine sediments covered most, if not all, of the Valley, but have been removed by erosion in many parts of the Valley.

The Paso Real Formation, the oldest terrestrial sediments in the Río General Valley, is redefined in this study to include two major lithologic units: (1) volcaniclastic sandstone and conglomerate and (2) volcanic-flow rock and agglomerate (fig. 2). The Paso Real is best exposed along the southeastern end of the Valley and can be traced northwestward as far as the Río Volcan River (fig. 1). Farther to the northwest in the vicinity of San Isidro it is absent. No fossils have been found in the Paso Real Formation and its possible age range is set by the Pliocene marine sediments that underlie it and late Pleistocene to Holocene age sediments that unconformably overlie it. A K-Ar date (R-3969, Geochron Laboratories) obtained from a volcanic boulder in the upper volcaniclastic unit of the Paso Real was 5.0 million years ($\pm$ 0.4 m.y.) old (see fig. 5). The boulder was presumed to have been derived from the lower volcanic unit of the Paso Real Formation and gives a maximum date for the upper unit. The age of the Paso Real Formation thus is considered to be from middle to late Pliocene to early Pleistocene.

The youngest sediments in the Valley have been designated in this study as the Brujo Formation and include an assemblage of sedimentary units of middle Pleistocene to Holocene age that unconformably overlie rocks of the Gatun and Paso Real Formations in the southeastern portion of the General Valley and the Gatun and unnamed Pliocene marine sediments in the northwestern portion (fig. 2). The Formation is nearly 600 meters thick in the southeast, but thins to less than 50 meters in the northwest at San Isidro.

The Brujo Formation can be informally subdivided into an upper and a lower unit based on lithology of sediment clasts. The lower portion, com-

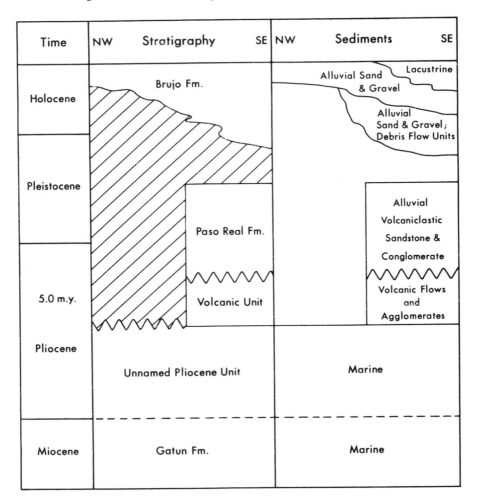

FIG. 2.   Stratigraphic sequences for Río General Valley.

posed of current-deposited sands and gravels and debris-flow units that lack clasts of plutonic rock, contains abundant clasts of augite porphyry like that in the underlying Paso Real Formation. The upper portion also contains current-deposited sands and gravels, debris-flow units along with lacustrine clays, but with an increasing proportion of plutonic clasts toward the top of the unit. These plutonic clasts were derived mainly from the Cordillera de Talamanca.

TABLE 1.   C-14 Dates from Río General Valley

I.D. Number Geochron Laboratories	Location	Age	Sediment type[2]
1. GX 3720	Queb. Guapinal	17,050 ($\pm$550)	Low energy fluvial or lacustrine
2. GX 3760	Río Catarata	26,515 ($\pm$1050)	Debris flow
3. GX 4031	Pacuor R. (Palma)	>37,000	Fluvial volcanic sands[3]
4. GX 4032	N.W. Buenos Aires	>37,000	Shallow marine (estuarine)[4]
5. GX 4113	S. Buenos Aires	8810 ($\pm$245)	Lacustrine clay
6. GX 4114	S. Buenos Aires	12,830 ($\pm$395)	Lacustrine clay
7. GX 4976	Brujo at River	>37,000	Debris flow
8. GX 4977	Brujo at River	>37,000	Debris flow
9. GX 4978	Brujo Bridge	>37,000	Fluvial sands and silts
10. GX 4979	Río Cabagra	18,600 ($\pm$1300)	Fluvial sand and gravel
11. GX 4980	Río General (Volcan)	>37,000	Lacustrine clay and silt

[1]Locations of sample sites shown on figure 4.
[2]Stratigraphic unit Brujo Formation except as noted.
[3]Gatun or Paso Real (?) stratigraphic unit.
[4]Pliocene (?) stratigraphic unit.

Quaternary History and Landform Evolution

The characteristics of the Tertiary strata point to submergence of the General Valley through this period, culminating in the development of subaerial to shallow-water conditions. The presence of Pliocene marine sediments overlain by Pliocene volcanic flow rocks (dated) indicates that major uplift of the area occurred in the middle to late Pliocene. From middle Pliocene to Holocene the Valley underwent widespread emergence and erosion of older strata followed by deposition of sands and gravels by braided streams on alluvial fans. The oldest of these deposits, which include the Paso Real alluvial sediments and the lower portion of the Brujo Formation, were derived from local active volcanic centers located along the southeastern margin of the Valley (fig. 3). Debris-flow units within the lower Brujo may represent lahar-type mudflows (Kesel, 1973). At this time nine radiocarbon dates of plant remains have been obtained from the Brujo Formation (Table 1). Four samples gave

FIG. 3.   One of several isolated hills in southeastern portion of the Río General Valley that are probably remnants of small volcanic cones or fissures.

dates of greater than 37,000 years B.P. The other samples yielded dates from 26,500 to 8,800 years B.P.

Uplift of the Cordillera de Talamanca continued during the Pleistocene, resulting in (further) construction of large alluvial fans along the base of the Cordillera. These fans are represented by the sands and gravels of the Brujo Formation. In the southeastern portion of the Valley plutonic debris begins to appear in the gravels within 200 meters of the base and becomes more abundant toward the top, where it may represent over 50 percent of the cobble and gravel-size debris. The only source for this plutonic debris is the Miocene intrusives within the Cordillera de Talamanca. The unroofing of these intrusive rocks by erosion occurred in this area sometime after 26,500 years B.P. (sample GX 3760), the youngest date from the Brujo sediments that lack plutonic clasts. Uplift of the Talamanca and relative downdropping of the Río General Valley has continued into Holocene time as indicated by faults that cut across Brujo gravels on the upper part of the alluvial fans.

The distal ends of the alluvial fans originating from the Talamanca have been uptilted by uplift of the Coast Range. The age of this uplift cannot be precisely dated; however, the presence of open marine Pliocene deposits suggests that the area was open to the sea at this time. The uplift of the Coast

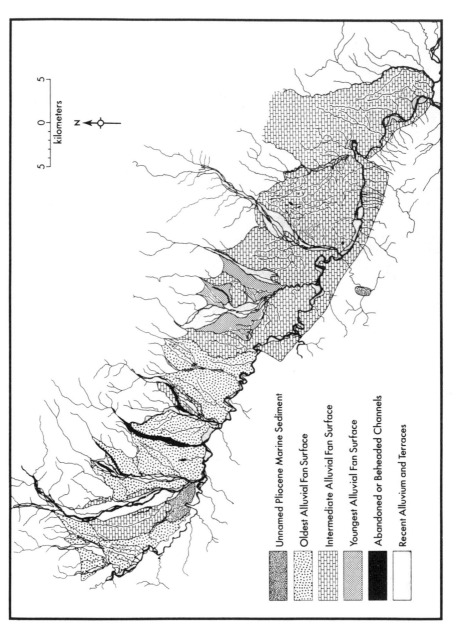

Legend:
- Unnamed Pliocene Marine Sediment
- Oldest Alluvial Fan Surface
- Intermediate Alluvial Fan Surface
- Youngest Alluvial Fan Surface
- Abandoned or Beheaded Channels
- Recent Alluvium and Terraces

FIG. 4.   Age relationships of alluvial surfaces in Río General Valley.

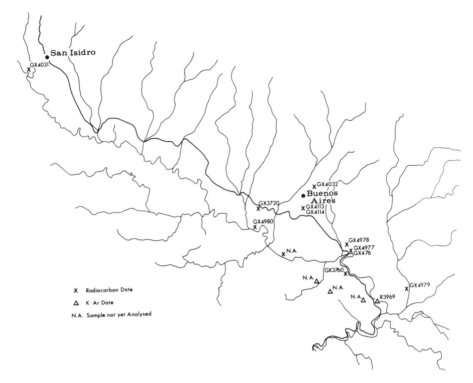

Fig. 5. Location of K-Ar and C-14 samples.

Range, forming a topographic barrier between the Río General Valley and the Pacific Ocean, probably began in early to middle Pleistocene and continued into the Holocene. Two radiocarbon samples (GX3720, GX4979) from tilted young Brujo gravels indicate that much of the uplift has occurred in the past 20,000 years. Uplift of the Coast Range has also caused a number of streams along the distal ends of the fans to reverse their direction of flow, in some cases forming lakes (fig. 4). One of these lakes contains two interstratified organic-rich zones overlying coarse alluvial gravel. Radiocarbon samples yielded dates of 12,830 ± 395 (GX4114) years B.P. for the lower zone and 8,810 ± 245 (GX4113) for the lower one. These dates indicate that significant uplift of the Coast Range has occurred into Holocene time.

Throughout the evolution of the Río General Valley, the northwestern part has remained structurally more positive than the area to the southwest. As a result, it is only in the northwest part of the Valley that the Gatun Formation contains shallow-marine and terrestrial sediments (Lowe and Kesel, in prep.). The Paso Real either was never deposited in the northwest or was removed by erosion before deposition of the Brujo Formation. The Brujo Formation is nearly 600 meters thick in the southeast, but is less than 50 meters in the northwest. The evidence indicates that from lower to middle Pleistocene through the Holocene the Cordillera de Talamanca and the Coast Range were undergoing uplift while the Río General Valley, particularly the southeastern part, was subsiding.

ALLUVIAL FANS

The alluvial fans in the Río General Valley are of Quaternary age and the fan surfaces are formed on the Brujo Formation. Plant remains found near the base of the Río Cabagra fan (fig. 5) yielded a radiocarbon date of 18,600 ± 1300 (GX 4979). It was estimated from this date that in the southeastern portion of the Valley the fan accumulated sediment at an average net rate of 16 meters per thousand years. In comparison, Beaty (1970), on arid alluvial fans in the White Mountains of California, determined a maximum accumulation rate of 15.2 centimeters per thousand years. The exceedingly high rate of fan accumulation in the Río General Valley may be caused by greater tectonic activity or greater intensity of geomorphic processes under humid tropical conditions; further conclusions, however, will have to await further investigation and comparative data.

The alluvial fan sediments consist of crudely stratified, poorly indurated gravel with intertonguing and interbedded sand units (fig. 6). Construction of the fans occurred as the main channel, depositing sediment, shifted its course from one part of the fan to another. Thus, while one portion of the fan surface was experiencing deposition, another part was undergoing weathering and soil formation. Some fans in the Valley exhibit as many as 4 to 6 buried soil profiles representing periods of no deposition.

Because streams flowing from the Talamanca have now incised their channels below the fan surfaces, deposition has not occurred during Recent time. The age relationships of the fan surfaces were determined, using the depth of soil development, to the top of the C-horizon.

The depth of soil development on alluvial surfaces is shown in the following tabulation:

Surface	*Depth to C-horizon* (m)
Oldest alluvial fan	3.0 - 4.0
Intermediate alluvial fan	1.5 - 3.0
Youngest alluvial fan	0.5 - 1.0
Recent alluvial flood plains and terraces	<0.3

FIG. 6.   Basal portion of alluvial fan sediments near Brujo.

Fig. 7. Weathered alluvial sediments beneath intermediate surface. Clasts have been completely altered to clay.

The oldest fan surfaces occur in the northwestern portion of the Valley and are younger toward the southeast (fig. 4). The oldest surfaces have a well-developed lateritic soil 3 to 4 meters deep, while soils on younger surfaces are progressively thinner and less developed. The most recent surface including the alluvial flood plain and terraces incised below the fan surface has minimal soil development, generally less than 0.3 meter in depth. The younger fan surfaces in the southeastern portion indicate sediment accumulation continued in this area after it had ceased farther to the northwest.

Further analysis of the alluvial fan data is expected to provide answers to several important questions, including causal factors for fan development and what initiated incision of fan surfaces by major streams.

I am currently examining the soils, including analyses of pH, extractable nutrients, organic matter, and heavy minerals. The relationship between soil development and landform evolution will be the subject of at least one future paper and will include a generalized soil map of the Río General Valley. One interesting aspect of the soils is their age of development. The maximum age of the soils developed on the intermediate age fan surfaces (fig. 4) can be estimated from radiocarbon sample GX 3720 at 17,000 years B.P. Soils on this surface range from 1.5 to 3.0 meters in thickness and are moderately to extremely weathered. This degree of soil development in such a short time period is contrary to most published data concerned with the time scale of tropical soil development (Birkeland, 1974, p. 175) and will necessitate further study. Another indication of the intensity of weathering during this period is the complete alteration of alluvial sediments beneath these soils to regolith. Boulders up to one meter in diameter have been completely altered to clay, leaving only an outline of the former clast (fig. 7).

DRAINAGE DEVELOPMENTS

The Río General and its major tributaries with source areas in the Talamanca Mountains are perennial streams, although there is a pronounced seasonality in discharge resulting from the wet-dry seasons. Lesser streams that originate on the alluvial fans generally cease flowing during the dry season. The course of the Río General, along the southwest margin of the Valley, is probably the result of alluvial fan deposition from the northeast causing the Río General to follow a course that is roughly coincident with the distal ends of the fans (fig. 4). Stream diversion or piracy is an important aspect in the evolution of the fans. Fan-building streams that emerge from the mountains can be diverted into channels rising on the fan but at lower elevations. The flow from Quebrada Cajon, for example, has been diverted to the lower-lying Río San Pedro (fig. 4) possibly during a flood overflow or by headward erosion

GX4113	GX4114	GX3720	GX4032	GX4980	GX4976	GX4977		
8,810	12,830	17,050	>37,000 (Estuarine)	>37,000 (fluvial volcanic sands)	>37,000 mudflow	>37,000① mudflow		
.08	.18	.09	.10	+	++	0	Quercus	MONTANE
.06	.07	.03	.09	0	+	0	Podocarpus	
0	+	0	0	0	0	0	Pinus	
.01	.05	.03	.04	0	0	0	Ericaceae	
0	0	.01	.02	0	0	0	Alnus	
.30	.30	.44	.17	+	+	++	Graminae	HERBS
.01	0	.06	.05	+	0	0	Umbelliferae	
.10	.04	.04	.06	+	++	0	Chenopodiaceae	
.05	.12	.03	.05	0	+	0	Composite (Hi-spine)	
.03	.02	.05	.12	0	+	+	Composite (Lo-spine)	
.12	.11	.09	.23	+	+	+	Cyperaceae	
.01	+	.01	.02	0	+	0	Solanaceae	
+	0	0	0	0	0	0	Polygonaceae	
.04	+	.01	.06	+	++	0	Moraceae	TROPICAL TREES & SHRUBS
.04	.01	.04	.01	0	0	0	Byrsonima crassifolia	
0	.02	.02	.01	+	+	+	Malpighiaceae	
+	0	+	.01	0	+	0	Rubiaceae	
.04	+	.03	0	0	+	0	Acacia	
.01	0	0	+	0	0	0	Palmae	
+	+	.01	0	0	0	0	Celtis	
+	+	.01	0	0	0	0	Hippocratea	
.02	0	0	.02	0	0	0	Zanthoxylum	
+	0	0	.06	0	0	0	Sapotaceae	
.01	0	0	+	0	0	0	Calliandra	
0	+	0	0	0	0	0	Piperaceae	
.03	.03	.01	.02	+	+	0	Alchornea	
0	+	0	+	0	0	0	Bombacaceae	
+	0	+	0	0	+	0	Ilex	
0	+	0	0	0	+	0	Myrica	
0	0	0	+	0	0	0	Erythrina	
+	0	+	0	0	0	0	Acalyphia	
.01	+	0	0	0	+	0	Melastomaceae	
0	+	0	0	+	0	0	Annonaceae	
250	322	212	318	46	72	12	Σ grains counted	
2.7	9.8	7.1	18.5	← low →			Grains/gm. dry weight X 1,000	

Data Presented as Frequencies   (.10 = 10%)

+ pollen present < 1%

① sample not useable for reconstruction

FIG. 8.   Pollen analyses for selected sites in the Río General Valley.

of the latter. The Río San Pedro has continued to cut down, leaving the abandoned Cajon channel about 15 meters higher. Similar diversions also are evident on the recent flood plain, although abandoned channels are generally only 1 or 2 meters above present channels. These abandoned channels elevated above the recent channels indicate current downcutting by these streams.

Uplift of the Coast Range has caused a number of streams along the distal ends of the alluvial fans to reverse their direction of flow (fig. 4). This disruption of drainage is most pronounced south of Buenos Aires (fig. 1) in the southeastern portion of the Valley probably because of closer proximity to the Coast Range. Some major streams were able to maintain their courses and continued to downcut, forming antecedent valleys. The amount of downcutting by these antecedent streams also increases toward the southeast.

The following tabulation shows the amount of dissection by major streams along distal ends of fans:

Stream	Amount of dissection below fan surface (m)	Direction
Quebrada Cajon	120	N.W.
Río Union	143	
Río Convento	150	
Río Sonador	155	
Río Volcan	214	
Río Ceibo	285	S.E.

Those streams unable to keep pace with uplift were forced to reverse their flow direction, forming large lakes. Since that period, deeply entrenched tributaries of the antecedent streams have eroded headward, integrating the drainage although many small lakes and swampy areas remain without external drainage (fig. 4).

The antecedent valleys occupied by major tributaries reflect the influence of uplift of the Talamanca and Coast Ranges. The streams have incised, steep-walled valleys near the alluvial fan apex and along the distal ends of the fans. The amount of incision is often more than 100 meters and reaches a maximum of 285 meters at the lower end of the Río Ceibo fan (see above tabulation). Along their distal ends, the streams have cut down through the unconsolidated fan deposits to the resistant rocks of the Gatun Formation. The radiocarbon date (GX 4114) from the overlying lacustrine clays discussed previously indicates that this magnitude of downcutting has occurred within the last 13,000 years.

Between the incised portions, the stream valleys are flat-floored up to several kilometers wide, may be incised only a few meters below the fan surface, and have braided channels (fig. 4). Stream activity in this portion of the Valley is controlled by the incision farther downstream, where the resistant rock of the Gatun Formation encountered by the stream acts as the local base level for the upstream section. Because of this fixed base level, valley flats have developed as the stream uses much of its energy for lateral erosion rather than downcutting.

Paleoenvironments and Climatic Change

During the Pleistocene cirque glaciers formed on the Cordillera de Talamanca. The elevation of this Pleistocene snow line has been calculated at 3,500 meters and moraine deposits have been found extending down to 3,320 meters (Weyl, 1956; Hastenrath, 1973). An absolute age for the glaciation has not been determined although Weyl (1956) believes it to be Wurm-Wisconsin based on the freshness of the landforms. Hastenrath (1973) recognizes, at least, three moraine stages. Weyl and Hastenrath found no evidence for Pleistocene periglacial activity in the valleys flowing from the Talamanca south to the Río General Valley. Hastenrath (1973) has, however, described abundant fossil periglacial forms above 3,300 meters in the Talamanca 30 kilometers farther to the northwest outside the Río General Valley.

The only pollen analysis in this part of Costa Rica was recorded by Martin (1964) from a bog in the Talamanca. From this analysis, it was estimated that the lower limit of the paramo during the late Wisconsin was 650 meters lower than its present elevation. The accuracy of this estimate is uncertain. In the northern Andes, for example, the tree line during the last glacial may have been 1,200 to 1,500 meters lower than at present (Van Der Hammen, 1974; Vuilleumier, 1971).

Several hundred pollen samples were taken during the course of this study and are now being prepared in the laboratory. Because coring equipment was unavailable at the time of sampling, many of the samples were taken from discrete locations and in only three locations were vertical profiles examined and sampled. One of the vertical profiles is a series of lacustrine beds and includes samples dated at 8,810 (GX 4113) and 12,830 (GX 4114) years B.P. Samples associated with radiocarbon dates were analyzed first and some of these results are presented in figure 8. These data represent the average of several samples taken at each site. They are present here as a first approximation.

The three youngest samples dating 17,050 to 8,810 years B.P. represent a time span that extends from what would correspond to a "full glacial" in North America into the postglacial period. Samples that correspond to the "full glacial" (GX 3720) suggest a drier period with a high percentage of

FIG. 9.   Leaf imprint in fluvial sediments of Brujo Formation (scale in centimeters).

grasses, and the presence of *Acacia, Byrsonima,* and *Acalypha.* These data would seem definitely to indicate the presence of a tropical grass savanna containing scattered woody species. This would, in fact, be the oldest recorded savanna in Latin America based on radiocarbon dates. Toward the end of the glacial (12,830 years B.P.) there appears to be a slight increase in precipitation represented by an increase in oaks and a decrease in the drier species. The period to 8,800 years B.P. indicates climatic conditions probably not much different from the present with grass savanna and scattered woodland.

Samples with ages beyond the range of radiocarbon dating are particularly interesting because of their antiquity. Three of the samples represent fluvial sand (GX 4978) and mudflow (GX 4976; GX 4977) environments. The large numbers of successional weeds and herbs indicate a highly disturbed environment probably related to a surface undergoing alluvial deposition and mudflow activity. On the basis of lithology and stratigraphic association, these samples are all included in the Brujo Formation, probably of later Pleistocene age.

The remaining sample greater than 37,000 years old comes from an estuarine environment that includes plant remains and shallow marine fossils. The sample tentatively is considered here to be later Pliocene in age and includes

FIG. 10.   Tree trunk and root systems buried by fluvial sands of Brujo Formation.

pollen from both a coastal wetland and from a tropical woodland, the latter possibly transported by rivers to the coastal area. The woody species suggest that the woodland was a dry forest type. It is interesting to note that *Byrsonima,* a major component of most savannas since late Pleistocene, is present.

Several sample localities, GX 4032 and GX 4978, in particular, contain large quantities of well-preserved vegetal material including leaves and seeds (fig. 9). In addition, at the latter site the deposition of alluvial sands and silts, most likely in a flood plain environment, has preserved large sections of trees and their root systems (fig. 10). Further analyses and identification of these materials is still being undertaken.

Human Occupation Sites

During the initial grant the analysis of one radiocarbon sample (GX 4032) provided by Geochron Laboratories indicated that the texture and the ash content along with the brittle fracture of the sample suggested partially burned bone. The sample yielded a radiocarbon date of greater than 37,000 years. One aspect of the continuation grant from the National Geographic Society was to examine the site where this sample was taken to determine if there was any evidence for an ancient human occupation site. Dr. William G. Haag, Louisiana State Archaeologist, and I spent five days in June 1977 excavating in and around the site. A sizable quantity of organic debris was found, but nothing that could be identified as either animal or human bone. In addition, a large number of artifacts, mainly pottery fragments, was found mostly on the ground surface. All this material was judged to be of very recent age. It was concluded that the site was not an ancient human occupation site and that the sample identified as possible burned bone was transported by fluvial processes or was another material similar to bone, possibly carbonized wood. The sample was given to the Museo Nacional in San Jose, Costa Rica, for further examination.

REFERENCES

BIRKELAND, P. W.
  1974.   Pedology, weathering and geomorphological research, 258 pp.   Oxford University Press, N.Y., 258 pp.

DENGO, G.
  1962.   Tectonic-igneous sequence in Costa Rica.   Pp. 133-161 *in* "Petrologic studies" (Buddington volume).   Geol. Soc. Amer.

HASTENRATH, S.
  1973.   On the Pleistocene glaciation of the Cordillera de Talamanca, Costa Rica.   Zeitschr. Gletscherkde. u. Glazialgeol., vol. 3, pp. 317-325.

HENNINGSEN, D.
  1966.   Notes on stratigraphy and paleontology of Upper Cretaceous and Tertiary sediments in southern Costa Rica.   Amer. Assoc. Petroleum Geologists Bull., vol. 50, pp. 562-566.

KESEL, R. H.
  1973.   Notes on the lahar landforms of Costa Rica.   Zeitschr. Geomorph. Neue Folge, suppl. bd. 18, pp. 78-91.

LOWE, D., and KESEL, R. H.
  ———.   Late Miocene to Holocene stratigraphy, sedimentology, and tectonic development of the Rio General arc-trench gap, Costa Rica. (In preparation.)

MARTIN, P.
  1964.   Palynological report on a Sierra de Talamanca bog.   VI Internatl. Congr. on Quaternary, Warsaw, 1961, vol. 2, pp. 319-323.

VAN DER HAMMEN, T.
  1974.   The Pleistocene changes of vegetation and climate in tropical South America.   Journ. Biogeogr., vol. 1., pp. 3-26.

VUILLEUMIER, B. S.
  1971.   Pleistocene changes in the fauna and flora of South America.   Science, vol. 173, pp. 771-780.

WEYL, R.
  1956.   Eiszeitliche Gletscherspuren in Costa Rica (Mittelamerika).   Zeitschr.
          Gletscherkunde und Glazialgeol., vol. 3, pp. 317-325.
  1957.   Beitrage zur Geologie der Cordillera de Talamanca Costa Ricas.   Neues
          Jahrb. Geol. und Palaontol., Abh., vol. 105, pp. 123-204.
  1971.   Die Morphologisch-Tektonische Gliederung Costa Rica (Mittelameri-
          ka).   Erdk., Arch. wiss. Geogr., vol. 25, pp. 223-230.

RICHARD H. KESEL

Coral Kill and Recolonization in American Samoa

Principal Investigator: Austin E. Lamberts, Grand Rapids, Michigan.

Grant Nos. 1372 and   For a study of coral reefs and coral-reef destruction in Ameri-
1945.   can Samoa, and of the recolonization of a selectively denuded
coral reef.

I. Coral Reef Destruction

During July 1973, John Flanigan, a high-school teacher with the Department of Education of American Samoa, discovered that most of his spectacular demonstration coral reef had inexplicably died. Both he and, independently, James Betcher had last visited this area in late November 1972 and had noted luxuriant coral growth. During July and August 1973 we reconnoitered the area and found extensive coral death of recent occurrence in the reefs bounded by Coconut Point, the Pago Pago Airport, and out to beyond the reef edge. Mr. Betcher had noticed the change about 2 months earlier.

Tutuila, American Samoa, located at lat. 14°20'S., long. 170° 40'W., is a small volcanic island surrounded by fringing reefs, the broadest extending about 1,000 meters from the shore in the south midportion of the island. Protected by this reef lies a shallow estuarian lagoon separated from it in part by a narrow sandy peninsula referred to as Coconut Point. In recent years the building of a modern airport across the lagoon to the reef edge was accompanied by much dredging of the lagoon, which now opens to the sea through Avatele Passage, a narrow gap between the runway embankment and the reef flats adjoining Coconut Point. The distance between these two landmarks is about 400 meters and encompasses partially dredged sand flats and coral reefs. Before 1973 great thickets of staghorn acroporid corals occupied the deeper areas. Some of these stands were over 30 meters across and 2 meters high.

Our survey showed that all the corals of the dominant suborder, Astrocoeniina, had died within an area of at least 8 hectares (20 acres). This included all the *Acropora, Montipora,* and *Pocillopora* corals, while members of two other suborders, Fungiina and Faviina, appeared healthy. It looked to us as if all the coral had succumbed at the same time, perhaps 3 or 4 months before, as all the skeletons were covered with the same-length strands of brown algae. Where this occurred in shallow water the demarcation point between living and dead coral was sharply delimited, and even over the reef edge scuba divers reported that most of the corals to a depth of 6 meters were dead. There was no

359

evidence of siltation, and a review of dredging records indicated almost no activity within a mile during the months when this happened. We found that mollusks, calcifying algae, and echinoderms were present in expected numbers. A rare angelfish, *Pomacanthus imperator* (Bloch), occupied the same niche under a rock that it had for two years with no apparent distress. There was no evidence of infestation by crown-of-thorns starfish *(Acanthaster)* on this or any reef on Tutuila.

Pala Lagoon has over 0.5 meter of tidal flow, the water all rushing in and out the narrow Avatele passage. During high tides water passes also over the reef crests and reef flats paralleling the Coconut Point peninsula to create an inshore stream running next to the beach. This is about 40 meters wide, and at high tide its greatest depth was about 1 meter. This streams toward the tip of the peninsula where it joins the outflow from Pala Lagoon to form a fan-shaped discharge sweep. Figure 1 indicates how all the dead coral lay within this precise area. On the west edge of the coral kill some banks of *Acropora* were only partially dead, with a western rim of living coral. The same was noted over the reef flat, so that coral death could be marked out almost to the meter. Finally, it was noted that in the stream channel the precise dividing line between normal coral growth and dead coral seemed to lie at a fish trap erected across the stream.

For many years Tongan fishermen have erected fish traps on various areas of this reef. These are weirs made of commercial chicken wire strung on sticks across the current so that fish are directed into a cul-de-sac where they are speared. It was noted that healthy *Pocillopora* grew within 30 meters upstream of this net, but all the dominant corals below the trap were dead. Circumstantial evidence suggested that something had occurred here to kill certain corals that had come in contact with water passing this point. It was as if some noxious agent, that had a selective action on the Astrocoeniina corals and nothing else, had been added to the water. We postulated that something may have been added to the water to aid in catching fish. Fish poisons have been used in the tropical Pacific for generations for this purpose, and pesticides would have been available for such a stunt, but nobody in the vicinity seemed to know anything about the dead coral, and certainly nobody volunteered information suggesting that an attempt had been made to poison fish since that was punishable by a $600 fine. The present study was then drawn up to investigate the effects of manufactured biocidal agents on living corals. A literature search uncovered no references on the effects of pesticides on reef corals.

FIG. 1.   Coconut Point coral kill of 1973, Tutuila, American Samoa (A and B are transect lines).

Laboratory Studies

All laboratory studies were performed during September and October 1974 at the Hawaii Institute of Marine Biology at Kaneohe, Oahu, Hawaiian

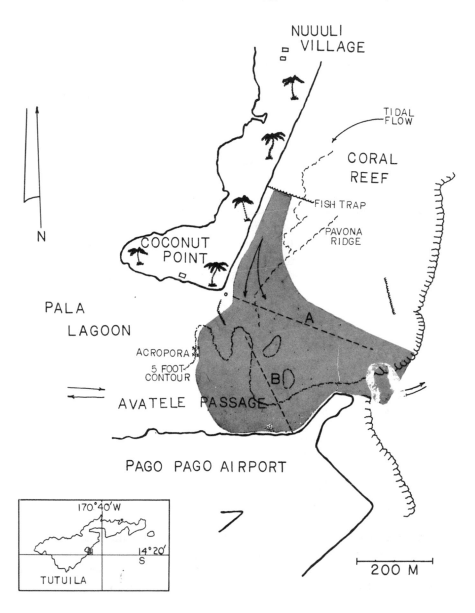

Islands. The purpose was to assess the effects of certain toxic agents on living corals. Following are the methods and the results:

Coral heads of *Pocillopora damicornis* (Linnaeus), the same species involved in the Samoan kill, were broken up and 10 similar growing tips were suspended in identical glass jars each containing 2 liters of freshly filtered sea water. To each of eight jars a measured amount of a toxic agent was added to give a decremental series ranging from 2 parts per million (ppm) concentration in the first jar to 10 parts per billion (ppb) in the eighth. The agents tested are listed in Table 1. Until recently they have all been available commercially. They were added directly to the sea water, or alcohol in small quantity was used as a vehicle. To nine of the jars I added the dye sodium alizarinate (Alizarin Red S) to give an ambient concentration of 10 ppm. This hydroquinone dye is an indicator of biological calcification, and when present in sea water during growth of corals it is incorporated into the skeleton in proportion to the amount of calcium carbonate deposited (Lamberts, 1973, 1975). The depth and distribution of the magenta color that remains after the living tissue has been removed can then be observed directly and can be compared with other specimens in the same or similar series to assess the ability of the organism to form skeletal tissues. In these experiments, the ninth bottle with alizarin and the tenth with clear sea water served as controls. Laboratory lighting, water temperature, and aeration were standardized and controlled.

TABLE 1.   Chemical Agents Tested to Assess Their Toxicity to Reef Corals

No.	Name	Type
1	DDT	Chlorinated hydrocarbon
2	Dieldrin	do.
3	Endrin	do.
4	Lindane	do.
5	Malathion	Organo-phosphate
6	Parathion	do.
7	2-4-D	Herbicide
8	Atrazine	do.
9	Carbanyl (Sevin)	Carbamate pesticide
10	Clorox	Bleach
11	Mercuric chloride	Heavy metal
12	Copper sulphate	do.

After each series was allowed to run for 24 hours the coral specimens were examined with magnification to check the vitality and reaction of the polyps against the controls. The specimens were then transferred to fresh sea water for 24 hours, then again examined, and then cleaned. I had shown in similar experiments with alizarin that there exists a considerable difference among coral heads of the same species in respect to growth during any given period. Quantitative comparisons are not feasible. In these studies all living corals exposed to alizarin dye showed some uptake, and no specimen died except some exposed to either mercury or bleach. When clean specimens in each series were ranked as to the amount and intensity of magenta color in the otherwise white skeletons an estimate was gained of the short-term biological effect of the additive on skeletal production in these corals. These could then be compared and are listed for that purpose in Table 2.

TABLE 2. Numerical Ranking of All Specimens of the Coral *Pocillopora damicornis*

Ranked according to the amounts of Alizarin dye deposited during a 24-hour period when they were exposed to a toxic agent. The rank numbers compare ten specimens in each series as to the amount of color observed from most (#1) to least against the amount of toxic material in the sea water.

| Toxic agent | Amount of toxic agent added in ppm | | | | | | | | Controls | |
	2.0	1.0	0.5	0.25	0.1	0.05	0.025	0.01	With dye	No dye
DDT	9	8	5	6	7	1	4	3	2	10
Dieldrin	4	1	2	3	7	9	6	5	8	10
Endrin	8	3	2	5	4	6	1	7	9	10
Lindane	3	9	8	5	6	2	1	4	7	10
Malathion	4	9	6	3	8	5	7	1	2	10
Parathion	2	4	3	8	9	7	1	6	5	10
2-4-D	3	5	1	2	9	7	6	8	4	10
Atrazine	8	1	2	5	6	9	7	3	4	10
Carbanyl	4	6	2	9	7	3	5	8	1	10
Average	5	5	3	5	7	5	4	5	5	10
Mercury	9	7	8	6	5	4	3	2	1	10
Copper	7	4	5	6	3	8	9	2	1	10

Also, we made other *in vitro* studies using a precision Cole-Parmer pump, which delivered a known constant flow of sea water and additives to test tanks. Three 10-liter glass aquaria were set up so that a constant flow of water would cascade from one to another. Corals of the genera *Pocillopora, Fungia,* and *Cyphastrea,* representing the three suborders involved, were placed in each tank. When possible, a single coral head was divided and part placed in each tank. The first and highest aquarium was supplied with filtered sea water and served to hold the controls. The second received the overflow from the first plus sufficient Alizarin Red S to give a constant concentration of 10 ppm. The third tank received the overflow from the second plus a solution of the biocide to be tested. DDT was added to give an ambient concentration of 0.5 ppm, and in the second series endrin was added to give a constant 1.0 ppm concentration. Each of these substances was added for 48 hours, after which the sea water was allowed to run clear for a day before coral tissue was removed with a jet of water so that alizarin deposition could be compared.

My observations on living corals subjected to pesticide and herbicides showed that with the greatest concentrations used in my laboratory, some of the terminal polyps died when exposed to DDT or endrin. With some others there was evidence of stress effect manifested by decreased tissue irritability and lack of vigor during the exposure to these chemical agents.

Mercury is a protoplasmic poison and is notoriously toxic to animal life, including corals. Stress reactions were noted in coral polyps exposed to a concentration of 10 ppb, and 0.5 ppm or greater was lethal. Copper, as $CuSO_4$, often used as an algicide, did not kill coral in these experiments at a concentration of 2 ppm. Commerical bleach (Clorox) killed coral tissue when the concentration was 2 parts per thousand if there was prolonged contact. Practically speaking, bleach in order to kill coral must be in a concentration of about 2 liters per cubic meter of sea water (1 gallon per 2 cubic yards).

Similar results were found using my tank studies. Corals were not killed and did not appear damaged by either DDT or endrin in these 48-hour trials. The presence of abundant alizarin in the cleaned corals indicated that skeletal calcium carbonate had been deposited in the amount and manner expected in normal growth. When all specimens from each series were compared, it appeared that high concentrations of pesticides might depress the formation of skeletal calcium slightly but did not eliminate it. Deposition of skeletal calcium, however, as deduced from observing the alizarin deposition, seemed enhanced over the normal controls when the chemicals were in the sea water in the 0.5 ppm range. This suggests that small amounts of such agents, toxic in large quantities, might stimulate the metabolism of the coral polyp during the time it is present. At this point nothing is known about long-term effects, if any.

Coral polyps are apparently very hardy animals. A level of certain pesticides such as endrin or parathion that would have been lethal to much of the marine life on the reef had little or no demonstrable effect on the living coral, which continued to deposit skeletal material in abundance. Each coral species and each individual colony of coral polyps has its own growth pattern and pace of growth; so there is always a variation in the amount and pattern of skeletalization and hence of the pattern of the alizarin dye visible. It was only after the above experiments had been concluded that I abandoned plans for in situ studies using the same pesticides and herbicides on living coral on the Samoan reefs themselves.

Observations in American Samoa

Tutuila, American Samoa, was revisited between October 15 and November 12, 1974, to resurvey the area of the coral kill. Climatic conditions allowed satisfactory observations of the reef but never optimum ones. The fish trap that had separated the living from the dead *Pocillopora* had been destroyed, but pieces of it remained submerged at the site and were found to consist of medium-mesh galvanized chicken wire. Samoans living in the vicinity claimed to have torn down the net. Hardly surprising! Samoans have been at enmity with the Tongans for centuries. Still, two new fish traps of similar design had been erected, one near the edge of the reef at the northern limit of the coral kill and the other within the western limits. The Tongan fishermen who managed them denied ever using any poisoning agents to catch fish.

The entire area was rechecked repeatedly by wading or swimming with face mask and recording data on an underwater slate. Healthy heads of *Pocillopora* were found in profusion 40 meters upstream from the fish-trap wreckage, some being over 15 centimeters in diameter, indicating an age of several years. Here was found also some *Montipora* of the suborder Astrocoeniina and moderate amounts of *Porites* and *Pavona*. Extensive banks of the latter continued on and served as a marker of the inner margin of the reef flat proper. Downstream below the trap, both in the inshore lagoon stream and in the deeper areas that had contained the extensive coral banks, most of the coral skeletons had now been broken up and washed away or reduced to rubble. In this entire area of destruction only one sparse 2-by-2-square meter patch of *Acropora formosa* (Dana) was found. It was this species that made up most of the big banks previously seen. There were a few small heads of *Pocillopora damicornis* usually growing on dead *Acropora* branches. It is probable that these early colonizers had become established after the massive destruction had occurred.

The boundaries of the coral kill were again verified and measured. Total area involved was about 8 hectares (20 acres); however, some of this was sandbar and the area of actual coral death was about 6 hectares (15 acres). Coral of the suborder Fungiina was alive and consisted of *Pavona* and *Porites,* both of finger and solid species. Suborder Faviina was represented by numerous healthy colonies of *Lepastrea purpurea* (Dana) and *Galaxea fascicularis* (Linnaeus). One of the chief contributors to the inshore reef edge was *Psammocora con-*

tigua (Esper), which was growing vigorously. Based on skeletal morphology *Psammocora* has been classified by various taxonomists as either in the suborder Astrocoeniina or in Fungiina. In this instance its response was like that of the members of the latter suborder.

During the latter visit to Samoa I had access to a study of the corals in this area done by Dr. James Maragos in 1972 (Helfrich, 1975). At that time a group of University of Hawaii scientists made an environmental impact study of the Pala Lagoon during which transects were laid out, two of them (labeled A and B) being in the area I was studying. He made coral counts and estimates of coral cover, and I repeated the same observations so that our results could be compared.

Water currents were also observed. At high tide an object floating with the surface currents along the inshore stream toward the tip of Coconut Point traveled at the rate of 10 meters per minute. The water depth was measured along the contour of the sandy bottom at the site of the wrecked fish trap. It was estimated that at high tide about 250 cubic meters of sea water passed this site per minute. It was obvious that if a toxic agent alone was responsible for the destruction noted, huge amounts must have been used or else it must have been far more toxic to live corals and more specific for certain kinds than anything I tested.

Living coral on the reef flat is usually interspersed with sand or rubble areas and patches of rock often overgrown with calcifying algae so that many species may be present and still the total area covered by live coral is usually less than 50 percent. In observations along transects A and B both in 1972 and in 1974 the diversity and amount of coral cover were virtually the same with the exception that all the Astrocoeniina corals reported as abundant in some points during the first study were entirely absent in the second. These transect lines missed all the large thickets of *Acropora* in the areas dredged for airport fill; still, *Acropora* corals alone constituted a fourth of all corals reported on these two transects. My survey showed that large areas previously covered with these corals now showed only rock or rubble and, in the deeper areas, sand. Voucher specimens of living and dead corals were taken for possible analysis as well as many photographs for future reference.

Two other areas of similar coral kill were observed on Tutuila reefs during the later visit. One, far out in the north shore bay of Masefau where it was not readily accessible to humans, covered about 2/3 hectare and had consisted mostly of *Acropora formosa* and *Pocillopora damicornis*. It was surrounded on all sides by living corals of the same genera. The dead branches were covered by strands of brown algae and showed no gross disintegration. The second, half the size but otherwise similar, was at the edge of moderately deep water in

Faga'itua Bay. These were observed with Dr. Ronald Needham, a resident marine zoologist who asserted that these areas had appeared healthy 4 months previously.

Conclusions

My studies indicate that reef corals are surprisingly tolerant to the pesticides and herbicides that I tested but will succumb to general protoplasmic poisons. There are thousands of such compounds known and many combinations were used in the Samoan agriculture industry. Only a preliminary survey using a few of the better-known and representative agents could be made and of these DDT and endrin have already been banned for commercial use in the United States. In many instances these substances are lethal to fish and marine invertebrates in much smaller concentration than that which caused only a mild decrease in the activity of the coral polyps (Portmann, 1970). Undoubtedly, higher concentrations of this select group of biocidal agents would have shown greater toxicity; however, I surmised that if reef corals continued to function well after continuous exposure to these agents for 24 hours there was little likelihood that there would be a deleterious effect from such agents if added to the sea water that swept over a coral reef to be immediately diluted in the open ocean. It appeared as if all the corals had been exposed to some noxious agent at the same time as it was being carried along by natural water currents. The contours of the area of dead coral suggested that this may have happened near high tide or as the waters were being swept out of Pala Lagoon on a falling tide.

The sea water passing over the reef and then across the fish trap in question was copious in any tidal cycle but far less than the volume exchange in Pala Lagoon. The University of Hawaii survey estimated that this could approach a million cubic meters per tidal cycle, or 10 times the amount that I estimated to be passing by the fish trap. It would have required that 500 grams of any biocidal agent be added to the inshore stream per minute to maintain a concentration of 2 ppm in the flowing water. Larger applications would certainly give heavy concentrations locally but the swift water overturn would make any effect transitory.

These reef corals must have been extremely sensitive to some toxic agent that was not a general protoplasmic poison but specific for only a select suborder of otherwise hardy animals. No biocidal agent that I encountered gave any effects like this. I could conclude only that the pesticides and herbicides I evaluated could not under ordinary circumstances have caused this kind of havoc.

Various studies of coral-reef destruction implicate the consequences of industrialization such as sedimentation, oil spills, blasting, and eutrophication. There are also many natural phenomena causing reef damage such as storms and earthquakes, thermal extremes, sea-water dilution, or reef drying, as well as predation by natural enemies that live on the reefs. Undoubtedly there are many other causes that singly or in combination serve to destroy coral reefs and reef corals.

Massive, unexplained coral die-offs may not be uncommon on Samoan reefs and probably happen elsewhere, but they have received little attention. It is probable that coral polyps like other living organisms are subject to diseases either intrinsic or caused by bacterial or viral invaders. It is possible that an epizootic malady could affect only one suborder among corals as it does in other zoological orders. Attributing this particular coral kill to an extraneous pollutant is entirely on circumstantial evidence which initially to me was convincing. If no toxic agent in itself would cause such a curious pattern of coral death, we can speculate that the suborder Astrocoeniina may have been weakened by some epizootic disease which may also have been present in other areas of Samoa as noted. The unusual configuration that began at a fish trap may have been coincidental; however, it is not beyond reason to believe that actual death may have resulted from a noxious agent acting on weakened corals. It is doubtful if a single process could have produced such an unusual result.

As with other natural disasters to coral reefs, the corals of Coconut Point will probably reestablish themselves if allowed to do so. It is hoped that the present survey may serve as a base line to chronicle the regrowth of another coral garden.

Summary

The dominant suborder of reef corals died suddenly in an 8-hectare area on an American Samoan reef while two nondominant suborders of coral and other life were spared. Circumstantial evidence linked this to a fish trap. Pesticides were suspected, but laboratory studies of representative biocides indicate that short-term exposure of reef corals to some commonly used pesticides caused no discernible harm.

II. Recolonization of a Denuded Coral Reef

The coral reefs of Tutuila, American Samoa, were well known to John Flanigan, a teacher in Samoa. As an avid naturalist he was dismayed when in July 1973 he found one of his favorite reef areas denuded of most of the previously living coral. At that time we mapped the area of Coconut Point, Figure 1, and found that scleractinian corals of the dominant suborder Astrocoeniina had recently died leaving their algae-covered unbroken skeletons in place. Two nondominant suborders of reef coral seemed unharmed. An 8-hectare area was involved, mostly reef flat swept by sea water which had passed through a fish-trap weir. We concluded that it was not coincidental that only certain corals, in the lee of this net made of chicken wire, were dead.

A year later I again surveyed the area, made coral counts, procured voucher specimens, and took photographs. I concluded then that this phenomenon was probably due to an epizootic infection of unknown type affecting only the astrocoeniinid corals, but that sudden death had been triggered by a chemical substance entering into the water, presumably to kill fish.

Coral reefs are complex structures of living animals and plants. Although to the casual observer they may appear immutable, they are a balanced ecosystem in which every element is subject to change; a constant reshaping takes place with a reciprocity between build-up and destruction—first one component being in ascendancy and then the other. Every organism is involved in both actions, including the hard corals which together with certain calcareous algae are the foundation builders of all coral reefs. Corals reproduce sexually, disseminating minute larvae which settle on some stable surface and increase by asexual division as they form a reef mass with their calcium carbonate skeletons. In time these die and others take their place. This study concerns such a succession and coral recolonization.

Studies of the recolonization of destroyed coral reefs have for the most part been directed toward the damage inflicted by the spiny starfish *Acanthaster plancii*. When such a massive infestation has passed over a reef there remain remnants of viable coral tissue, and remarkable recovery can occur in as little as five years (Randall, 1973; Pearson, 1977); however, the coral species profile may then be altered. Shinn (1976) noted that reef recovery following a hurricane is often rapid and is accomplished mostly by asexual regeneration of scattered coral debris. Recovery of a reef destroyed by cold is much slower and is accomplished by settling of viable planula larvae. This is similar to the phenomenon which follows the destruction of a coral reef by a lava flow. Grigg and Maragos (1974) estimate that it may take 50 years for complete recovery of a sheltered reef, while in exposed areas with rapid seawater turnover, complete recolonization and substantial recovery may occur in 20 years. I have uncovered no reports on the recolonization of a reef which was selectively denuded of its dominant corals while leaving substantial numbers of nondominant species, as well as the algae, echinoderms, mollusks and fish, relatively undisturbed except through loss of habitat. The following is an assessment of the recolonization of such a reef suddenly bereft of the coral genera *Acropora*, *Montipora*, and *Pocillopora* five years before.

Methods

During an environmental impact assessment for a Pala Lagoon dredging project, Maragos (Helfrich, 1975) recorded the bottom cover and coral counts of two transects that lay within my study area. The exact location of these transects could only be estimated from the published maps, so specific transects were established during my 1974 study (see Part 1, fig. 1). Transect A extends 400 meters at a compass heading of 95° mag. from a concrete bunker erected in 1942 on the southeast tip of Coconut Point almost to the reef edge. Transect B runs from the same bunker at 135° mag. across Avatele Passage 400 meters to where Avatele Point meets the Pago Pago International Airport runway embankment. Where practical, iron stakes were driven every 50 meters to mark transects. Following previous methods, bottom cover estimates were made at 10-meter intervals along these transects. The percentage of bottom coral species was determined along transect A at 25-meter intervals to give 16 determinations. Live corals were identified, voucher specimens procured, and at a favorable low tide selected photographs of the area were taken.

The entire 8-hectare area was again examined as well as the surrounding reef areas during November 1978 to estimate coral growth and recolonization. Work was done on foot at low tide in the shallows or with mask and snorkel in Avatele Passage and in the deep borrow pits excavated when the airport runways were constructed. I was assisted by Mr. Flanigan on three of these excursions.

Findings and Discussion

Erosional changes have occurred along the Coconut Point shoreline (Catell, 1977). The bunker from which transect A begins, although constructed on land, was on the beach in 1969 and by 1978 was separated from land by 35 meters, with much water from the inshore lagoon flowing west of it except at low low tides. The sand which has been eroded has been deposited on an extensive sand flat immediately south of Coconut Point and also in the borrow pits. Huge thickets of *Acropora formosa* occupied these same deeper areas prior to 1973 at which time they all died.

Water levels have changed over portions of the reef flat so the water depth along transect A is now considerably less than when I first waded in it in 1969. This is very noticeable in the midsection and terminus of the transect

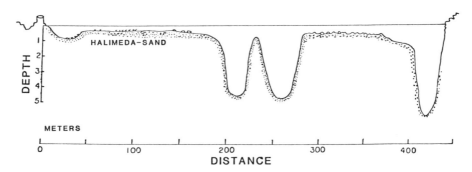

FIG. 2.   Reef contour and substrate composition of Coconut Point transects A and B,
1978 (20 times vertical exaggeration).

which is now a continuation of the long Nu'uuli reef crest and is fully exposed
at low tide (fig. 2). This change in contour of the reef is reflected in the coral
counts taken in different years. Table 3 lists both the bottom cover and the
coral counts by species. There are significant differences between the counts
and estimates of Maragos in 1972 and my figures of 1974. Some of these result
from variations in interpretation, such as what was counted as benthic algae
and what was sediment; however, I believe the coral estimates are reasonably
accurate. Coral counts recorded by transect quarters are given in Table 4.
While there are no appreciable differences in the numbers of corals recorded in
the first three quarters of transect A in 1972 and 1974, it is noteworthy that
they were made by different examiners. There is a marked disparity in the terminal quarter. The lower coral count in 1974 is largely due to the absence of
Astrocoeniinae corals and two species of *Porites*. The changing contours of the
reef are thought to have resulted in further decrease in Transect A coral
counts, despite some recolonization by species absent in 1974. Bottom cover
distribution for 1978 is given in Figure 3. This shows a general pattern similar to that found in 1974 but not identical to it.

In 1978 further reconnaissance on both sides of transect A revealed no vestiges of Astrocoeniina corals within 200 meters north of the transect, whereas

TABLE 3.   Transect A: Bottom Cover and Coral Growth in 400 meters

	Percent of cover		
	1972	*1974*	*1978*
Bottom cover			
Living coral	38.3	26.6	21.8
Rubble	29.0	24.4	40.6
Benthic algae	15.5	3.7	13.0
Consolidated			
coral rock	6.2	28.7	14.1
Sediment	7.0	16.6	10.5
Sponges, basalt,			
echinoderms, etc.	4.0	−	−
	100	100	100.0
Coral growth			
Psammocora contigua	11.0	8.0	4.7
Pavona frondifera	7.8	12.9	14.5
Porites of lutea	4.8	4.9	1.6
Synarea convexa	3.8	−	.77
Pocillopora damicornis	3.2	−	.23
Porites andrewsi	2.2	8	trace
Acropora formosa	2.0	−	trace
Montipora foveolata	3.5	−	−
	38.3	26.6	21.8

TABLE 4.   Coral Counts for Transect A, in Percent of Cover, by Quarters

Quarter	Coral count—Percent of Cover		
	1972	*1974*	*1978*
0 - 100 m	8.75	7.36	9.81
101 - 200 m	12.94	11.54	3.48
201 - 300 m	7.05	7.05	6.61
301 - 400 m	9.54	.64	1.87
	38.38	26.59	21.77

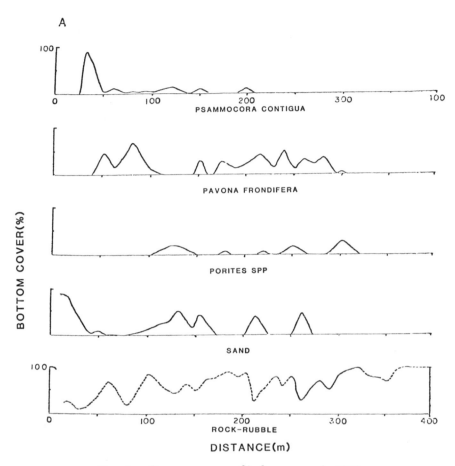

FIG. 3.   Bottom cover profile for transect A, 1978.

in 1974 there were substantial numbers of these species over the reef flat. At that time *Pocillopora damicornis* was very abundant near the *Pavona* ridge about 50 meters north of the fish trap remnants. These had all disappeared and had been replaced by *Pavona* sp.; however, 150 meters further north the species distribution and abundance were much like that found near the fish trap in 1974.

These changes in coral distribution suggest that the epizootic disease process hypothecated as one factor in the coral death of 1973 (see Part I, p. 359) actually extended far beyond the limits of denudation outlined at that time. Eventually this had resulted in a coral death over a much wider area than first reported. The establishment of *Pavona* sp. in certain areas is better understood

TABLE 5.   Transect B: Bottom Cover and Coral Growth in Distal 40 Meters. (Data for first 200 meters given as 1978 (2).)

| | Percent of Cover | | | |
	1972	*1974*	*1978(1)*	*1978(2)*
Bottom Cover				
Living coral	24.5	24.0	21.2	7.5
Rubble	18.7	32.2	39.25	20.5
Benthic algae	15.9	–	8.0	22.8
Sediment	40.7	32.5	31.3	44.7
Rock, etc.	–	11.2	–	4.5
	99.8	100.0	99.7	100.0
Coral Growth				
Porites andrewsi	11.5	4.0	4.0	–
Porites lutea	6.9	20.0	20.0	2.0
Acropora formosa	6.0	dead	–	–
Psammocora contigua	.3	–	–	4.2
Pavona spp.	–	–	–	1.3
Alveopora sp.	–	–	–	Occ.
Leptastrea purpurea	–	–	–	Occ.
	24.5	24.0	24.0	7.5

when it is realized that the leaves of this species are easily broken off and washed downstream and continue to grow wherever they lodge on the reef flat. Thus many of the heads of *Pavona frondifera* recorded in Table 3 were embedded in rubble and not attached to any firm substrate. This also happens to a lesser degree with *Psammocora* but not with the other species recorded here to any great extent.

Between 1973 and 1978 in the area south and within 30 meters of the terminus of transect A many colonies of *Acropora formosa* and *Pocillopora damicornis* had established themselves in water that was 40-120 centimeters deep at low tide. Had the reef profile not changed during these years, it is conjectured that the coral profiles on the 1978 study would have resembled that recorded in 1972 with the exception of the genus *Montipora,* which did not reestablish itself in this area. *Montipora,* although not ordinarily regarded as a colonizing genus, is common on most Samoan reefs. Its total absence anywhere near the transects remains unexplained.

Transect B data is recorded in Table 5. Bottom cover for only the distal 90 meters was available for 1972 and 1974. These data together with recent data are given under 1978(1). In addition, the bottom cover of the proximal half of the transect is recorded under 1978(2). Those areas not included encompass the deeper borrow pit areas that formerly were filled with thickets of *Acropora formosa*. These thickets were dead but standing in 1973, but by 1974 they had crumbled to rubble, resulting in a bottom of mostly sand and silt. By 1978 there were some new banks of *A. formosa* in these areas, some of which were 6 by 10 meters in size with individual stalks to 50 centimeters tall. Also in the deeper areas are patches of the calcareous branching algae, *Halameda* sp. as extensive as the coral and not previously recorded. In the intermediate depths are large areas which have been continuously covered with *Porites andrewsi* but for the most part, the silt appears too soft at present to afford a settling site for any coral larvae.

Avatele Channel was at one time lined on the reef flat side by extensive banks of *Acropora formosa* which had disappeared by 1974. The survey of 1978 showed occasional heads of *A. humilis* and *A. nana* toward the seaward end while heads of *A. hyacinthus* up to 30 centimeters in diameter were common throughout. Large patches of *A. aspera*, *A. exigua*, and *A. formosa* were noted in the Pala Lagoon end of the channel. Also, *Pocillopora damicornis* and *P. verrucosa* had been established. *Montipora* sp. was present but in small colonies and scarce.

Besides the reestablished astrocoeniinid corals and the species found on the reef flat, others were encountered including *Fungia fungites*, *F. scutaria*, *Favia* cf. *rotumana*, *Platygyra rustica*, *Galaxia fascicularis*, *Lobophyllia* cf. *costata* and *Euphyllia glabrescens*. Fish were numerous, as were echinoderms and other invertebrates. While many Samoan reefs are heavily infested with the starfish *Acanthaster planci* at this time (Birkeland and Randall, 1979), only two small ones have been encountered in the entire study area, both in deeper water at the seaward end of Avatele Channel.

Conclusions

A portion of Coconut Point reef was denuded of many of its scleractinian corals 5 years before the present study. Recolonization by natural processes has occurred since then and is proceeding rapidly. Most of the species that had died out have reestablished themselves and do not appear abnormal. Although reef contours have been changing since they were formed and will continue to do so, these natural processes have been modified by human interference, in this instance by the dredging of landfill borrow pits. This may in part account for increased beach erosion along Coconut Point. Many of the huge coral thickets had occupied these transient deep areas which are gradually being filled in by sediment. Initially these corals were established on a firm substrate immediately following the initial dredging. It has yet to be shown what growth patterns will follow a destruction as recorded on this reef.

The *Acropora* thickets previously found in these particular areas will probably never be reestablished as they were in 1969 because of changes in substrate; however, it is reasonable to predict that an extensive well-developed reef can be established in as little as ten years provided the physical conditions remain adequate and there are nearby reefs to furnish viable larva for settlement. Only five years have passed since an extensive coral kill was documented and the Nu'uuli reef is well on its way to renewing itself, although it will take many more years before this reef can be considered to be mature.

REFERENCES

BIRKELAND, C., and RANDALL, R. H.
  1979.   *Acanthaster plancii* (Alamea) studies in American Samoa, 53 pp.   Amer. Samoa, Dep. Mar. Resources.
CATELL, S. A. (for Environmental Consultants, Inc.)
  1977.   Marine reconnaissance survey for Coconut Point shoreline erosion control project. Nu'uuli American Samoa study, 119 pp.   U. S. Army Eng., Pac. Div., Rep. ECI-139.
FLANIGAN, J. M., and LAMBERTS, A. E.
  1981.   *Acanthaster* as a recurring phenomenon in Samoan history.   Atoll Res. Bull., no. 255, pp. 59-62.
GRIGG, R. W., and MARAGOS, J. E.
  1974.   Recolonization of hermatypic corals on submerged lava flows in Hawaii.   Ecology, vol. 55, pp. 387-395.
HELFRICH, P.; MARAGOS, JAMES E.; et al.
  1975.   An assessment of the expected impact of a dredging project for Pala Lagoon, American Samoa, 76 pp.   Honolulu, University of Hawaii Sea Grant Program.
LAMBERTS, AUSTIN E.
  1973.   Alizarin deposition by corals, 163 pp.   Ph.D. dissertation, University of Hawaii.
  1975.   Measurement of alizarin deposited by coral.   Proc. 2d Int. Coral Reef Symposium 2, pp. 241-244. Great Barrier Reef Committee, Brisbane.
LAMBERTS, AUSTIN E., and GARTH, JOHN S.
  1978.   Coral-crab commensalism in xanthids.   Pacific Science, vol. 31, no. 3, pp. 245-247.
PEARSON, R. G.
  1977.   Coral reef recovery following *Acanthaster* infestations.   Mar. Res. in Indonesia, vol. 17, p. 119.
PORTMANN, J. E.
  1970.   The toxicity of 110 substances to marine organisms.   Shellfish information leaflet. Min. Agr. Fish and Food, vol. 19, pp. 1-10.

RANDALL, R. H.
  1973.   Coral reef recovery following extensive damage by "Crown of thorns" starfish *Acanthaster plancii* (L.).   Proc. Second Int. Symp. on Cnidaria. Publ. Seta Mar. Biol. Lab., vol. 20, pp. 469-489.
SHINN, E. A.
  1976.   Coral reef recovery in Florida and the Persian Gulf.   Environmental Geol., vol. 1, pp. 241-254.

AUSTIN E. LAMBERTS

Exploration and Research at Olduvai Gorge and Laetoli, Tanzania, 1974-1980

Principal Investigators: Mary D. Leakey, Centre for Prehistory and Palaeontology, Nairobi, Kenya; Richard L. Hay, Department of Geology and Geophysics, University of California, Berkeley, California.

Grant Nos. 1298, To Leakey, in support of archeological and paleontological
1445, 1591, 1723, excavations at Olduvai Gorge, Tanzania, and the Laetoli
1782,[1] 1861, 1886,[2] Beds, and in support of the Centre for Prehistory and Pa-
1992, 2138, 2205.[3] laeontology, Nairobi.

Grant Nos. 1593, To Hay, for investigation of the stratigraphy and geology of
1863, 2041, 2177, the Laetoli area in northern Tanzania.
2346.

I. ARCHEOLOGICAL AND PALEONTOLOGICAL INVESTIGATIONS

Olduvai Gorge 1974-1980

1974

Fauna. An intensive search for microvertebrate fauna was carried out in Beds II, III, and IV over a period of three months. A fair number of specimens was obtained from various sites, but the numbers did not compare with the amount of material obtained from Bed I.

Miss M. Jackes, of the University of Toronto, discovered an unusual accumulation of faunal remains in Bed I. It consisted of a mass of bones, teeth, and horn cores about 3 meters long and 1 meter wide, and it contained an exceptionally high proportion of carnivores. Included were parts of the large sabretooth cat *Megantereon* and the skull of a wolflike animal, *Canis africanus.* No stone tools were found at this site and the accumulation of bones seems to have been of natural origin and not the result of hominid activity, as is usually the case at Olduvai Gorge.

---

[1] Contribution from Marpro, Ltd., for Olduvai Gorge and Laetoli research project.
[2] Contribution from C. Terry Brown for Early Man Program in Tanzania.
[3] Contribution for Early Man Program in Tanzania.

Study of the faunal material from Beds III and IV was completed.

The JK Pits. A contoured map of the pits was made by Dr. Celia Kamau. It may be noted that a present-day equivalent of these pits was observed by Philip Leakey when flying over northern Kenya. It is believed that the modern pits are used for extracting salt from saline earth to supply livestock. A visit to this area will be made during 1982.

Fossil Pollen. Dr. Raymonde Bonnefille obtained some results from samples collected in Beds I and II. The pollen from lower Bed I indicates humid conditions. Grasses predominate higher in Bed I, and it seems that the climate became increasingly dry during the course of Bed I, but wetter again in lower Bed II, where the vegetation resembles that of lower Bed I.

Geology. Dr. Richard Hay completed his volume on the geology of Olduvai Gorge.

The Camp. Thanks to the generosity of Mr. Gordon Hanes and the building expertise of Mr. George Dove, a permanent stone building was erected at the campsite. Two large underground cisterns were also constructed to collect rainwater from the roof. A second-hand Land Rover was purchased to replace the Toyota Land Cruiser, which had proved an unsatisfactory vehicle. The Peugeot 404 used for traveling to and from Nairobi was capsized by the driver and a 504 station wagon purchased in its place.

1975

Members of the Research Committee of the National Geographic Society and of the Board of Trustees visited Olduvai during June, camping in the Side Gorge. They also made a day trip to Laetoli and were able to see exposures of the Laetoli Beds which have since proved so important in the study of human evolution.

Further extensive sampling of Beds I and II for pollen was carried out by Dr. Raymonde Bonnefille. Also, Professor Allan Cox of Stanford University collected a large number of samples for paleomagnetic readings. Particular attention was given to trying to locate the exact level in the Olduvai sequence at which the transition from the Matuyama Reversed Epoch to the Brunhes Normal Epoch took place (it is now known that even upper Bed IV has reversed polarity).

The JK Pits. A site museum, financed by Mr. Gordon Hanes, was constructed over the pits.

The Camp. Mr. Gordon Hanes, accompanied by two friends, installed two wind-operated generators to supply electricity to the camp. The entire camp was wired for electric light and storage batteries were set up.

Fieldwork for this year was concentrated on the Pliocene site of Laetoli, 30 miles south of Olduvai.

1976

The most important research at Olduvai during this year was experimental stone tool manufacture by Mr. P. R. Jones from Oxford, who spent four months endeavoring to identify the methods employed by early man for making the types of stone tools used at different periods in the Olduvai sequence. Conditions are particularly favorable at Olduvai for this research, since the sources of all the principal raw materials used by early man are known and still available today. The results of Mr. Jones's work will form a chapter in the forthcoming monograph on Beds III and IV. As a result of this work it has become evident that the nature of the rocks employed is an important factor in the nature and extent of trimming on stone tools.

During 1976 a total of 25,989 persons visited Olduvai Gorge, a figure higher than ever before.

1977

This year was devoted almost entirely to research at Laetoli and study of the results in the laboratory at Olduvai. Dr. and Mrs. Alan Gentry, from the British Museum (Natural History), visited the Olduvai camp and prepared a report on the Laetoli Bovidae.

Owing to the closure of the Kenya-Tanzania border, the number of visitors to the Gorge was greatly reduced.

1978 AND 1979

Research at Laetoli and laboratory work again occupied the greater part of the year, but Dr. W. Auffenburg, paleontologist from the University of Florida, who is a specialist on reptiles, examined the collections of fossil tortoises from Olduvai and prepared a report.

Maintenance of sites, repairs to roads and fences, etc. was carried out by a reduced staff when fieldwork at Laetoli was not in progress. Wages and expenses were refunded by the Antiquities Department.

1980

The Olduvai Monographs. No progress was made on the volume describing the sites and the artifacts from Beds III and IV, owing to delay in the computer analysis of the bifacial tools by Drs. D. A. Roe and Paul Callow.

A meeting was held in London, during the Royal Society Symposium on the Emergence of Man, between Mr. Robin Derricourt of the Cambridge University Press, Professor P. V. Tobias, Professor Michael Day, and myself to discuss the publication date for the volume on *Homo habilis*. Professor Day undertook to forward his descriptions of the postcranial material to Professor Tobias before the end of the year and Professor Tobias agreed to write his concluding chapter and finalize the volume by the end of the year.

Olduvai Fauna.   Dr. C. S. Churcher completed the description of the Olduvai equids. He kindly undertook the study in place of Dr. D. A. Hooijer, who was forced by ill health to retire. It seems that the fossil equids include forms ancestral to the living Grevy and Burchell's zebras as well as *Hipparion,* the three-toed horse. The earliest known wild ass is recorded from Bed II, Olduvai.

An overall study of the Olduvai fossil bird collection was begun by Mrs. D. Matthiesen at the University of Florida, Gainesville. Her research has been made possible by a grant from the L. S. B. Leakey Foundation.

The Olduvai and Laetoli Collections.   The Antiquities Department completed the Laetoli laboratory at Olduvai. This has enabled the entire collection of fauna and footprint casts to be housed in the new building, while the Olduvai artifacts and fauna from Beds III, IV, and from the Masek Beds, are housed separately in the old building. With the help of two Tanzanian students and a student from Bedford College, London, both collections have now been catalogued and stored in covered boxes with insect repellants.

Fieldwork.   Mr. P. R. Jones returned from Oxford, where he obtained a diploma in prehistoric archeology, and initiated excavations in Bed II, with funding from the L. S. B. Leakey Foundation. He plans to excavate a series of early Acheulean sites of approximately the same age, where the tools are made from different materials, and so to continue his study of the effects of raw materials on the technology of bifacial tools.

Laetoli Beds, 1974-1980

Results of exploration of the tuffs of the Laetoli Beds in Tanzania during the period 1974-1980, supported by grants from the National Geographic Society, were published by Mary D. Leakey and Richard L. Hay in *Nature* (1979, see References). The following paragraphs update that report.

THE HOMINID FOOTPRINTS AT LAETOLI

A trail of hominid tracks made by three individuals was found in 1978 at Site G by Dr. Paul Abell, Professor of Chemistry at Rhode Island University.

He first noticed the impression of a heel that appeared to be hominid, although all the front part of the footprint had been removed by erosion. Excavation of the surface soil south of the heel print revealed more prints made by the same individual as well as another set of prints to the east. These were at first considered to be single prints made by a much larger foot, but when the southern part of the trails was uncovered in 1979 it was found that the large prints were double, made by two individuals, with the second placing his or her feet in the steps of the first.

The trails were made by three individuals walking to the north. Judged by the equal alignment of the trails and the similar state of preservation of the prints, they appear to have been walking together at a slow pace. A total length of 27 meters has been excavated, in which there are 39 prints of the smallest individual and 30 of the dual prints. In the southern part of the trail, 5 to 10 centimeters of the upper unit of the Footprint Tuff covered the surface with the footprints; as a result, they are entirely unweathered and in an excellent state of preservation.

The smallest individual, who made the trail of single prints, had an average foot length of $7\frac{1}{4}$ inches and the third individual, who overprinted the footsteps of the second, an average length of $8\frac{1}{2}$ inches. On the basis of modern man, in whom the foot length represents approximately 15 percent of stature, these two individuals would not have stood more than 4 to $4\frac{1}{2}$ feet tall. The greater part of the footprints of the leading individual in the dual trail have been obliterated by the second, but the toe impressions and the front part of the footprints are generally preserved. These are bigger and wider than either of the other two, and indicate that this was probably a larger individual. The distribution of weight appears to have been entirely human and it is noticeable that in the prints of the smallest individual the heels are particularly deeply imprinted.

Interpretation of the behavior pattern evinced by these three trails can only be hypothetical, but it is possible that they represent a male followed by a female, with a juvenile walking alongside on the left. Whatever the mode of progression may have been, the Laetoli hominid footprints have given us unequivocal proof that as long ago as $3\frac{1}{2}$ million years some Pliocene hominids were fully bipedal, with a free-striding, upright gait and feet similar to those of modern man. It is perhaps surprising, in view of the fact that the hands were thus free for carrying objects or any other activity, that no stone tools, nor even utilized stones have been found in the Laetoli Beds. Accumulations of broken animal bones representing food debris, such as occur two million years ago at Olduvai Gorge, are equally unknown. It seems likely that the Laetoli hominids existed as roving bands, getting whatever food was available, and had not yet become either hunters or habitual meat eaters, although they would probably have scavenged when possible. Once the need arose to cut through the skins of animals in order to obtain meat, sharp instruments would have been required, since their canine teeth were relatively small and not suitable for this purpose. In fact, it may have been the need to cut through hides that first gave rise to the use of sharp stones and eventually to the manufacture of stone tools.

MARY D. LEAKEY

II. STRATIGRAPHY AND GEOLOGY OF THE LAETOLI AREA

Grants for 1976, 1978, and 1979 (nos. 1593, 1863, and 2041, respectively) supported geologic fieldwork in the Laetoli area of northern Tanzania as part of the exploration of Pliocene hominid-bearing deposits by Dr. Mary D. Leakey. The aim of my work was to establish the stratigraphy, age, and origin of the sedimentary rocks.

Prior to this fieldwork with Dr. Leakey's expedition, only the Laetoli Beds (Pliocene, $\sim$ 3.6-3.8 myr BP) and Ngoloba Beds (late Pleistocene) had been recognized. Fossils were assigned to one or the other of these units, with consequent paleontologic confusion. The stratigraphy proved to be much more complex than this, and the following sequence was established.

Ngaloba Beds ($\approx$ Ndutu Beds of Olduvai Gorge; $\sim$ 50-150,000 yr BP),

Olpiro Beds ($\approx$ middle Bed II of Olduvai Gorge),

Naibadad Beds ($\sim$ 2.1 myr BP; in part correlative with Bed I),

Ogol Lavas (2.4 myr BP),

Ndolanya Beds ($\sim$ 2.5-3.5 myr BP; composed of two units separated by disconformity),

Laetoli Beds ($\sim$ 3.6-4.0 myr BP).

Much of the 1978 and 1979 field seasons was spent studying the Footprint Tuff of the Laetoli Beds, which contains many thousands of footprints, including at least 75 of early hominids. The tuff, almost 15 centimeters thick, was subdivided on a fine scale and individual laminae representing thin ash falls were correlated over the Laetoli area ($\sim$ 70 kilometers squared). Detailed study indicated that the Footprint Tuff was deposited over a relatively short period—a few weeks to perhaps as much as a few months. The lower part of the tuff was deposited during the latter part of the dry season, and the upper part of the tuff was deposited during the rainy season. The stratigraphic distribution of footprint types fits with this hypothesis, and the nature and abundance of footprints in the upper part of the tuff appears to represent the rainy-season migration characteristics of the East African savannah. This tuff gives a most remarkable glimpse of animal life at a geologic instant in time.

Several publications have already resulted from this work (see References), and the general stratigraphic geology is described by me as part of the monograph being prepared on the results of Dr. Leakey's expeditions in the Laetoli area.

This report, which has been completed, describes all the stratigraphic units in the Laetoli area. These are from oldest to youngest, the Laetoli Beds, Ndolanya Beds, Ogol Lavas, Naibadad Beds, Olpiro Beds, and Ngaloba Beds. The Laetoli and Ngaloba Beds have yielded hominid remains, and other fossils have been collected from all units but the Ogol Lavas and Naibadad Beds. Only the Laetoli and Ngaloba Beds have been previously described in scientific literature.

Fieldwork at Laetoli in 1981 was carried on during the period July 8 to July 30, supported by grant 2346. It resolved the remaining stratigraphic problems and provided a proper geometrical and chronological framework for the archeologic materials and faunal remains.

The stratigraphy and paleontology of the Ndolanya beds were finally worked out. These fossiliferous deposits lie between the Laetoli Beds (~3-6 myr BP) and the Ogol Lavas (~2-4 myr BP). The Ndolanya Beds are subdivided into upper and lower units separated by a disconformity. Preliminary identifications suggest that the fauna from one locality was on the order of 0.5 myr BP older than remains from other localities. Work in 1981 showed that all the fossils are from the upper unit, which casts doubt on the older faunal age assignments. Restudy of the supposedly older fauna showed it to be of substantially the same age as that of the other remains.

Another important accomplishment was assignment of the faunal and archeological site excavated by J. W. K. Harris to the Ngaloba Beds (< 0.4 myr BP) rather than the Olpiro Beds (~1.2 myr BP). Moreover, the Ngaloba Beds were subdivided into lower and upper units. The lower unit, to which Harris's site belongs, is characterized by Acheulian tools, whereas the upper unit contains MSA (Middle Stone Age) artifacts.

The stratigraphy of the Footprint Tuff of the Laetoli Beds was worked out in more detail than previously (Leakey and Hay, 1979). The tuff is now subdivided into 18 ash layers, each of which was the product of a single eruption or closely spaced series of eruptions. Additional observations confirm that these ash layers accumulated over a few weeks from the latter part of the dry season into the rainy season. New inferences can now be made about the climate, environment, and fauna over this short period.

RICHARD L. HAY

REFERENCES

HAY, RICHARD L.
  1978.   Melilitite-carbonatite tuffs in the Laetolil Beds of Tanzania.   Contribu-
            tions to Mineralogy and Petrology, vol. 67, pp. 357-367.
  1981.   Paleoenvironment of the Laetolil Beds, northern Tanzania.   Pp. 7-24
            in "Hominid Sites: Their Geologic Settings," G. Rapp and C. F. Von-
            dra, eds. American Association for the Advancement of Science, Selected
            Symposium 63, 310 pp.
HAY, R. L., and LEAKEY, M. D.
  1982.   The fossil footprints of Laetoli.   Scientific American, vol. 246, pp. 50-
            57.
LEAKEY, MARY D.
  1971.   Olduvai Gorge, vol. 3. Excavations in Beds I and II, 1960-1963, pp.
            xxix+306. Cambridge University Press.
  1981.   Discoveries at Laetoli in N. Tanzania.   Proc. Geol. Assoc., London.
  1981.   Tracks and Tools. Pp. 95-102 *in* "the Emergence of Man."   Royal Soci-
            ety-British Academy Symp., Phil. Trans. Roy. Soc., London, vol. B
            192.
LEAKEY, MARY D.; DAY, M. H.; and MAJORI, C.
  1980.   New hominid fossil skull (L.H. 18) from the Ngaloba Beds, Laetoli, N.
            Tanzania.   Nature vol. 284, pp. 55-56.
LEAKEY, MARY D., and HAY, RICHARD L.
  1979.   Pliocene footprints in the Laetolil Beds at Laetoli, northern Tanza-
            nia.   Nature, vol. 278, pp. 317-323.
LEAKEY, MARY D.; HAY, RICHARD L.; CURTIS, G. H.; DRAKE, R. E.; JACKES,
          M. K.; and WHITE, T. D.
  1976.   Fossil hominids from the Laetolil Beds.   Nature, vol. 262, pp.
            460-466.

Paleoecology of Grasshopper Pueblo, Arizona

Principal Investigator: W. A. Longacre, Department of Anthropology, University of Arizona, Tucson, Arizona.

Grant No. 1370:   In support of prehistoric habitat reconstruction by mammalian microfaunal analysis at Grasshopper Pueblo, Arizona.

The aim of this study was to reconstruct the prehistoric environment of Grasshopper Pueblo by analysis of mammalian microfaunal remains. Grasshopper was a large masonry pueblo occupied during the 14th century. Elucidation of the details of the paleoecology of the area is of particular interest, because several types of data indicate that the climate is different now than at the time of occupation (Thompson and Longacre, 1966; Longacre and Reid, 1974; Olsen and Olsen, 1970; Dean and Robinson, 1982).

Mice, because of their extremely small size (10-40 grams) and largely nocturnal habits, were probably not an important food source for the prehistoric peoples of Grasshopper Pueblo. Rather, these small mammals were living in and around the site, especially in storage rooms and trash heaps, during and after its occupation. At death, some of them were buried and subsequently preserved by sediments filling the site. Because many species of mice are known to be restricted to characteristic habitats, the presence of some of these ecologically informative species in the microfaunal collections from Grasshopper enables inferences about the prehistoric habitats surrounding the site.

Once microfaunal material is identified to the species level and ecological data about the extant mouse community in the vicinity of the site are gathered, comparisons between the extant and prehistoric faunas can be made. Both the taxonomic composition of the faunas and the relative abundances of the animals in them are of potential interest. However, because of the vagaries of the processes of death, deposition, and preservation, relative abundances of fossil and extant communities are difficult to evaluate and compare directly. This study, therefore, concentrated mainly on differences in species compositions of the faunas. Because mice living in habitats in the direct vicinity of a site are included in an archeological fauna, differences between species compositions of prehistoric and modern microfaunas may be the result of real differences in the past and present environments—and therefore the mouse communities—in the area. Other factors, however, such as sampling effects or introduction of bone material into the site by the activities of its human occupants or of animals (carnivores, predatory birds), may also be operative. It is necessary to determine which of these are important before accurate paleoecological interpretations of archeological microfaunas are possible. Taxa present in the extant fauna yet missing from the archeological fauna can often be attributed to sampling errors. The animals in question may have been present prehistorically, but simply might not have been included in or successfully preserved by the sedimentation processes at the site. Or, they may not have been recovered during the course of the excavations. Conversely, mice represented in the prehistoric fauna but seemingly absent from the present fauna may actually be living in the area of the site, but perhaps they are rare or extremely secretive, thus escaping detection by the field biologist.

Comparisons between the present and prehistoric microfaunas at Grasshopper enabled reconstruction of the prehistoric environment in the area. Combined with the analysis and interpretation of other data, such as the results of dendroecological, faunal, and pollen analyses, it was possible to estimate the magnitude of the temporal differences in the environment and to postulate the relative importance of climatic-induced versus human-induced variables in the process of environmental change.

Study Area

Grasshopper Pueblo, occupied from about A.D. 1275-1400, is located in east-central Arizona (110° 40' E, 34° 5' N) on the Salt River drainage, 17.4 kilometers northwest of Cibecue on the Fort Apache Indian Reservation. Elevation is about 1,850 meters. The surrounding area, the Mogollon Rim, is a geological transition zone between the Colorado Plateau to the north and the Basin and Range Province to the south. The vegetation is also transitional, with components from both the Upper Sonoran Desert and the Evergreen Woodlands (Lowe, 1964). Topographic diversity in this region enhances its biotic diversity.

The current vegetation in the vicinity of Grasshopper consists of upland stands of pinyon pine *(Pinus edulis)*, juniper *(Juniperus)*, and ponderosa pine *(Pinus ponderosa)*, with a mixture of grasses *(Bouteloua, Euphorbia, Erigeron, Agropyron,* and *Plantago)* in the valley bottoms. Extensive areas support open shrub associations of oak *(Quercus)*, manzanita *(Arctostaphylous)*, sumac *(Rhus)*, juniper *(Juniperus)*, and mountain mahogany *(Cercocarpus)*. The mean annual precipitation is 475 millimeters and comes as late summer thunderstorms and winter rain and snow (U. S. Department of Commerce, climatological data).

The most common nocturnal rodents in the area are *Peromyscus boylii* (Allen) (brush mouse), *Peromyscus maniculatus* (Merriam) (deer mouse), and *Neotoma stephensi* (Goldman) (Stephen's wood rat). *P. maniculatus* is the most widespread, occupying many habitats including ponderosa pine and mixed coniferous forests and sagebrush *(Artemisia)*-grass associations (Bailey, 1931; Findley et al., 1975). *P. boylii* inhabits shrublands and pinyon-juniper woodland (Holbrook, 1975; Harris, 1963); *N. stephensi* is associated with pinyon-juniper woodland (Harris, 1963). Several other species are present in the vicinity of Grasshopper, including Ord's Kangaroo rat *Dipodomys ordii* (Merriam), the Mexican vole *Microtus mexicanus* (Mearns), and the Western harvest mouse *Reithrodontomys megalotis* (Baird).

Methods

IDENTIFICATION OF ARCHEOLOGICAL MICROFAUNA

Taxonomic efforts focused on the identification of archeological mouse mandibles to species level, because they are more abundant and often better preserved than postcranial skeletal elements. In addition, mandibles are more readily identifiable to lower taxa than most other bones. The Grasshopper microfaunal collection is dominated by species of the white-footed mouse *Peromyscus,* a genus with 8 species occurring in a large range of habitats in the Southwest.

Subtle interspecific morphological differences preclude reliable identification to species level of isolated *Peromyscus* mandibles by comparison to reference specimens from museum collections. Archeological specimens of *Peromyscus* present even greater taxonomic difficulties because they can be fragmentary and lack teeth. Even complete mandibles with relatively unworn teeth pose difficulties; Hooper (1957) showed considerable intraspecific variation and interspecific similarities in molar structure of *Peromyscus* species. However, the proper use of multivariate statistical procedures, whereby many characters are evaluated simultaneously, provides the most potent approach to archeological microfaunal taxonomy; discriminant function and canonical variates analyses greatly aid reliable species-level identification of mandibles. In these analyses, a series of measurements taken on each unknown specimen is compared to measurements taken on groups of modern specimens of known identity. The archeological specimen is placed in the cluster (i.e., modern species) it most closely resembles statistically.

Each archeological specimen was identified to the genus level by inspection; subsequent multivariate analyses allowed species-level identifications. The reference species and sample sizes used for each genus were: *Peromyscus maniculatus* (32), *Peromyscus boylii* (37), *Peromyscus difficilis* (27), *Peromyscus truei* (24), *Peromyscus leucopus* (37), *Peromyscus crinitus* (15), *Peromyscus eremicus* (18), *Reithrodontomys megalotis* (12), *Reithrodontomys montanus* (11), *Microtus mexicanus* (12), *Microtus montanus* (9), *Microtus pennsylvanicus* (9), and *Microtus longicaudus* (13). Although many of these species do not currently occupy east-central Arizona, the possibility that some of these might have occurred in the Grasshopper area in the past needed to be considered. The reference specimens were adult animals from the collections of the Museum of Vertebrate Zoology (University of California, Berkeley), the Museum of Southwestern Biology (University of New Mexico), and the Museum of Vertebrate Biology (University of Arizona).

Up to 17 measurements (Holbrook, 1975) were made to the thousandths of a millimeter on each mandible with an EPOI Measuring Shopscope. Broken mandibles had missing measurements. Most mandibles with 9 to 17 measurements were readily identifiable.

ECOLOGICAL INVESTIGATION

The study of the extant nocturnal rodent fauna in the vicinity of Grasshopper entailed documenting what species occur there currently and what local habitats each occupies. This information was necessary to any interpretations of the significance of species in the prehistoric (archeological) rodent fauna. The ecological investigation consisted of two approaches. First, during 1975 a series of rodents was collected from a variety of habitats in the area, including ponderosa pine forest, manzanita-oak shrubland, juniper-oak shrubland, pinyon-juniper woodland, grassland, etc. Elevation of the sampling sites ranged from 1,575 to 1,880 meters. The skin and skeleton of each trapped animal were saved; these enabled positive identification of each specimen.

Second, three local habitats within 2 kilometers of the Grasshopper ruin underwent detailed ecological study. In each of these habitats, two 1.5-hectare study sites were established. Live trapping (mark and recapture) studies of the rodents on each site during the summers of 1975-1977 revealed the details of vegetational use by the resident species. The vegetation on each 100-trap-station grid was mapped in detail, including the estimated size and diameter of each woody plant. Rodent captures could be examined with respect to the frequency of occurrence of certain plant species and also the total density and three-dimensional structure of the vegetation. In addition, on each grid 40 "arboreal" trap stations were established by permanently affixing to a log, bush, or tree a horizontal wooden platform on which the trap was placed. Captures of rodents at the arboreal trap stations enabled a delineation of the amount and nature (if any) of arboreal activity of each rodent species. For each grid, the total season captures for each individual animal and each species were analyzed in the light of vegetation use, arboreal activity, and spatial distribution with respect to other individuals and other species.

During the 1976 and 1977 field seasons, several ecological experiments helped to reveal the existence of possible competitive interactions and habitat selection among the 3 most common nocturnal species in the area—*Peromyscus maniculatus, Peromyscus boylii,* and *Neotoma stephensi.* These included the removal (by live trapping) of 1 or 2 resident species on a grid and documentation of any changes in spatial occurrence, population density, or habitat use by the species remaining on the plot. Presumably, if a competing species was removed from an area, the remaining species might compensate by expanding or altering their patterns of resource utilization. Since the relationships between vegetation and rodent species were of primary concern in this study, these aspects were monitored during the removal experiments. Several different removals, each with a paired control (undisturbed) grid, provided data about competitive interactions and how these influence rodent species use of the vegetational resources in several local habitat types. In the second ecological experiment, the habitat on one-half of a study plot in manzanita-oak shrubland was altered and the rodent species response monitored. During a one-week period in the middle of the 1976 field season, the crowns of all woody plants on the treatment plot were cut at ground level and removed from the area. The root systems of the plants remained intact; there was a minimum of disturbance to the substrate. Trapping of the cleared area during the second half of the field season documented the response of *P. boylii, P. maniculatus,* and *N. stephensi.* Continued trapping of the grid during 1977 delineated the longer term response of the rodent populations to the cleared area.

Results

Both the snap trapping and live trapping revealed that 4 species of mice and 2 species of rats occur at present in the vicinity of Grasshopper. Of the 179 snap trapped animals, 112 were *Peromyscus boylii,* 45 *P. maniculatus,* 10 *Reithrodontomys megalotis,* 1 *Dipodomys ordii,* and 11 *Neotoma stephensi.* Total captures during 1975 to 1977 on the live-trapping grids were: *P. maniculatus* 236, *P. boylii* 1467, *R. megalotis* 58, *Microtus mexicanus* 5, *N. stephensi* 468, and *D. ordii* 176. During the past three years, *P. boylii* has been by far the most common mouse in the vicinity of Grasshopper. It occurs in a wide variety of woodland and shrub habitats, including pinyon-juniper woodland, manzanita, oak, and juniper shrublands, and ponderosa pine forests. Grass-covered valley bottoms are the only local habitats in which *P. boylii* does not occur. Throughout most of its range in the Southwest, *P. boylii* is usually closely associated with oak and/or chaparral habitats. *P. maniculatus* is ubiquitous throughout most of the Southwest. Near Grasshopper, it is most abundant in grassland and sparse shrubland habitats; it is less common in the more thickly vegetated habitats. It has been considered to be competitively excluded from woodland and shrubland habitats by other *Peromyscus* species, being left to exploit the more sparsely vegetated, less preferred local habitats (Findley et al., 1975). Both *M. mexicanus* and *R. megalotis* were captured less frequently than the 2 *Peromyscus* species. Typically, *M. mexicanus* occupies grassy areas in ponderosa pine forest, although it occasionally occurs in pinyon-juniper woodlands. The few captures of this species in the vicinity of Grasshopper occurred in grass areas in manzanita-oak shrubland. Since *Microtus* construct runways in grass, it is usually easy to tell if they are present in an area. I never found runways near Grasshopper, even in apparently suitable habitat, but at higher elevations (2,120 m) about 9 kilometers away, there was abundant evidence of *Microtus* near small ponds and other sources of permanent moisture. The species, thus, seems to be a very uncommon member of the mouse fauna extant near Grasshopper.

Reithrodontomys megalotis occurred in shrubland habitats, especially those dominated by manzanita and oak. I never trapped it in pinyon-juniper woodland or ponderosa pine forest. This species might actually be more abundant near Grasshopper than its relatively few trapping records indicate. Its small size and apparently secretive habits make it a difficult animal to catch.

As is typical of the species, I caught *Neotoma stephensi* in pinyon-juniper woodlands or stands of young juniper and oak. It did not occur in open habitats such as grassland, or in ponderosa pine forest. *Dipodomys ordii* lived only in areas of loose soil and sparse vegetation, either grass or shrubs.

Live trapping revealed the details of vegetational use, particularly arboreal activity, by *Peromyscus maniculatus, P. boylii,* and *Neotoma stephensi*. These are fully described in Holbrook (1979a, b). *P. boylii* and *N. stephensi* spend about half of their time climbing in foliage and on logs. By contrast, *P. maniculatus* is almost exclusively terrestrial. Removal of *P. boylii* from a habitat in which the 3 species were sympatric (juniper-oak shrubland and grassland) resulted in a slight increase in the population density of *P. maniculatus,* an increase in its activity on the plot and an expansion in the range of vegetational resources it used to include some previously utilized by *P. boylii*. This increased activity and expansion in resource use occurred within the area of the grid *P. maniculatus* had previously shared with *P. boylii*. *P. maniculatus* did not invade the more heavily vegetated areas on the grid which had been exclusively occupied by *P. boylii* and *N. stephensi*. *N. stephensi* also responded to the removal of *P. boylii*. It began to be caught in vegetation usually used by *P. boylii*, and it climbed in the highest vegetational strata which *P. boylii* had previously monopolized. When both *P. boylii* and *N. stephensi* were removed from the plot, *P. maniculatus* increased the range of its resource use even further, and it displayed increased arboreal activity. By contrast, in a pinyon-juniper woodland and manzanita-oak shrubland where only *P. boylii* and *N. stephensi* occurred, the removal of *N. stephensi* had almost no significant (or measurable) effect upon population density, spatial occurrence, arboreal activity, or vegetational utilization of *P. boylii*.

These experiments suggest that the 3 species have evolved preferences for certain habitat types. Competitive interactions temper these preferences and help account for their observed patterns of habitat use. The results of the habitat alteration experiment further supported this idea; *Peromyscus boylii* and *Neotoma stephensi* would not occupy the opened habitat, just as they will not use naturally occurring open habitats such as grassland. Thus, even in the absence of potentially competing species, each of the 3 species selects only certain gross habitat types to occupy. Competitive interactions then help to determine the details of vegetational use within each habitat.

I identified a total of 303 archeological mandibles, 285 of these to the species level. Eight species occurred in the prehistoric fauna; 3 of them were common: *Peromyscus maniculatus* (106), *P. eremicus* (87), and *P. leucopus* (51). Six species were rare: *P. boylii* (6), *P. truei* (15), *Reithrodontomys megalotis* (14), *Onychomys leucogaster* (2), and *Microtus mexicanus* (3). Most of the microfauna was recovered from room occupation levels, primarily floors (88), subfloors (19), roofs (3), fill between first-story floors (76), fill between roof and floor (95), pre-room occupation surfaces (5), and unknown provenience within the room (17). The 5 rodent species which have sample sizes greater than six did not have significantly different occurrence in the strata ($X^2 = 23.4$, NS). Specimens recovered from room overburden near the present ground surface could be the result of postoccupational burrowing and are not considered here.

The microfaunal collections from the rooms in Grasshopper Pueblo contained 1 to 7 species. Thus, I considered the microfauna from each room separately, to see what factors might influence the number of species occurring in a room. A multiple regression analysis ("Stepwise" of Barr et al., 1976) of the number of species in each room sample (dependent variable) on the total number of specimens in the room, the room construction phase (1-8), the room abandonment phase (1-4), the size of the room (m²), and the number of occupation floors (independent variables) revealed that both the number of specimens in the collection and the abandonment phase of the room account for 59 percent of the variance in and are positively associated with the number of species occurring in each room. I also tried to delineate other relationships between the architecture of the room and the number of species in the samples. There was no apparent influence of room block on the total number of species. Five species occurred in the rooms of Room Block 1 ($N=14$), and Room Blocks 2 and 3 had 7 species ($N=84$ and $N=201$, respectively).

The total number of mouse species identified in the prehistoric fauna is 8; at present 4 of these species occur at Grasshopper. No room collection contained all 8 species; only 2 rooms had 6 or more. Of the 26 room faunas, 19 had 3 or fewer species.

Table 1 shows the species composition for rooms (and strata) in four abandonment classes: floors of early abandoned rooms; trash above floors of early abandoned rooms and floors of probable early abandoned rooms; floors of probable late abandoned rooms; and floors and fill of late abandoned rooms. The room abandonment classes are from Reid (1973). Three species predominate in the prehistoric fauna from Grasshopper: *Peromyscus maniculatus*, *P. eremicus*, and *P. leucopus*. Even though relative abundances in fossil faunas do not necessarily reflect actual prehistoric species abundances, the large numbers of these 3 species indicate that prehistorically they were common near Grasshopper.

In summary, the Grasshopper microfauna has several interesting characteristics. First, the modern small rodent fauna in the vicinity is only half as diverse as the prehistoric fauna (4 versus 8 species), and all of the present-day species occur in the prehistoric fauna. Second, 2 of the numerically most abundant species in the fossil fauna, *P. leucopus* and *P. eremicus*, do not live in the vicinity of Grasshopper today. Third, although the present and prehistoric faunas are quite different in species composition and diversity, there are no conclusive indications of faunal turnover during the occupation span of the pueblo.

Discussion

The Cibecue area is of inherent biogeographic interest because of its proximity to the Mogollon Rim, a zone of rapid topographic and ecological transition which bisects east-central Arizona. The marked habitat changes in this part of Arizona present a barrier to the distribution of many rodent species. Some species reach the southern limits of their distribution at the Mogollon Rim; others only extend as far north as the Salt River. Thus, Grasshopper is located in an area at which the ranges of many rodent species abut, and fairly small alterations in climatic regimes, resulting in vegetational changes in this area, could potentially result in range extension or reduction for a variety of rodent species. Species distributions in the transitional area within a radius of about 60 kilometers of Grasshopper are not well known; this makes the interpretation of the paleoecological significance of the prehistoric fauna from Grasshopper somewhat difficult. Paleoecological reconstruction, however, must be based on whatever is currently known or inferred about the habitat associations of the species in the fauna.

Of the 8 small rodent species that occur in the prehistoric fauna, 4 currently live in the immediate vicinity of Grasshopper. These are *Peromyscus maniculatus, P. boylii, Reithrodontomys megalotis,* and *Microtus mexicanus.* Populations of *P. truei* might occur near Grasshopper now as well. Cockrum (1960) includes southern Navajo County in the Arizona range of *P. truei;* specimens have been collected within 50 kilometers of Grasshopper. Throughout most of its geographic range in the Southwest, *P. truei* is associated with pinyon and juniper, but the species is occasionally found in riparian vegetation, or in stands of oak, pine, and fir. *P. truei* is usually most abundant in pinyon-juniper woodland (Bailey, 1931; Findley et al., 1975; Wilson, 1968; Harris, 1963). Although apparently suitable habitat for this species occurs near Grasshopper, the species seems not to occupy the area. It may be that *P. truei* is simply very rare there and more trapping effort might reveal its presence. It would certainly not be surprising to catch this species near Grasshopper.

The current geographic ranges of the other 3 species in the prehistoric fauna—*Peromyscus leucopus, P. eremicus,* and *Onychomys leucogaster*—do not include the Grasshopper area. Presumably, they could be excluded from the area now by either adverse climatic conditions, lack of suitable habitat (vegetation or soil types), or biotic factors such as competition from other rodent species.

Populations of *Peromyscus leucopus* reach their western limit in Arizona; currently they almost surround Grasshopper. The species has been trapped about 60 kilometers west of Grasshopper and about 60 kilometers east of Grasshopper in the vicinity of McNary. Populations are also known to occur on the Little Colorado River near Winslow, St. John's, and Springerville. The species is abundant on the Verde River near Camp Verde. In the Southwest, *P. leucopus* is often associated with fairly well developed riparian vegetation or with river bottom brush and grass communities. It has been trapped in marshes, cottonwood and willow groves, in mesquite thickets, and in grasslands (Burt, 1933; Findley et al., 1975; Bailey, 1931; Hoffmeister and Goodpaster, 1954; Calahane, 1939). *P. leucopus* is definitely not a woodland or forest dwelling species. Since the species often occupies relatively mesic habitats along streams or arroyo bottoms, it could conceivably occur along Cibecue Creek, Canyon Creek, or Carrizo Creek, all within a few miles of Grasshopper. Prehistorically, conditions of somewhat increased moisture, resulting in enhanced stream flow in the general vicinity of Grasshopper, might

TABLE 1.   Species Composition of Rooms in Each Room Abandonment Class

Species	Room abandonment class (See notes below)			
	1	2	3	4
Peromyscus maniculatus	2	5	4	95
Peromyscus eremicus	4	6	5	72
Peromyscus leucopus	2	2	2	45
Peromyscus truei	0	3	1	12
Peromyscus boylii	0	0	0	6
Peromyscus sp.	0	1	0	17
Reithrodontomys megalotis	0	1	1	12
Onychomys leucogaster	0	0	0	2
Microtus mexicanus	3	0	0	0

1. Floors of early abandoned rooms (Rooms 41, 47, 146, 16, 23, 164, 270, 274).
2. Trash above floors of early abandoned rooms; floors of probable early abandoned rooms (Rooms 18, 24, 40, 187).
3. Floors of probable late abandoned rooms (Rooms 22, 69).
4. Late abandoned rooms, fill, and floors (Rooms 279, 280, 269, 21, 183, 210, 246, 62, 68, 19, 215, Great Kiva).

have enabled *P. leucopus* populations to move into the area. If Salt Draw contained a perennial stream, appropriate habitats for this species would certainly have been available adjacent to Grasshopper Pueblo.

Populations of *Peromyscus eremicus* now inhabit areas to the south and west of Grasshopper. Specimens of this species have been obtained on the Salt River, about 30 kilometers south of Grasshopper, and near Roosevelt Lake about 50 kilometers to the southwest. The species is primarily associated with dry, rocky grasslands and brushlands, but it is also found in pinyon-juniper woodland as well as in well-developed riparian vegetation. It is a species of valley bottoms, arroyos and riverbeds, and foothills (Hoffmeister and Goodpaster, 1954; Calahane, 1939; Hoffmeister, 1956; Findley et al., 1975; Hoffmeister, 1971). Like *P. leucopus,* it is not a montane species.

Gennaro (1968) studied populations of *Peromyscus eremicus* in New Mexico and hypothesized that the northern limit to the range of this species in New Mexico was determined in part by the absence of mesquite and in part by temperature. He noted that the average annual maximum temperature is 71°F. at the northernmost occurrence of New Mexico populations of *P. eremicus* and suggested that temperatures lower than this might be unfavorable for the species. The distribution of *P. eremicus* in Arizona includes only areas where the average January temperature is 35°F. or higher; the average July temperature in these areas is above 75°F. (Sellers and Hill, 1974; Cockrum, 1960). The average January temperature near Cibecue is between 35° and 40°F., but the average July temperature is a few degrees less than 75 (Sellers and Hill, 1974). Thus, climatic conditions—too low summer temperatures—might partially account for the absence of *P. eremicus* in the Grasshopper area at present.

The Grasshopper microfauna includes 2 specimens of *Onychomys leucogaster*. The range of this species apparently does not include the Grasshopper area now, but like *Peromyscus leucopus,* populations of *O. leucogaster* occur in several directions within about 50 kilometers. The species is mainly an occupant of grassland, mesquite thickets, and other relatively open habitats (Findley et al., 1975; Hoffmeister, 1971; Harris, 1963; Hoffmeister and Goodpaster, 1954).

Paleoecological inferences based on the species composition of the mammalian microfauna suggest that environmental conditions during the prehistoric occupation of Grasshopper were somewhat different than at present. Salt Draw might have been permanently flowing, with well-developed riparian vegetation, perhaps due to somewhat increased precipitation. Summer temperatures might have been a few degrees higher than at present, resulting in a longer growing season for agriculture. Some of the rodent species which must have been living adjacent to the pueblo (e.g., *Peromyscus boylii, P. eremicus*) indicate that relatively open shrublands and woodlands probably predominated in the area, instead of the current ponderosa pine forest.

These interpretations generally coincide with other available evidence about the Grasshopper paleoenvironment. Stratigraphic trenching operations revealed that a stream flowed prehistorically in Salt Draw, and that at one time a dam impounded water to form a small pond. Olsen and Olsen (1970) analyzed the fish and amphibian faunas from Grasshopper. The presence of 2 toad species *(Bufo alvarius* and *Bufo cognatus),* a frog *(Rana pipiens),* and the Sonora Mud Turtle in the fauna, each dependent on a water supply during all or part (the breeding season) of the year, suggests the Salt River Draw probably contained a permanent stream. In addition, the Sonora Mud Turtle *(Kinosternon sonoriense)* now lives only below 1,530-meter elevation in Arizona. If the specimen was indigenous, perhaps the Grasshopper climate was somewhat less montane.

Analyses of tree-ring specimens (Dean and Robinson, in press) revealed that the late 1200's were characterized by increased aridity at Grasshopper, corresponding to the "Great Drought" in other portions of the Southwest. This was followed by a period of increased effective moisture during the early 1300's.

There is additional evidence that environmental conditions were different during the 1300's in Arizona. For instance, Minckley and Alger (1968) analyzed fish remains from a Pueblo IV site near Perkinsville (Yavapai County) and suggested that the Verde River had a much higher water level during the

1300's. Woodbury (1961) argued that the modern distribution of trees at
Point of Pines extends to lower elevations than prehistorically. He based this
on the observed distribution of occupation and agricultural sites with respect
to the current distribution of trees. Similarly, Stein (1963) identified the he-
teromyid rodent *Perognathus* in the fauna from the Canyon Creek Phase (A.D.
1325-1400) of Point of Pines. Species of this genus occupy fairly warm, arid
habitats and apparently the genus does not occur now at Point of Pines. Several species of *Perognathus* reach the limits of their distribution within less than
80 kilometers of the site. Perhaps increased warmth and/or aridity would result in the spread of one or more of these species to Point of Pines.

Hevly (1964) reconstruced the prehistoric environment of the upper Little Colorado River by pollen analyses and use of dendroclimatological data.
From about A.D. 1100 to 1300, conditions of decreased effective moisture
with heavy summer rainfall prevailed in the area. After A.D. 1300, however,
increased effective moisture and a biseasonal pattern of precipitation developed. This could have led to perennial stream flow of previously ephemeral
rivers. Thus, a variety of evidence indicates that during the 1300's more
streams in east-central Arizona were flowing year round. In addition, at least
during the late 1200's somewhat warmer conditions than at present prevailed.

Could a habitat disturbance by the human occupants of Grasshopper Pueblo rather than climatic change account for the prehistoric occurrence of the 4
additional species nearby?

It is possible to estimate the amount of land utilized for farming by the
prehistoric inhabitants of Grasshopper. Longacre (1975) estimated the peak
population of Grasshopper to be about 1,000 people during the mid A.D.
1300's. Estimates of planted acreage needed for per capita support by Southwestern agriculturalists vary, but ethnographic studies suggest that from 0.2
to 1.2 hectares per person would be needed (Woodbury, 1961; Cook, 1972).
Thus, from 200 to 1,200 hectares might have been in production near Grasshopper by A.D. 1350. Whether this land was originally forested and had to be
cleared or whether it was mostly relatively open habitat to begin with is unclear. Dean and Robinson (in press) argued that the conditions of increased
warmth and decreased moisture in the late 1200's would have resulted in a
thinning of the local forest cover, making the area much more suitable for agriculture. Even if local habitats were vegetated more sparsely than they are at
present, much land in the general vicinity of the pueblo had to be opened for
farming; felled trees undoubtedly were used for building and firewood. As
some fields fell into disuse and other plots were cleared for farming, a mosaic
of habitats representing different stages of plant succession probably was
formed. Thus, the area consisted of patches of agricultural land, untouched

habitats such as shrubland and woodlands, and a variety of plots with mixtures of grasses and herbaceous and shrub species which are typical of early and middle stages of succession. This spatial and temporal diversity of local habitats could probably have supported a rather diverse range of rodent species.

Habitat disturbance and recovery, therefore, can account for the high diversity of rodent species, representing a range of local habitat types, in the archeological collection. Following a habitat disturbance such as clearing (by logging or fire), rodent populations quickly recover their total density (Hooven and Black, 1976; Turkowski and Watkins, 1976), but the species composition of the disturbed plot might remain basically the same or it might change in response to the vegetation change (Beck and Vogl, 1972; Krefting and Ahlgren, 1974; Sims and Buckner, 1973; Turkowski and Reynolds, 1970; Lillywhite, 1977). Usually, previously forested plots during early succession tend to support populations of species which prefer open habitats with little three-dimensional structural diversity. Later in succession, these species could be replaced by woodland and forest dwelling rodent·. Some rodent species with flexible habitat preferences might persist on the plot during the entire succession. However, the particular species present in the disturbed area as it recovers (i.e., undergoes plant succession) depend entirely on what species are locally available to colonize the plot. It is unlikely that species living farther away than a mile or two would have much opportunity to colonize a disturbed area. Thus, the human impact on the land in the vicinity of Grasshopper, which must have been substantial, probably resulted in an array of local habitat types, each with different rodent species inhabiting it. Continual habitat disturbance, in the form of clearing new plots for fields and letting others revegetate via succession, could maintain the total rodent species diversity at a relatively high level (Connell, 1978). Any of these would be likely to become incorporated in the Grasshopper microfauna. This helps account for the fact that species characteristic of different local habitats comprise the fauna of the Pueblo. This, however, does not adequately explain the occurrence of species such as *Peromyscus leucopus, Peromyscus eremicus,* and *Onychomys leucogaster* in the Grasshopper fauna, because populations of these do not now occur in the vicinity. Even if a habitat disturbance comparable to the prehistoric one occurred today, the local species diversity would probably not be increased, because source populations of additional species are too distant. Thus, prehistoric environmental conditions (over a wider range than that disturbed by humans for agriculture) must have been different to enable populations of these 3 species to enter the study area. The period of drying and increased warmth in the late 1200's probably enabled *O. leucogaster* and *P. eremicus* to spread into the Grasshopper area; the enhanced stream flow in the Salt Draw during at least part of the occupation might indicate the availability of perennial streams and riparian vegetation that would provide habitat for *P. leucopus*. In sum, several lines of evidence indicate that the prehistoric species diversity at Grasshopper Pueblo is the result of both areal climatic change and local human impact.

Acknowledgments

This work was supported by grants from the National Science Foundation, the Wenner-Gren Foundation, the National Geographic Society, and the Academic Senate of the University of California. I am grateful to W. A. Longacre and M. Graves, who contributed to the research in many ways. The Arizona Game and Fish Department issued permits for the fieldwork. I deeply appreciate the hospitality of the White Mountain Apache Indian Tribe, on whose lands this study was conducted.

REFERENCES

BAILEY, V.
  1931.   Mammals of New Mexico, 412 pp.   North American Fauna no. 53, U. S. Department of Agriculture, Bureau of Biological Survey.
BARR, A. J.; GOODNIGHT, J. H.; SALL, J. P.; HELWIG, J. T.
  1976.   A user's guide to SAS 76, 329 pp.   Sparks Press, Raleigh, North Carolina.
BECK, A. M., and VOGL, R. J.
  1972.   The effects of spring burning on rodent populations in a brush prairie savannah.   Journ. of Mammalogy, vol. 53, pp. 336-346.
BURT, W. H.
  1933.   Additional notes on the mammals of Southern Arizona.   Journ. of Mammalogy, vol. 14, pp. 114-122.
CALAHANE, V. H.
  1939.   Mammals of the Chiricahua Mountains, Cochise County, Arizona. Journ. of Mammalogy, vol. 20, pp. 418-440.
COCKRUM, E. L.
  1960.   The recent mammals of Arizona: their taxonomy and distribution, 276 pp.   University of Arizona Press, Tucson, Arizona.
CONNELL, J. H.
  1978.   Diversity in tropical rain forests and coral reefs.   Science, vol. 199, pp. 1302-1310.
COOK, S. F.
  1972.   Prehistoric demography.   Addison-Wesley Module 16, pp. 1-42, Reading, Massachusetts.
DEAN, J. S., and ROBINSON, W. J.
  ———.   Dendrochronology of Grasshopper Pueblo.   *In* "Multidisciplinary Studies at Grasshopper Pueblo, Arizona," W. W. Longacre, S. J. Holbrook, and M. W. Graves, eds.   Anthrop. Pap., University of Arizona Press, Tucson, Arizona. (In press.)

FINDLEY, J. S.; HARRIS, A. H.; WILSON, D. E.; and JONES, C.
　1975.　Mammals of New Mexico, 360 pp.　University of New Mexico Press, Albuquerque.
GENNARO, A. L.
　1968.　Northern geographic limits of four desert rodents of the genera *Peromyscus, Perognathus, Dipodomys,* and *Onychomys* in the Rio Grande Valley.　American Midland Naturalist, vol. 80, pp. 477-493.
HARRIS, A.
　1963.　Ecological distribution of some vertebrates in the San Juan Basin, New Mexico, 63 pp.　Museum of New Mexico Pap. in Anthrop. No. 8.
HEVLY, R. H.
　1964.　Pollen analysis of Quaternary archaeological and lacustrine sediments from the Colorado Plateau.　Ph.D. dissertation. University of Arizona, Tucson, Arizona.
HOFFMEISTER, D. F.
　1956.　Mammals of the Graham (Piñaleno) Mountains, Arizona.　American Midland Naturalist, vol. 55, pp. 257-288.
　1971.　Mammals of the Grand Canyon, 183 pp.　University of Illinois Press, Urbana, Illinois.
HOFFMEISTER, D. F., and GOODPASTER, W. W.
　1954.　The mammals of the Huachuca Mountains, southeastern Arizona, Illinois Biological Monographs, vol. 24, part 1.
HOLBROOK, S. J.
　1975.　Prehistoric paleoecology of northwestern New Mexico.　Ph.D. dissertation. University of California at Berkeley.
　1979a.　Habitat utilization, competitive interactions, and coexistence of three species of cricetine rodents in east-central Arizona.　Ecology, vol. 60, pp. 758-769.
　1979b.　Vegetational affinities, arboreal activity, and coexistence of three species of rodents.　Journ. Mamm., vol. 60, pp. 528-542.
HOOPER, E. T.
　1957.　Dental patterns in mice of the genus *Peromyscus,* 59 pp.　Misc. Publ. Museum of Zoology, University of Michigan, no. 99.
HOOVEN, E. F., and BLACK, H. C.
　1976.　Effects of some clearcutting practices on small mammal populations in western Oregon.　Northwest Science, vol. 50, pp. 189-208.
KREFTING, L. W., and AHLGREN, C. E.
　1974.　Small mammals and vegetation changes after fire in a mixed conifer hardwood forest.　Ecology, vol. 55, pp. 1391-1398.
LILLYWHITE, H. B.
　1977.　Effects of chaparral conversion on small vertebrates in southern California.　Biological Conservation, vol. 11, pp. 171-184.
LONGACRE, W. A.
　1975.　Population dynamics at the Grasshopper Pueblo, Arizona.　Memoirs of the Society for American Archaeology, no. 30, pp. 71-74.
LONGACRE, W. A., and REID, J. J.
　1974.　The University of Arizona Archaeological Field School at Grasshopper: Eleven years of multidisciplinary research and teaching.　Kiva, vol. 40, pp. 3-38.

LOWE, C. H., ed.
  1964.   The vertebrates of Arizona, 270 pp.   University of Arizona Press. Tucson, Arizona.
MINCKLEY, W. L., and ALGER, N. T.
  1968.   Fish remains from an archaeological site along the Verde River, Yavapai County, Arizona.   Plateau, vol. 40, pp. 91-97.
OLSEN, S. J., and OLSEN, J. W.
  1970.   A preliminary report of the fish and herpetofauna of Grasshopper Ruin. Kiva, vol. 36, pp. 40-43.
REID, J. J.
  1973.   Growth and response to stress at Grasshopper Pueblo, Arizona.   Ph.D. dissertation, University of Arizona, Tucson, Arizona.
SELLERS, W. D., and HILL, R. H., eds.
  1974.   Arizona climate, 1931-1972, 616 pp.   University of Arizona Press, Tucson, Arizona.
SIMS, H. P., and BUCKNER, C. H.
  1973.   The effect of clearcutting and burning of *Pinus banksiana* forests on the populations of small mammals in southeastern Manitoba.   American Midland Naturalist, vol. 90, pp. 228-231.
STEIN, W. T.
  1963.   Mammal remains from archaeological sites in the Point of Pines Region, Arizona.   American Antiquity, vol. 29, pp. 213-220.
THOMPSON, R. H., and LONGACRE, W. A.
  1966.   The University of Arizona Archaeological Field School at Grasshopper, east-central Arizona.   Kiva, vol. 31, pp. 255-275.
TURKOWSKI, F. J., and REYNOLDS, H. G.
  1970.   Response of some rodent populations to pinyon-juniper reduction on the Kaibab Plateau, Arizona.   Southwestern Naturalist, vol. 15, pp. 23-27.
TURKOWSKI, F. J., and WATKINS, R. K.
  1976.   White-throated woodrat *(Neotoma albigula)* habitat relations in modified pinyon-juniper woodland of southwestern New Mexico.   Journ. of Mammalogy, vol. 57, pp. 586-591.
UNITED STATES DEPARTMENT OF COMMERCE
  1965.   Climatological Data.   National Oceanic and Atmospheric Administration, Environmental Data Service.
WILSON, D. E.
  1968.   Ecological distribution of the genus *Peromyscus* in the Sandia Mountains, New Mexico.   Southwestern Naturalist, vol. 13, pp. 267-274.
WOODBURY, R. B.
  1961.   Prehistoric agriculture at Point of Pines, Arizona, 48 pp.   Memoirs of the Society for American Archaeology, no. 17.

S. J. HOLBROOK

Calibration of the Age of Mammals in Argentina

Principal Investigator: Larry G. Marshall, Department of Geology, Field Museum of Natural History, Chicago, Illinois.

Grant Nos. 1329,   In support of geochronologic (stratigraphic, biostratigra-
   1698, and 1943.   phic, paleomagnetic, and radioisotopic) studies of Cenozoic mammal-bearing beds in Argentina, and systematic studies of associated land mammal faunas (especially marsupials).

The Problem

During the age of mammals South America was, as Australia is today, an island continent. As a result of this feature the terrestrial faunas of South America developed in isolation and are dominated by autochthonous groups. South America's isolation ended about 3 Ma (million years before present), when the Panamanian land bridge came into existence. Thereafter the fossil record documents an intermingling of long-separated North and South American terrestrial faunas (Patterson and Pascual, 1972).

In South America, as in North America, Cenozoic land mammals from scattered localities are used by vertebrate paleontologists for subdivision of geologic time. This scheme has resulted in recognition of land mammal ages which are based on aggregates of genera and species of fossil land mammals whose members are inferred to have existed during a restricted interval of geologic time (Evernden, Savage, et al., 1964). A relative time scale for mammalian faunal evolution within South America is now generally agreed upon, although controversies still exist. The unique nature of South American terrestrial faunas until the latest Tertiary prevents precise paleontologic intercontinental correlation. In addition, the lack of extensive interdigitations of fossiliferous marine and nonmarine strata in South America has deterred further refinement.

Radioisotopic age determinations and/or paleomagnetostratigraphic studies of rocks associated with mammal-bearing strata and attempts to calibrate land-mammal ages in terms of an "absolute age" time scale were virtually non-existent for the South American Cenozoic. One of the three best Cenozoic land mammal records in the world thus stood virtually outside the growing framework of isotope dating despite the fact that volcanic rocks suitable for dating are commonly associated with Argentine fossil land-mammal faunas.

403

The fossil land-mammal faunas of Argentina are well known and they represent a "key" to understanding mammalian evolution on the South American continent. This stems from the fact that all but one (the Friasian) of the South American land-mammal ages here recognized (fig. 2) were defined originally on Argentine beds and faunas. It is thus important first to have a clear understanding of the Argentine succession before precise correlations of beds and faunas can be made from elsewhere in South America. In view of this priority, the goal of this research program was to establish a radioisotope time scale for the continental mammal-bearing beds and faunas of Argentina.

Such a time scale will ultimately permit paleontologists to distinguish between ecologic and temporal relationships of local faunas or faunal assemblages and to resolve ages of faunal assemblages in which primitive and advanced forms occur together (Evernden, Savage, et al., 1964). The dates will serve also as a basis for establishing rates of evolution among the faunas as a function of time; they will improve accuracy and precision of intra- and intercontinental faunal correlations; and they will govern a comparison of stages of faunal evolution between South American and faunas of other continents. The data will be of importance to evolutionary biologists, paleontologists, stratigraphers, and biogeographers, and are thus of interdisciplinary significance.

The Research—Geochronology

In January and February 1975 I visited a large number of known middle Tertiary age mammal-bearing localities in the provinces of Santa Cruz and Chubut, Patagonia, southern Argentina (fig. 1). Supported by a grant (no. 1329) from the National Geographic Society, and with the help of Dr. Rosendo Pascual, Museo da La Plata, and Mr. Orlando Gutierrez, Museo de Ciencias Naturales "Bernardino Rivadavia," Buenos Aires, I collected volcanic rocks associated with the known mammal-bearing horizons. Nine of these rocks were dated (some several times) by Drs. Garniss H. Curtis and Robert E. Drake at the Department of Geology and Geophysics, University of California, Berkeley. These dates permitted verification and refinement of ages, boundaries, and hiatuses between beds of Deseadan (early Oligocene) through Friasian (middle Miocene) age (fig. 2).

Two separate basalts from between the Deseadan and Colhuehuapian horizons at the west end of the Great Barranca ("cliff") south of Lago Colhué-Huapí gave dates of 28.8 and 24.3 Ma (million years before present), and a basalt from the same stratigraphic interval at Cerro Blanco gave a date of 35.4 Ma (figs. 1, 2). The dates from the Great Barranca are taken to represent minimal (basal) ages for the Colhuehuapian, while the 35.4 Ma date from Cerro

Blanco apparently lies conformably above the Deseadan horizon at that locality. A basalt capping the Deseadan at the east end of the Great Barranca gave a date of 27.7 Ma and is apparently of pre-Colhuehuapian age, as are the other basalts at that locality. Samples of two basalts from Pico Truncado (fig. 1) gave dates of 33.6 Ma and 27.6 Ma. The first basalt directly overlies the Deseadan horizon and the second lies 37 meters up-section from the first (Marshall, Pascual, Curtis, and Drake, 1977).

Two periods of volcanic activity are recorded by these dates, one around 34-35 Ma and the other around 25-29 Ma. The former is tentatively accepted as a terminal date for known Deseadan, and 25.0 Ma is tentatively taken as a basal age for known Colhuehuapian. The apparent paleontological hiatus between known Deseadan and known Colhuehuapian is thus in the order of 9.0 Ma (fig. 2).

Until recently, the only potassium-argon (^{40}K-^{40}Ar) date available for the whole of the Argentine mammal-bearing Cenozoic was based on a plagioclase concentrate obtained from a tuffaceous matrix from the inside of a glyptodont (order Edentata) carapace. The specimen was collected from the Santa Cruz Formation along the north side of the Río Gallegos east of Felton's Estancia (fig. 1). The tuff sample gave a date of 21.7 Ma (Evernden, Savage, et al., 1964, p. 170).

A second date of 18.5 Ma was obtained on a tuff from 116 meters above the base of the Santa Cruz Formation at Monte León (fig. 1). This sample is from a level (>100 m.) stratigraphically above the sample dated from near Felton's Estancia which is consistent with the somewhat younger age. The two dates ($\bar{x}=20.1$ Ma) indicate that at least the greater part, if not all, of the coastal Santa Cruz Formation correlates with the Aquitanian Marine Stage of Europe (fig. 2).

Biotite and plagioclase concentrates from an ignimbrite underlying the mammal-bearing tuff horizon in the Collón-Curá Formation of Friasian Age along the Río Collón Curá (fig. 1) were dated and gave ages ranging from 14.0 Ma to 15.4 Ma ($n=4$; $\bar{x}=14.5$ Ma). These dates correlate with the Barstovian land-mammal age in North America (see fig. 2) and the latest Burdigalian to Langhian marine stage of Europe (Marshall, Pascual, et al., 1977).

It now appears probable that the Colhuehuapian, Santacrucian, and Friasian are based upon a successive and relatively continuous evolutionary sequence without such hiatuses as those recognized between the lower Tertiary mammal ages. For this reason, and because of the precise stratigraphic tie-ins of the Santa Cruz beds and Colhué-Huapí beds with the intervening late Chattian Monte León marine beds, I am led to assign the Colhuehuapian age to the late Oligocene and the rest of the successive units (see fig. 2) representing the

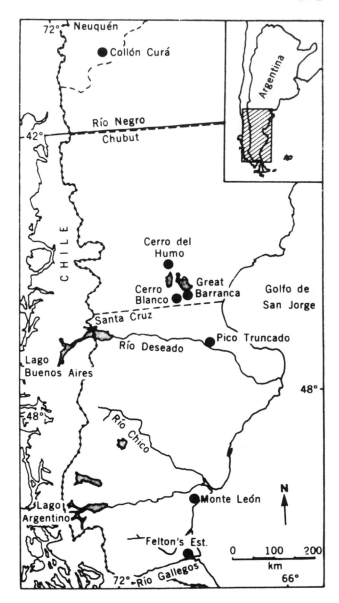

FIG. 1. Map of Patagonia, southern Argentina, showing
some mammal-bearing localities for which radioisotope
dates are available.

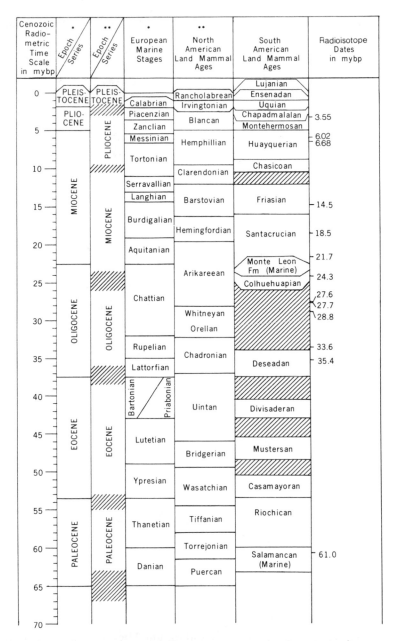

FIG. 2. Cenozoic radioisotopic time scale and chronostrati-
graphy showing approximate correlations of South American
land mammal ages and marine stages with North American
land mammal ages and European marine stages.

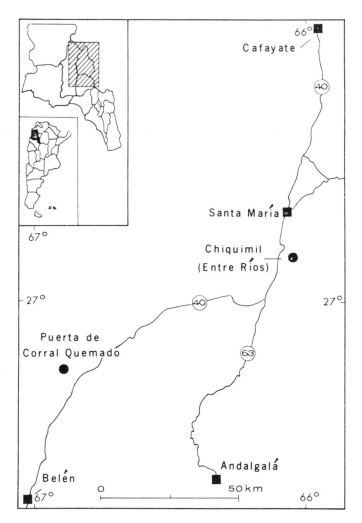

FIG. 3.   Map of Catamarca Province, northwest Argentina,
   showing the Chiquimil and Punta de Corral Quemado
   localities.

Santacrucian and Friasian to the early and middle Miocene (Marshall, Pascual,
et al., 1977; Marshall and Pascual, 1978).

   A second grant from the Society (no. 1698) permitted refinement of ages
of Late Tertiary land-mammal beds and faunas in Argentina. Beds of Huayquerian and Montehermosan Age were studied at the localities of Chiquimil

and Puerta de Corral Quemado in the province of Catamarca, northwest Argentina (fig. 3). The fieldwork was conducted between May 7 and June 3, 1977, by Dr. Robert F. Butler, Department of Geosciences, The University of Arizona, Tucson, and myself, and was carried out under the auspices of a joint expedition with Dr. Rosendo Pascual, and Sr. Galileo J. Scaglia, Museo Municipal de Ciencias Naturales "Lorenzo Scaglia," Mar del Plata. Samples of tuffs were dated by the ^{40}K-^{40}Ar method by Drs. Curtis and Drake, and block samples suitable for paleomagnetic analyses were processed by Butler.

A mean age of 3.55 Ma was obtained on several mineral concentrates from a tuff from Unit 29 in the upper part of the Corral Quemado Formation of Riggs and Patterson (1939) at Puerta de Corral Quemado. The mammal faunas from the Corral Quemado Formation are of Montehermosan Age (fig. 2). Given this age constraint, a correlation of the paleomagnetic section below this tuff suggests correlation with the normal polarity events in the Gilbert epoch (Marshall, Butler, et al., 1979).

A mean age of 6.02 Ma was obtained on several mineral concentrates of a tuff from Unit XIX of the "Araucanense" Formation of Riggs and Patterson (1939) at Chiquimil, and a mean age of 6.68 Ma was obtained on a tuff sample from Unit 8 of the Chiquimil A Formation of Riggs and Patterson (1939) at Puerta de Corral Quemado. A paleomagnetic section was also obtained through Unit 8 at Puerta de Corral Quemado. The age of 6.68 Ma for Unit 8 near the top of the paleomagnetic section constrains the polarity zonation to within Epoch 7. With this initial confinement, the polarity zonation shows a strong correlation with the greater part of Epoch 7. Faunas of Huayquerian age (see fig. 2) have been collected from above and below these units (Riggs and Patterson, 1939).

The radioisotopic and magnetostratigraphic data from Chiquimil and Corral Quemado thus permit refined estimates of durations and boundaries of faunas of Huayquerian and Montehermosan Age. Huayquerian age fossils are abundant in Unit XVII of the Chiquimil section, some 75 meters below the tuff from Unit XIX dated at 6.02 Ma. The base of the Huayquerian at that locality is thus older than 6.02 Ma. Accepting a median age of 14.5 Ma for the Friasian (Marshall, Pascual, et al., 1977), and the existence of a paleontological hiatus between known Friasian and the temporally restricted Chasicoan, the Chasicoan-Huayquerian boundary (see fig. 2) is tentatively placed at about 9.0 Ma (Marshall, Butler, et al., 1979).

The 3.55 Ma date from Unit 29 near the top of the Corral Quemado Formation provides a minimum age for the Montehermosan at that locality. The magnetostratigraphic data indicate that the Corral Quemado fauna occurs at least within the middle part of the Gilbert epoch with a maximum age of about 4.4 Ma. These data favor placement of the boundary between known Montehermosan and known Huayquerian (see fig. 2) at about 5.0 Ma (Marshall, Butler, et al., 1979).

Establishment of the Montehermosan-Chapadmalalan boundary is based on the 3.55 Ma data for Unit 29 of the Corral Quemado Formation and on biostratigraphic data. The virtually synchronous appearance of seven South American genera in North America in beds dated around 2.5 Ma favors the existence of the Panamanian land bridge by that time. If the beginning of the extensive late Pliocene faunal interchange between the Americas indicates temporal synchronization there is strong evidence for approximate equivalence of Chapadmalalan with late Blancan. Furthermore, the report that the faunas from the Chapadmalal Formation and the Monte Hermoso Formation are remarkably similar favors placement of the boundary for known Chapadmalalan and known Montehermosan (see fig. 2) at around 3.0 Ma (Marshall, Butler, et al., 1979).

Refinement of the age of beds and faunas of the earliest recognized land mammal age in South America, the Riochican, was made possible by grant no. 1943 from the Society. During January and February 1979, Robert Butler and I collected samples of volcanic rocks and oriented samples of sedimentary rocks for paleomagnetic analyses which bear directly upon the age of these earliest known land-mammal faunas in Patagonia. We were assisted by Drs. Malcolm C. McKenna of the American Museum of Natural History, and William D. Turnbull of Field Museum. Localities visited are shown in Figure 4.

The marine Salamanca Formation underlies the terrestrial Rio Chico Formation, in which the oldest described mammals in the Argentine succession occur. Two basalts which directly underlie the Salamanca Formation east of the Estancia La Angostura were dated at 62.8 Ma and 64.0 Ma. These dates provide basal ages for the Salamanca Formation at those localities (Marshall, Butler, Drake, and Curtis, 1981).

A late Danian (early Paleocene) age for the Salamanca Formation is indicated by studies of planktonic foraminifera (Bertels, 1975). This age is supported by a K-Ar date of 61.0 Ma (Andreis, 1977) on a vitric tuff from the Salamanca Formation at Cañadón Hondo (fig. 4).

Samples for paleomagnetic analyses were collected from 35 sites in a 140-meter section of the Rio Chico Formation at Cerro Redondo, and from four sites in a 5-meter section at Punta Peligro (fig. 4). The "Banco Negro Inferior" comprises the total section at Punta Peligro and is the basal-most unit at Cerro Redondo. This unit is of reversed polarity in both sections and the reversed polarity zone emcompasses approximately the lower 80 meters of the Rio Chico section at Cerro Redondo. Above this thick basal reversed zone are

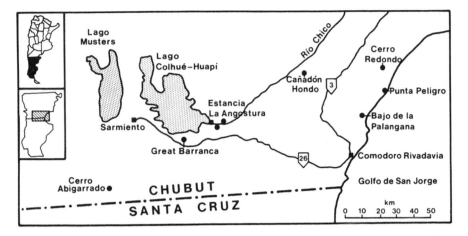

FIG. 4.   Map of central Patagonia, southern Argentina.

two normal polarity zones separated by a 15-meter reversed polarity zone. The two normal polarity zones are correlated with magnetic anomaly 25 and 26 chrons of the magnetic polarity time scale on the following evidences (Marshall, Butler, Drake, and Curtis, 1981):

1. Radioisotope dates corroborate a late Danian age for the Salamanca Formation. The late Danian includes magnetic anomaly 27 chron. Thus, none of the polarity zones in the Cerro Redondo section can be as old as anomaly 27 chron.

2. Our field observations indicate no significant unconformity between the Salamanca and Rio Chico Formations at Cerro Redondo. These observations and the demonstrated late Danian age for the Salamanca Formation require that the Salamanca-Riochican boundary be placed near the Danian-Thanetian boundary (fig. 2).

3. Given these age constraints, the magnetic polarity sequence observed at Cerro Redondo shows a strong correlation with the magnetic polarity time scale in the interval following 27 chron into anomaly 25 chron. The implied age range of the Rio Chico Formation at Cerro Redondo thus encompasses middle and late Paleocene, and corresponds in time with Torrejonian and Tiffanian land-mammal age faunas (see fig. 2) in North America (Marshall, Butler, Drake, and Curtis, 1981).

The exposures at Cerro Redondo terminate below the Riochican-Casamayoran contact, suggesting that latest Riochican time is not recorded in that section. Given the present lack of geochronologic calibration of latest Riochican, it is convenient to recognize the Riochican-Casamayoran boundary (see fig. 2) as the boundary between the Paleocene-Eocene Epochs (Marshall, Butler, Drake, and Curtis, 1981).

The geochronologic results of these studies are summarized in Figure 2. Although we have come a long way in advancing knowledge of the ages of these South American land mammal faunas, there are still many areas for which geochronologic data are still lacking. The research supported by the Society has permitted the initiation of pilot projects into these remote areas of Argentina. Recently, the National Science Foundation and the Consejo Nacional de Investigaciones Cíentificas y Técnicas in Argentina have jointly sponsored a 3-year program to continue these studies. This work is being carried out as a collaborative effort by Drs. G. H. Curtis and R. E. Drake, University of California, Berkeley; Dr. R. F. Butler, The University of Arizona, Tucson; Dr. R. Pascual, Museo de La Plata; and myself. This ambitious program would not have been possible without the initial help, encouragement, and support of the Society.

The Research—Systematic Studies

In conjunction with these geochronologic studies there has been a major effort to continue systematic studies of Cenozoic land mammal faunas of Argentina. I have emphasized studies of one group, the Marsupialia, which includes opossums and their relatives. This group is well represented in the fossil record of South America, and specimens are known from each of the recognized land-mammal ages. Circumstances thus permit a rare opportunity to study the evolutionary history of a particular group in detail. These faunal studies are tangent to those on geochronology, but much of my initial work was made possible by these grants from the National Geographic Society (see References for a listing of titles).

REFERENCES

(References marked with an asterisk (*) are the result of research done during the present study.)

ANDREIS, R. R.
  1977.   Geología del area de Cañadón Hondo, Depto. Escalante, Provincia del Chubut, República Argentina.   Obra del centenario del Museo de La Plata, no. 4, pp. 77-102.
BERTA, A., and MARSHALL, LARRY G.
  *1978.   Fossilium catalogus: South American Carnivora. pars 125, 48 pp.   W. Junk, The Hague.
BERTELS, A.
  1975.   Bioestratigrafia del Paléogeno en la República Argentina.   Revista Española de Micropaleontología, vol. 7, pp. 429-450.

CLEMENS, WILLIAM A., and MARSHALL, LARRY G.
*1976.   Fossilium catalogus. I: Animalia. American and European Marsupialia. pars 123, 114 pp. W. Junk, The Hague.
EVERNDEN, JACK F.; SAVAGE, DONALD E.; CURTIS, GARNISS H.; and JAMES, GIDEON T.
1964.   Potassium-argon dates and the Cenozoic mammalian chronology of North America. Amer. Journ. Sci., vol. 262, pp. 145-198.
MARSHALL, LARRY G.
*1975.   The Handel T. Martin paleontological expedition to Patagonia in 1903. Ameghiniana, vol. 12, no. 1, pp. 109-111.
*1976a.   Evolution of the family Thylacosmilidae, extinct saber-tooth marsupials of South America. Mus. Paleont., Univ. Calif., Berkeley, PaleoBios, no. 23 (July), 30 pp.
*1976b.   Notes on the deciduous dentition of the Borhyaenidae (Marsupialia: Borhyaenoidea). Journ. Mamm., vol. 57, no. 4, pp. 751-754.
*1976c.   Fossil localities for Santacrucian (early Miocene) mammals, Santa Cruz Province, southern Patagonia, Argentina. Journ. Paleont., vol. 50, no. 6, pp. 1129-1142.
*1976d.   Revision of the South American fossil marsupial sub-family Abderitinae. Publ. Mus. Munic. Cienc. Nat., Mar del Plata, vol. 2, no. 3, pp. 57-90.
*1976e.   On the affinities of *Pichipilus osborni* Ameghino 1890 (Marsupialia, Caenolestinae) from the Santa Cruz beds of southern Patagonia, Argentina. Ameghiniana, vol. 13, no. 1, pp. 56-64.
*1976f.   A new borhyaenid (Marsupialia, Borhyaenidae) from the Arroyo Chasicó Formation (lower Pliocene), Buenos Aires Province, Argentina. Ameghiniana, vol. 13, no. 3-4, pp. 289-299.
*1977a.   Evolution of the carnivorous adaptive zone in South America. Pp. 709-721 *in* "Major Patterns in Vertebrate Evolution," Max K. Hecht, Peter C. Goody, and Bessie M. Hecht, eds., NATO Advanced Study Institute Series, Series A: Life Sciences. Plenum Press, New York and London.
*1977b.   First Pliocene record of the water opossum, *Chironectes minimus* (Didelphidae, Marsupialia). Journ. Mammal., vol. 58, no. 3, pp. 434-436.
*1977c.   Cladistic analysis of didelphoid, dasyuroid, borhyaenid, and thylacinid (Marsupialia) affinity. Syst. Zool., vol. 26, pp. 410-425.
*1978.   Evolution of the Borhyaenidae, extinct South American predaceous marsupials. Univ. Calif. Publ. Geol. Sci., vol. 117, pp. 1-89.
*1979a.   Review of the Prothylacyninae, an extinct subfamily of South American "dog-like" marsupials. Fieldiana: Geology, new. ser., no. 3, 50 pp.
*1979b.   A model for South American cricetine (Rodentia) paleobiogeography. Paleobiology, vol. 5, pp. 126-132.
*1980a.   Marsupial paleobiogeography. Pp. 345-386 *in* "Aspects of Vertebrate History," L. L. Jacobs, ed. Museum of Northern Arizona Press, Flagstaff, 407 pp.
*1980b.   Systematics of the South American marsupial family Caenolestidae. Fieldiana: Geology, new ser., no. 5, 145 pp.

MARSHALL, LARRY G. (continued)

*1981a.   The great American interchange—an invasion induced crisis for South American mammals.   Pp. 133-229 *in* "Biotic Crises in Ecological and Evolutionary Time," M. Nitecki, ed.   Academic Press, New York.

*1981b.   Review of the Hathlyacyninae, an extinct subfamily of South American "dog-like" marsupials.   Fieldiana: Geology, new ser., no. 7, p. 120.

MARSHALL, LARRY G.; BERTA, A.; HOFFSTETTER, R. J.; PASCUAL, ROSENDO; REIG, O. A.; BOMBIN, M.; and MONES, A. ·

*In press.   Geochronology of the continental mammal-bearing Quaternary of South America.   Ch. 8, *in* "Cenozoic Mammals: Their Temporal Record, Biostratigraphy, and Biochronology," M. O. Woodburne, ed. University of California Press, Berkeley.

MARSHALL, L. G.; BUTLER, R. F.; DRAKE, ROBERT E.; and CURTIS, GARNISS H.

*1981.   Calibration of the beginning of the age of mammals in Patagonia. Science, vol.212, pp. 43-45.

MARSHALL, L. G.; BUTLER, R. F.; DRAKE, ROBERT E.; CURTIS, GARNISS H.; and TEDFORD, RICHARD H.

*1979.   Calibration of the great American interchange.   Science, vol. 204, pp. 272-279.

MARSHALL, LARRY G.; CLEMENS, WILLIAM A.; HOFFSTETTER, R. J.; PASCUAL, ROSENDO; PATTERSON, BRYAN; TEDFORD, RICHARD H.; and TURNBULL, W. D.

*1977.   Acyonidae Ameghino, 1889 (Mammalia): proposed suppression under the plenary powers.   Bull. Zool. Nomen., vol. 33, pp. 212-213.

*1978.   Acyonidae Ameghino, 1889 (Mammalia): supplement to proposal to suppress this name.   Bull. Zool. Nomen., vol. 35, pp. 12-14.

MARSHALL, LARRY G., and HECHT, M. K.

*1978.   Mammalian faunal dynamics of the Great American Interchange: an alternative interpretation.   Paleobiology, vol. 4, pp. 203-206.

MARSHALL, LARRY G.; HOFFSTETTER, R.; and PASCUAL, ROSENDO

*In press.   Geochronology of the continental mammal-bearing Tertiary of South America.   Ch. 7, *in* "Cenozoic Mammals: Their Temporal Record, Biostratigraphy, and Biochronology," M. O. Woodburne, ed. Univ. Calif. Press, Berkeley.

MARSHALL, LARRY G., and PASCUAL, ROSENDO

*1977.   Nuevos marsupiales Caenolestidae del "Piso Notohipidense" (SW de Santa Cruz, Patagonia) de Ameghino. Sus aportaciones a la cronología y evolucion de las comunidades de mamíferos Sudamericanos.   Mus. Munic. Cienc. Nat., Publ. Mar del Plata, vol. 2, no. 4, pp. 91-122.

*1978.   Una preliminar escala temporal radiometrica de las edadesmamífero del Cenozoico medio y tardio Sudamericano.   Museo de La Plata, no. 5, pp. 11-28.

MARSHALL, LARRY G.; PASCUAL, ROSENDO; CURTIS, GARNISS H.; and DRAKE, ROBERT E.

*1977.   South American Geochronology: Radiometric time scale for middle to late Tertiary mammal-bearing horizons in Patagonia.   Science, vol. 195, pp. 1325-1328.

MARSHALL, LARRY G., and PATTERSON, B.
  1981.   Geology and geochronology of the mammal-bearing Tertiary of the Val-
          le de Santa María and Río Corral Quemado, Catamarca Province,
          Argentina.   Fieldiana: Geology, new ser., no. 9, pp. 1-80.
MARSHALL, LARRY G., and TEDFORD, R. H.
  *1978. Caenolestidae Trouessart, 1898, and Palaeothentidae Sinclair, 1906
          (Mammalia): proposed conservation under the plenary powers.   Bull.
          Zool. Nomen., vol. 35, pp. 58-64.
PATTERSON, B., and MARSHALL, LARRY G.
  *1978. The Deseadan, Early Oligocene, Marsupialia of South America.
          Fieldiana: Geology, vol. 41, pp. 36-100.
PATTERSON, BRYAN, and PASCUAL, ROSENDO
  1972.   The fossil mammal fauna of South America.   Pp. 247-309 *in* "Evolu-
          tion, Mammals and Southern Continents," A. Keast, F. C. Erk, and B.
          Glass, eds.   State Univ. of New York Press, Albany, 543 pp.
RIGGS, E. S., and PATTERSON, BRYAN
  1939.   Stratigraphy of late Miocene and Pliocene deposits of the Province of Ca-
          tamarca (Argentina) with notes on the faunae.   Physis, vol. 14, pp.
          143-162.

LARRY G. MARSHALL

Biology of the Cave Swallow in Texas

Principal Investigator: Robert F. Martin, Texas Memorial Museum and Department of Zoology, University of Texas at Austin, Texas.

Grant Nos. 1301, 1418, and 1721. In support of comparative reproductive and range dynamics studies of cave swallows *(Petrochelidon fulva)* and their hirundinid nesting associates in Texas.

I. Range Extension, Reproduction, and Hybridization

The cave swallow *(Petrochelidon fulva)* previously has been thought to be isolated ecologically from other hirundinids in Texas, narrowly restricted in its breeding sites to sinkholes and caverns (Selander and Baker, 1957; Whitaker, 1959; Baker, 1962; Reddell, 1967; see Wauer and Davis, 1972, for isolated exception). Recently, its spatial relationships have changed: *P. fulva* has expanded its breeding niche in the United States to include habitats strongly modified by man and has entered into more intimate contact with other swallows. The purposes of this study are: 1, to document this range expansion; 2, to describe and compare reproductive patterns and success in cave and culvert populations of cave swallows; and 3, to describe reproductive and other interactions between culvert-nesting cave, barn, and cliff swallows.

The project was sponsored by the National Geographic Society and the Texas Memorial Museum, University of Texas at Austin. Sallie, Mark, Wayne, and Shân Martin, Michael Lewis, George Miller, Dean Hector, and Mr. and Mrs. Robert Erekson made important contributions to this portion of the research.

Study Area

Dunbar Cave, 37 kilometers west-southwest Rocksprings, Texas, a typical Edwards Plateau limestone cavern entered by a vertical sinkhole, was the site of our baseline reproductive studies of *P. fulva* (fig. 1). In the entrance chamber of this cave, a colony of from 200-300 breeding pairs nests (fig. 2) in isolation from other swallows. Temperature from May to August within the chamber varies from 17° to 22°C; daily fluctuation usually does not exceed 2°C. This breeding site is considered typical of the original nesting habitat of *P. fulva* in the United States.

417

Reproductive and other interactions between *P. fulva* and the barn swallow *(Hirundo rustica)* are studied primarily along a transect coincident with U. S. Highway 90, lying just south of the southern margin of the Edwards Plateau and spanning an east-west distance of 200 kilometers (fig. 3). Tributaries of the Nueces and Rio Grande Rivers drain the Edwards Plateau and pass through concrete culverts beneath this highway. Cave and barn swallows nest colonially or semicolonially in these culverts, sometimes isolated by species but usually intermingled in intimate syntopy. Interactions between culvert-nesting cave, barn, and cliff swallows were investigated in three culverts in the vicinity of Moore, Texas; in these culverts cliff swallows *(Petrochelidon pyrrhonota)* tend to segregate at the western ends of passageways. Data from these sites and Dunbar Cave were taken either daily or twice weekly during the breeding season, depending upon results desired.

Ongoing studies of range dynamics encompass these and other cave and culvert sites lying within that portion of Texas west of long. 98°E. and south of lat. 32°N. Within this area transects are run at least annually, and usually at more frequent intervals.

Methods

Nests were marked individually by inserting numbered nails into nest bases (Dunbar Cave) or by marking adjacent surfaces with pen or pencil. To estimate incubation period, nestling period, and fledging times of barn and cave swallows, nests were visited daily, and eggs and nestlings were marked individually. Incubation times were taken from the laying of the last egg to its hatching (Nice, 1937). To minimize the effects of disturbance by investigators, survival figures were based on data taken from nest sites visited at 3- to 4-day intervals. This latter sampling schedule generated data for which hatch time frequently was not known precisely. In these instances, reference was made to the average period of time required for incubation determined at different locations or times by daily nest visitation. Twice-weekly sampling also potentially biased "hatch" data toward underestimation of true hatch in that some very early nestling mortality may have been included with prehatching losses; approximately 30 percent of clutches scored were subject to this potential error. Egg loss and nestling mortality to 19 days (cave swallow) and 16 days (barn swallow) were determined by interpolation to midpoints of sampling gaps. Since cave and barn swallows usually laid daily until clutch completion, clutch initiation was determined by counting in reverse from the sampling day on which an egg or eggs first were found in the nest; clutch completion was determined by counting forward.

Fig. 1.   Entrance to Dunbar Cave, Edwards County, Texas.

Results, Dunbar Cave

Timing of Events.   Cave swallows were present on March 26, 1974, the date on which nest marking began. On April 2, an estimated 250-300 birds were present. Repair of previously existing nests and construction of new nests of mud and guano on chamber ceiling and walls were underway on April 9; on this date we estimated that 350 adults were present. Nests were being lined with dried grass and occasional feathers on April 16, and approximately 400 *P. fulva* were present; on this date several broken eggshells were found on the floor of the chamber. Two-thirds of the marked nests were lined by April 19; we noted several instances of the use of wool for this purpose. On April 23, 1974, approximately 500 adults were present and one egg had been deposited in nest 62. Nest 62 possessed a completed clutch of 4 on April 27 and laying had begun in 20 other marked nests. By comparison, laying began on April 22 in 1975. By May 5, eggs had been laid in 52 additional nests; 32 of these held completed clutches. Clutch starts were less numerous on successive visits. From April 27 to June 18 clutches were begun in 115 nests.

At Dunbar Cave most hatches occurred during the 15th or 16th 24-hour period following laying (N = 14; x̄ = 15.79; range = 15-18; standard error (SE) = 0.24). Ability to fly successfully was achieved at between 20 and 22 days; first nest egress of nestlings of the cave population probably normally occurs at between 22 and 26 days (table 1).

TABLE 1.   Flight Capability of Juvenile Dunbar Cave *Petrochelidon fulva* in 1975

Day post-hatch	N	Flight capability (in meters) when dropped from 1.5 m
18	17	most birds achieve < 3
19	19	majority achieve < 18 many < 3
20	22	majority achieve < 18
21	20	majority achieve 18 or > 18
22	17	majority achieve > 36
23	8	majority achieve ⩾ 36

On approximately June 18, 1974, laying again began in previously occupied nests and continued until early July. Seventy-three nests that previously had held eggs incubated to or beyond term or that had initially held young were laid in a second time (table 2). No nests in which initial laying had begun after May 22 received subsequent clutches. The latest date at which near-fledging young were present in nests in which two clutches were deposited was August 16. Three clutches were laid in only one nest; in this nest, near-fledging young still were present on August 23.

TABLE 2.   Frequency of Clutch Sizes in Nests of *Petrochelidon fulva* at Dunbar Cave, Edwards County, Texas, in 1974

	Number of eggs in clutch						Total clutches
	1	2	3	4	5	6	
First clutch (in nest)	1	2	22	76	14	0	115
Second clutch (in nest)	3	3	34	31	1	1	73

Productivity, Hatchability, Success.   In 1974, the maximum clutch size reported was 6, and the minimum, 1 (table 2). Four was the most common clutch size during the first laying period, while clutches of 3 and 4 were most

FIG. 2.   Cave swallow nests in entrance chamber of Dunbar Cave.

common and appeared in approximately equal frequencies in nests in which subsequent deposition of eggs occurred. Data on clutch size in 1974 were partitioned according to whether the eggs represented the initial or only deposition of the season in a particular nest or the subsequent clutch deposited in that nest. Within each of these categories data were partitioned semi-arbitrarily according to waves of moderately synchronous laying or to discontinuities in clutch starts; means and standard errors are presented for data within categories (table 3). Data for hatchability and survival to 19 days are presented similarly in Table 3. Table 3 also summarizes results of statistical testing (Mann-Whitney U-Test) between means of major categories. Additionally, percentages of eggs that hatched, hatched young that survived to 19 days, and eggs that hatched young that survived to 19 days are provided in Table 3.

Clutch size decreased significantly between early and late first depositions ($P < 0.05$), between early and late second depositions ($P < 0.01$), and between first and second depositions ($P < 0.001$). "Hatches" declined between

TABLE 3.   Reproductive Statistics and "Hatch"-Survival Percentages for Nests of *Petrochelidon fulva* at Dunbar Cave, Edwards County, Texas, in 1974

Vertical lines join means representing samples between which Mann-Whitney U-Tests were performed. Solid lines indicate significant difference exists (P < 0.05 or ≤ 0.05). See text for levels of significance.

Clutch sequence [1]	N	Clutch size $\bar{x}$	SE	Young "hatched" $\bar{x}$	SE	Survival (19 days) $\bar{x}$	SE	"Hatch"/ laid	Survive/ "hatch"	Survive/ laid
First clutch (early) Before May 10	87	3.95	.069	3.26	.133	2.78	.145	.82	.85	.70
First clutch (late) May 11-29	19	3.47	.159	2.42	.299	2.05	.270	.70	.84	.59
First clutch (very late) June	9	3.89	.200	3.78	.277	1.11	.351	.97	.29	.28
First clutch, late (total) May 11-July 1	28	3.61	.129	2.86	.250	1.75	.227	.79	.61	.49
Second clutch (early) Before June 30	65	3.45	.102	2.55	.140	1.31	.141	.74	.51	.38
Second clutch (late) July	8	2.75	.163	1.00	.499	.63	.419	.36	.63	.23
Total first clutch	115	3.87	.062	3.17	.118	2.53	.129	.81	.80	.65
Total second clutch	73	3.37	.096	2.40	.146	1.22	.136	.71	.52	.37
Total over-all								.78	.71	.54

[1] Chronology by nest, not adult pair; adults unmarked.

early and late first depositions (P < 0.05), between early and late second depositions (P < 0.01), and between first and second depositions (P < 0.001). Survival to 19 days decreased significantly between early and late first depositions (P < 0.001), between early and late second depositions (P < 0.05), and between first and second depositions (P < 0.001). Over-all, and within most categories, success percentages diminished with time (table 3).

Results, Culvert Populations

Distribution.   Table 4 presents the distribution of culvert-nesting cave and barn swallows along the main transect during our initial year of research; additional off-transect records are presented in Figure 3. More recent records that delineate the 1976 range margin of *P. fulva* in central and south-central Texas are presented in Figure 4. At present, the northern boundary of the

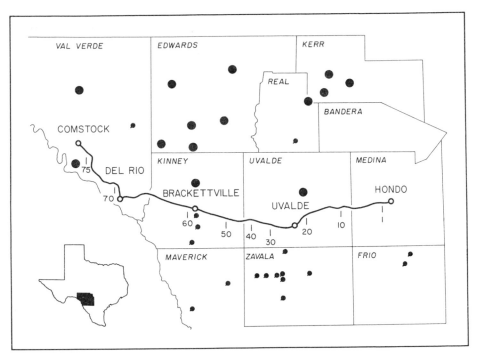

FIG. 3.   Distribution of cave swallows in central Texas in 1973. Counties italicized;
cities located by open circles. Initial, terminal, and each tenth culvert of main
study transect indicated by numbered vertical dashes. Small tagged dots represent
off-main-transect culverts occupied by both cave and barn swallows. Large dots
represent central Texas cave and sinkhole colonies of cave swallows reported recently active by Selander and Baker (1957).

range of the cave swallow is to some degree uncertain, and further exploration
of this area is planned (see Martin and Martin, 1978).

Hybridization.   Early surveys disclosed young of two phenotypes occupying a nest in culvert 8, 24.3 kilometers west of Hondo, at the eastern edge of
cave–barn swallow breeding syntopy. One of the nestlings was *H. rustica*-like
in plumage color and pattern, whereas the plumages of the other two were intermediate between those of *H. rustica* and *P. fulva*. Repeated observation indicated that both adults attending the nest were phenotypically *H. rustica*.
Originally the nest had held 5 eggs (within normal clutch size range of both
species) that apparently were laid in normal temporal sequence. However, one
nestling from this clutch disappeared from the nest in the period from 2 to 4
days after hatching, and another individual was lost either as an egg or as a

TABLE 4.   Distribution of Syntopic Culvert-Nesting Cave and Barn Swallows Along U. S. Highway 90 in Texas in 1973

(Symbols: C = cave swallows nesting; B = barn swallows nesting; CC = cave and cliff swallows nesting (Culvert 31).)

Culv. no.	7 Apr	18 Apr	2 May	15 May	30 May	15 Jun	4 Jul	18 Jul	1 Aug	15 Aug	30 Aug	15 Sep	# C	# B
1-7	Non-syntopic			(*Hirundo rustica* only)										
8	–	–	CB	CB	CB	CB	CB	CB	CB	B	–	–	2	9
9	–	B	B	B	B	B	CB	CB	CB	B	–	–	1	8
10-21	Non-syntopic			(*Hirundo rustica* only)										
22	–	–	CB	CB	CB	CB	CB	CB	B	B	B	–	3	14
23	CB	CB	CB	CB	CB	CB	CB	B	B	B	B	–	5	39
24	B	B	B	B	B	B	B	B	B	B	–	–	0	10
25	–	–	C	CB	CB	CB	CB	CB	CB	B	–	–	14	3
26	–	–	B	B	B	B	B	B	B	B	B	–	0	16
27	–	C	C	CB	CB	CB	CB	CB	CB	B	B	–	20	9
28	CB	CB	CB	CB	CB	CB	CB	CB	CB	CB	B	–	21	22
29	B	B	CB	CB	CB	CB	CB	CB	CB	–	–	–	3	8
30	–	B	B	B	B	B	B	B	B	B	–	–	0	9
31	–	–	CCB	CCB	CCB	CB	CB	CB	CB	CB	CB	–	20	12
32	CB	CB	CB	CB	CB	CB	CB	CB	CB	CB	CB	–	20	26
33	–	–	–	C	C	CB	CB	CB	CB	B	–	–	2	2
34	B	B	CB	CB	CB	CB	CB	CB	–	–	–	–	9	12
36	B	B	CB	C	C	C	CB	CB	CB	CB	CB	–	27	6
37	C	CB	CB	CB	CB	CB	CB	CB	CB	CB	B	B	14	13
38	–	–	C	C	C	CB	CB	CB	B	–	–	–	9	2
39	–	–	B	B	B	–	–	–	–	–	–	–	0	3
40	B	CB	CB	CB	CB	CB	CB	CB	CB	CB	CB	–	70	64
41	B	B	CB	CB	CB	B	B	B	–	–	–	–	4	8
42	–	–	CB	CB	CB	CB	CB	CB	B	B	B	–	6	17
43	–	B	CB	CB	CB	CB	CB	CB	B	B	B	–	12	26
44	–	–	CB	CB	CB	CB	CB	CB	CB	CB	CB	–	14	38
45	–	–	B	CB	CB	CB	CB	CB	CB	B	–	–	2	15
46	–	–	B	CB	CB	B	B	B	B	B	B	–	0	10
47	–	–	B	B	B	B	CB	CB	CB	B	B	–	1	9
48	–	–	CB	CB	CB	CB	CB	CB	CB	CB	CB	–	42	54
49	C	C	C	C	C	C	CB	C	–	–	–	–	15	1
50	–	–	B	B	B	B	CB	CB	B	B	B	–	1	4
51	–	C	CB	CB	CB	CB	CB	CB	B	B	B	–	39	3
52	–	–	CB	CB	CB	CB	CB	CB	B	–	–	–	25	7

					Date								Total clutches hatched	
Culv. no.	7 Apr	18 Apr	2 May	15 May	30 May	15 Jun	4 Jul	18 Jul	1 Aug	15 Aug	30 Aug	15 Sep	# C	# B
53	–	–	–	B	B	CB	CB	CB	B	B	–	–	1	6
54	C	C	CB	CB	CB	CB	CB	CB	CB	CB	CB	B	97	15
55	–	–	C	C	C	CB	CB	C	C	C	C	–	26	2
56	–	–	CB	CB	CB	CB	CB	CB	CB	B	B	–	14	19
57	–	–	C	CB	CB	CB	CB	CB	CB	CB	B	–	24	9
58	B	B	CB	CB	CB	CB	CB	CB	B	–	–	–	12	18
60	–	–	B	B	B	B	B	B	B	B	B	–	0	22
61	–	B	CB	CB	CB	CB	CB	CB	CB	B	–	–	4	13
62	B	B	B	B	B	B	B	B	B	B	B	–	0	19
63	–	–	B	B	B	B	B	B	B	B	B	–	0	8
64	–	–	B	CB	CB	B	B	B	B	B	B	–	1	43
65	–	B	B	CB	CB	CB	CB	CB	B	B	B	–	4	18
66	–	–	B	CB	CB	CB	CB	CB	CB	–	–	–	2	15
67	–	–	–	B	B	B	B	B	B	B	B	–	0	25
68	–	–	CB	CB	CB	CB	CB	B	B	B	B	–	2	19
69-75	Non-syntopic			(*Hirundo rustica;* some *P. pyrrhonota;* see text)										

nestling a day or so after hatching. On May 30 the *H. rustica*-like juvenile flew from the nest as it was being inspected. The two young of intermediate plumage were collected from the nest at night on June 1, but the adults escaped from the nest and were not collected.

In the two apparent hybrids the color of most of crown, nape, and back is intermediate between the glossy blue-black of juveniles of *H. rustica* and the duller dark brown of those of *P. fulva.* The breast and abdomen are cinnamon as in *H. rustica,* not white (with some cinnamon laterally) as in *P. fulva.* The rectrices have prominent subterminal white spots on their inner webs as in *H. rustica* and are not immaculately dark brown as in *P. fulva.* Most conspicuously, the rump is buffy orange as in *P. fulva,* not blue-black as in *H. rustica.*

Protein variation was analyzed in extracts of breast muscle, heart muscle, and liver of the two apparent hybrids and of eight specimens of *H. rustica* and eight specimens of *P. fulva* from the transect area. Techniques of electrophoresis and enzyme-specific staining follow those of Selander et al. (1971), as adapted for birds by Nottebohm and Selander (1972).

Most of the proteins assayed are invariable or nearly so in electrophoretic mobility in our samples of *H. rustica* and *P. fulva;* no allozymic variation within or between species was detected in 18 of the 22 proteins examined (Martin and Selander, 1975). As far as we are able to determine by electrophoresis, all individuals in our samples are homozygous for the same allele at each locus encoding these proteins. Similarly, both species have the same common allele at the albumin locus; the sample of *P. fulva* is monomorphic, but one individual of *H. rustica* is heterozygous for the common allele and another encoding a slower-migrating band. The darkest staining (anodal) esterase in liver extracts is highly variable individually in number and position of bands, but this enzyme could not be scored as a single-locus system.

Only three proteins, 6-Phosphogluconate dehydrogenose, Isocitrate dehydrogenase-1, and Adenylate kinase, showed consistent interspecific differences and thus provided a basis for confirmation of hybridization. For each of these the phenotypes of the two presumed hybrids were intermediate; detailed descriptions of banding patterns of these proteins are presented by Martin and Selander (1975).

The biochemical evidence of heterozygosity at three structural gene loci strongly supports the morphologically based interpretation of the two juveniles as interspecific hybrids. Two hypotheses concerning the origin of the hybrids may be advanced. One posits that introgressive hybridization is occurring: both adults attending the nest were parents of all nestlings, at least one parent was a hybrid (perhaps a backcross), and the disparate phenotypes of the young are the result of recombination. The second (and more attractive) hypothesis is that both attending adults were "pure" *H. rustica;* the nestling of *H. rustica* phenotype was their issue; and the two young of intermediate phenotype were the result of a mismating of the female *H. rustica* and a male *P. fulva,* possibly that associated with nest B.1 on the opposite wall of the culvert, 10 feet from nest B.5. Since this time, eleven additional instances of hybridization between these genera have been discovered; these occurred at or near the margins of the range of *P. fulva* (Martin, 1980). All hybrid young were similar in phenotype to those described above.

Discussion

North American swallows have adapted well to environments modified by human activity; several have become strongly associated with man and his works (Bent, 1942; Allen and Nice, 1952; Mayhew, 1958; Samuel, 1971). Until recently, however, this has not been the case for the cave swallow in the United States. Although occasionally reported to nest in buildings in north-central Mexico (Whitaker, 1959; Baker, 1962), prior to 1972 its breeding north of the Mexican boundary appears to have been confined exclusively to

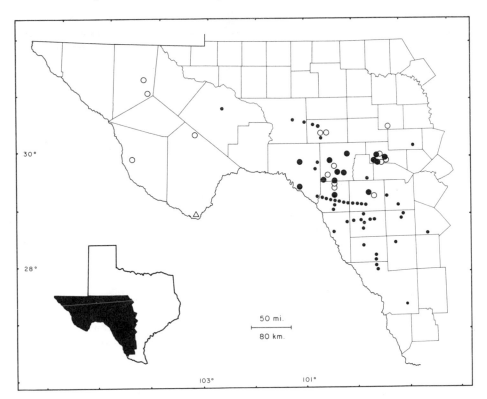

FIG. 4.   Distribution of cave swallows in Texas in 1976. Large dark circles represent
cave and sinkhole sites reported recently active by Selander and Baker in 1957.
Large open circles and open triangle represent more recently reported cave and
sinkhole sites (see text). Small dots represent recently active culvert breeding sites
(1976); two species syntopy is present at most. Northern edge of range partially
undetermined.

natural caverns and sinkholes. In 1957, Selander and Baker described only 14
active breeding sites in central Texas. By 1972 an additional 15 cave-nesting
colonies had been reported from Texas (Reddell, 1967, 1971; Wauer and Davis, 1972). Several cave-breeding colonies have been reported from New Mexico (Kincaid and Prasil, 1956; Baker, 1962). An important feature of this
exclusive use of caverns in the United States has been the isolation from other
swallows associated with it.

The situation recently has altered. The type of nesting site utilized in
Texas has broadened and an increased number of suitable sites continues to be
made available. As a consequence, the range of the species has increased con-

siderably to the east and south into flatland noncave topography and wide-spread nesting syntopy has developed with barn swallows. At several locations, intimate breeding contact exists with both barn and cliff swallows. Martin (1974) suggested several potential hazards that the species involved might face in the new situation: breakdown of reproductive isolating mecha-nisms, increased vulnerability to disease or parasitism, and enhanced competition.

Isolating mechanisms have broken down; hybridization between cave and barn swallows presently occurs at relatively low frequency, usually toward the periphery of the range of *P. fulva*. At least a portion of hybrid pairings are sta-ble for more than one laying cycle. The fate of hybrids not collected is un-known; no evidence for introgression presently exists. The repeated occurrence of such hybridization and the very high interspecies coefficient of genic similarity of 0.860 derived from our electrophoretic data (see Martin and Selander, 1975, for greater detail) cast further question upon the generic limits of *Petrochelidon* and *Hirundo*.

Data on comparative reproduction between cave and culvert populations of cave swallows are published elsewhere (Martin, 1982a); comparative repro-ductive data, between barn swallows breeding in culverts with and without nesting cave swallows, and between contact populations of cave, cliff, and barn swallows are in analysis; however, some brief summary statements may be made here. Culvert colonies of cave swallows usually begin laying earlier than the Dunbar Cave colony (Martin et al., 1977; Martin 1982a). Culvert-nesting cave swallows display significantly higher clutch size and nesting sur-vival than cave *P. fulva*. Culvert cave swallows average slightly smaller clutch-es than barn swallows at midtransect, but have similar or superior fledging percentages. Culvert-nesting barn and cave swallows begin laying at similar times of the year and have the potential to rear two to three clutches. When nesting syntopy occurs between three species of swallow, breeding success is moderate in cave and barn swallows, but usually lower in cliff swallows. Cliff swallow nests appear to be more heavily infested with ectoparasites than those of the other two species. Additionally, cave and cliff swallows are sibling spe-cies that forage at greater height than do barn swallows. I speculate that cliff swallows may be at a competitive disadvantage in foraging in these situations and that disturbance (damage to cliff swallow nest entries) by the investigator may further reduce food intake by nestlings.

In summary, the cave swallow appears to have made a successful initial transition in Texas from an isolated natural nesting habitat to an artificial sit-uation occupied by two related species. Many details of this transition are in analysis; others await future research. The situation may remain geographical-ly and competitively stable or future alteration in range or density, or both, of the cave swallow may occur, with concurrent competitive exclusion of one or several of the three species presently involved in contact.

II. Reproduction and Hybridization of Culvert-Nesting Colonies

Here I outline the pattern of reproduction of culvert-nesting colonies of cave swallows and report at length on recent instances of hybridization between barn swallows *(Hirundo rustica)* and cave or cliff swallows *(P. fulva, P. pyrrhonota)* at culvert sites. Sallie Martin, Michael Lewis, and George Baumgardner made important contributions to this portion of the study.

Study Areas and Methods

Basic reproductive data for cave swallows were gathered in 1974 at 4 culvert sites located along a 23-kilometer stretch of Highway 90, beginning and extending eastward from 13 kilometers east of Brackettville. The sites lie just to the east of the eastern boundary of the Chihuahuan Desert in a region of gently rolling hills dissected by semi-permanent streams, approximately 73 kilometers southeast of our Dunbar Cave swallow colony (Martin et al., 1977). Climatological conditions (NOAA, 1974, 1976) at Brackettville were considered representative of those occurring at the culvert sites (see also Martin, 1982a).

The culverts visited were selected from a series that averaged 1.6 kilometers apart; larger colonies usually alternated with smaller colonies within this series. Sample culverts held from 6 to 32 nesting pairs of cave swallows; although barn swallows formed 49 percent of the swallows breeding at these culverts, no hybridization occurred here. Culverts were of multiple-passageway construction; passages were rectangular in cross-section and ranged from 12.2 to 17.3 meters in length, 1.2 to 1.8 meters in width and 1.2 to 2.1 meters in height. Nests usually were constructed on the upper 15 percent of culvert walls.

Nest contents were examined at 2- to 3-day intervals. When not known exactly, clutch initiation was determined by backdating, clutch completion by foredating; hatch time not known exactly was estimated by use of the 15-day incubation characteristic of *P. fulva* (Martin et al., 1977). Egg loss and nestling mortality to 19 days post-hatch (1 day prior to flight potential) were determined to midpoints of sampling gaps. Unless stated otherwise, statistical comparisons employed the Mann-Whitney U-Test; results were considered significant at $P < .05$.

Data on hybridization were accumulated during regular (twice weekly) visitation of culvert nests of our main research transect (Hwy 90, Hondo to Comstock; Martin, 1974, 1980) and in culverts occupied by cave, cliff and barn swallows near Moore. When possible, nests that contained young morphologically intermediate between cave (or cliff) and barn swallows (see pp. 423-426; and Martin, 1980, for details of hybrid morphology) were observed, young and/or attending adults were collected, and extracts of their tissues were subjected to electrophoretic analyses of 6-Phosphogluconate dehydrogenase (6-PGD) and Isocitrate dehydrogenase-1 (IDH-1) enzyme mobilities to confirm species or hybrid identity (see Martin and Selander, 1975, for description of procedures).

Results: Reproductive Pattern at Culvert Sites

A total of 81 cave swallow nests formed our first clutch sample; a second clutch was deposited in 49 of these; 8 nests received a third clutch. Distributive statistics on clutch size, hatch, and survival to 19 days for these nests are presented in Table 5; additionally, percentages of eggs that hatched, hatched young that survived to 19 days, and eggs that hatched young that survived to 19 days are provided here.

TABLE 5.   Reproductive Statistics and Hatch/Survival Percentages for Nests of Cave Swallows in Culverts near Brackettville, Texas

Clutch sequence [1]	N	Clutch size		Young hatched		Survival (19 days)		Hatch/ laid	Sur- vive/ hatch	Sur- vive/ laid
		$\bar{x}$	SE	$\bar{x}$	SE	$\bar{x}$	SE			
Clutch 1	81	4.31	.065	3.44	.119	3.25	.127	.79	.94	.75
Clutch 2	49	3.96	.087	3.22	.166	2.92	.184	.81	.90	.74
Clutch 3	8	3.50	.188	2.38	.564	1.63	.497	.68	.16	.11
Total over-all	138							.79	.90	.72

[1] Chronology by deposition in nest; adults unmarked.

Clutch size, hatch, and survival decreased from first to second clutches; of these decreases, only that between respective clutch sizes was significant (P < .005; 2 > P > .15; .1 > P > .05). Reproductive parameters declined further in the few third clutches laid; no statistical comparisons utilizing these data were made. Hatch and survival percentages of first and second clutches were similar, but were considerably lower in third clutches.

Results: Hybridization at Culvert Sites

Clutches containing hybrid young occur at yearly frequencies of approximately .003 (1977 data) when data for all clutches of syntopic culvert nesting barn, cave, and cliff swallows are combined. Observations on nests containing hybrids during 1974, 1975, and 1977 are reported briefly below and detailed elsewhere (Martin, 1982a, b).

1974 HYBRIDIZATION AT CULVERT SITES

Culvert 9, Nest 9A6 (Medina Co. 27 km W. Hondo). Examination of nest 9A6 on May 24, 1974, indicated that the 4 juveniles present were of 2 phenotypes. Three of the nestlings present were similar to *H. rustica* in plumage color and pattern, while the plumage of the fourth was similar to that of a juvenile *P. fulva*. At this time the nest was attended by two adults of *H. rustica* phenotype; among 9 other nests active in this culvert, only nest A7, approximately 3 meters north of 9A6 and containing 3 young slightly older than those occupying 9A6, was attended by *P. fulva* adults. Originally, nest 9A6 held 5 eggs, apparently laid in normal temporal sequence. One egg (or very young nestling) was lost during a sampling interval. As the suspect hybrid developed, it assumed the plumage characteristic of an *H. rustica* × *P. fulva* hybrid, while the other young developed typical *H. rustica* plumage. On June 5, the hybrid alone remained in the nest *(H. rustica* fledge earlier than *P. fulva)*. On June 7 it was gone from the nest, presumably fledged normally. This nest subsequently was active from June 19 to July 20; 2 young of *H. rustica* phenotype were fledged (Martin, 1982b).

Culvert 9, Nest A8. Examination of nest A8, approximately 6 meters west of nest 9A6 and 3 meters west of nest A7 (*P. fulva* occupation), on July 17, 1974, disclosed 4 young of 2 phenotypes: 3 *H. rustica*-like individuals and 1 similar in plumage to *P. fulva*. Two adults of *H. rustica* phenotype previously had attended this nest, rearing in normal sequence 4 *H. rustica*-like young that fledged about June 7. Subsequent observations of A8 on the night of June 25-26 indicated that both adults attending a clutch of 5 eggs were typically *H. rustica* in appearance; at that time, of 10 active nests in culvert 9, only nest A7 was attended by *P. fulva* adults. The clutch in A8 was laid in normal sequence; 1 young was lost at between 2 to 7 days post-hatch. Three young developed juvenile plumage characteristic of *H. rustica* and fledged on July 26 in my presence; on this day, the other young had developed hybrid plumage, was photographed, and returned to the nest. Later that day, it flew from the nest in the presence of a co-worker at an age not exceeding 20 days post-hatch.

Nest 9A7, positioned between nests 9A6 and A8, was attended by 2 *P.*

fulva and was active continuously from April 27-28 through July 13. Two clutches of 4 eggs were laid (the second while fully feathered young still occupied the nest); two groups of 3 young fledged successfully. The first egg of the clutch of 9A6 that contained the hybrid was laid within 1 day of the date upon which the first clutch was completed in A7. The final clutch laid in A7 was completed approximately 1 week before the first egg of the hybrid-containing clutch in A8 was laid (Martin, 1982b).

Since nest A7 was the only cave swallow nest active during the period during which laying took place in hybrid-producing nests A6 and A8, and since clutch size, laying sequence, and observed attendants of all nests appeared normal morphologically, I hypothesize that all juveniles of *H. rustica* phenotype produced in nests A6 and A8 were the issue of *H. rustica* nest attendants, and that both young of hybrid phenotype were the result of "mismatings" of the A7 male *P. fulva* and the *H. rustica* females attending nests A6 and A8. Alternate hypotheses exist, but are less parsimonious.

Culvert 300, Nest Bx13 (Frio Co., vic. Moore).   Visitation of nest Bx13 on May 18, 1974, indicated that the 5 juveniles present were of 2 phenotypes; as development continued, 3 assumed *H. rustica* plumage, while 2 acquired hybrid plumage. The nest had existed since the previous season and was of apparent cave swallow-type construction. Beginning approximately April 24, 5 eggs had been laid in apparently normal temporal sequence. Observations on the night of May 22 disclosed that 2 birds, one of *H. rustica* and one of *P. fulva* phenotype perched at the nest. On May 29, 4 fully-feathered young (2 *H. rustica*-like; 2 hybrid) were in the nest; 1 of each type was collected. Beginning on June 12, a second clutch of 4 eggs was laid in this nest. Observations on June 15 indicated that adult *H. rustica* and *P. fulva* still attended the nest. Four young hatched subsequently, but before they could be identified, the nest failed (vacant nest, July 6). Beginning on July 17, a third clutch of 4 eggs was laid in the nest; all hatched. Subsequently, 1 young was lost before it could be identified and the remaining 3 young developed plumage typical of *H. rustica*. During observation on August 10, an adult attendant of this nest was identified as *H. rustica;* a cave swallow fluttered nearby and scolded the investigator, but a positive association between this bird and nest Bx13 could not be established. Biochemical analyses later confirmed the hybrid (Martin, 1980).

The simplest hypothesis concerning events at this nest involves a female *H. rustica* "losing" her conspecific male and accepting a *P. fulva* male that remained with her through the second clutch. Nest Bx14, 1.6 meters distant, attended by (at least) 1 *P. fulva,* and fledging *P. fulva* young, was in close synchrony with this nest for two laying-rearing cycles; possibly a polygynous system existed. Positing that the third clutch (young of *H. rustica* phenotype) of Bx13 was the result of the mixed pair necessitates involving previous and continuing introgressive hybridization; lacking evidence of this, it is simpler to assume that nest Bx13 was abandoned by the mixed pair after their second clutch, and was reoccupied by a different (conspecific) pair of birds. Alternatively, if a polygynous system existed between nests Bx13 and 14, the female *H. rustica* of Bx13 remated conspecifically when the pair of *P. fulva* attending Bx14 left after their second rearing cycle. Other, more complicated, hypotheses also exist.

Culvert 300, Nest Ay21. Examination of Nest Ay21 on May 18 disclosed that 2 young of different phenotypes were present. Observations on May 22 indicated that both attending adults were of *H. rustica* phenotype. This nest was of typical barn swallow construction, started in the vicinity of April 16. It originally had held 4 eggs, apparently laid in normal temporal sequence beginning on April 27 or 28. One bird was lost as a hatchling; the other in the egg or as a hatchling. As development of the remaining young progressed, one assumed juvenile plumage typical of *H. rustica;* the other, that characteristic of *H. rustica* × *P. fulva* hybrids. The young left or disappeared from the nest between June 1 and 5. A second clutch of 4 was begun in this nest on June 12; observations on June 15 indicated that both adults at the nest were *H. rustica.* The nest suffered a loss of 3 eggs late in incubation and lost the last egg (or hatchling) subsequently. No further activity at the nest occurred. Several *P. fulva* nests were active during this time approximately 10 meters distant in the same passageway; additionally, a small colony of *P. pyrrhonota* nested approximately 100 meters distant at the far end of the culvert. Since I assume that nestling hybrids between *H. rustica* and either *P. fulva* or *pyrrhonota* would be exceptionally difficult to distinguish morphologically, and I have no known *H. rustica* × *P. pyrrhonota* nestlings for reference, one parent of the hybrid in Ay21 can only be identified to genus.

Culvert 302, Nest RR1 (Frio Co., vic. Moore). Examination of nest RR1 on July 27 indicated that one of 4 near-fledging young was an *H. rustica* × *Petrochelidon* species hybrid. This individual and one nestmate of *H. rustica* morphology was collected. Nest RR1 had not been visited regularly previously; it was the only nest built beneath a railroad bridge 25 meters downstream from Culvert 302. Five eggs had been deposited in the nest in early May, and 4 young of *H. rustica* phenotype had fledged in mid-June. A second clutch of 5 was deposited from June 22-26 and gave rise to the clutch described above. Several pairs of *P. fulva* and *H. rustica* nested approximately 30 meters distant at the proximal end of culvert 302 during the entire period nest RR1 was active. A small colony of *P. pyrrhonota* nested approximately 100 meters distant at the far end of culvert 302 during the earlier part of the season. This *P. pyrr-honota* colony was not active after June 15; and although it is possible that a male from this colony was one parent of the hybrid young, it is simpler to hypothesize that a male *P. fulva* from the proximal end of culvert 302 was involved in the hybrid event. Biochemical analyses later confirmed hybridization.

Culvert 403 (Dimmit Co. 5 km S. Asherton).   A survey trip on July 16, 1974, produced the sighting of a probable *H. rustica* × *Petrochelidon* hybrid. Culvert 403 sheltered 48 *H. rustica*-type nests and 6 *P. fulva*-type nests. Over 30 *H. rustica* and at least 2 *P. fulva* flew and scolded overhead. The putative hybrid flew within the flock; it possessed a deeply-forked tail, pale reddish breast, and orange rump. Its vocalizations appeared to be similar to those of *H. rustica*.

1975 HYBRIDIZATION AT CULVERT SITES

Culvert 300, Nest 300Bx12 (Frio Co., vic. Moore).   Examination of the single nestling in nest Bx12 on July 17 indicated that it possibly was a hybrid; subsequently it developed plumage characteristic of *H. rustica* × *P. fulva* hybrids and fledged at approximately 20 days post-hatch. This nest was begun on approximately June 15 and was of typical *H. rustica* construction; beginning on June 22, 4 eggs had been deposited in it in apparently normal temporal sequence; incubation also appeared to be of normal duration. Two eggs late in incubation or 2 young within 2 days of hatch disappeared from the nest; one nestling was lost from the nest at a later time during the first week post-hatch. No observations could be made of adults attending this nest.

Nearby *P. pyrrhonota* (within 2 meters on same culvert wall) had fledged young several days before eggs were deposited in nest Bx12; these nests were not active after this time (*P. pyrrhonota* are usually single-clutched in central Texas). A proximate *P. fulva* nest (8 meters distant on opposite culvert wall) had received a second clutch (completed on June 13); this nest failed during incubation approximately 4 days before clutch deposition began in Bx12. Since central Texas *P. pyrrhonota* usually are not reproductively active beyond one clutch, it seems more conservative to hypothesize that the hybrid young in Bx12 was of *H. rustica* × *P. fulva* parentage; however, *P. pyrrhonota* parentage also must be considered an alternative.

1977 HYBRIDIZATION AT CULVERT SITES

Culvert 301, Nest AE11 (Frio Co. vic. Moore).   On May 21, 1977, this *H. rustica*-type nest held 5 young of 2 phenotypes; earlier, 6 eggs had been laid in it in apparently normal sequence. One egg or nestling had been lost

near the time of hatching. As development continued, 4 nestlings developed
H. rustica plumage while the remaining individual developed hybrid plumage. Weights of nestlings were taken at approximately 11 and 16 days post-
hatch; at both weighings, the hybrid was the heaviest nestling, with a weight
intermediate between that typical of similarly aged *H. rustica* and *P. fulva*
nestlings (Miller, 1974). On May 27, attending adults (male and female *H.
rustica*) were trapped serially as they visited the nest; subsequently, all
nestlings were collected. Study skins later were prepared; tissue extracts were
subjected to starch gel electrophoresis; gels were scored for IDH-1 and 6-PGD
enzyme mobilities. Birds of *H. rustica* phenotype had protein mobilities typical of *H. rustica;* the putative hybrid juvenile had banding patterns typical of
H. rustica × *P. fulva* hybrids (Martin and Selander, 1975; Martin, 1980).

No *P. fulva* nested in this passageway of culvert 301, although *P. fulva*
nests were active in several serial passageways. Several *P. pyrrhonota* nests,
from 10 to 20 meters distant in the same passageway, were active in loose synchrony with nest AE11, and other *P. pyrrhonota* nested in serial tubes of culvert 301, as well as at other sites within a 2-kilometer radius. Probably due to
interference by English sparrows *(Passer domesticus)*, cliff swallow eggs in this
culvert were broken frequently, and none successfully hatched. Several *P.
pyrrhonota* nests were usurped by sparrows. Under these circumstances, it is
possible to assume that a male of either *P. pyrrhonota* or *P. fulva* was involved
in this hybrid event.

Culvert 301, Nest AW11. On June 16, 1977, this nest (recent repair; *H.
rustica*-type construction) held a single very young nestling of non-*H. rustica*
phenotype; at this time it was the only survivor of a clutch of 5 eggs that previously had hatched 4 young too small to identify to phenotype on the previous visit. The survivor developed plumage typical of an *H. rustica* × *P. fulva*
hybrid; it was collected on June 26, 1977, after attempts to observe adults attending the nest failed. The young was sacrificed; a study skin was prepared,
and tissue extracts were subjected to starch gel electrophoresis and enzyme
specific staining for IDH-1 and 6-PGD. On these diagnostic systems, the
specimen showed banding patterns typical of *H. rustica* × *P. fulva* hybrids.
Two *P. fulva* nests were active 10+ meters east of nest AW11; one of these
had fledged young at a time which suggests that its male may have been in reproductive synchrony with the female of nest AW11, but neither of these *P.
fulva* nests reared a second clutch. Other *P. fulva* nests were active synchronously in other locations of this 6-passageway culvert, and a few disturbed (see
above) *P. pyrrhonota* nests were active approximately 100 meters distant. Considering proximity, and the fact that *P. pyrrhonota* were declining in reproductive activity at this time (most young of the single clutch were near fledging at

other sites), it is more parsimonious to hypothesize that a male of *P. fulva* was one parent of the hybrid.

    Culvert 8, Nest B8 (Medina Co. 24.3 km W. Hondo).   Inspection of nest 8B8 on May 21, 1977, disclosed nestlings of 2 phenotypes. Three of these subsequently developed plumage characteristic of *H. rustica;* the fourth, that of *H. rustica* × *P. fulva* hybrids. Weights of nestlings were taken twice during development. The hybrid exceeded each of its nestmates in weight in both instances and approximated that of similarly-aged *P. fulva* nestlings. Weights of the remaining nestlings were similar to those of similarly aged *H. rustica.* On May 29, attending adults (male and female *H. rustica*) were trapped together at the nest; subsequently all young were collected. Study skins were prepared; tissue extracts were subjected to starch-gel electrophoresis. Parents and juveniles of barn swallow morphology had IDH-1 and 6-PGD mobilities typical of *H. rustica;* the juvenile of intermediate phenotype possessed enzyme patterns typical of *H. rustica* × *P. fulva* hybrids. (Martin, 1980).

    Nest 8B8 was of typical barn swallow construction, freshly built in 1977. Four eggs were deposited in it between April 25 and 30. During the same period, 4 eggs were laid in a *P. fulva* nest (8B2) approximately 3 meters distant on the opposite wall of the culvert; 4 *P. fulva* fledged from this nest. The only other *P. fulva* nest (8B6) active in this culvert at this time was located 3 meters west of 8B8 on the same wall. This nest had earlier (April 13) held 4 eggs, which were not present on visits of April 19, 25, and 30. During the period of May 1-7, a second clutch (5 eggs) was deposited in the nest. *P. fulva* adults attended the nest and fledged 5 young. No *P. pyrrhonota* nested in the vicinity of this culvert.

    Culvert 8, Nest B5.   On June 1, this nest contained 4 young of 2 phenotypes. Two of these developed plumage characteristic of *H. rustica;* two, plumage typical of *H. rustica* × *P. fulva* hybrids. Four eggs had been deposited in this nest during the approximate period of May 9-12. Two cave swallow nests (8B2, 8B6) also were active nearby at the same time (see above, for chronologies of these, and of nest 8B8); both fledged full complements of young. Observations made on June 5 indicated that the young in 8B5 were attended by 2 *H. rustica,* which, judging by relative tail length, appeared to be an adult male and female. During these observations, several attacks were made by the putative male of this pair on cave swallows attending young in nest 8B6. The attacks involved a darting flight from nest 8B5 to 8B6, followed by what appeared to be a single peck or wing strike to the resident *P. fulva,* followed by immediate retreat to nest 8B5. The *P. fulva* responded only passively or moderately defensively to this aggression. No other interactions were noted between birds visiting nests in this culvert.

On June 11, only 1 nestling of each phenotype remained in the nest; these were collected, sacrificed and made into study skins. Adults were not trapped in the hope that another clutch would be started; it was not. Examination of gels following electrophoresis and staining of tissue extracts indicated again that concordance existed between phenotype and genotype of diagnostic systems (Martin, 1980).

Considering the chronology of reproductive events for both hybrid-containing nests and both active *P. fulva* nests in this culvert, it appears that either male *P. fulva* (nest 8B2 or 8B6) could have been involved in the hybrid event involving nest 8B8, but that the male of 8B6 was the more likely participant in the hybrid events involving nest 8B5. Since no *P. pyrrhonota* nested near this culvert, participation by this species is discounted as far less parsimonious.

Discussion

These observational data indicate that heterospecific matings involve female barn swallows and either cave or cliff swallow males; these pairings usually are transitory. Excepting the unsexed mixed species pair attending nest 300 Bx13, only adults of *H. rustica* phenotype (which, if collected, were of *H. rustica* genotype) were observed attending nests containing hybrids. With 2 *potential* exceptions (300Bx12; 301AW11), hybrids never were observed to be the exclusive progeny of a nest and nonhybrid nestlings in hybrid-containing nests were never of other than *H. rustica* morphology. All juveniles of hybrid morphology examined biochemically had protein patterns characteristic of hybrids; all nestmates of hybrids showed enzyme patterns characteristic of *H. rustica*. Taken together, these data provide no evidence of introgressive hybridization; but suggest that generic merger is in order.

REFERENCES

ALLEN, ROBERT W., and NICE, MARGARET M.
  1952.   A study of the breeding biology of the purple martin *(Progne subis)*. Amer. Midland Nat., vol. 47, pp. 606-665.
BAKER, JAMES K.
  1962.   Associations of cave swallows with cliff and barn swallows.   Condor, vol. 64, p. 326.
BENT, ARTHUR CLEVELAND
  1942.   Life histories of North American flycatchers, larks, swallows, and their allies.   U. S. Nat. Mus. Bull. 179, 555 pp., illus.
KINCAID, EDGAR, and PRASIL, RICHARD
  1956.   Cave swallow colony in New Mexico.   Condor, vol. 58, p. 452.

MARTIN, ROBERT F.
  1974.   Syntopic culvert nesting of cave and barn swallows in Texas.   Auk, vol. 91, pp. 776-782.
  1980.   Analysis of hybridization between the hirundinid genera *Hirundo* and *Petrochelidon* in Texas.   Auk, vol. 97, pp. 148-159.
  1982a. Reproductive correlates of environmental variation and niche expansion in the cave swallow in Texas.   Wilson Bull., vol. 93, no. 4.   (In press.)
  1982b. Proximate ecology and mechanics of "intergeneric" swallow hybridization *(Hirundo rustica* x *Petrochelidon fulva)*.   Southwestern Nat., vol. 27, no. 2. (In press.)
MARTIN, ROBERT F., and MARTIN, SARAH R.
  1978.   Niche and range expansion of cave swallows in Texas.   Am. Birds, vol. 32, pp. 941-946.
MARTIN, ROBERT F., and SELANDER, ROBERT K.
  1975.   Morphological and biochemical evidence of hybridization between cave and barn swallows.   Condor, vol. 77, pp. 362-364.
MARTIN, ROBERT F.; MILLER, GEORGE O.; LEWIS, MICHAEL R.; MARTIN, SARAH R.; and DAVIS, WALTER R.
  1977.   Reproduction of the cave swallow: A Texas cave population.   Southwestern Nat., vol. 22, pp. 177-186.
MAYHEW, WILBUR W.
  1958.   The biology of the cliff swallow in California.   Condor, vol. 60, pp. 7-37, illus.
NATIONAL OCEANOGRAPHIC AND ATMOSPHERIC ADMINISTRATION (NOAA)
  1974.   Climatological Data. Annual Summary, Texas.   U. S. Department of Commerce.
  1976.   Climatological Summary, Brackettville, Texas.   U. S. Department of Commerce.
NICE, MARGARET M.
  1937.   Studies in the life history of the song sparrow. I.   Trans. Linn. Soc. New York, vol. 4, pp. 1-247.
NOTTEBOHM, FERNANDO, and SELANDER, ROBERT K.
  1972.   Vocal dialects and gene frequencies in the chingolo sparrow (*Zonotrichia capensis*).   Condor, vol. 74, pp. 137-143, illus.
REDDELL, JAMES R.
  1967.   A checklist of the cave fauna of Texas. III. Vertebrata.   Texas Journ. Sci., vol. 19, pp. 184-226.
  1971.   A checklist of the cave fauna of Texas, VI: Additional records of Vertebrata.   Texas Journ. Sci., vol. 22, pp. 139-158.
SAMUEL, DAVID E.
  1971.   The breeding biology of barn and cliff swallows in West Virginia.   Wilson Bull., vol. 83, pp. 284-301.
SELANDER, ROBERT K., and BAKER, JAMES K.
  1957.   The cave swallow in Texas.   Condor, vol. 59, pp. 345-363, illus.

SELANDER, ROBERT K.; SMITH, MICHAEL H.; YANG, SUH Y.; JOHNSON, WALTER
E.; and GENTRY, J. B.
1971. Biochemical polymorphism and systematics in the genus *Peromyscus*, I:
Variation in the old-field mouse *(Peromyscus polionotus)*. Studies in Genetics 6 (Univ. Texas Publ. no. 7103), pp. 49-90.
WAUER, ROLAND H., and DAVIS, DONALD G.
1972. Cave swallows in Big Bend National Park, Texas. Condor, vol. 74, p.
482.
WETMORE, ALEXANDER, and SWALES, BRADSHAW H.
1931. The birds of Haiti and the Dominican Republic. U. S. Nat. Mus.
Bull. 155, 483 pp.
WHITAKER, LOVIE M.
1959. Cave swallow nesting in building near Cuatro Ciénegas, Coahuila, Mexico. Condor, vol. 61, pp. 369-370.

ROBERT F. MARTIN

Excavations of Ancient Canals at Edzna, Campeche, Mexico

Principal Investigator: Ray T. Matheny, Department of Anthropology and Archaeology, Brigham Young University, Provo, Utah.[1]

Grant No. 1302: In support of the excavation of ancient canals and reservoirs at Edzna, Campeche, Mexico.

Investigations at Edzna, Campeche, Mexico, revealed huge hydraulic works including a network of canals and reservoirs, and a water-filled moat surrounding a fortress-like structure (for details see Matheny, 1976). When a special investigation using heavy machinery was required, a grant application to the National Geographic Society was made.

The Edzna Valley is one of the few places on the Yucatán Peninsula that has a deep soil accumulation suitable for intensive agricultural practices (such as repeated planting). Flanking hills have scant soil deposits and are more typical of the low, hilly terrain of the peninsula. A swidden type of agriculture can be practiced on these shallow-soil hills but intensive agriculture can be done only with terracing or other kinds of land modification.

The site of Edzna lies in the northern part of the valley of the same name at an estimated elevation of 196 meters above sea level. The valley is located about 70 kilometers northeast of Campeche City, the capital of the Mexican Gulf state of Campeche. Edzna is a large site and most properly should be called a city. The ancient city sprawls over 17 square kilometers and is about 4.5 kilometers across at its east-west axis. Until recently the site was little known and was considered to be a minor site. The large acropolis with the five-storied temple, called "Cinco Pisos," was well known as well as several other large buildings and a number of stelae. Work by George F. Andrews (1969) and by the author has shown that the site was a major center with urban characteristics.

Recent discoveries made by the author and his colleagues at Edzna revealed 31 canals, totaling 23 kilometers in length, 27 reservoirs, and a moated fortress (fig. 1). We have discerned this extensive hydraulic system through the use of infrared aerial photography taken at the peak of the rainy

---

[1] Participants in this project were Deanne L. Gurr, Richard F. Hauck, and Don Forsyth, New World Archaeological Foundation archeologists.

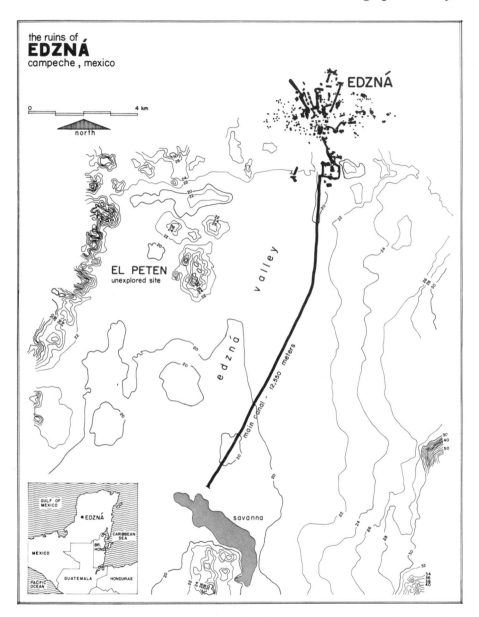

FIG. 1.   Map of the Edzna Valley. Heavy dark lines show canals, reservoirs and public buildings. The valley drains from north to south.

FIG. 2. Excavation of the south moat of the fortress at Edzna, using the 22-ton Poclain 1-cubic-meter bucket excavator.

season. The ancient canals and reservoirs still could be seen filled with rainwater even though they had become choked with soil and vegetation. Because these old water constructions had been dug into heavy clay, they continue to absorb water after sufficient rain has fallen.

The National Geographic Society research grant permitted a detailed investigation of some of the canals and reservoirs by excavation. The canals were large, and an attempt to excavate by the available manpower during the dry season was not satisfactory. Machine excavation in the heavy clay soil was desirable but finding suitable machinery to do the job was a problem.

Campeche must be regarded as a frontier state in a land not easily tamed. There is one railroad and, at the time of research, there were only two roads that traversed the country. Conditions in Campeche are such that no manufacturing takes place except small handcrafted items. Heavy machinery, therefore, is rare.

Because of the high cost of heavy machinery, the governor of Campeche has required that some of the state's major roads be built by hand in order to employ a large number of men. We needed a backhoe and after looking in several towns we located a bucket excavator in the Campeche City rock quarry. It was a 22-ton crawler-type, French-built Poclain, powered by an air-cooled diesel engine made in Germany. Negotiating with Campeche City engineers to use the machine took one week. The next problem was finding a suitable truck and trailer to transport the excavating machine to Edzna, some 70 kilometers away. No contractors in the states of Campeche, Tabasco, or Yucatán had a truck and trailer adequate for the job. Finally, we saw a truck and trailer on the highway suitable for our task. We stopped the truck and the driver told us that his rig belonged to S.O.P. *(Secretaria de Obras Publicas),* and that permission to use it would have to come through that office in Campeche. It took two days to negotiate with S.O.P. personnel to use their vehicles. We arrived at a date agreeable to all parties to use and to transport the large excavation machine to Edzna.

We began working in some of the north-sector reservoirs, making practice excavations in order to learn how to use the 1-cubic-meter bucket (fig. 2).

Next we cut 1-meter-wide by up to 3-meter-deep trenches through two large, well-defined canals in the north sector (fig. 3). The cuts were made from bank-to-bank to insure complete information. House mounds found on the banks served as convenient starting points from which to excavate, as they provided information on the relationship between the canals and house mounds associated with them.

The excavation machine was moved about 3 kilometers across the ancient city to the moated fortress. Since it was May, temperatures were 40° to 44°C.;

marking the height of the hot season. The Poclain excavator did not stand up well in the heat, because of inadequate cooling for the hydraulic system. Hydraulic lines kept bursting but fortunately we were able to have new ones made by Campeche boatbuilders, who help keep the shrimp fleet operational.

The main canal, where it joins the moated fortress, and the southwest corner of the fortress had trenches cut by the excavating machine. All together, more than 300 meters of trenches were cut through the ancient hydraulic constructions. Without the use of machinery, excavation in these huge features would not have been feasible.

The test trenches showed that the prominent canals in the north sector were originally cut by the ancient Maya to a depth of 3 meters. These canals were about 40 meters wide on the average and were flanked by banks consisting of soil removed by the original excavation. The trenches also cut through house mounds placed on top of the banks. These mounds proved to have been successively occupied over at least three cultural periods.

FIG. 3.   Cross section of Canal 5, north sector, Edzna. The mound on the right is of the Late Preclassic period.

Cross-section drawings and photographs of the trenches clearly show the nature of the original excavations. Figure 4 is a photograph of canal number 4 of the north sector. Here the dark-stained deposits mark the extent of the original excavation. The cuts near banks show trash from mound occupation which help date canal construction. Late Preclassic ceramics are found in the bottom layers of the house mounds on the canal banks. These artifacts in turn date the construction of the canal at least to the Late Preclassic period (about 150 B.C. at Edzna). Successive occupations of Proto-Classic and Early Classic periods are found in the house mounds. Late Classic house mounds are found on the canal banks and in fields between canals.

The association of Late Preclassic culture with the construction of canals at Edzna is consonant with the results of 151 test excavations placed elsewhere at the site, which showed that the major occupation was of that period. The site was first occupied at the Middle Preclassic period (ca. 600 B.C.), but no canal or reservoir association is known for this time. Excavation in the north-sector canals, main canal to the south, fortress moats, and the fortress, all show strong association with the Late Preclassic period. The conclusion drawn from the above evidence is that the basic hydraulic system of Edzna was constructed shortly before the beginning of the Christian era. Some materials that were dated by radiocarbon age determinations and by thermoluminescence techniques strongly suggest 150 B.C. for the main building phase at the site.

The canal system was laid out in a peculiar symmetry that can be seen in figure 1. Canals were aligned toward the center of the city forming long radial arms similar to the spokes of a wheel. The alignment is not precise in every case but most of the canals align directly toward Cinco Pisos, the principal building at the city. Cinco Pisos is a Classic building but the platform upon which it rests has been dated to the Late Preclassic period (Ruz, 1945). The full extent of Preclassic occupation in the city center is unknown but numerous test pits suggest heavy occupation of this area. It is conceivable that some of the canals were added to the system after the Late Preclassic period but this remains an unknown factor.

Machine excavations in the main canal showed it originally to have been dug down about 1.5 meters and averaged 50 meters in width. This canal connects with the moated fortress and probably kept the moats supplied with water. The canal runs 12 kilometers to the south and terminates in a savanna called the "Pic." The canal makes a perfect alignment with Cinco Pisos up to 5 kilometers south of that building, then it curves southwest to connect with the savanna. The canal represents an enormous public work involving the removal of about 900,000 cubic meters of soil. This figure is tenuous at the present time because excavation of other locations of the canal to determine its depth have not been made. The canal is wide and deep enough to have supported canoe traffic and movement of goods along its 12-kilometer course. At present there is no evidence that canoes were used on the canal; however, since the Classic Maya have a tradition of canoe use, it is likely that the canal was used in that way.

The Poclain excavating machine was moved to the main canal, and positioned on the west bank of the canal, at 300 meters south of the fortress. Excavation was made through the bank and progressed for 25 meters toward the middle of the canal. The trench profile shows that the original Maya excavation was 2.25 meters below the surface. Also, that the canal was redug, deepening it for about 20 meters of its 50-meter width. This second excavation was not dated, but the original one was dated to the Late Preclassic Period.

Machine excavations in the south moat of the fortress and up into the fortress show that the moat was only about 1.5 meters deep. It was, however,

Fig. 4. Cross-section excavation by machine of Canal 4. Dark, organically stained soil indicates original excavation profile.

about 75 meters wide. Hand excavations in other parts of the south moat and connecting to the fortress confirm this depth. Also, some soil from the original excavation was thrown up on the fortress side, creating a low profile wall along the south bank. The south moat connects with the 12-kilometer-long canal at the southwest end of the fortress. The south moat represents a sizable public work which required the removal of about 56,000 cubic meters of earth.

The north and south moats of the fortress were wide, averaging about 80 meters. The east and west moats were narrow, averaging about 25 meters. Excavations by a series of pits across the west moat showed it to be up to 3 meters in depth. Considering the depth and amount of water, all moats of the fortress would have been a difficult place to attack, requiring invaders to wade over 80 meters in some places in water up to 1.5 meters deep or to swim the 3-meter-deep west moat. The fortress was a secure place as long as water could have been maintained in it. Fish, edible snails, crawfish, and alligators have been found in the main canal and the fortress moats. If alligators had been kept in the moats by the ancient Maya, then an enemy may have been more surely deterred from attack.

The entire hydraulic system at Edzna consisted of 25 large reservoirs, 31 canals, and several small aguadas. Some reservoirs and canals were connected, allowing water to flow from the north sector into downtown sections. The layout of canals shows that a grand plan of city design had been conceived and carried out to near-completion. One canal in the southwest sector of the site was begun and oriented toward the center of the city, but was never completed. This plan forces all of the radiating canals into a scheme, which I call a system. The purpose of the layout is unknown but it may have had an esoteric value in Maya cosmology that is now unknown.

The canals and reservoirs had to have been dug by hand, which required the removal of more than 2,000,000 cubic meters of earth. This monumental task must have been accomplished under a sophisticated social order that was able to conceptualize the water collection from rainfall, store it in planned reservoirs and canals, and mobilize a labor force over a period of time to do the job. Once built, maintenance must have been another manpower consideration, especially with some of the canals and reservoirs that were connected together. I have calculated that approximately 4,000,000 man-days of labor were required to construct the water system of Edzna. This, along with construction of the city, amounts to a grand feat equal to building the ceremonial area, including both pyramids of the Sun and Moon at Teotihuacan in the Valley of Mexico.

We have here at Edzna a record of civilized life equal to that found with some of the largest cities of the Old World that were built or in existence at the time of Christ. It is little realized that the civilizations of the New World were producing large cities at or shortly after the time of Christ with many extremely sophisticated features.

REFERENCES

ANDREWS, GEORGE F.
   1969.   Edzna, Campeche, Mexico—settlement patterns and monumental architecture, 149 pp., illus.   University of Oregon, Eugene.
MATHENY, RAY T.
   1976.   Maya lowland hydraulic systems.   Science, vol. 193, pp. 639-646.
RUZ, ALBERTO LHUILLIER
   1945.   Campeche en la arqueologia Maya.   Acta Anthropologica, vol. I, nos. 2-3, pp. 52-61, Mexico.

RAY T. MATHENY

Geological Investigations of the Skaergaard Intrusion, East Greenland

Principal Investigator: Alexander R. McBirney, Center for Volcanology, University of Oregon, Eugene, Oregon.

Grant No. 1359: In support of geological studies of the Skaergaard Region, East Greenland.

The Skaergaard intrusion is an extraordinarily complete and well exposed body of highly differentiated gabbro, approximately 6 by 11 kilometers in surface extent, that was intruded into Eocene basalts and ancient metamorphic rocks at the time of the opening of the North Atlantic about forty million years ago. It was discovered and first described by L. R. Wager and his co-workers (1939, 1968) and has become a classic example of igneous differentiation.

The most remarkable aspect of the intrusion is the succession of structural and mineralogical features that developed as the large mass of molten magma slowly cooled and crystallized. The rocks contain a wealth of basic information on the physical and chemical processes by which magmas differentiate when emplaced into shallow levels of the earth's crust, and the theoretical insights that have been gained from it have had a pervasive influence on a wide range of petrological concepts.

Detailed geochemical studies of specimens collected by Wager and his students have provided an invaluable set of standards to which other examples of igneous differentiation are often compared, but because the intrusion is in a remote Arctic region and is inaccessible to most geologists, most interpretations of the field relations of the rocks and the mechanisms by which they formed have been based on the early observations recorded by Wager and his co-workers. Despite the high quality of this fieldwork, it was less than complete, mainly because the studies were carried out more than three decades ago at a time when the interpretations were based on what are now considered to be outdated views of the physical and chemical nature of magmatic processes.

The expedition carried out in 1974 with the help of the National Geographic Society was designed to reexamine the intrusion and to obtain new material that could provide better insights into how the intrusion crystallized and differentiated. A group of 13 geologists, petrologists, and geochemists, mainly from the University of Oregon but also from other institutions in the

451

United States and abroad, was organized under the leadership of Alexander R. McBirney. The group sailed from Reykjavik, Iceland, on the Norwegian sealing vessel MS *Signalhorn* at the beginning of August, spent nearly a month in Greenland, and returned to Iceland when weather conditions began to deteriorate. With the exception of a 3-day period of stormy weather, it was possible to devote the entire period to fieldwork.

One of the primary objectives of the expedition was to complete an accurate geologic map of the intrusion and its surroundings on a new topographic base that had been prepared specifically for this study by the Danish Geodetic Institute. The task of mapping the geologic features was divided among four groups, each of which undertook to investigate a particular area and group of rocks. The work was coordinated with that of Dr. K. C. Brooks of the University of Copenhagen who, together with his students, has been working in an area near the southern part of the intrusion. The major part of the mapping was completed during the 1974 expedition; minor details were filled in by subsequent work in the summers of 1976 and 1978. Although laboratory studies of the rocks are still in progress, several notable results have already emerged. The mapping, together with geophysical surveys to determine the subsurface form of the body, has provided a much clearer view of the structural, stratigraphic, and volumetric relations of the intrusion and its surroundings.

Several significant new aspects of the geologic relations were found in the ancient metamorphic rocks north of the intrusion in a region being studied by Dr. M. A. Kays of the University of Oregon. Radiometric ages of 3.0 billion years obtained by W. P. Leeman and his co-workers (1976) have shown that these rocks are among the oldest on earth, and it is now possible to correlate them with equivalent units, both in Greenland and northern Europe. It was also discovered that this sequence includes a body of ultramafic rocks that lies immediately north and structurally below the intrusion. Blocks of these peridotites and olivine-rich gabbros are abundant as inclusions in the basal layers of the intrusion and have hitherto been interpreted as fragments of the lower unexposed part of the intrusion. As such, they would represent the initial stages of differentiation of the Skaergaard magma. It is now apparent, however, that they are xenoliths with no direct genetic relation to the Skaergaard magma. This discovery removes one of the long-standing constraints on the inferred trend of differentiation and the nature of that part of the body that cannot be seen at the surface. As a result, it is now possible to make a more reasonable interpretation of the early history of crystallization.

Work within the interior of the intrusion has also produced a wealth of important new data. In the southern part of the intrusion, a group of rocks known as the Upper Border Group crystallized from the roof downward to form a differentiated series that is a crude mirror image of the Layered Series that crystallized from the floor upward. For the first time, the Upper Border Group has been thoroughly mapped and sampled, and laboratory studies of the rocks have revealed several significant ways in which the mineralogical assemblages differ from those that were previously inferred for these rocks on the basis of their analogous relations to the Layered Series. The most notable differences are in the compositions of co-existing minerals. The plagioclase co-existing with olivine or pyroxene of a given Fe/Mg content is more anorthite rich than it is in the Layered Series. In addition, the order of appearance of minerals is different. Apatite, for example, is found as large primary crystals throughout the Upper Border Group but does not appear in the Layered Series until very late in the sequence of crystallization. These differences can probably be attributed, at least in part, to accumulation of water and other volatile components under the roof.

Detailed mapping and sampling of the Layered Series has shown similar mineralogical variations on a horizontal scale across the floor of the intrusion. Individual units vary markedly in thickness from one side to the other, and there are also differences in the compositions of co-existing minerals. Again, these variations may have resulted from differing concentrations of volatile components, but differing rates of heat loss and crystallization must also have affected the nature and efficiency of fractionation between crystals and liquid.

During the course of experimental studies of the high-temperature relations of the differentiated gabbros, it was noted that the liquids from which the late-stage members of this series were precipitated have an immiscible relationship to the silica-rich granophyres in the upper part of the intrusion (McBirney, 1975). It appears that during the last stages of differentiation the magma split into two liquids, one that was low in silica and rich in iron and a second that was silica rich and iron poor. The siliceous liquid, though small in volume, had an important effect on controlling the compositional evolution of the magma as a whole. Liquid immiscibility, though often suggested as a possible mechanism of magmatic differentiation, has rarely been documented and the relations in the Skaergaard intrusion provide one of the best examples of the process in natural silicate liquids.

This is not to say, however, that all of the granophyres in the Skaergaard intrusion evolved through immiscibility. The largest bodies are most likely the products of melting of the metamorphic basement rocks. They have isotopic and trace-element compositions that strongly support such an origin, and their total volume is too great for them to be products of differentiation of the Skaergaard magma.

Perhaps the most far-reaching result to come out of the studies has been a reinterpretation of the basic mechanisms of crystallization and differentiation that are responsible for the principal compositional and structural features of intrusions of this kind (McBirney and Noyes, in press). It has long been believed that as magmas cool, crystals form under the roof and rain down to accumulate in a steadily thickening pile on the floor. A number of structural features, such as rhythmic graded layering in sedimentary rocks, have been interpreted as evidence that some of the crystals were deposited by density currents sweeping down the walls and across the floor. It has been noted, however, that there are important differences between these structures and those that would result from gravitational deposition, and some of the anomalous relations found in the Skaergaard intrusion are difficult to reconcile with the earlier interpretations. First, the density of plagioclase crystals is less than that of the iron-rich liquid from which they were thought to have settled. Moreover, the grains are not hydraulically equivalent in the sense that small grains of minerals of high density are not found in the same layer with larger crystals of minerals having a lower density. Detailed examination of "sedimentary" features in the layering has revealed that they differ in several other ways from true sedimentary deposits. The distributions and configurations of layers, especially near the walls and around obstructions to flow are not consistent with the pattern that would result from a density current sweeping across the floor.

As a result of these various observations, the basic theory has been re-examined and rejected in favor of a mechanism of in situ crystallization, in which the layering is explained as the result of oscillatory nucleation and crystal growth. Although this reinterpretation has not been accepted by steadfast proponents of the classical sedimentary mechanism, it has resulted in an entirely new view of the basic processes of igneous crystallization and differentiation.

Although the investigations are continuing, the results that were gained from fieldwork during the 1974 expedition have clearly contributed a major increment to our understanding of the evolution of differentiated igneous rocks.

REFERENCES

LEEMAN, W. P.; DASCH, E. J.; and KAYS, M. A.
   1976. $^{207}Pb/^{206}Pb$ whole-rock age of gneiss from the Kangerdlugssuaq area, eastern Greenland.   Nature, vol. 263, pp. 469-471.
McBIRNEY, A. R.
   1975.   Differentiation of the Skaergaard intrusion.   Nature, vol. 253, pp. 691-694.

McBirney, A. R., and Noyes, R. M.
_____. Factors governing crystallization and layering in igneous intrusions. Amer. Jour. Sci. (In press.)

Naslund, H. R.
1976. Mineralogical variations in the upper part of the Skaergaard intrusion, East Greenland. Carnegie Inst. Washington Yrbk., vol. 75, pp. 640-644.

Wager, L. R., and Brown G. M.
1968. Layered igneous rocks, 588 pp. Oliver and Boyd, Edinburgh.

Wager, L. R., and Deer, W. A.
1939. Geological investigations in East Greenland, Part III, The petrology of the Skaergaard intrusion, Kangerdlugssuaq, East Greenland. Meddr. Gronland, vol. 105, pp. 1-352.

Alexander R. McBirney

Glacial and Floral Changes in Southern Argentina since 14,000 Years Ago

Principal Investigator: John H. Mercer, Institute of Polar Studies, Ohio State University, Columbus, Ohio.

Grant No. 1407: To conduct a field study of glacial and floral changes in southern Argentina during the past 14 millennia.

The last (Late Wisconsin-age) glacial maximum in temperate latitudes of South America is known to have occurred at about the same time—20,000-18,000 years B.P.—as in temperate latitudes bordering the North Atlantic. Both areas are now experiencing interglacial conditions. However, this broad similarity of major climatic events disguises important differences in shorter-term events in the two hemispheres, especially during the interval 18,000-10,000 B.P. At present, a disproportionate amount of terrestrial data originates from around the North Atlantic Ocean, and especially from Europe, whose climatic history is widely believed to be globally applicable. However, the opposite may be nearer the truth: the North Atlantic was a highly atypical part of the world ocean during glacial maxima, being bordered east and west by large ice sheets and to the north, probably, by extensive ice shelves. During general deglaciation, decaying ice sheets and disintegrating ice shelves must have exerted a disturbing influence on climate in the North Atlantic area, not only delaying the onset of fully interglacial warmth but probably also causing temporary reversals of the warming trend such as the well-known European Younger Dryas Stade, 11,000-10,000 B.P. In the Southern Hemisphere, by contrast, the decrease in the volume of land ice since the last glacial maximum has been minor—the main change has been shrinkage in the area covered by sea ice—so that the ocean-cryosphere-atmosphere system was probably able to respond more quickly to climatic stimuli. Consequently, an area such as southern South America is likely to give clearer and less ambiguous evidence about the factors that controlled climatic change during the last glacial-interglacial transition than are the well-studied areas around the North Atlantic.

During earlier investigations of glacial fluctuations in southern South America, Mercer (1972) had concluded that after a final advance, probably about 14,500-14,000 B.P., deglaciation continued without reversal until, by 11,000 B.P., the glaciers had shrunk to within their present borders, where

457

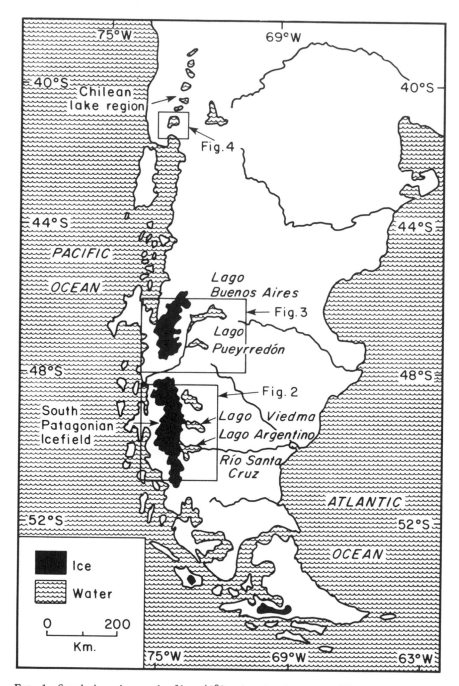

FIG. 1. South America south of lat. 40°S., showing locations of figures 2, 3, and 4.

they remained throughout the European Younger Dryas Stade 11,000-10,000 B.P. This uninterrupted glacial shrinkage implied rapid and continuous rise in temperature after 14,000 B.P. to present levels of warmth by 11,000 B.P., a time when ice still covered most of Canada and Scandinavia. However, the temperature curve deduced from the pollen record in Chile is significantly different, with the warming trend reversed during 11,000-10,000 B.P., that is, during Younger Dryas time; temperatures were then 4°C. below today's, and present-day temperature was not reached until ca. 8,500 B.P. (Heusser, 1974).

After ca. 8,500 B.P. there is no major disagreement in the global evidence of glacial variations. After the end of the postglacial warm interval ca. 6,000 B.P., three episodes of widespread Neoglacial readvances are known from both hemispheres, culminating ca. 4,500 B.P., ca. 2,500 B.P., and during recent centuries. However, in southern South America the ca. 4,500 B.P. readvance seems, on the evidence of a few dates, to have been much the greatest, whereas in the Northern Hemisphere it was, in general, surpassed by one or both of the later readvances.

Aim of the Study

The aim of the study was to reconstruct climatic change in southern Argentina during the past 14 millennia by obtaining (1) a detailed chronology of ice marginal fluctuations and (2) a history of the vegetation over this same interval, from pollen analytical studies. Our party consisted of John Mercer, glacial geologist, and Thomas Ager, palynologist, both from the Ohio State University; and Walter Sander, geologist, from the Departamento Geotécnico, Agua y Energía Eléctrica, Buenos Aires. We arrived in southern Argentina (see fig. 1) at the beginning of October 1975; this was the beginning of spring and rather early for such high latitudes (lat. 48-51°S.), but it would enable Ager to observe and collect plants during their flowering and pollination. This was important for interpreting the past changes in pollen rain. Patagonia is notorious for its strong and persistent summer winds; in winter, however, winds are much lighter, with frequent calms. The spring climate is less predictable, but we had hoped that October would combine comparative warmth with light winds, making for good working conditions. However, we experienced nearly constant strong winds and gales, but with low temperatures and snowfalls down to lake level even in early December. Thus, field conditions were not so pleasant as we had hoped.

A perennial problem in Patagonia is obtaining a reliable field vehicle. We had arranged to use a Jeep belonging to a farmer near Lago Argentino; but it was in poor condition to start with and deteriorated so rapidly that halfway through the field season it had become virtually unusable. These problems with the vehicle forced us to revise our field program, and during the last month we worked in an area that we could investigate on foot.

This report is in two parts: Narrative and Glacial Geology (by Mercer) and Vegetation History (by Ager).

I. Narrative and Glacial Geology

Our first objective at the start of the season was the Moreno Glacier and features associated with it (fig. 2). Since first observed at the end of the last century, this glacier has been slowly advancing across the lake. In recent decades it has repeatedly dammed the southern arm of the lake, now known as Lago Rico, but so far the ice dam has always broken before Lago Rico has risen sufficiently to overflow and reoccupy its "late glacial" outlet. This ancient channel was occupied in the waning stages of the last glaciation and was not abandoned until the Moreno Glacier had shrunk almost to its present size. The channel is now filled with peat; a radiocarbon age of 10,000 ± 140 years B.P. (I-2209) for the basal peat had been obtained earlier (Mercer, 1968, p. 93), showing that the glacier has not been appreciably larger than it is now for at least that length of time. With the Hiller borer, Ager penetrated to the base of this bog, in order to analyze the changes in vegetation over the last ca. 10,000 years, but unfortunately pollen preservation was very poor. Ager next penetrated to the base of a bog only 1 kilometer from the Moreno Glacier front. I had previously dug pits in this bog on two occasions in order to obtain basal peat for dating. On the first occasion I had misinterpreted the stratigraphy. I thought I had reached the base of the bog where peat covered material identified at the time as sand (Mercer, 1968, p. 98). Later, however, I realized that the "sand" was volcanic ash, and I dug a deeper pit to the true base, where the age of the peat is 9,510 ± 210 years B.P. (RL-119) (unpublished). The age of the peat immediately above the ash is 3,830 ± 115 years B.P. (I-2201). A detailed description of the pollen sequence, accompanied by a pollen diagram, is given in the section on vegetation history.

The Moreno Glacier for over 10,000 years has not been appreciably larger than it is today, but the great majority of glaciers in this area have two or three belts of Neoglacial moraines in front of their present termini. At the south end of Lago Rico, several small moraines dating from recent centuries lie within 1 kilometer of the present ice front of the Frías Glacier, and a belt of massive early Neoglacial moraines lies 8 kilometers beyond, reaching the shore of the lake. I have obtained a date of 3,465 ± 130 years B.P. (GX-4164)

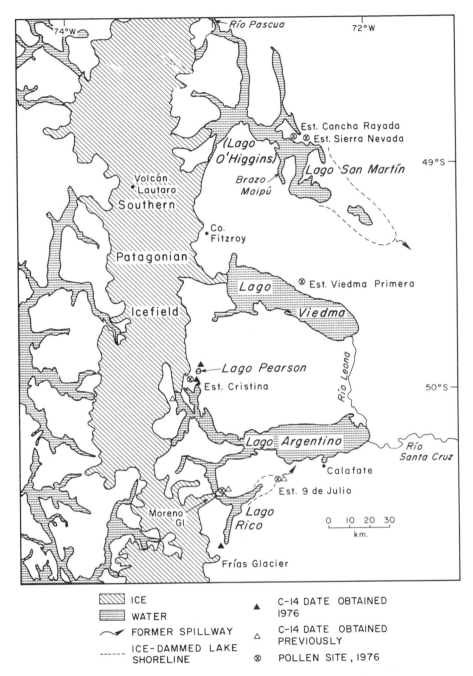

FIG. 2. Lago Argentino, Lago Viedma, and Lago San Martín and vicinity, showing sites sampled for pollen analysis and C-14 age determinations, and the former shoreline and spillway of ice-dammed Lago San Martín.

for wood 10 centimeters above the base of 150 centimeters of organic sediments in a former drainage channel through the outermost moraine, giving a minimal age for its formation. One kilometer in front of the moraine, rooted stumps buried beneath 10 feet of sandy clay are 850 ± 120 years old (GX-4165). The burial of these trees evidently had nothing to do with the formation of the moraine.

From Lago Argentino we drove north to Lago Viedma (see fig. 2). After necessary repairs to the vehicle in Calafate we crossed the Río Santa Cruz in a ferry powered by the 7-knot current of the river. The Río Santa Cruz, which carries the outflow from both Lago Argentino and Lago Viedma, was the river that Charles Darwin and a group from HMS *Beagle* ascended in 1834, hoping to reach the Cordillera; but the slow headway they made man-hauling their boat against the strong current forced them to turn back only 15 kilometers from the lake, whose existence they never suspected. After crossing and re-crossing the Río Leona, the outlet of Lago Viedma that flows into Lago Argentino, we turned west along the north shore of Lago Viedma. Our objective was an extensive bog near the Estancia Viedma Primera. Above us rose a snow-covered volcanic plateau, the Meseta Desocupada, 1,600 meters in elevation, where I had earlier found evidence for an early glaciation of this area about 3.5 million years ago (Mercer, 1976a, p. 131).

After boring this bog we headed for Lago San Martín 50 kilometers to the north. The eastern end of the lake has many bays and narrow inlets, in contrast to the simple lobate outlines of its neighbors to the south, Lago Viedma and Lago Argentino. This topography seemed ideal for the former presence of ice-marginal lakes during late glacial time, dammed in the inlets and bays by the glacier in the main channel. We had hoped that some of the present inlets might have been temporary ice-marginal lakes during the final late glacial readvance, whose end moraines could be seen in aerial photographs to lie at the mouths of at least one inlet. If so, the resulting rise in water level might have drowned vegetation along the shores, and preserved it beneath glacial lake sediments. However, wide-ranging search for such a sequence in exposures above present lake level between Brazo Maipú and Estancia Cancha Rayada (fig. 2) was unsuccessful.

Lago Argentino and Lago Viedma are the only piedmont lakes on the east side of the Andes between lat. 45°S. and the Strait of Magellan at lat. 54°S. that drain eastward to the Atlantic; the others, surprisingly, drain westward through the Cordillera to the Pacific, Lago San Martín by the Río Pascua (fig. 1), and Lago Pueyrredón and Lago Buenos Aires by the Río Baker (fig. 3). These three lakes all extend into Chile where they are known as Lago O'Higgins, Lago Cochrane, and Lago General Carrera, respectively. These piedmont

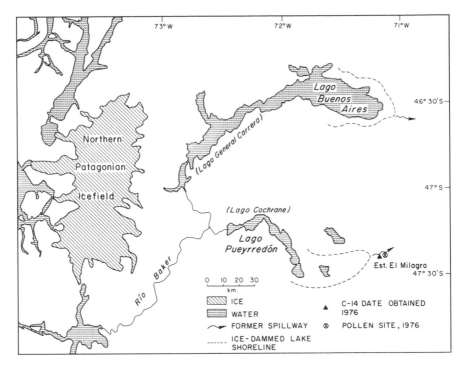

FIG. 3. Lago Pueyrredón and Lago Buenos Aires and vicinity, showing sites sampled for pollen analysis and C-14 age determinations, and the shorelines and spillways of the former ice-dammed lakes.

lakes came into being in the closing stages of the last glaciation as the ice began to recede from the massive terminal moraines at their eastern ends. At first all of them drained eastward to the Atlantic, but deglaciation of the Cordillera unblocked lower outlets for the present Pacific-draining lakes, and the outlets at their eastern ends were abandoned. These former glacial drainage channels are well-marked features of the landscape. We intended to dig or, failing that, to bore to the base of the sediments that have accumulated in the old drainage channels of Lago San Martín, Lago Pueyrredón, and Lago Buenos Aires since they were abandoned. We reasoned that, if these basal sediments were rich in organic matter, a radiocarbon age of the basal layer would give us a minimal age for the timing of deglaciation of the present outlets. Pollen analyses of the channel fill would give a history of local vegetation since deglaciation. We first investigated the old outlet of Lago San Martín, situated southeast of the present Lago Tar; but the channel had filled with windblown sand and silt, and no peat or organic mud had accumulated. Mechanical trouble forced us to return from Lago San Martín to Calafate, and after considerable delay, we set out again northward. Two days' travel brought us to the abandoned outlet of Lago Pueyrredón. Much of this channel also was filled with windblown sand, but near the Estancia El Milagro a considerable stretch was occupied by a peat bog. We bored to the base of this bog, which was about 4 meters deep, taking samples for pollen analysis at regular intervals and also obtaining a 12-centimeter-long sample of peat from near the base. The age of this basal sample has been determined at 11,245 ± 245 years B.P. (GX-4168). The next site we investigated was the old outlet of Lago Buenos Aires, a short distance southeast of the town of Perito Moreno; but the lower part of the sediments filling the channel were inorganic sands and clays, unsuitable for either radiocarbon dating or pollen analysis.

The present outlet of Lago Pueyrredón (Cochrane) is a tributary of the Río Baker, the great river that flows to the Pacific Ocean from the western end of Lago Buenos Aires (General Carrera). The Río Baker now flows between the northern and southern Patagonian icefields, and it would take a comparatively minor readvance of the southern outlet glaciers of the northern icefield to close it (figs. 1 and 3). This date from the late glacial outlet of Lago Pueyrredón is important because it gives a minimal age for deglaciation of the Río Baker and shows that the glaciers have not been much larger than they are today for the past 11,200 years; probably the channel was abandoned at least several centuries earlier, because (1) the dated sample did not come from the very base of the channel fill, and (2) the sample is known to have been slightly contaminated by younger material. This age determination is valuable supporting evidence for my tentative conclusion, based mainly on two age determinations from the Chilean channels region, that the European Younger Dryas cold interval 11,000-10,000 B.P. did not affect southernmost South America (Mercer, 1976a, p. 156). The Younger Dryas interval was an episode of severe cooling which began and ended abruptly. Its end at about 10,000 B.P. is widely taken, especially by Europeans, as an important global climatic boundary—the glacial-postglacial transition. For example, the global occurrence of this event has been assumed in attempts to calibrate the isotopic record from Byrd Station, Antarctica (Johnsen et al., 1972). A global Younger Dryas cooling is also necessary for the ca. 2,500-year astronomically determined climatic cycle proposed by Denton and Karlén (1973). The apparent absence of the Younger Dryas episode from southernmost South America casts doubt on all these lines of reasoning.

Increasing mechanical trouble with the vehicle forced us to return to Calafate directly from Lago Buenos Aires, without investigating the late glacial and Neoglacial features closer to the Cordillera, as had been our intention. In

Calafate we turned the vehicle in and, it being impossible to obtain another, decided to spend the remainder of our time based at Estancia Cristina, the isolated home of Mr. and Mrs. Herbert Masters, on the northern shore of Lago Argentino (fig. 1). In the immediate vicinity of the farm we were assured of important late glacial and Neoglacial features including peat bogs to investigate within walking distance.

The farm is on the floor of a valley close to the Upsala Glacier, the largest outlet glacier on the eastern side of the southern Patagonian icefield. Slightly above the level of the valley floor, outside the Neoglacial moraines and about 4 kilometers from the present ice margin, we found a peat bog that appeared to give a good record of the interval since the Upsala Glacier had reached approximately its present dimensions. With the Hiller borer we penetrated just over 3 meters before reaching a hard bottom. Of this the lower meter was blue-gray clay; this was covered by 10 centimeters of gyttja and 2 meters of peat with bands of volcanic ash. The age of the lowest peat, resting on gyttja, is 9010 ± 215 years (GX-4166). This gives a minimal duration of time elapsed since the Upsala Glacier shrank to approximately its present size; to this must be added the unknown length of time for accumulation of 1 meter of clay and 10 centimeters of gyttja.

At its greatest Neoglacial extent, ice from the Upsala Glacier spilt over a ridge and formed a lobe that occupied the present Lago Pearson. To the south, outwash gravels dating from this readvance cover the valley floor. The farm buildings are on some higher ground rising above this gravel. The north side of the ice lobe impounded a lake behind a massive end moraine; after glacial recession, the lake level gradually dropped as the outlet cut down through the moraine. About 1 meter of sediments of the former lake is now exposed in the banks of tributary streams. We were unable to reach the base of these sediments to determine the age of any drowned vegetation beneath, but we found two driftwood logs embedded in sand 4 and 5 meters below the surface. These logs date from 1265 ± 120 B.P. (GX-4162) and 1425 ± 130 B.P. (GX-4163), respectively. They are younger than the moraine, but by how much is uncertain because we do not know how long the lake took to drain by downcutting of its outlet stream after the glacier had receded from the moraine. Previously, I had obtained an age of 2310 ± 120 B.P. (I-988) for a time when the Upsala Glacier was advancing toward its Neoglacial maximum (Mercer, 1965, p. 404); together these dates suggest that the glacier reached its Neoglacial maximum about 2,000 years ago.

At the beginning of December we left Estancia Cristina and returned to Calafate. Ager felt satisfied with the palynological work he had accomplished, and the samples obtained promised many months of laboratory study. The

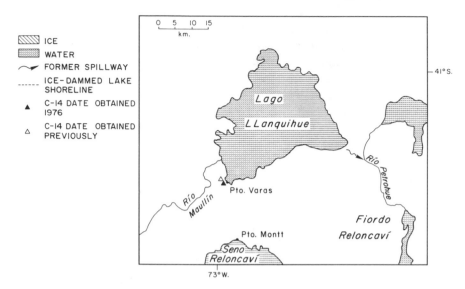

FIG. 4. Lago Llanquihue, Chile, showing site sampled for C-14 age determination and a former spillway of the lake.

glacial geological studies, however, had not been as fruitful as I had hoped; in particular, I had not succeeded in dating the late glacial moraines that lie partway down the lakes. I therefore decided to finish the field season by spending a short time in the Chilean lake region, on the west side of the Andes at about lat. 41°S., where incompatible dates had been obtained for late glacial events.

Investigations were carried out on the shores of Lago Llanquihue (fig. 4). When the glacier was receding from the lake—it had already receded from the western shores by about 17,400 B.P.—drainage was westward by the present outlet, the Río Maullín. Continued recession of the glacier unblocked a lower outlet leading southeast to the Fiordo Reloncaví; this outlet was occupied until readvancing ice closed it once more. After final recession of the ice the lake continued to drain by the Río Maullín, presumably because its channel had been deepened below the level of the southeastern outlet.

At Puerto Varas on the western shore of Lago Llanquihue, peat covering and covered by lake sediments is exposed. This peat accumulated during the low-water stage and was drowned when readvancing ice closed the southeastern outlet. Two conflicting dates had previously been obtained for the uppermost peat: 14,800 ± 230 B.P. (I-5033) and 13,300 ± 550 B.P. (GX-2947)

(Mercer, 1972, p. 1118; Heusser, 1974, p. 308). It was important for inter-hemispheric comparisons to determine whether the final stage of the last glaciation in southern South America occurred ca. 14,500 or 13,000 B.P., and so two more samples were obtained: uppermost peat, and a wood fragment at 2 centimeters depth in the peat. The age determinations obtained, 13,200 ± 320 (GX-4169) and 13,760 ± 295 B.P. (GX-4170), show that the readvance culminated around 13,000 B.P. (it could not have been much later because the glaciers are known to have finally receded from the lakes by 12,200 B.P.). These two dates, and the date of 11,245 ± 245 B.P. for deglaciation of the Río Baker, show that the transition from full glacial to full interglacial conditions in this region occurred in no more than 2,000 years, between 13,000 and 11,000 B.P. (Mercer, 1976b, p. 1009).

The glacial geological results obtained during this field investigation have been incorporated into an article that brings together the results of several seasons' fieldwork in southern South America (Mercer, 1976a).

JOHN H. MERCER

II. VEGETATION HISTORY

The second major objective of the 1975 field season was to conduct a reconnaissance investigation of the Holocene history of vegetation in the vicinity of the lakes Argentino, Viedma, San Martín, and Buenos Aires. The only previous pollen work done in the region was that by Auer (1958), who cored several bogs near these lakes as part of his extensive investigation of Patagonian Quaternary history. The cores he obtained lacked radiocarbon control, and several had very poor preservation and low concentrations of pollen. It was therefore hoped our effort would contribute a more useful chronology and vegetation history. Previous research conducted elsewhere in Patagonia is of course relevant to this study. Most of the pollen work done in southern Chile is that of Heusser (1960, 1966a, 1966b, 1971, 1972a, 1972b). The only other pollen work in southern Argentina is that of Markgraf in Tierra del Fuego (1976) and Bariloche (unpublished).

The fieldwork portion of this investigation involved three projects, all of which contribute to the objective of reconstructing vegetation history. These projects were : (1) collecting of vascular plant specimens from throughout the region; (2) collecting surface sediment samples from ponds and bogs for later analysis of modern pollen rain; and (3) coring of peat bogs and shallow ponds from which pollen profiles could be derived.

Vascular Plant Collection

More than 700 plant specimens were collected during the 1975 field season, representing about 160 species of vascular plants from steppe and forest habitats. Since the field season was during the austral spring, a high proportion of the plants collected were in flower. This makes the collection particularly useful for the purposes of producing pollen reference slides. The field season ended before the time of flowering of many species, however, and consequently a significant number of plants that contribute to the pollen rain were not represented by pollen reference material. This problem was partly solved by referring to published pollen descriptions for Chile and Argentina (Heusser, 1971; Auer et al., 1955). In addition, some pollen reference material was obtained by trade with Dr. Paul Colinvaux and Dr. Vera Markgraf.

The plant collection also provided information about the regional flora and plant ecology to supplement published reports on those subjects (e.g., Dimitri, 1972; Muñoz Pizarro, 1966; Macloskie, 1903-1905; Anliot, 1964; Perez Moreau, 1960; Auer, 1958; Correa, 1969; 1971). Identifications of many of the plants collected proved to be a tedious task, because of the paucity of identified Patagonian plant specimens in the United States herbaria, and the incomplete status of the published Patagonian Flora (Correa, 1969; 1971). Most of the plants in the collection have now been identified with the aid of the above-listed publications and that of S. F. Anliot of Wilmington College, Ohio, and Lyman B. Smith of the U. S. National Herbarium. Voucher specimens were deposited in the collections of the U. S. National Herbarium, Duke University Herbarium, and the Center for Northern Studies, Wolcott, Vermont.

Surface Pollen Spectra

The second project contributing to the vegetational history of the region was the collecting of surface sediments from bogs, ponds, and lakes in the region. Such samples were collected from a variety of vegetation types and habitats, from both steppe and forest areas, and from altitudes ranging from about 30 to 1000 meters. The object of such a collection is to provide an understanding of the relationships between particular vegetation types and the pollen spectra associated with them in the present environment (Markgraf et al., 1981). Once these relationships are understood, one can proceed to the stage of reconstructing ancient vegetation on the basis of fossil pollen assemblages. Whenever possible, one seeks modern analogs for past vegetation types by comparing modern pollen spectra from known vegetation types with ancient pollen spectra from unknown vegetation types.

Auer (1958) discovered in his pollen research in Patagonia that peat and other sediments in the steppe areas generally contained low concentrations of pollen, and often preservation was poor. I also found this to be the case. The pollen production of the steppe area vegetation is evidently very low; many of the plants are insect pollinated, and therefore rare contributors to the pollen rain, and conditions for preservation of pollen are often poor. Several samples proved to be completely barren of palynomorphs, and others contained sparse, corroded pollen. Sites moistened by springs are rare in the steppe, but I collected samples from several such sites, only to find the usual problems of poor preservation and sparse concentrations, and a heavy overrepresentation by wet-site plants such as sedges. Surface samples of this type sometimes produced 95 percent sedge pollen, and such a pollen spectrum does not reflect accurately the region immediately beyond the perimeter of the spring-moistened site. Thus a detailed reconstruction of steppe vegetation history is difficult or impossible for most sites within the steppe. Two sites investigated during the 1975 field season may yield useful results for reconstructing steppe vegetation of the past, based on pollen spectra from the surface sediments. These are shallow spring-fed ponds in the abandoned late-glacial outlet of glacial Lago Pueyrredón (Estancia El Milagro) and from near Estancia Viedma Primera on the north shore of Lago Viedma.

Surface sediments from bogs within the *Nothofagus*-forested portions of the region tend to contain moderate to abundant concentrations of well-preserved pollen, although some samples proved to be nearly barren even within this area. Pollen spectra tend to be overwhelmingly dominated by *Nothofagus* pollen in the forested areas, and this accurately reflects the dominance of the three southern beeches found in the region: *Nothofagus pumilio, N. antarctica,* and *N. betuloides,* listed in order of abundance in most areas.

Sites at or near the steppe-forest ecotone yield pollen spectra that suggest a sharp drop in pollen production and deposition as the forest grades into steppe. Transition zone sites tend to contain more shrub pollen than steppe sites farther removed from the forest, but they contain far less *Nothofagus* pollen than one would expect so near the forest edge. Evidently very little *Nothofagus* is transported beyond the forest edge. This has also been noticed by Dr. Vera Markgraf in Tierra del Fuego and Bariloche (pers. comm., 1976).

Coring of Peat Bogs

The third project was of course the actual coring of bogs and shallow ponds in a variety of habitats throughout the region. Coring was done by hand with a Hiller Peat Borer. Better cores could be obtained by using a Living-

TABLE 1.   Radiocarbon Age Determinations

Laboratory sample number	Age in years B.P.	Location and significance of sample
GX-4162	1,265 ± 120	Log 4 meters below surface of lacustrine sediments on floor of former lake dammed by Neoglacial moraine of Upsala Glacier, lat. 49°55′S., long. 73°05′W. Gives minimal age for moraine.
GX-4163	1,425 ± 130	Same site as GX-4162, log 5 meters below surface.
GX-4164	3,465 ± 130	Wood 10 cm above base of 150 cm of organic sediments in former watercourse through outermost Neoglacial moraine 9 km from terminus of Frías Glacier, lat. 50°43′S., long. 73°00′W. Gives minimal age for recession of glacier from moraine.
GX-4165	850 ± 120	Stump in growth position 1 km in front of GX-4164 site, buried beneath 3 m of clayey sand. Burial of tree evidently had no connection with formation of moraine.
GX-4166	9,010 ± 215	Peat from 198-200 cm depth resting on 10 cm of gyttja and 103 cm of clay on hard bottom. Cristina bog 4 km from present margin of Upsala Glacier, lat. 49°48′S., long. 73°10′W. Gives minimal age for recession of ice.
GX-4167	7,820 ± 195	Basal peat in bog composed of 90 cm of peat covering 15 cm of clay covering 24 cm of peat on cobbles. Elevation 1,140 m, lat. 49°49′S., long. 73°03′W. Gives minimal age for recession of ice.
GX-4168	11,245 ± 245	Peat from 4 m depth, 10 cm above an impenetrable floor, in El Milagro bog in former outlet of ice-dammed Lago Pueyrredón, lat. 47°19′S., long. 70°58′W. Gives minimal age for deglaciation of the Río Baker.
GX-4169	13,200 ± 320	Uppermost peat beneath 15 m of lake sediments, Puerto Varas, Lago Llanquihue, Chile, lat. 41°19′S., long. 72°59′W. Gives approximate date for submergence of site as readvancing ice closed former outlet at southeast end of lake.
GX-4170	13,760 ± 295	Wood fragment 2 cm below sample GX-4169
GX-4535	5,455 ± 175	Cristina bog; peat at 140-143 cm depth, covered by 2 cm of volcanic ash.
GX-4536	4,570 ± 170	Cristina bog; peat at 109-111 cm depth, covering 10 cm band of clay.
GX-4537	3,425 ± 140	Cristina bog; peat from 70-75 cm depth, overlying upper ash layer.
GX-4538	3,785 ± 145	Peat from 162-163 cm depth, covered by volcanic ash. 9 de Julio bog, in old outlet of ice-dammed Lago Rico, lat. 50°25′S., long. 72° 40′W.

stone Piston Corer to penetrate lake sediments, but that method was not employed during the 1975 field season because of severe logistic limitations.

A total of 8 cores was raised, plus several duplicate cores, from sites in both steppe and forest areas. Unfortunately, some of the cores have proved to be nearly barren of pollen, but it is likely that at least 4 of the cores will be usable for pollen analysis.

Cores were obtained from the following localities: Moreno Glacier, Estancia Cristina, and Estancia 9 de Julio (Lago Argentino); Estancia Viedma Primera (Lago Viedma); Estancia Cancha Rayada and Estancia Sierra Nevada (Lago San Martin) (fig. 1); and Estancia El Milagro (Lago Pueyrredón) (fig. 2).

Volcanic ash layers occur commonly throughout the region, and such layers were used by Auer (1958) as a means of correlation throughout Patagonia prior to the availability of radiocarbon dating. The ash is believed to be derived from Volcán Lautaro, in the middle of the icefield west of Lago Viedma (fig. 1). Most of the cores taken during the 1975 field season had at least one, and often two or three, noticeable ash layers. Radiocarbon dates from peat associated with the ash layers provide an ashfall chronology for the area independent of Auer's scheme as he applied it to all of Patagonia. Table 1 lists radiocarbon dates from the 1975 field season.

Present-day Regional Vegetation

The contemporary vegetation of the region under investigation can be subdivided into two main components—forest and steppe. The forested portion of the region corresponds to the area of highest precipitation, along the eastern flank of the southern Andes. The forest vegetation in this region is dominated by the deciduous southern beeches *Nothofagus pumilio* and *N. antarctica*. The evergreen *Nothofagus betuloides* occurs in scattered localities where moisture is abundant. Other trees in the area include *Drimys winteri* and occasional patches of *Pilgerodendron uvifera*. Important shrubs include *Maytenus magellanica*, *Embothrium coccineum*, *Escallonia rubra*, and *Berberis* sp. Common low shrubs and herbs include *Ribes* sp., *Pernettya mucronata*, *Empetrum rubrum*, *Chiliotrichum amelloides*, *Gunnera magellanica*, and others. A more extensive treatment of the vegetation of the forest of this region is provided by Anliot (1964) and Perez Moreau (1960).

The steppe areas of the region also are discussed in the above publications. The steppe vegetation can be subdivided into three categories: shrub steppe, *Stipa-Festuca* steppe, and semidesert, reflecting a moisture gradient from somewhat moist to very dry as one travels eastward from the eastern flank of the Andes.

The shrubby steppe includes *Berberis heterophylla, B. buxifolia, Anarthrophyllum* sp., *Senecio* sp., *Verbena tridens,* and *Azorella* sp. The shrubby steppe also includes bunch grasses such as *Stipa,* but with decreasing moisture, the bunchgrasses tend to become more abundant.

The bunchgrass steppe dominated by *Stipa* and *Festuca* grasses also includes *Anarthrophyllum* sp., some *Verbena tridens, Armeria bella,* scattered *Berberis* sp., *Cerastium arvense, Margyricarpus* sp., and others.

The semidesert areas are often sandy areas with patchy vegetation of bunchgrasses, occasional cacti *(Echinocactus, Opuntia), Ephedra, Oxalis* sp., *Sisyrinchium* sp., and others.

Research by Auer (1958), Anliot (1964), accounts provided by turn-of-the-century pioneers in the region, and evidence of glacial recession all suggest that the region is undergoing a significant drying trend that began early this century. Regional vegetation has been undergoing gradual change in response to this climatic change, as well as responding to considerable influence of man's activities that include burning and clearing of forests and heavy grazing pressure from sheep, horses, and cattle. It is difficult to separate these natural and man-caused influences when evaluating the changes in vegetation, but it is clear that steppe and semidesert vegetation is expanding at the expense of the forest vegetation. It is quite probable also that the steppe vegetation has undergone considerable change in character as a result of very heavy grazing pressure from sheep in particular. This pressure tends to alter the vegetation by favoring those plants that are inedible to sheep because they are poisonous, protected by thorns, or unpalatable.

Pollen Analysis of Cores

The three projects conducted in the field provided the samples and basic information necessary to proceed to the stage of pollen analysis of cores from the study area. Analysis of one core has been completed, and a second has been processed but abandoned due to poor preservation (9 de Julio), and a third (Cristina I) is undergoing analysis. Analysis of the first core proceeded slowly because of my unfamiliarity with the pollen flora and the presence of many unknowns unrepresented in the available pollen reference collection. The core selected for the initial analysis was the Moreno Glacier bog core, because the preservation was good, and pollen was abundant. In addition, the bog had been investigated previously by John Mercer, who obtained two radiocarbon dates from a pit dug near the coring site.

The sediment profile obtained by coring in 1975 consisted of 325 centimeters of peat underlain by at least 25 centimeters of blue-gray clay. According to a radiocarbon date from a nearby pit on the peat immediately overlying the clay, deposition of limnic peat began about 9,500 years B.P.

Two volcanic ash layers occur in the profile, at depths of 70-85 centimeters and at 130-138 centimeters.

Pollen Profile of the Moreno Glacier Bog, Lago Argentino

The 325-centimeter peat sequence that overlies at least 25 centimeters of clay represents about the past 9,500 years, based on a radiocarbon-dated sample of peat immediately overlying the clay in an adjacent pit dug in a previous field season by John Mercer (9,510 ± 210 years B.P. [RL 119]). The clay underlying the peat may contain pollen, but the Hiller Peat Borer used to core the bog tends to contaminate clayey sediments, and so the samples have not been analyzed. The peat has yielded sufficient pollen to produce a pollen profile based on samples collected in most cases at 10-centimeter intervals (fig. 5).

The lowermost peat samples are characterized by low percentages of *Nothofagus* pollen and relatively high percentages of sedge, grass, heath, and Compositae pollen. This suggests that at the earliest stage of peat deposition at this site, presumably about 9,500 years ago, *Nothofagus* had already begun to invade the immediate vicinity of the site. It is not known how much time elapsed between the recession of glacial ice from the bog site and the initiation of peat deposition, nor is it known how far the *Nothofagus* and accompanying plants had to migrate to reach the site. It is reasonably likely that the vegetation did not have far to travel, and if that proves to be true, it obviously requires a local refugium where the forest vegetation was able to survive the last full glacial interval of the late Pleistocene.

The initial pollen assemblage at the site suggests, on the basis of pollen percentages, that the initial peat samples were deposited at a time when colonization of the bog area was still in progress. This is strongly suggested by the low *Nothofagus* pollen percentages and high percentages of heath pollen (represented by *Empetrum rubrum*, *Pernettya*, *Gaultheria*, and others), and relative abundance of herbs that imply open meadows rather than closed-canopy forest. *Embothrium* pollen is present in trace amounts at the base of the core, and its presence also suggests open areas existed near the site. According to Anliot (1964, p. 10), *Pernettya* and *Empetrum* are among the first pioneers or invaders in sites exposed by receding ice in this region. According to Anliot (1964, p. 3), *Nothofagus antarctica* is sometimes able to colonize nearly barren moraines, whereas *Nothofagus pumilio* may possibly require modification of the substrate by shrubs and herbs prior to its becoming established. On the basis of pollen

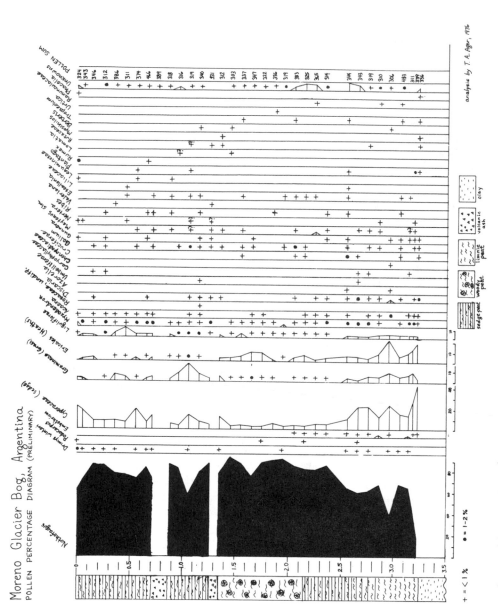

Fig. 5. Moreno Glacier bog, Lago Argentino, Argentina: Pollen percentage diagram (preliminary).

evidence, however, it is not known which species of *Nothofagus* initially colonized the site.

The lowermost segment of the peat core (250-325 centimeters) constitutes a pollen subzone characterized by several previously mentioned indicators of open-forest conditions, and the abundance of sedge pollen suggests that perhaps the immediate vicinity was wet boggy vegetation, perhaps with open water in a pond now occupied by the peat deposit. Assuming a basal date of 9,500 years B.P. and a constant sedimentation rate, we may conclude that the colonization and open forest interval of the pollen record spanned roughly the interval 7,200 to 9,500 years B.P.

The core interval 150 to 250 centimeters (roughly 4,300-7,200 years B.P.) is characterized by high percentages of *Nothofagus* pollen and very low percentages of sedge, grass, Compositae, and other pollen types. This suggests close-forest conditions and/or somewhat drier conditions reducing the area of sedge habitat. *Embothrium* pollen disappears locally midway through this pollen subzone, which also suggests elimination of open forest conditions.

The uppermost 150 centimeters of the core, representing roughly the past 4,300 years, records a slight drop in pollen percentages of *Nothofagus* and heaths and an increase in sedge, grass, and Compositae pollen percentages. The increase suggests a trend to slightly more open vegetation, perhaps a few openings in the forest cover, and the increase in sedge pollen suggests a return to slightly moister conditions.

These interpretations are by necessity very preliminary, and the completion of the core from Cristina will be necessary prior to making any firm interpretations. The Cristina bog record should be particularly useful because the site occupies a more sensitive position close to the boundary between forest and steppe, whereas the Moreno Glacier bog site is well within the forest boundary.

REFERENCES

ANLIOT, S. FREDRIK
    1964.   Observations of vegetation in the vicinity of two glacial piedmont lakes, southern Patagonia.   Inst. Polar Stud. Rpt. no. 13, 25 pp.   Ohio State University Research Foundation, Columbus, Ohio.
AUER, V.
    1958.   The Pleistocene of Fuego-Patagonia, pt. 2: The history of the flora and vegetation.   Ann. Acad. Sci. Fennicae, ser. A, III, Geologica-Geographica, no. 30, 239 pp. Helsinki.

AUER, V.; SALMI, M.; and SALMINEN, K.
1955.   Pollen and spore types of Fuego-Patagonia.   Ann. Acad. Sci. Fennicae III, Geologica-Geographica, vol. 43, pp. 1-10.
CORREA, M. N.
1969.   Flora Patagónica, pt. 2: Typhaceae a Orchidaceae (excepto Gramineae). Col. Cient. INTA, 219 pp. Buenos Aires.
1971.   Flora Patagónica, pt. 7: Compositae.   Col. Cient, INTA, 451 pp. Buenos Aires.
DENTON, GEORGE H., and KARLÉN, W.
1973.   Holocene climatic variations—their pattern and possible cause. Quaternary Res., vol. 3, pp. 155-205.
DIMITRI, M. J.
1972.   La región de los bosques Andino-Patagónicos, sinopsis general.   Col. Cient. INTA, vol. 10, 381 pp. Buenos Aires.
HEUSSER, CALVIN J.
1960.   Late-Pleistocene environments of the Laguna de San Rafael area, Chile. Geogr. Rev., vol. 50, pp. 555-577.
1966a.   Late-Pleistocene pollen diagrams from the Province of Llanquihue, southern Chile.   Proc. Amer. Philos. Soc., vol. 110, pp. 269-305.
1966b.   Polar hemispheric correlation: Palynological evidence from Chile and the Pacific Northwest of America.   Pp. 124-141 *in* "World Climate from 8000 to 0 B.C." Proc. Int. Symposium held at Imperial College, London, April 18-19, 1966.   Royal Meteorological Society, London.
1971.   Pollen and spores of Chile, 167 pp.   University of Arizona Press, Tucson.
1972a.   On the occurrence of *Lycopodium fuegianum* during late-Pleistocene inter-stades in the Province of Osorno, Chile.   Torrey Bot. Club Bull., vol. 99, pp. 176-184.
1972b.   An additional postglacial pollen diagram from Patagonia Occidental. Pollen and Spores, vol. 14, pp. 157-167.
1974.   Vegetation and climate of the southern Chilean lake district during and since the last interglaciation.   Quaternary Res., vol. 4, pp. 290-315.
JOHNSEN, S. J.; DANSGAARD, W.; CLAUSEN, H. B.; and LANGWAY, C. C.
1972.   Oxygen isotope profiles through the Antarctic and Greenland ice sheets. Nature, vol. 235, pp. 429-434.
MACLOSKIE, G.
1903-   Flora Patagónica: Flowering plants.   Rpts. Princeton Univ. Exped.
1905.   Patagonia, 1896-1899, vol. 8, no. 1, pp. 139-466.
1905-   Idem, vol. 8, no. 2, pp. 467-905.
1906.
MARKGRAF, VERA
1976.   New data on the late and postglacial vegetational history of "La Misión," Tierra del Fuego, Argentina, 13 pp.   Paper presented at Symposium on Quaternary Vegetational History of Savannah and Deserts, IV International Palynological Conference, Lucknow, India, December 1976.
MARKGRAF, VERA; D'ANTONI, H. L.; and AGER, T. A.
1981.   Modern pollen dispersal in Argentina.   Palynology, vol. 5, pp. 43-63.

MERCER, JOHN H.
    1965.   Glacier variations in southern Patagonia.   Geogr. Rev., vol. 55, pp. 390-413.
    1968.   Variations of some Patagonian glaciers since the late glacial.   Amer. Journ. Sci., vol. 266, pp. 81-109.
    1972.   Chilean glacial chronology 20,000-11,000 carbon-14 years ago. Science, vol. 176, pp. 1118-1120.
    1976a.   Glacial history of southernmost South America.   Quaternary Res., vol. 6, pp. 125-166.
    1976b.   Interglacial-glacial and glacial-interglacial temperature trends in the Southern Ocean, as inferred from events in southern Chile.   Abstracts with Programs, Geological Society of America annual meeting, Denver, p. 1009.
MUÑOZ PIZARRO, CARLOS
    1966.   Sinopsis de la flora Chilena, 500 pp. 2d ed.   University of Chile.
PEREZ MOREAU, R. A.
    1960.   Reseña botánica sobra el Lago Argentino.   Inst. Nac. Hielo Cont. Patagónico, Buenos Aires, no. 1, 35 pp.

THOMAS A. AGER[1]

---

[1] Current address: Mail Stop 970, U. S. Geological Survey, Reston, Virginia.

A Survey of the Cave Fauna of the Yucatán Peninsula, Mexico

Principal Investigator: Robert W. Mitchell, Department of Biological Sciences, Texas Tech University, Lubbock, Texas.

Grant Nos. 1365 and   In support of a survey of the cave fauna of Yucatán.
1486.

Yucatán was the first area of Mexico to be biologically investigated with respect to its cavernicole fauna. The classic studies of A. S. Pearse and his colleagues of the Carnegie Institution of Washington revealed the presence of a rich endemic troglobite and troglophile fauna (Pearse, 1936; 1938). The only other major investigation of the cavernicole fauna of Yucatán was made by B. F. Osorio Tafall and M. Cárdenas Figueroa in 1947 (Cárdenas Figueroa, 1950). The first comprehensive study of the caves and cave fauna of the Yucatán Peninsula was begun in the spring of 1973 when numerous caves were visited by Mary Butterwick, David McKenzie, Martha Helen McKenzie, Stuart Murphy, and James Reddell. The unexpected discovery of several undescribed species of troglobite indicated that the Peninsula was deserving of additional study. The National Geographic Society sponsored two expeditions to Yucatán. The first was conducted from September until December 1974 and included David McKenzie, Robert W. Mitchell, James Reddell, and Suzanne Wiley. This expedition emphasized the states of Yucatán and adjacent Campeche. The second expedition was in the summer of 1975 with the personnel consisting of Andrew Grubbs, David McKenzie, Robert W. Mitchell, James Reddell, and Suzanne Wiley. Although some additional time was spent in the state of Yucatán, the emphasis of this expedition was on Quintana Roo and Campeche.

The Yucatán Peninsula was chosen for intensive biospeleological research because of its ease of access, abundance of caves, and the light it might shed on the evolution of troglobites in the lowland tropics. It has been considered almost an axiom of biospeleology that terrestrial troglobites are virtually absent from tropical regions. Yucatán seemed, therefore, to be an ideal area to verify or disprove this picture of troglobite evolution.

About 565 species are known from the caves and cenotes of the Yucatán Peninsula, of which 115 are known only from large open-air cenotes and should not be considered a part of the true cave fauna. During the course of the present study 160 species were added to the known cave fauna, of which 31 were previously undescribed. Large collections of isopods, mites, millipedes, centipedes, diplurans, collembolans, roaches, crickets, and beetles remain unstudied. The exploration of 4 caves in Tabasco, 19 in Campeche, 18 in Quintana Roo, and 53 in Yucatán have resulted in the discovery of additional specimens of poorly known species and provided us with much information on faunal distribution.

Faunal Survey

The following brief discussion of the fauna of the Yucatán Peninsula emphasizes only the more significant species. For a more detailed discussion of the cave fauna of the Peninsula refer to Reddell (1977a; 1977b).

Order Oligochaeta.   Two rare species of earthworm are known only from caves in Yucatán. One of these species, *Balanteodrilus pearsei* Pickford, was rediscovered and has been redescribed by Gates (1977).

Order Copepoda.   A small collection of copepods in Grutas de Xtaxumbilxunam, Campeche, included a rare South American species, *Mesocyclops ellipticus* Kiefer, which has been redescribed by Yeatman (1977).

Order Isopoda.   The troglobitic cirolanid *Creaseriella anops* (Creaser) has been found in 20 caves in the coastal plain of Yucatán and Quintana Roo. The terrestrial isopod fauna of the Peninsula is still under study, but Schultz (1977) has described a new blind species of the family Philosciidae, *Troglophiloscia laevis,* from Actún Xpukil, Yucatán.

Order Amphipoda.   Holsinger (1977) has described the first troglobitic amphipods from the Peninsula. One species, *Mayaweckelia yucatanensis,* is known only from Grutas de Xtaxumbilxunam, Campeche, while the other, *M. cenoticola,* is widespread throughout the peninsula.

Order Mysidacea.   The mysid *Antromysis cenotensis* Creaser, previously known from 12 caves in northern Yucatán, is now known to be widespread throughout Yucatán and Quintana Roo and has been collected from an additional 21 localities. It was redescribed by Bowman (1977).

Order Decapoda.   Hobbs and Hobbs (1976) have summarized our knowledge of the shrimps of the Yucatán Peninsula. The palaemonid shrimp *Creaseria morleyi* (Creaser), previously known from 10 caves in northern Yucatán, has now been recorded from 30 caves in Campeche, Quintana Roo, and Yucatán. The atyid shrimp *Typhlatya pearsei* Creaser is also known now from many caves throughout the Peninsula. Hobbs and Hobbs (1976) described 2 additional species of atyid: *T. campecheae* from 2 caves in Campeche and *T. mit-*

chelli from 16 caves in Quintana Roo and Yucatán.

Order Scorpionida.   The discovery of 2 species of troglobitic scorpion of the family Diplocentridae is perhaps the most significant biological discovery made during the course of exploration in Yucatán. This represents a second independent line of blind scorpions in Mexico. Prior to the discovery of these species the only troglobitic scorpions in the world belonged to the genus *Typhlochactas* in the family Chactidae. Francke (1977) reviewed the genus *Diplocentrus* in the Peninsula and described the 2 troglobites: *D. anophthalmus* from Actún Chukum, Yucatán; and *D. mitchelli* from Actún Halmensura, Campeche. He also described a troglophilic species, *D. reddelli,* from Actún Xpukil, Yucatán. Wagner (1977) redescribed 2 species of the genus *Centruroides* from the Peninsula and synonymized the problematic *C. yucatanus* (Chamberlin and Ivie) with *C. ochraceus* (Pocock).

Order Pseudoscorpionida.   Muchmore (1977) has summarized the information available on the pseudoscorpion fauna of the Peninsula. His work includes the description of one new species of troglobite, *Vachonium cryptum,* from Actún Xkyc, Yucatán.

Order Schizomida.   The only schizomid known from caves in the Yucatán Peninsula is *Schizomus portoricensis* (Chamberlin and Ivie). This species, present in virtually every cave in the Peninsula, was redescribed by Rowland and Reddell (1977).

Order Amblypygida.   The blind amblypygid *Paraphrynus chacmool* (Rowland), previously known from only 2 caves, has now been found in many caves throughout the Peninsula.

Order Araneae.   The spider fauna of the caves of the Yucatán Peninsula is extremely rich, with a total of more than 50 species known, of which 7 are troglobites (Gertsch, 1977b). The only agelenid known from Yucatán caves is *Cicurina maya* Gertsch, known only from Actún Tucil, Yucatán. The ochyroceratid spider, *Theotima martha* Gertsch, is an apparent troglobite known from one cave each in Quintana Roo and Yucatán. The oonopid, *Oonops coecus* (Chamberlin and Ivie), originally described from one specimen, is now known from 9 caves in Campeche, Quintana Roo, and Yucatán. Three species of pholcid spider are known as troglobites in the Peninsula. *Metagonia chiquita* Gertsch was described from Cenote Chen Mul, Yucatán; *M. torete* Gertsch is known from 6 caves in Campeche, Quintana Roo, and Yucatán; and *Pholcophora pearsei* (Chamberlin and Ivie) was redescribed on the basis of specimens from 5 caves in Quintana Roo and Yucatán. A still undescribed species of the rare family Tetrablemmidae has been collected from 2 caves in Campeche.

Order Ricinuleida.   The ricinuleid *Cryptocellus pearsei* (Chamberlin and Ivie), previously known from 3 caves in Yucatán, has now been found in 7 additional localities (Gertsch, 1977a). The presence of this species in several caves in vast numbers is of considerable interest.

Order Opilionida.   Goodnight and Goodnight (1976) based a study of the opilionid *Erginulus clavotibialis* (Cambridge) in part on material obtained from Yucatán. Goodnight and Goodnight (1977) reported the first cave-dwelling opilionids from the Peninsula and described new species of troglophile from caves in Yucatán and Campeche.

Order Acarina.   The most significant acarine discovery made was of a new genus and species of argasid tick of considerable phylogenetic importance. This species was described from Grutas de Xtaxumbilxunam, Campeche, by Keirans and Clifford (1975) as *Nothoaspis reddelli*. The species was also later obtained from caves in Yucatán and Tabasco (Keirans, Clifford, and Reddell, 1977).

Class Diplopoda.   Causey (1977) has presented a preliminary report on millipedes collected in Yucatán, but most of this material remains unstudied. The only unquestioned troglobitic millipedes known from the Peninsula are 2 species of spirostreptid of the genus Orthoporus. *Orthoporus zizicolens* (Chamberlin) was a poorly described species known only from 2 caves. Causey (1977) redescribed the species and reported it from 4 additional localities. A second troglobitic species, *O. spelaeus* Causey, was described from Cenote de Catzín, Yucatán.

Order Coleoptera.   Most of the beetles obtained from the peninsula are still under study, but Peck (1977) has reported 2 apparently troglophilic species of leiodid beetle of the subfamily Catopinae from caves in the Peninsula.

Class Teleostomi.   Both species of troglobitic fish known from Yucatán were found. Specimens of *Ophisternon infernale* (Hubbs) were used by Rosen and Greenwood (1976) in a study of the phylogeny and distribution of this and related genera. This species is now known from 4 caves in Yucatán; specimens seen but not captured in 2 caves in Quintana Roo probably also represent this species. The brotulid *Typhliasina pearsei* (Hubbs) was obtained from 5 caves in Yucatán.

Cave Exploration and Mapping

Although the principal goal of the National Geographic Society expeditions was to conduct a faunal survey, a number of the larger caves were mapped in order to lay the basis for future ecological studies. Since many of these caves are also of considerable archeological importance, the mapping of the caves will serve several purposes. Prior to this study the only meaningful information on caves in Yucatán was to be found in the classic studies of Stephens (1843) and Mercer (1896). No complete maps of caves appear in the literature and our knowledge of the nature of caves and the extent of karst development in the Peninsula was almost entirely limited to Mercer's work in the Sierra de Ticul. The following very briefly summarizes the major surveying projects carried out in the Peninsula. A complete list and brief descriptions of caves visited and mapped is in Reddell (1977a).

Tabasco.   The commercial cave, Grutas del Coconá, was mapped in its entirety. This cave is of particular importance as the type locality of several distinctive species of troglobite, including the marine relict planarian *Opisthobursa mexicana* Benazzi.

Sierra de Bolonchén.   Several large caves were discovered and mapped in this region of Campeche. Most notable was the famed Grutas de Xtaxumbilxunam, described so vividly by Stephens (1843). Exploration and mapping of the cave is still not complete because of the size and complexity of the cave, but it is among the longer and deeper in the Peninsula. Other notable caves surveyed in this region include Grutas de San Antonio (the deepest in the Peninsula at −120 meters) and Grutas de Xkalumkín in the ruins of Xkalumkín.

Sierra de Ticul.   Actún Xpukil near Calcehtok was completely surveyed and found to be far more extensive than previously believed. Exploration of inner rooms in the cave, not previously known, revealed the presence of numerous unbroken pots, skeletons, stone walls, and other artifacts in undisturbed condition. Actún Chac, described in detail by both Stephens (1843) and Mercer (1896), was also surveyed. A map of the important archeological cave, Grutas de Loltún, was begun and about half of the cave surveyed.

Coastal Plain.   The coastal plain of Yucatán was previously believed to be characterized almost entirely by large open-air cenotes, with caves believed to be rare and small. Exploration of many caves throughout the Coastal Plain revealed this to be untrue. Extensive cave systems were found in several areas and doubtless many large caves still remain to be discovered. Grutas de Balankanche, one of the more remarkable archeological sites in the peninsula, was surveyed and the map made available to archeologists working in Yucatán. Cenote Chen Mul, located at the base of the main pyramid in the ruins of Mayapán, was also completely mapped. The longest cave in the peninsula and among the longer in Mexico is Actún Kaua. This cave is a complex maze with more than 7 kilometers of surveyed passage. At least 3 kilometers of passage have been explored but remain unsurveyed and numerous passages continue beyond the point of farthest exploration. This cave is also of potential archeological significance; a vast amount of clay fill has been removed from the cave floor and may have served as a source of clay for the potters of Chichén Itzá.

Summary

The cavernicole fauna of the Yucatán Peninsula was shown by this study to be far more diverse and abundant in terms of species than was previously known. Of particular interest was the diversity of terrestrial troglobites. It was clearly demonstrated that terrestrial troglobites *have* evolved in a tropical karst region. A comparison of other karst regions in North America have shown no significant difference in the number of terrestrial troglobites from one region to another. Four regions have thus far been compared, each of which is well known. The Yucatán Peninsula was shown to have 24 terrestrial and 11 aquatic troglobites; the Sierra de El Abra of Tamaulipas and San Luis Potosí has 28 terrestrial and 7 aquatic troglobites; the highland Sierra de Guatemala of Tamaulipas has 26 terrestrial and 6 aquatic troglobites; and the Mammoth Cave Region of Kentucky has 29 terrestrial and 14 aquatic species. As the unstudied collections from Yucatán are described it is expected that the number of terrestrial troglobites will increase.

These data clearly demonstrate that the terrestrial troglobite fauna of a lowland tropical region is as abundant as that of temperate and subtropical regions. There is, however, a striking difference in the groups which are represented. The dominant group in temperate caves are the Coleoptera, with many species of troglobite in several families; no troglobitic beetles were found in Yucatán and are generally rare in tropical caves in general. It is believed that the predator niches occupied by beetles in temperate caves are filled by arachnids in tropical caves. The arachnid fauna of tropical regions is more diverse than that of temperate regions and such tropical orders as the Schizomida, Amblypygida, and Ricinuleida are frequently abundant in tropical caves.

Recent studies have demonstrated that changes in vegetation and climate occurred in tropical regions during the Pleistocene. These changes, however, were far less severe and of shorter duration than in temperate regions. It is probable that groups with low vagility, such as the soil and litter fauna, became isolated in caves for a sufficiently long period to allow speciation and subsequent cave adaptation to occur. The more vagile groups, such as beetles, reinvaded the cave regions before the speciation process could be completed. With few exceptions all of the troglobites known from tropical regions belong to groups which are normally very limited in distribution and which would be severely affected by relatively small climatic or vegetational changes.

Acknowledgments

In addition to funding by the National Geographic Society, this study was supported in part by The Museum, Texas Tech University, Lubbock, Texas.

The following are thanked for their assistance in the field: Mary Butterwick, Deborah Denson, Linda Elliott, Andrew Grubbs, Masaharu Kawakatsu, Charles Loving, Jeannie Loving, David McKenzie, Martha Helen McKenzie, Marsha Meredith, Rexell Mitchell, Robert Mitchell, Jr., Scott Mitchell, Sharon Mitchell, Stuart Murphy, J. Mark Rowland, Wataru Teshirogi, and Suzanne Wiley.

Reynaldo Solis of Mérida and Eleuterio Gonzalez and Manuel Ay Canul of Muna not only helped in making field collections but assisted in many other ways as well.

Mrs. Joann Andrews of Mérida helped in the field and gave freely of her time and hospitality and access to her superb library. Sr. Norberto Gonzalez of the Instituto Nacional de Antropología e Historia very kindly provided the necessary permission to work in Grutas de Balankanche, Grutas de Loltún, and other archeological zones.

REFERENCES

BOWMAN, THOMAS E.
  1977.   A review of the genus *Antromysis* (Crustacea: Mysidacea), including new species from Jamaica and Oaxaca, México, and a redescription and new records for *A. cenotensis*. Assoc. Mexican Cave Stud. Bull., no 6, pp. 27-38.

CÁRDENAS FIGUEROA, MAURO
  1950.   Los recursos naturales de Yucatán. IV.-Informe hidrobiologico y faunístico de Yuçatán. Bol. Soc. Mex. Geogr. Estadist., vol. 69, pp. 135-159.

CAUSEY, NELL B.
  1977.   Millipedes in the collection of the Association for Mexican Cave Studies. IV. New records and descriptions chiefly from the northern Yucatán Peninsula. México (Diplopoda). Assoc. Mexican Cave Stud. Bull., no.6, pp. 167-183.

FRANCKE, OSCAR F.
  1977.   The genus *Diplocentrus* in the Yucatán Peninsula with description of two new troglobites (Scorpionida: Diplocentridae). Assoc. Mexican Cave Stud. Bull., no 6, pp. 49-61.

GATES, G. E.
  1977.   On some earthworms from North American caves. Assoc. Mexican Cave Stud. Bull., no 6, pp. 1-4.

GERTSCH, WILLIS J.
1977a.   On two ricinuleids from the Yucatán Peninsula (Arachnida: Ricinulei). Assoc. Mexican Cave Stud. Bull., no. 6, pp. 133-138.
1977b.   Report on cavernicole and epigean spiders from the Yucatán Peninsula. Assoc. Mexican Cave Stud. Bull., no. 6, pp. 103-131.
GOODNIGHT, CLARENCE J., and GOODNIGHT, MARIE L.
1977.   Laniatores (Opiliones) of the Yucatán Peninsula and Belize (British Honduras).   Assoc. Mexican Cave Stud. Bull., no. 6, pp. 139-166.
GOODNIGHT, MARIE L.; and GOODNIGHT, CLARENCE J.
1976.   Observations on the systematics, development, and habits of *Erginulus clavotibialis* (Opiliones: Cosmetidae).   Trans. American Micros. Soc., vol. 95, pp. 654-664.
HOBBS, HORTON H., III, and HOBBS, HORTON H., JR.
1976.   On the troglobitic shrimps of the Yucatán Peninsula, México (Decapoda: Atyidae and Palaemonidae).   Smithsonian Contr. Zool., no. 240, pp. 1-23.
HOLSINGER, JOHN R.
1977.   A new genus and two new species of subterranean amphipod crustaceans (Gammaridae s. lat.) from the Yucatán Peninsula in México.   Assoc. Mexican Cave Stud. Bull., no. 6, pp. 15-25.
KEIRANS, JAMES E., and CLIFFORD, CARLETON M.
1975.   *Nothoaspis reddelli,* new genus and new species (Ixodoidea: Argasidae), from a bat cave in México.   Ann. Entomol. Soc. America, vol. 68, pp. 81-85.
KEIRANS, JAMES E.; CLIFFORD, CARLETON M.; and REDDELL, JAMES R.
1977.   Description of the immature stages of *Nothoaspis reddelli* (Ixodoidea: Argasidae) from bat caves in México.   Ann. Entomol. Soc. America, vol. 70, pp. 591-595.
MERCER, HENRY C.
1896.   The hill-caves of Yucatan, 183 pp., illus.   Lippincott, Philadelphia.
MUCHMORE, WILLIAM B.
1977.   Preliminary list of the pseudoscorpions of the Yucatán Peninsula and adjacent regions, with descriptions of some new species (Arachnida: Pseudoscorpionida).   Assoc. Mexican Cave Stud. Bull., no. 6, pp. 63-78.
PEARSE, A. S.
1936.   The cenotes of Yucatan, 304 pp., illus.   Carnegie Institution of Washington Publ. no. 457.
1938.   Fauna of the caves of Yucatan, 304 pp., illus.   Carnegie Institution of Washington Publ. no. 491.
PECK, STEWART B.
1977.   The subterranean and epigean Catopinae of México (Coleoptera: Leiodidae).   Assoc. Mexican Cave Stud. Bull., no. 6, pp. 185-213.
REDDELL, JAMES R.
1977a.   A preliminary survey of the caves of the Yucatán Peninsula, México. Assoc. Mexican Cave Stud. Bull., no. 6, pp. 215-296.
REDDELL, JAMES R., ed.
1977b.   Studies on the cavernicole fauna of the Yucatán Peninsula.   Assoc. Mexican Cave Stud. Bull., no. 6, pp. 1-296, illus.

ROSEN, DONN ERIC, and GREENWOOD, P. HUMPHRY
1976.   A fourth neotropical species of synbranchid eel and the phylogeny and systematics of synbranchiform fishes.   Bull. American Mus. Nat. Hist., vol. 157, pp. 1-70.
ROWLAND, J. MARK, and REDDELL, JAMES R.
1977.   A review of the cavernicole Schizomida (Arachnida) of México, Guatemala, and Belize.   Assoc. Mexican Cave Stud. Bull., no. 6, pp. 79-102.
SCHULTZ, GEORGE A.
1977.   Two blind species, one new, of terrestrial isopod crustaceans (Oniscoidea: Philosciidae) from Yucatán and Guatemala.   Assoc. Mexican Cave Stud. Bull., no. 6, pp. 9-13.
STEPHENS, JOHN L.
1843.   Incidents of travel in Yucatan, 2 vols., illus.   Harper and Brothers, New York.
WAGNER, FREDERICK W.
1977.   Scorpions of the genus *Centruroides* (Arachnida: Scorpionida: Buthidae) from the Yucatán Peninsula.   Assoc. Mexican Cave Stud. Bull., no. 6, pp. 39-47.
YEATMAN, HARRY C.
1977.   *Mesocyclops ellipticus* Kiefer from a Mexican cave.   Assoc. Mexican Cave Stud. Bull., no. 6, pp. 5-7.

ROBERT W. MITCHELL

The Cluster of Galaxies Abell 910

Principal Investigator: Thomas W. Noonan, Physics Department, State University of New York, Brockport, New York.

Grant No. 1398:   In support of a study of the sizes of distant clusters of galaxies.

The study of clusters of galaxies is relevant to several lines of inquiry. First, it is hoped to use their angular sizes, as a function of redshift, as a test for cosmological models. Second, the question of possible cluster evolution will be answered by the accumulation of data on the properties of clusters. Third, galaxies themselves may be better understood through their interactions with each other in clusters.

Procedure

Photographic plates of the cluster Abell 910, located at (1950) 09^h59^m, $+67°24'$, were studied by microscope to obtain the distribution of galaxies. The analysis followed the lines of the investigator's previous work (Noonan, 1972). The use of plates in two colors allowed the determination of color effects.

Conclusions

The cluster, at a redshift of 0.20 (Wilkinson and Oke, 1978), has an overall radius of 15' or, when converted to linear measure with a Hubble constant of 100 km s^{-1}Mpc^{-1}, 2.6 Mpc, somewhat larger than the radius of a typical cluster. The average distance of cluster galaxies from the cluster center is 5'.9 on the red plate, compared with 6'.9 on the yellow plate, indicating a tendency for redder galaxies to be more centrally concentrated, an effect found in several other clusters.

Acknowledgments

This study was made possible by a grant in 1974 from the National Geographic Society for which I am grateful. Thanks are also due to Sidney van den

Bergh for the use of the facilities of the Dominion Astrophysical Observatory, Victoria, British Columbia, in June 1978.

REFERENCES

NOONAN, THOMAS W.
  1972. The cluster of galaxies Abell 1413. Astronomical Journ., vol. 77, pp. 9-12.
WILKINSON, ALTHEA, and OKE, J. B.
  1978. Spectral variations in brightest cluster galaxies. Astrophysical Journ., vol. 220, pp. 376-389.

THOMAS W. NOONAN

Field Study of Joint and Fracture Patterns in the Middle East

Principal Investigator: Amos M. Nur, Stanford University, Stanford, California.

Grant No. 1408:   In partial support of a field study of joint and fracture patterns in Middle East earthquake sites.

During the period March to September 1975 I spent approximately 45 days in field investigations of faults and fractures in the Jordan River rift valley and the southern part of the Sinai Peninsula. Although the original goal of the study was confined to problems of distribution and scale of fracturing in the earth's crust, it became apparent during the course of the work that the role of fractures is tightly linked with fault slip and earthquake activity. Consequently, serious effort was made to compile and interpret historical evidence for earthquake activity. This led not only to seismological investigation of recent earthquakes but also to a search for Biblical, historical, and archeological evidence.

Geological and Geophysical Results

In 1927, the central part of Palestine was hit by a destructive earthquake (estimated magnitude $M = 6.5$), which destroyed homes and some public buildings in Jerusalem, Jericho, Nablus, and several villages in Galilee and Transjordan. From the distribution of the damage it is easy to infer that this event was similar to many prior earthquakes that occurred once or so per century and presumably originated on the same fault segment. The 1927 event, however, was the first of these ever recorded on seismic instruments the world over. No such event has occurred since that time. The analysis of the seismic records generated by the 1927 earthquake revealed that the location of the event and several of its aftershocks delineate a line running approximately north-south into the Dead Sea. The motion during the 1927 quake, also inferred from the seismic data, yielded a left lateral strike slip displacement indicating that the horizontal shear slip occurred on a north-south-trending vertical fault, with the eastern side moving north relative to the western side. This result is in very good agreement with the motion predicted by the theory of global plate tectonics.

Next, the 1927 data were combined with more recent seismic measurements of radiation from small earthquakes in the Dead Sea, further suggesting

491

the existence of a fault trace in the middle of the Jordan rift valley. (This fault trace is very subtle and does not coincide with the spectacular but geophysically relatively unimportant normal faults that define the Jordan rift boundaries.)

The faint fault trace, inferred from the seismicity, was then identified by disturbances in the geology (tilted beds), morphology (linear array of small oasis and springs along the fault), air photos, and, most exciting, historical evidence. Two independent pieces of evidence indicate that the ground surface was clearly fractured during the 1927 event. A Jerusalem-based geographer visited the area a few days after the event and discovered fresh ground cracks. An anonymous photographer from the American Colony in Jerusalem actually obtained a picture of the cracks.

During the 1927 event, water flow in the river Jordan ceased for a half day or so. This was due to a mud slide, triggered by the earthquake, where Wadi Zarka joins with the river Jordan.

Historical and Biblical Evidence

A perusal of historical data revealed that pre-1927 earthquakes with similar intensity and damage were repeatedly associated with stoppage of flow in the river. Furthermore the Monastery of John the Baptist, located near the river bank, was totally destroyed repeatedly by past earthquakes. The monastery is located where Jesus presumably was baptized, and according to legend this is also where Joshua crossed the Jordan into the promised land. There is a truly remarkable similarity between the details of the 1927 event and the Old Testament's description of the fall of Jericho. According to the book of Joshua (3:1, 15-16):

> And Joshua rose early in the morning; and they removed from Shittim, and came to the Jordan, he and all the children of Israel, and lodged there before they passed over.
> And, as they who bore the ark were come unto the Jordan and the feet of the priests who bore the ark were dipped in the brim of the water (for the Jordan overfloweth all its banks all the time of harvest),
> That the waters which came down from above stood and rose up upon an heap very far from the city Adam, that is beside Zarethan; and those that came down toward the sea of the plain, even the salt sea, failed, and were cut off; and the people passed over right against Jericho.

The Old Testament describes this stoppage of flow *prior* to the fall of the city walls (which we infer were destroyed by the earthquake), but it is reasonable to assume that the actual sequence was as follows: The Israeli nomads were camping for a long time on the eastern bank of the river, unable to take the lush city of Jericho, which was heavily enclosed by walls. An earthquake (very similar to the 1927 event), occurred on the tectonic fault and this caused the walls to collapse. Joshua's army, realizing what happened, ran across the river to take the city. As they crossed it, they found the river to be dry, presumably owing to a mud slide farther north, as described in the above paragraph from the book of Joshua.

The historian Josephus Flavius describes in his book how the town of Qumran, south of Jericho, was destroyed by an earthquake in the year 31 B.C. In particular, he details the fracturing of the central water cistern in this desert village. This fractured cistern was unearthed recently, with an offset of 25 centimeters. The town lies 2 kilometers west of our inferred Dead Sea rift fault and was probably destroyed by slumping on a secondary fault. Qumran is the site of the discovery of the Dead Sea scrolls.

Several churches, monasteries, and mosques, particularly in Jerusalem, have repeatedly suffered heavy damage from 1927-type earthquakes. There is a collection of broken columns near the El Aksa mosque, which were collected over the years. Parts of the Church of the Holy Sepulchre have also repeatedly suffered from the Jericho fault earthquakes.

During the unearthing of the ruins of Masada, at the southern end of the Jericho fault, the archeologists noted that whole walls had collapsed intact, indicating that an earthquake or earthquakes were responsible.

Zechariah (14: 4) prophesying the doom of Jerusalem invokes an earthquake . . . "and the Mount of Olives shall cleave in its midst toward the east and toward the west, . . . and half of the mountain shall remove toward the north, and half of it toward the south." This suggests that a large 1927-type event, which damaged Jerusalem heavily, occurred during Uziah's reign (ca. 500 B.C.), and produced enough offset on the fault to be observed as a left lateral strike slip.

An independent and separate series of earthquakes in the southern Sinai Peninsula is associated with the Santa Katherina monastery area, where the patchy defense walls bear evidence of repeated damage by earthquakes.

REFERENCES

NUR, AMOS M.
   1976.   Tectonics, seismicity and structure of the Afro-Eurasian junction: The breaking of an incoherent plate.   Physics of the Earth and Planetary Interiors, vol. 12, pp. 1-50.
   _____.   The origin of fracture lineaments.   Vol. 3 of "New Basement Tectonics." (In press.)

AMOS M. NUR

Feeding Ecology and Social Organization of Brown Hyenas (*Hyaena brunnea,* Thunberg) of the Central Kalahari Desert

Principal Investigators: Mark J. Owens and Delia D. Owens, Wildlife Department, Maun, Botswana.[1]

Grant No. 1392:   For behavioral study of cheetahs, emphasizing population dynamics and reproductive biology.

In 1974 the study area chosen for the research of cheetahs in the Okanango Delta was severely flooded, making initiation of the study impossible. Consequently, a behavioral and ecological study of the brown hyena was undertaken while we waited for the Delta to dry. Unfortunately the record rainfall continued for the next four years. Since we were unable to undertake the cheetah study, the Society's support was switched to the subject herein reported.

On May 2, 1974, a study on the behavioral ecology of brown hyenas inhabiting the Deception fossil river system in the Central Kalahari Game Reserve of Botswana was initiated. The research continued through 1980 under sponsorship from the Frankfurt Zoological Society. Past sponsors have been the National Geographic Society during 1975, the Okavango Wildlife Society in 1976 and 1977, Mr. and Mrs. A. M. Price through the California Academy of Sciences, and the Frankfurt Zoological Society during 1978 and 1979.

Prior to this project no research had ever been conducted on the brown hyena or any other wildlife population within the Central Kalahari Game Reserve. After a study of the brown hyena in the Southern Kalahari coincidental with this project, Mills (1976) and Skinner (1976) reported the brown hyena to be a solitary scavenger.

The primary research objectives of this project have been (1) to develop a qualitative and quantitative description of the brown hyena's diet in a typical Central Kalahari fossil river system; (2) to ascertain the degree to which brown hyenas are social, and to describe the social system and its relationship with feeding ecology; and (3) to describe the influence of lion feeding ecology and

---

[1] Present address, P.O. Box 86, Montreat, North Carolina 28757.

495

range movement on that of brown hyenas along the Deception fossil river system.

Methods

Lion and brown hyena research subjects are equipped with ear tags and/or radio transmitter collars. Range movements and habitat associations are monitored on a daily basis, using the project aircraft (donated by the Frankfurt Zoological Society) and a 4-wheel drive vehicle for ground surveillance. The day-to-day positions of the hyena clan and lion pride members are plotted on a map of the research area developed from aerial photographs. To better describe total range movements night flights are made each month during the full moon when lion and hyena positions are fixed midway during the forage period. Individual lions and brown hyenas are followed at night with the use of the radiotelemetry equipment and the truck for up to 12 hours. A game census is flown over the research area four times annually and ungulate concentrations are plotted according to habitat type.

Brown hyena food item selection and foraging behavior has been described through direct observation while following hyenas over the range and through fecal analysis.

The research is being conducted in Botswana's 55,000-square-kilometer Central Kalahari Game Reserve. The focus is on two brown hyena clans and five lion prides along the Deception Valley, one of the fossil river systems which transect the Central Kalahari.

Summary of Results

Brown hyenas are primarily scavengers, and 35.9 percent of the times they were observed feeding it was on the remains of kills left by other predators. Such food items as bones, skin, hooves, and small amounts of meat are obtained from carcasses abandoned by lions. Often, however, brown hyenas acquire fresh carcasses by chasing leopards, cheetahs, and jackals from their kills. These may be quite entire, depending on how soon a hyena discovers the kill, and provide an important source of fresh meat and moisture.

During the dry season, typically from June through December, the hyena supplements its diet with small prey it kills itself. Sixteen percent of feeding observations involved small prey such as springhare, mice, rats, reptiles, and insects. Miscellaneous scavenged material, including dung, eggs, old bones, and horns, made up 33.9 percent of direct feeding observations. Wild fruits, especially melons, are an important source of moisture for the hyena in the dry season and they represent 12.5 percent of the feeding observations. Brown hyenas, lions, jackals and other predators of the Central Kalahari survive long periods of 8 months or more with nothing to drink and only the fluids of prey and the moisture from melons keep them alive. During droughts they may survive indefinitely without water. (Owens and Owens, 1978).

Brown hyenas forage alone, and this is undoubtedly why they have been described as solitary animals by Mills (1976), Smithers (1971), Skinner (1976), and others. In fact, however, brown hyenas exhibit a unique social organization which has been molded by the arid and semiarid Kalahari environment.

Brown hyenas exist in clans of from 10 to 13 individuals, including the young. A clan typically consists of four or five adult females, their offspring of varying ages, a dominant male, and one or two subordinate males (Owens and Owens, 1979a).

Clan members jointly defend a territory of approximately 170 square kilometers against other clans along the fossil river system (Owens and Owens 1978, 1979b).

As they forage solitarily, individuals follow a network of olfactory pathways which are maintained through scent marking or pasting. The paste from anal gland secretions deposited on grass stalks or bush apparently contains information on sex, social status, estrus status of individuals, and temporal-spatial information which enables other clan members to avoid or locate a foraging individual. Thus, although brown hyenas have no loud vocalizations, this sophisticated olfactory communication allows them to meet, greet, and engage in a variety of social interactions, including ritualized fighting for social status within the clan's rank order heirarchy (Owens and Owens, 1978).

Vocalizations are limited to short range communications, as for example, the "purring" by a female with cubs soliciting their exit from the den, the "growl-bark" used as a warning, or the "squeak" used by cubs in begging or by a subordinate adult in appeasement.

Brown hyena cubs are born in a maternity den where they are suckled and attended by the female until they are approximately 2.5 months old. During this period the female moves them to several different den sites, usually aardvark or porcupine dens that are enlarged for use by the mother.

The last of these maternity dens is normally quite close to the clan's communal den where cubs of all clan females are raised together (Owens and Owens, 1979a). In this last maternity den, cubs are introduced for the first time to adult and subadult hyenas moving to and from the communal den.

Once cubs are established in the communal den all clan females participate in raising them collectively. Females suckle other cubs besides their offspring for up to 14 months of age. However, the estrus of clan females is staggered so that normally only one litter of from two to four *infant* cubs is present in the communal den at one time.

Whenever carrion is located, all clan females and the clan males most related to the infant cubs provision the den.

In the Central Kalahari food items for the scavenging brown hyena are scarce for much of the year. After the rains the large herds of springbok, oryx, hartebeest, and other large ungulates migrate from the river systems. As a result, carrion from the predation on these herds by lions, leopards, and other large predators greatly diminishes. Brown hyena clan members must expand their ranges and forage time in order to locate sufficient food resources to sustain themselves and their cubs during the long dry months. Thus, females with cubs can afford to spend little time attending their young at the den.

The communal den frees the female with cubs, relieving her of many of her maternal responsibilities so that she can spend most of her nocturnal activity period in foraging. For example, the den affords cubs their only protection against predators. At the first sound of an animal approaching through the grass, the cubs dive into the den and stay beneath the ground until the danger is past.

The communal den allows greater collective forage time by clan females and enhances food provision to the cubs. At any one time during the night all or nearly all clan females are foraging while their cubs are within the den. This increases the chances that one or more of the females will locate a food surplus which can be shared by all the cubs at the den.

The den is also a center for important social development and learning. Early each evening there is a "happy-hour" of play where cubs practice neck-biting, muzzle-wrestling, chasing, and greeting each other and visiting adults. All of these behavior patterns exhibited in play are important in establishing a place in the social hierarchy as an adult (Owens and Owens, 1979a).

As hyena cubs reach adolescence they begin leaving the den for short periods each night to forage on their own. But the den retains its importance as a social center and for learning. Adolescents return to the den each night where they await the arrival of one of the adult females. After greeting the adult, the adolescent follows it as it moves off to forage. It appears that considerable learning about forage pathways, techniques, hunting behavior and appropriate response to potential predators takes place during these periods.

When the young hyenas reach subadulthood, adults begin rebuffing them through vigorous neck-biting and muzzle-wrestling. By the time they are 30 months of age some of the male and female cubs have been excluded by the clan.

A large portion of the brown hyena diet consists of the remains of lion kills. Aerial and ground surveillance has shown that the range movements and feeding ecology of lions greatly influences the same in brown hyenas. The hyena clan home range is contained within that of the local lion pride and both expand to nearly twice the wet season area during the dry months. The expansion incorporates more woodland habitat types out from the river bed but there is no expansion along it. On the river bed, lion and hyena clan territory bounds overlap.

The brown hyena exhibits a binary social mode in response to the limitations of its food resources. It is solitary in its foraging, yet social in its communal denning and congregation for communal scavenging at large carcasses left by other predators.

REFERENCES

MILLS, M. G. L.
  1976.   Ecology and behaviour of the brown hyena in the Kalahari with some suggestions for management. *In* "Proceedings of a Symposium of Endangered Wildlife in Southern Africa." University of Pretoria, Pretoria.
OWENS, DELIA D., and OWENS, MARK J.
  1979a. Communal denning and clan associations in brown hyenas (*Hyaena brunnea,* Thunberg) of the Central Kalahari Desert. African Journ. Ecol., no. 17, pp. 35-44.
  1979b. Notes on social organization and behaviour in brown hyenas (*Hyaena brunnea*). Journ. of Mammalogy, vol. 60, no. 2, pp. 406-408.
OWENS, MARK J., and OWENS, DELIA D.
  1978.   Feeding ecology and its influence on social organization in brown hyenas (*Hyaena brunnea,* Thunberg) of the Central Kalahari Desert. East African Wildlife Journ., no. 16, pp. 113-135.
  1979.   The secret social life of the brown hyena. African Wildlife, vol. 33, no. 3, pp. 26-29.
  1979.   Dark and shaggy ghosts of the Central Kalahari. Wildlife, vol. 21, no. 4, pp. 8-11.
  1980.   The semi-social brown hyena. Natural History, vol. 89, no. 2, pp. 44-53.
SKINNER, JOHN D.
  1976.   Ecology of the brown hyena *Hyeana brunnea* in the Transvaal with a distribution map for Southern Africa. South Africa Journ. of Science, no. 72, pp. 262-269.
SMITHERS, RAY H. W.
  1971.   Mammals of Botswana. Museum Memoir no. 4, Trustees of the National Museums of Rhodesia, Salisbury.

MARK J. OWENS
DELIA D. OWENS

Interstellar Deuterium and Its Relation
to Cosmology

Principal Investigator: Jay M. Pasachoff, Director, Hopkins Observatory, Williams
College, Williamstown, Massachusetts.

Grant No. 1344:   In support of studies of interstellar deuterium and its relation
to cosmology.

The future of the universe—whether it will expand forever or eventually begin to contract—can best be determined by an investigation of the interstellar abundance of deuterium (heavy hydrogen). National Geographic Society grant 1344 supported the expenses of my observing run to observe interstellar deuterium with the 210-foot radio telescope of the Australian National Radio Observatory in Parkes, New South Wales. The observations were carried out in the direction of the center of our Milky Way Galaxy, which rises much higher in the sky and is much longer above the horizon in the southern hemisphere than it is for sites in the northern hemisphere of the earth.

Over the years, since the discovery in 1929 by Hubble that the universe is expanding, several attacks have been made on the problem of determining whether and by how much the expansion is slowing down. Some of the methods, including direct observation of the velocities of recession of distant galaxies and counts of radio sources at diminishing strengths, have been pursued for many years, but the data do not permit a definite answer to the question whether the universe's expansion will continue forever—an open universe—or whether the expansion will eventually reverse—a closed universe. A different fundamental method of attack considers the amount of gravity in the universe, and calculates whether this is sufficient to reverse the expansion. Simple counts of the visible matter in the universe, however, are not sufficient to establish the amount of gravity, for invisible matter in the form of intergalactic gas, black holes, or other as yet unobserved objects, also has gravity. Moreover, some methods indicate that 90 percent or more of the matter may be invisible, the so-called "missing mass problem."

Theoretical models of the first few minutes after the big bang indicate that the light elements and isotopes were formed then. The amount of helium that results, however, is relatively insensitive to the assumptions one makes about initial conditions, while the amount of deuterium (the isotope of hydrogen with one proton and one neutron) is very sensitive to the initial mass density. In brief, if the density is high, as soon as any deuterium is formed it quickly meets another proton and is "cooked" into an isotope of helium; if, however, the density is low, when any deuterium is formed, it tends to remain. Thus a high abundance of deuterium relative to ordinary hydrogen indicates a high mass density, and a low deuterium abundance indicates a low mass density. One can calculate what the critical density is at which the univese becomes closed, in that there is sufficient gravity to pull back the expanding matter, and compare with this critical density the density calculated from the observed deuterium abundance. One further crucial advantage to studying deuterium is that deuterium is apparently formed only at the big bang, and not in stellar interiors later on.

The abundance of deuterium had never been observed in interstellar space prior to observations I made together with Diego A. Cesarsky (now of l'Observatoire de Paris) and Alan T. Moffet of the California Institute of Technology at the Owens Valley Radio Observatory in California during the summers of 1972 and 1973. Our observations indicated that the abundance of deuterium was sufficiently high that the mass density of the universe was too low for the expansion to ever cease. Our observations involved a lengthy observation (3 months long) in the direction of the galactic center at the 92-centimeter wavelength of the fundamental deuterium line.

Simultaneously to the announcement of our first deuterium abundance, a group announced that they had used another radio method to observe a deuterated molecule. The results, however, have a large uncertainty because processes involved in the formation of the molecule must be considered. Subsequent results in the ultraviolet from NASA's Copernicus satellite, which carries a telescope, involved first a deuterated molecule, with the same problem of interpretation, and then observations of the Lyman lines in the ultraviolet that have given a good value for the deuterium abundance in the directions of several stars located within a distance from the sun of one-tenth of the radius of the galaxy. Our 92-centimeter radio method involves longer distances in our galaxy, and all the methods must be pursued. One result from comparison of the conclusions from different methods is an assessment of the homogeneity of the distribution of deuterium by the galaxy, which leads to a check of our understanding of methods of the formation and destruction of deuterium.

The 130-foot telescope at Owens Valley had reached the limit of its usefulness, and the 210-foot antenna at Parkes had three potential advantages. First, it is larger and its resolution is consequently better; thus, the strength of the sources is less diluted by contributions from the sky background. Second, because of the telescope's location in the southern hemisphere, the source was observable for a much longer period each day than it had been in the northern hemisphere. Third, the new electronic system that followed the antenna in the chain of electronics (the so-called "back end," as opposed to the "front end," the dish itself), was potentially more efficient at Parkes.

Ten days of observing time were granted by the Australian National Radio Astronomy Observatory (ANRAO) for the project, and Nicholas Fourikis and John D. Murray of the ANRAO staff were assigned to work with me on the project. Additional time was spent in the ANRAO headquarters in Epping, New South Wales, both before and after the observing run at the telescope. A series of instrumental problems with the telescope, with its electronics, and with the controlling computer severely limited the amount of observing time available to the project. Nonetheless, many hours of data were collected, but the total observing time was too small to allow the data to be an improvement on existing observations from the Owens Valley. Since my return from Australia, I have worked to arrange further observing runs at Parkes and elsewhere. It remains desirable to improve the level of uncertainty associated with our existing 92-centimeter deuterium observations, in order to limit still further the uncertainties in the associated conclusions about the future of the universe.

REFERENCES

CESARSKY, DIEGO A.; MOFFET, ALAN T.; and PASACHOFF, JAY M.
  1972.   327 MHz observations of the galactic center: Possible detection of the
          deuterium absorption line.   *In* "Sixth Texas Symposium on Relativistic
          Astrophysics, 1973, Proceedings."   Annals New York Acad. Sci., vol.
          224, pp. 295-300.
  1973.   Possible discovery of interstellar deuterium.   Astrophys. Journ. Letters, vol. 180, pp. L1-L6.
PASACHOFF, JAY M., and CESARSKY, DIEGO A.
  1974.   Further observations at the interstellar deuterium frequency.   Astrophys. Journ., vol. 193 (pt. 1), pp. 65-67.
PASACHOFF, JAY M., and FOWLER, WILLIAM A.
  1974.   Deuterium in the universe.   Scientific American, vol. 230, no. 5
          (May), pp. 108-118.

JAY M. PASACHOFF

A Pantropical Comparison of
Lowland Forest Bird Community Structure

Principal Investigator: David L. Pearson, Department of Biology, Pennsylvania
State University, University Park, Pennsylvania.

Grant Nos. 1346   For a comparison of bird community structure in Old World
and 1634.   and New World tropical forests.

Lowland tropical forests offer an interesting and exciting opportunity to test ideas concerning the composition and ecological relationships of bird communities. Because of the large number of species in these forests, the chances of observing and measuring interactions is much greater than in areas of higher latitudes where species numbers are relatively low. Besides this professional reason for using the tropical lowland forest for studies is the more emotional reason that lowland forests may be eliminated within the next twenty years, and relatively little is known of their ecology. Experts have predicted that except for a few national parks, the onslaught and destruction by "civilized" man will make these forests only a memory before the turn of the century.

Following a total of two years study in western Amazonia, sponsored by the National Science Foundation (Pearson, 1971, 1972, 1974, 1975a, 1975b, 1975c, 1977; O'Neill and Pearson, 1974), I found that the answers to several of the questions I asked about bird communities were not clear. I felt that a comparison of these South American birds to an area where the birds were unrelated but most other factors were similar would give a much clearer idea of what factors were important in the evolution of the birds present and their interactions (in other words the effects of convergent evolution).

The lowland forests of Indonesian Borneo (Kalimantan), Papua New Guinea, and Gabon in West Central Africa (fig. 1) have only a few bird families in common with South America and none of the same species. If I could find that communities of birds in these Old World areas showed predictably similar or dissimilar patterns of interactions, ecological roles, and composition (community structure), I would have a better idea of the most important natural selection factors influencing the general evolution of bird communities.

With a major part of the support from the National Geographic Society, together with grants from the New York Zoological Society, and the Frank M. Chapman Memorial Fund from the American Museum of Natural History, my wife Nancy and I left for Jakarta in June 1974. After 2 weeks of meeting government officials, obtaining the many permits necessary, and purchasing some supplies, we flew to the Balikpapan airport in Kalimantan Timur, and then proceeded immediately via taxi, and water taxi to Samarinda. This city, the capital of Kalimantan Timur, was our last chance to buy all the tinned food and most of the supplies for the next 6 weeks. After waiting for 3 days, we found a water taxi going to the Sangatta River. The crowded 22-hour ride took us down the Mohakum River, out onto the ocean, 120 kilometers north along the coast, and 2 hours up the Sangatta River to the Pertamina Oil Company Unit IV. Mr. PakSahar, the resident caretaker of the camp we were to stay in, met us in his motorized canoe and took us another 4 hours up the Sangatta River. Our camp was located on an orangutang refuge called the Kutai Reserve, and the facilities there were maintained by the University of Washington Regional Primate Center and the Indonesian Department of Forestry. We stayed in this comfortable but isolated setting until September.

The primary forest began at the back door of our cabin and my study site started only 20 meters from the door. The bird life was much less diverse (Pearson, 1975d) than the South American sites but ecologically just as interesting. In addition to birds, the orangutangs, gibbons, several species of monkeys, wild pigs, barking deer, flying lizards, and a myriad of insects and plants made every day significant and exciting. Little or no hunting has taken place in this area in the last 20 years, so the animals were relatively tame.

At the end of our stay, we were able to arrange a ride out on the Pertamina Oil Company helicopter and catch the jet to Jakarta right after landing in Balikpapan. The trip that had taken us almost 5 days to come into the Sangatta camp took only 5 hours on the way out.

After short stopovers in Singapore and Darwin, we arrived in Port Moresby, Papua New Guinea. Through the cooperation of the Summer Institute of Linguistics, we arranged a flight to their main base in the Eastern Highlands District, Ukarumpa. From there we chartered a single engine plane and flew to Maprik, East Sepik District, in the northwestern part of the country. Our 6 weeks in this area was ideal weather-wise. The dry season had ended, but the wet season was not yet in full force. My study area was a 40-kilometer drive over all-weather gravel road toward the Sepik River. The members of the Summer Institute of Linguistics graciously made a cabin and car available and provided a welcome relief from the extreme isolation of the Borneo site. An enthusiastic local ornithologist, Geoffroy Swainson, saved me days of exploring by pointing out the best lowland forest in the vicinity. His experience with the local birds also made my job of learning a whole new avifauna much easier.

In form and structure the forest on this site was remarkably similar to the South American forests. The birds, however, were quite different taxonomically from South America, and only one species was shared with the Borneo site, wreathed hornbill *(Aceros plicatus)*. Instead of monkeys, tree kangaroos jumped from limb to limb. Megapodes had their large mound nests scattered throughout the plot on the forest floor, cassowary sign was common, and three species of birds-of-paradise were performing elaborate courtship behavior, apparently in anticipation of the wet season.

The total diversity of birds here, however, was much lower (Pearson, 1975e) than in South America or on the Borneo site. In addition, common families such as woodpeckers are completely absent from New Guinea. The resources, especially insects, available on the tree trunks and branches where woodpeckers should have been, however, did not go unused. A small parrot *(Micropsitta pusio)* could be found hitching up and down the trees like an overgrown nuthatch. This bird is thought to eat fungi, but it also included insects and other arthropods in its diet.

By November the wet season was present in full force. My paths became rushing streams and all but impassable. But by this time I had spent over 225 hours of observation on the site and had sufficient data for preliminary comparisons.

From September 16 to November 14, 1976, my graduate assistant, Ms. Ann Rypstra, and I extended this worldwide comparison by conducting daily 8-hour surveys of a 2.5-kilometer circular transect of primary forest in eastern Gabon. The French Laboratoire de Primatologie et d'Ecologie Equatoriale provided research facilities and housing as well as access to a large forest reserve under their protection, and the National Geographic Society funded transportation and daily expenses. During this period we gathered 300 hours of observational data on bird foraging strategies, made measurements of foliage density, and preliminary measurements of insect abundance. Data were obtained for over 120 bird species occurring in the forest plot, a number greater than the two island sites but less than any of the three South American sites. The Gabon forest plot was not so tall as the other plots and was noticeable for its lack of palms and bromeliad epiphytes. In the area were 13 species of primates, including gorilla, and our night observations were sometimes restricted by small bands of forest elephants foraging on the study.

Using these similar-sized study plots in Old World and New World tropical lowland forests, I examined some of the major biotic factors involved

Fig. 1. World map showing the location of major tropical lowland forest areas (stippled) and the six sites used in this study: (1) Limoncocha, Ecuador; (2) Yarinacocha, Peru; (3) Tumi Chucua, Bolivia; (4) Kutai, Kalimantan (Borneo); (5) Maprik, Papua New Guinea; (6) Makokou, Gabon.

in the evolution and present state of avian community structure on these sites by comparing (1) historical factors and island or islandlike effects, (2) seasonality of rainfall and its effect on insect and fruit abundance, (3) habitat heterogeneity, and (4) the influence of nonavian competition. This study is the first to sample and quantitatively compare birds in similar-sized plots of representative habitat in all the world's major tropical lowland forest areas.

Historically, Borneo and New Guinea have been connected to their respective mainlands (Sunda and Sahul continental shelves) several times when worldwide sea levels lowered. In South America and Africa, long-term dry climates apparently prevailed at intervals of thousands of years. These dry periods permitted grasslands to invade and take over all but the wettest areas, where forest survived to form islandlike refugia. Isolation is considered by most biogeographers to be essential for speciation, and these islands or islandlike isolates may have permitted many new species to develop. When the islands reconnected (return of rainy period to South America and Africa to reconnect forests, or lowering of sea level for New Guinea and Borneo), new species encountered one another. If they were or could become ecologically compatible enough to coexist, the number of species in the area was greater than before the isolation. This cycle of isolation and reconnection may have been a major factor in the extremely high species numbers of many plant and animal groups now found in these tropical forests. Geographical differences in this isolation cycle are the best explanation for the differences in species numbers between different tropical areas. The fact that Borneo and New Guinea are presently islands where extinction rates are generally higher than on mainlands may best explain the smaller number of bird species on the two island plots.

The foliage complexity of these six forest plots was also assessed. Vertical foliage profiles indicate that the Borneo plot was the most complex, next the New Guinea plot, followed by the Amazonian plots, and finally by the Gabon plot. Numbers of plant species is often another indicator of foliage complexity, and this index followed the same rank order as the foliage profiles. The physical and species complexity of plants on these plots seems to be most important in providing the amount of space and resources available for the birds.

Seasonality was similar on the Gabon, Peru, Bolivia, and New Guinea plots with a distinct dry and rainy season. The Ecuador and Borneo plots had no distinct dry season, and rainfall was generally high all year around. This difference in seasonality affects insect and fruit abundance and becomes another important ecological factor influencing the structure of the bird community.

Finally I looked at the potential influence of nonavian competitors on the bird community. One major correlation was seen in the number of fruit-eating mammals on each plot. The more fruit-eating mammals present the fewer fruit-eating birds present. Where birds such as woodpeckers were absent, other animals like carnivorous beetles, dragonflies, spiders, and squirrels seemed to replace them and use the same resource and substrate. Even some plants may be competing with the birds for the insect resource. Entomophagous fungi regularly attacked many large insects at certain seasons and could have contributed to a general reduction of insect abundance that affected insectivorous birds.

To sort out all these factors and to rigorously test the importance of each will take long-term studies by teams of experts. What my initial results do show, however, is that historical factors were likely the major influence on how many bird species were available to enter a forest. Then ecological factors and interactions within the forest acted through exclusion, extinction, and morphological or behavioral changes to mold the bird community that now exists (Pearson, 1978).

REFERENCES

Asterisk indicates publications resulting from research sponsored by The National Geographic Society.

MANDL, K. and PEARSON, D. L.
*1978.   *Therates pseudorothschildi,* eine neue *Therates*-Art aus Neu-Guinea. (Coleoptera, Cicindelidae).   Zeitschrift der Arbeitsgemeinschaft Österr. Entomologen, vol. 30, pp. 33-36.

O'NEILL, J. P., and PEARSON, D. L.
1974.   Un estudio preliminar de las aves de Yarinacocha, Departamento Loreto, Perú.   Publicaciones del Museo de Historia Natural "Javier Prado," Lima, Ser. A. vol. 25, pp. 1-13.

PEARSON, D. L.
1971.   Vertical stratification of birds in a tropical dry forest.   Condor, vol. 73, pp. 46-55.

1972.   Un estudio de las aves de Limoncocha, Provincia de Napo, Ecuador. Boletín de Informaciones Científicas Nacionales, Quito, vol. 13, pp. 335-346.

1974.   Use of abandoned cacique nests by nesting Troupials *(Icterus icterus):* precursor to parasitism?   Wilson Bull., vol. 86, pp. 290-291.

1975a.   The relation of foliage complexity to ecological diversity of three Amazonian bird communities.   Condor, vol. 77, pp. 453-466.

1975b.   Un estudio de las aves de Tumi Chucua, Departamento del Beni, Bolivia.   Pumapunku, La Paz, vol. 8, pp. 50-56.

1975c.   Range extensions and new records for bird species in Ecuador, Peru, and Bolivia.   Condor, vol. 77, pp. 96-99.
*1975d.   A preliminary survey of the birds of the Kutai Reserve, Kalimantan Timur, Indonesia.   Treubia, vol. 28, pp. 157-162.
*1975e.   Survey of the birds of a lowland forest plot in the East Sepik District, Papua New Guinea.   Emu, vol. 75, pp. 175-177.
1977.   Ecological relationships of small antbirds in Amazonian bird communities.   Auk, vol. 94, pp. 283-292.
*1977.   A pantropical comparison of bird community structure on six lowland forest plots.   Condor, vol. 79, no. 2, pp. 232-244.

PEARSON, D. L.
1980a.   Patterns of limiting similarity in tropical forest tiger beetles (Coleoptera: Cicindelidae).   Biotropica, vol. 12, no. 3, pp. 195-204.
1980b.   Patterns of foraging ecology for common and rarer bird species in tropical lowland forest communities.   Proc. XVII International Ornithologist Congress, Berlin.
———.   Historical factors and bird species richness.   *In* "The Biological Model of Diversification in the Tropics," G. T. Prance, ed.   Columbia Press. (In press.)

RYPSTRA, A. L.
1979.   Foraging flocks of spiders, a study of aggregate behavior in *Cyrtophora citricola* Forskål (Araneae; Araneidae) in West Africa.   Behavioral Ecology and Sociobiology, vol. 5, pp. 291-300.

DAVID L. PEARSON

Butterflies of the Western North Slope and Victoria Island, with Special Reference to Arctic Butterfly Zonation

Principal Investigator: Kenelm W. Philip, Institute of Arctic Biology, University of Alaska, Fairbanks, Alaska.

Grant Nos. 1312   In support of the Alaska Lepidoptera Survey expeditions to
and 1456.   the Utukok and Kivalina rivers (western North Slope, 1974) and the Kuujjua River (Victoria Island, 1975).

Despite widespread sporadic collecting over many years, and the efforts of the Canadian Northern Insect Survey 1947-1957 (Freeman, 1959), the North American arctic regions have not been systematically surveyed for Lepidoptera. In Alaska the early collecting was concentrated along the southern coast and the Yukon and Kuskokwim rivers. In the 1930's the McKinley Park area was collected, but even as late as 1970 there had been little collecting north of the Yukon River. In Canada (and to some extent in Alaska) the Northern Insect Survey collected Lepidoptera at numerous locations, but the stations were widely separated and Lepidoptera were not emphasized at the expense of other orders of insects. In particular, the greater parts of Banks and Victoria islands, and much of Baffin Island, are still essentially uncollected.

In 1970 I started the Alaska Lepidoptera Survey (ALS), with the aim of improving our knowledge of the butterflies and moths of Alaska. This project later expanded its coverage to parts of northern Canada (and more recently to northeastern Siberia), since distributional and taxonomic problems of northern Lepidoptera cannot properly be studied within a restricted range of longitude. The northern half of Alaska was the least studied part of the state, and the ALS has been concentrating on tundra habitats on the Seward Peninsula and North Slope/Brooks Range. Major field stations from 1970-1973 were Anaktuvuk Pass, Nome vicinity, Harris Dome (Seward Peninsula), Meade River, Noluck Lake, and Schrader Lake. A number of volunteer collectors sent in material from many other northern sites, including representative samples from Prudhoe Bay and the Itkillik River. As of 1973, however, all of the thoroughly sampled localities (with the exception of Noluck Lake) from the North Slope/Brooks Range were in the central and eastern sections, and more collecting sites were needed in northwestern Alaska.

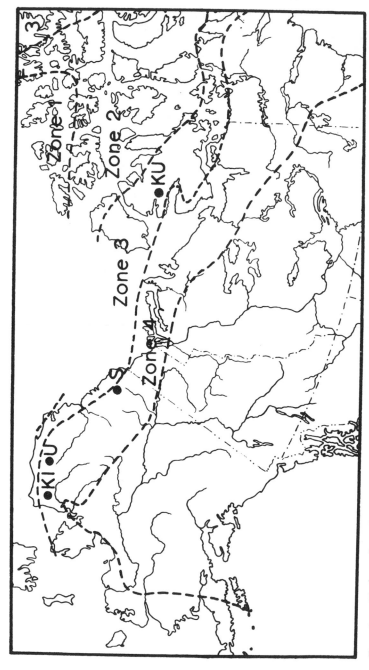

FIG. 1.   Alaska and northwestern Canada, with floristic zones (Young, 1971) and major Alaska Lepidoptera Survey collecting sites 1973-1975: KI=head of Kivalina River; U=Utukok River north of Noluck Lake; S=Schrader Lake; KU=Kuujjua River, Victoria Island.

Arctic Butterfly Zonation

It has long been known (Downes, 1964, 1966) that the diversity of the arctic butterfly fauna decreases rapidly from south to north; and the holarctic ranges of many arctic species imply only small changes in faunal composition as a function of longitude. Latitude alone, however, is by no means the only factor affecting faunal diversity; and cloud cover, wind, and other local climatic factors must be taken into account. A recently developed floristic zonation scheme (Young, 1971) appears to present a very useful conceptual framework on which to build an improved picture of arctic butterfly distribution. Young divides the arctic (defined as the region north of treeline) into four zones, purely on floristic grounds. One climatic parameter—the sum of the mean temperatures of all months having means above 0°C—proved to be fairly well correlated with the floristic zones. Figure 1 shows Young's zones for Alaska and northwestern Canada, as well as the major ALS collecting localities discussed below.

Zone 1 (McAlpine, 1964, 1965) has no butterflies. Zone 2 (Oliver, 1963; Downes, 1964, 1966) has 5 species: *Colias hecla, Lycaena phlaeas, Agriades aquilo, Boloria polaris, B. chariclea.* The faunal composition for Zones 3 and 4 was not known in sufficient detail to allow any precise correlation between Young's zones and the butterfly fauna before the fieldwork discussed below had been carried out. Zone 3 covers much of the Arctic Coastal Plain in Alaska, most of Banks and Victoria islands, and much of Baffin Island. A comparison of the fauna of those three islands with that of the Alaskan North Slope should yield an excellent test of the applicability of Young's zones to butterfly distribution.

The Utukok/Kivalina Rivers Expedition

In 1974 National Geographic Society support was obtained to help improve our knowledge of the western North Slope fauna (Zone 4). Dr. Olavi Sotavalta (University of Oulu, Finland) and I collected on the Utukok River 13 kilometers southwest of its junction with Carbon Creek (June 23-July 7), and at the head of the Kivalina River in the Wulik Peaks, DeLong Mountains (July 7-19). The Utukok River site is in the outer northern foothills of the Brooks Range, where the river cuts through the Archimedes Ridge/Lookout Ridge formation before dropping into the Arctic Coastal Plain. Elevations range from 150-550 meters; habitats range from river floodplain with willow thickets through sedge meadow, tussock tundra, and tundra meadow to scree and blockfield on the ridgetops. The Kivalina River site is a steep-walled mountain valley in the Wulik Peaks, and the landscape is almost devoid of the *Eriophorum* tussock tundra which covers so much of the North Slope (and is a rather poor butterfly habitat). Elevations (collected) range from 335-625 meters, habitats from dry gravel riverbeds through tundra meadow to vast expanses of scree and blockfield on the surrounding peaks. Columns 1 and 2 of Table 1 show the species of butterflies obtained, while column 3 shows, for comparison, the species found at Schrader Lake the previous summer (June 5-August 5). All three sites are Zone 4. The Kivalina River site (col. 2) yielded 30 species of butterflies, matching Schrader Lake for the largest species diversity yet found at a single North Slope site. Most of the differences between the Kivalina River and Schrader Lake lists are believed to reflect incomplete sampling of the fauna, except for the *Colias boothii/thula* difference. *C. boothii* appears to replace *C. thula* on the eastern North Slope, and examination of this complex over the entire North American arctic has raised the possibility that they are conspecific. If any North Slope species have alternate-year flights, as some taiga and tundra species do in interior Alaska, then two successive years of collecting at any one site would be required for thorough sampling of the fauna.

The overall similarity of the Kivalina River and Schrader Lake fauna indicates that Zone 4 has a fairly homogenous fauna over the Alaskan North Slope. Column 4 in Table 1 shows the entire butterfly fauna of the North Slope as known to date (1979). The North Slope is here defined as all land north of the Brooks Range watershed, which covers most (but not all) of Zone 4 in northern Alaska. The more southern parts of Zone 4 (south slope of the Brooks Range to treeline) contain a very complex interdigitation of tundra and taiga, and a number of taiga species stray into tundra habitats making it difficult to specify the Zone 4 fauna with much precision. The current North Slope fauna stands at 40 species (assuming *C. boothii* and *thula* are conspecific)—just over half of the total Alaska butterfly fauna.

Some of the more significant results of this expedition, aside from general distributional data for the western North Slope, were:

1. Westward or northwestward extensions of the known range of several species, particularly *Pyrgus centaureae, Euchloe creusa, Boloria distincta* (its Alaskan range, since it was already known from Chukotka), and *Erebia theano*.

2. A demonstration that the "rare" species *Boloria distincta* is common and widespread in northwestern Alaska wherever its habitat (scree and blockfield) occurs.

3. Collection of long series of a new and undescribed species of *Erebia* ("*E. sp.*" in Table 1) previously found on the Seward Peninsula and in the Brooks Range and its northern foothills by ALS collectors.

The Victoria Island Expedition (Zone 3)

Previous collecting on Victoria Island had concentrated on coastal sites. The Northern Party of the Canadian Arctic Expedition 1913-1918 collected butterflies at Walker Bay and Armstrong Point (northwest coast) and at one or more unspecified sites on the Wollaston Peninsula, one of which may have been as much as 40 kilometers inland (Gibson, 1920). At none of these sites was anything approaching the complete local fauna obtained. The Northern Insect Survey collected at Cambridge Bay (1950) and Holman (1952), and the collection from the latter site is representative of the fauna. I know of no Victoria Island collecting since 1952, which leaves only five general localities collected on the island, and only one (coastal) site thoroughly sampled.

In 1975 National Geographic Society support was obtained (and logistic support from the Polar Continental Shelf Project) to place Dr. D. M. Wood and G. Wood (Biosystematics Research Institute, Agriculture, Canada) and me at a carefully chosen field site in the Kuujjua River valley, Diamond Jenness Peninsula, northwestern Victoria Island (see fig. 1). The site is about 8 kilometers west of the southwest corner of the Saneraun Hills (an extension of the Shaler Mountains), 50 kilometers southeast of the head of Minto Inlet, and more than 60 kilometers north of Prince Albert Sound. Ignoring the inlets, the site is about 170 kilometers inland from Amundsen Gulf and Viscount Melville Sound—and was thus considered characteristic of the inland regions of northwestern Victoria Island.

Collections were made at elevations from 150-370 meters within an approximately 40-square-kilometer east-west oriented rectangle around base camp (71°17'N, 114°0.5'W). Any form of continuous plant cover was rather rare in the study area, and was limited to sedge meadows in depressions, hillsides receiving meltwater from snowbanks, or to the margins of lakes and streams. With the exception of those species preferring a scree/blockfield habitat most butterflies were restricted to (or much more abundant in) closed tundra or its near vicinity—and with the exception of such favorable habitats the remainder of the landscape (stony clay flats) was unproductive for Lepidoptera in general. Less than 10 percent of the land area supported populations of butterflies, and within that area most butterflies were concentrated into narrow bands along banksides and bank edges. Really dense butterfly populations were thus limited to about 1-2 percent of the land surface within the study area.

Within the study area there were five sites at which the majority of the 785 butterfly specimens obtained were collected: (1) A narrow linear sedge meadow in a long trough at the base of the 370-meter hill just west of camp,

TABLE 1. Butterflies of the North Slope and Arctic Coastal Plain (Alaska), and Banks, Victoria, and Baffin Islands (Canada)

The North Slope (including Utukok and Kivalina rivers, and Schrader Lake) and the Arctic Coastal Plain records are all from the Alaska Lepidoptera Survey, except *Erebia inuitica* (Wyatt, 1966). The Canadian records have been compiled from the Canadian National Collection (all three islands) and the Alaska Lepidoptera Survey (Banks and Victoria islands). Columns 1-8 indicate the following localities:

1. Utukok River   4. North Slope   6. Banks Island
2. Kivalina River   5. Arctic Coastal Plain 7. Victoria Island
3. Schrader Lake   8. Baffin Island

Species	1	2	3	4	5	6	7	8
Hesperiidae								
Hesperia manitoba (Scud.)				x				
Pyrgus centaureae (Ramb.)		x		x				
Papilionidae								
Parnassius eversmanni Men.	x	x	x	x				
Papilio machaon L.		x	x	x	x[a]			
Pieridae								
Pieris occidentalis Reak.			x	x				
P. napi (L.)	x	x	x	x				
Colias hecla Lef.	x	x	x	x	x	x	x	x
C. boothii Curt. } (same			x	x				x
C. thula Hov. } species?)	x	x		x	x	x	x	
C. philodice Godt.				x				
C. gigantea Stkr./*pelidne* Bdv. & Lec.				x				
C. palaeno (L)		x	x	x	x			x[b]
C. nastes Bdv.	x	x	x	x	x	x	x	x
Euchloe creusa (Dbldy.)		x	x	x				
Lycaenidae								
Lycaena phlaeas (L.)			x	x	x	x	x	x
Lycaeides argyrognomon (Bergs.)		x	x	x	x[a]			
Vacciniina optilete (Knoch)		x		x				
Agriades aquilo (Bdv.)	x	x	x	x	x	x	x	x
Glaucopsyche lygdamus (Dbldy.)			x	x				
Nymphalidae								
Nymphalis antiopa (L.)					x[c]			
Polygonia gracilis (G. & R.)					x[a]			
Boloria napaea (Hoff.)	x	x	x	x	x			
B. frigga (Thun.)	x	x	x	x	x	x	x	x
B. improba (Butl.)	x	x	x	x	x	x	x	x
B. polaris (Bdv.)	x	x	x	x	x	x	x	x
B. freija (Thun.)	x	x	x	x	x		x	x

(2) Scree and blockfield at the summit of the 370-meter hill, (3) A "muskox meadow" (Porsild, 1955) $2\frac{1}{2}$ kilometers south-southeast of camp, with gravelly banks on its northern rim, (4) An isolated gravel hill east of site number 3, (5) A steep-walled erosion gully near the Kuujjua River 5 kilometers east of camp. (Another large sedge meadow complex 4 kilometers west of camp might have been a productive site, but we were unable to collect it during good weather.)

Some butterflies occurred outside these sites. *Boloria polaris* in particular tended to be ubiquitous, although its density was much higher along the edges of sedge meadows. Other habitats (as for example the southeast slope of the hill west of camp, below a line of cliff-base snowbanks) were well worth collecting even though the density of butterflies was much lower than in the five sites listed above. On the other hand, the stony clay flats that comprised most of the landscape were exceedingly unproductive, barring an occasional *Boloria polaris* or *Oeneis melissa*.

Species	1	2	3	4	5	6	7	8
Nymphalidae (continued)								
B. *distincta* (Gibs.)	x	x		x				
B. *chariclea* (Schneid.)	x	x	x	x	x	x	x	x
B. *eunomia* (Esp.)		x	x	x				
Satyridae								
Coenonympha kodiak Edw.		x		x				
Oeneis uhleri (Reak.)				x				
O. *bore* (Schneid.)	x	x	x	x			x	
O. *melissa* (Fabr.)	x	x	x	x	x	x	x	x
O. sp.				x				
O. *polixenes* (Fabr.)	x	x	x	x	x	x	x	x
Erebia rossii (Curt.)	x	x	x	x	x		x	x
E. *disa* (Thun.)	x	x	x	x				
E. *mackinleyensis* Gund.			x	x				
E. *fasciata* Butl.	x	x	x	x	x	x	x	
E. *theano* (Tausch.)		x	x	x				
E. *inuitica* Wyatt				x				
E. *youngi* Holl.	x	x	x	x				
E. sp.	x	x	x	x				

[a] These species are believed to be strays from Zone 4 rather than residents of Zone 3. All records to date are of single specimens only.

[b] Older papers refer to Baffin Island *palaeno* as *pelidne*.

[c] A sight record (by the author) of a single specimen on the Kavik River. The determination is certain. The butterfly was seen in a dense willow (the larval foodplant) thicket, and the possibility exists (unconfirmed) that *N. antiopa* breeds on the Kavik River.

Collecting was carried out (weather permitting) from June 27 (first butterfly emergence) through August 1. Severe weather limited the butterfly
flight period (and collecting) to only 18 days or parts thereof during this 5-
week period. Apparently 1975 was a poor summer for collecting, but it was
obvious that the effective total butterfly flight season at this site must in general be very short indeed. The seventh column in Table 1 lists the currently
known butterfly species for Victoria Island, of which all but two *(B. improba,
E. rossii)* were found in the Kuujjua Valley.

The remaining columns (5-8) in Table 1 list the butterfly species for the
Arctic Coastal Plain in Alaska (col. 5, compiled from ALS records from Meade
River, Barrow, Colville delta, Prudhoe Bay, Barter Island, and Beaufort Lagoon; and Canadian National Collection (CNC) records from Collinson
Point), Banks Island (col. 6, ALS and CNC records), and Baffin Island (col. 8,
CNC records). All these localities are Zone 3, except for the very southern end
of Baffin Island which lacks Zone 4 butterflies (perhaps from its isolation from
the mainland by Hudson Strait). If Young's zonation scheme is relevant to
butterfly distribution, Victoria Island should be expected to show striking
faunal similarity to the Arctic Coastal Plain in Alaska. If one removes from the
Arctic Coastal Plain list the 4 species believed to be strays from Zone 4 rather
than bona fide residents of Zone 3, one has 16 species for Zone 3 in northern
Alaska. Victoria Island (col. 7), more than 1,500 kilometers to the east, has
15 species of which 14 (93%) are resident on the Arctic Coastal Plain. Banks,
Victoria, and Baffin islands have a total fauna of 16 species, one of which (assuming *Colias boothii* and *thula* are conspecific) does not occur on the Arctic
Coastal Plain (and vice versa) The entire Zone 3 strip in North America,
4,000 kilometers in length, has 17 species of butterflies of which 15 (88%)
are common to both ends of the zone. We may thus conclude that the butterfly fauna of Zone 3 in North America is quite homogenous along a 4,000-
kilometer east-west band from northwestern Alaska to Baffin Island.

The exceptions are of interest. The two Alaskan species not on Victoria Island are *Colias palaeno* and *Boloria napaea,* which have generally somewhat
similar distributions in Canada (Freeman, 1956). *Boloria napaea* gets to the
coast at Coppermine (CNC record) but apparently has not crossed Dolphin
and Union Strait to Victoria Island. Careful collecting in southwest Victoria
Island might yet turn this species up, since Freeman (op. cit.) has observed
that the distribution of *B. napaea* correlates with sedimentary rocks and does
not extend over the Canadian Shield. The Kuujjua Valley (and the Shaler
Mountains) are in a belt of Pre-Cambrian rocks, which may relate to the absence of *B. napaea* at our field site. The southwest portion of the island is Pa-
laeozoic sedimentary rock (Porsild, 1955), and *B. napaea* might occur there.

Colias palaeno (for no known reason) stays back from the coast near Victoria Island, and would not seem a candidate for the island fauna. Both these species are *very* abundant in Zone 4 in Alaska, and it is not surprising that they have moved up into lower Zone 3. *Oeneis bore,* on the other hand, presents a real problem. It is well established on Victoria Island, but has not yet shown up at any Zone 3 site collected in Alaska, although it is quite common in Zone 4.

On the whole, considering both distance and the presence of a water barrier between Alaska and the Canadian Arctic Archipelago, the results indicate that Young's zones are indeed a useful way of looking at arctic butterfly distributions. Preliminary results from my 1978 field trip to northeastern Siberia indicate that the Zone 3 correlation may extend to Chukotka as well. There are some limited problem areas (Melville Island, Wrangel Island) which need careful investigation. According to Young (personal communication) these apparent problems may end up confirming the overall picture, since later floristic data indicate revisions to the zones in the direction suggested by the butterflies.

Acknowledgments

The Alaska Lepidoptera Survey has received support for its North Slope/ Victoria Island investigations as follows:

1971, Meade River: Explorers Club; C. F. dos Passos; Tundra Biome, International Biological Program; Naval Arctic Research Laboratory, Barrow.

1972, Noluck Lake: American Philosophical Society.

1973, Kavik River and Schrader Lake: National Museum of Natural History, Smithsonian Institution.

1974, Utukok and Kivalina Rivers: National Geographic Society.

1975, Victoria Island: National Geographic Society; Polar Continental Shelf Project (Canada Department of Energy, Mines and Resources). Particular thanks are due Walter Burke and F. P. Hunt, who arranged helicopter transportation from Holman to the Kuujjua River, and Dr. D. M. Wood and G. Wood, who undertook a major share of coordinating the logistics of the Victoria Island expedition.

Finally, the overall comparison between material from the Alaskan North Slope with material from the Canadian Arctic Archipelago was made possible only through the efforts of Alaska Lepidoptera Survey volunteer collectors from 1970 to the present. There have been too many volunteers to list here, but I wish to express my deep appreciation to all the people who took time from their own work to collect tundra butterflies for the Alaska Lepidoptera Survey.

REFERENCES

DOWNES, J. ANTONY
   1964.   Arctic insects and their environment.   Canad. Ent., vol. 96, pp. 297-307.
   1966.   The Lepidoptera of Greenland; some geographic considerations. Canad. Ent., vol. 98, pp. 1135-1144.

FREEMAN, THOMAS N.
   1956.   The distribution of arctic and subarctic butterflies.   Proc. Tenth Int. Congr. Ent., Montreal, vol. 1, pp. 659-672.
   1959.   The Canadian Northern Insect Survey, 1947-1957.   The Polar Record, vol. 9, pp. 299-307.

GIBSON, ARTHUR
   1920.   Lepidoptera.   Pp. 3I-57I *in* "Report of the Canadian Arctic Expedition 1913-18," vol. III: Insects.   King's Printer, Ottawa.

MCALPINE, J. FRANCIS
   1964.   Arthropods of the bleakest Barren Lands: composition and distribution of the Arthropod fauna of the northwestern Queen Elizabeth Islands. Canad. Ent., vol. 96, pp. 127-129.
   1965.   Insects and related terrestrial arthropods of Ellef Ringnes Island.   Arctic, vol. 18, pp. 73-103.

OLIVER, DONALD R.
   1963.   Entomological studies in the Lake Hazen area, Ellesmere Island, including lists of species of Arachnida, Collembola, and Insecta.   Arctic, vol. 16, pp. 175-180.

PORSILD, A. ERLING
   1955.   The vascular plants of the western Canadian Arctic Archipelago, 226 pp.   Bull. National Museum of Canada, no. 135.   Queen's Printer, Ottawa.

WYATT, COLIN W.
   1966.   Eine neue Erebia-Art aus Alaska.   Ziet. der Wiener Ent. Ges., vol. 51, pp. 93-94.

YOUNG, STEVEN B.
   1971.   The vascular flora of St. Lawrence Island with special reference to floristic zonation in the arctic regions.   Contr. Gray Herb., no. 201, pp. 11-115.

KENELM W. PHILIP

Ichneumonidae (Hymenoptera) in the Coastal Desert of Peru and North Chile

Principal Investigator: Charles C. Porter,[1] Department of Biological Sciences, Fordham University, Bronx, New York.

Grant Nos. 1287,   In support of field research on parasitic wasps of the Family
1440 and 1987.   Ichneumonidae.

Introduction

Under grants awarded by the Committee for Research and Exploration of the National Geographic Society, I spent June through August of 1974, 1975, and 1979 in Mexico and South America doing field research on parasitic wasps of the Family Ichneumonidae. Ichneumonids elicit special interest not only because they are poorly studied taxonomically and ecologically (only 10% of the Latin American species is described) but also because they attack the immature stages of destructive crop pests (e.g., Lepidoptera, such as alfalfa cutworms, corn-ear worms, cotton-boll worms, sugarcane borers, etc.).

Study areas in Latin America given special emphasis during this work were northeast Mexico (and adjoining Texas), the Peruvian and Chilean Coastal Desert, Bolivian tropical forests and thorn scrub near Santa Cruz, and subtropical northern Argentina. So far, 19 articles and monographs (see References) have been published as a result of these studies, and 3 more have been accepted for publication. These include short taxonomic and natural history notes, as well as major revisions of the genus *Epirhyssa* (Porter, 1978a), of mesostenine ichneumonids in the Lower Río Grande Valley (Porter, 1977), and of ephialtine ichneumonids in north Chile (Porter, 1979), plus a zoogeographic analysis of the Latin American ichneumonid fauna (Porter, 1980d). Approximately 17,700 specimens were collected, by hand and by malaise trap, during the course of these investigations and most of them are being deposited in the Florida State Collection of Arthropods at Gainesville.

This report concerns the taxonomic composition, zoogeographic relationships, and ecology of ichneumonids in the Peruvian and north Chilean Coastal Desert. I have chosen to emphasize the Coastal Desert because it is one of the

---

[1] Research Associate, Florida State Collection of Arthropods, Florida Department of Agriculture and Consumer Services, Gainesville, Florida.

biotically least-known areas in the world and because much of my fieldwork was concentrated there. Solbrig (1976, p. 34), speaking of the desert flora, maintains that it is poorly studied and that "relative lack of communications in this region, the almost uninhabited nature of large parts of the territory, and the harshness of the climate and the physical habitat have made exploration very difficult." As for ichneumonids, the Coastal Desert fauna was essentially unknown before I commenced fieldwork there. I can now report 83 genera from the desert, of which 74 are new records and of which I was able personally to collect and observe 81.[2] Only 2 genera, *Pimplopterus* and *Diadegma* (Townes, 1966, pp. 131, 151) are cited from this biome in previous literature but not represented among collections assembled by me since 1975. The Coastal Desert ichneumonid fauna thus emerges as depauperate and lacking in generic endemisms but with numerous endemic species. It forms a coherent and distinctive taxonomic and zoogeographic unit. In future studies, I plan to describe, key, and illustrate the desert species (most of which are new) and, to that end, envision field research in the still unexplored regions between Chiclayo and the Ecuadorian border, between Lima and Trujillo, and between Lima and Arequipa.

ACKNOWLEDGMENTS

In north Chile, my activities were supported by the Universidad del Norte, which provided museum and laboratory facilities plus field vehicles. For their uniquely generous cooperation, patience, and kindness I am indebted to Dr. Raul Cortés P., Ing. Alfonso Matta V., Ing. Héctor Vargas C., Tec. Agr. Nelson Hichins O., and to Aux. Gerardo Díaz P., all of the Universidad del Norte's C.I.C.A. (Centro para Investigación y Capacitación Agrícola). Charles W. Calmbacher, then of Fordham University, served as assistant collector and preparator during the initial phases of this work. In 1979, I was accompanied and assisted by Anthony F. Cerbone, currently of Texas A&M University. Dr. Lionel A. Stange of the Florida Department of Agriculture, also working under a National Geographic Society grant, collaborated during the Peruvian phase of my research. Collecting in Peru also was facilitated by Hans Stein and Francis Wise of Northern Peru Mining Co., who arranged for use of company guesthouses in remote areas. Similar assistance was provided in Chile by the Chilean National Park Service and by the Chilean National Electric Co. (Endesa). During 1976 and 1977, my research was funded by National Science Foundation Grant DEB-75-22426.

---

[2] *Netelia, Brachycyrtus, Isdromas, Trachysphyrus, Compsocryptus, Venturia,* and *Diplazon* were obtained by me in the desert but also had been collected by earlier workers (Townes, 1966).

The Coastal Desert of Peru and North Chile

LIFE ZONES IN THE DESERT

The Coastal Desert comprises the coastal plain and adjacent west Andean slopes of Ecuador, Peru, and north Chile between about 1° and 23° S. lat. Rigorous barriers separate it from other biotic provinces. It commences dramatically in Ecuador, where wet forest cedes to thorn scrub as the cold Humboldt Current begins to affect adjacent land areas and causes rainfall to diminish abruptly. Eastward it is bounded by 4,000-6,000-meter Andean peaks and westward by the Pacific Ocean. Southward, below Iquique in Chile, there is a more than 1,000-kilometer stretch of wasteland practically untraversed by rivers and attaining 3,000-meter altitude. Thus, at the present day, there is little biotic exchange between the Peruvian Desert and northwest South American wet forests or the semiarid scrub of central Chile, while only those species adapted to extreme climates above 3,000 meters can enter the desert from the east.

At least six altitudinally determined life zones may be distinguished in the desert. Despite egregious differences, they form a unit because of their isolation from the rest of South America, because they belong to a single watershed, and because vagile, euryplastic animals often range through several or even all of them. These life zones are listed below.

1. *Coastal Lowlands.* These extend in a narrow strip along the Pacific Coast. In the southern, drier part of the desert, vegetation in this zone is mostly limited to river valleys. At Arica, Chile, for example, yearly precipitation averages 0.5 millimeter and even along rivers one sees only an impoverished flora of *Equisetum, Distichlis, Geoffroea, Acacia, Prosopis, Schinus, Salix, Grindelia, Baccharis,* and *Atriplex.* North of Trujillo, Peru, where frequent displacement of the Humboldt Current brings some heavy rain, thorn scrub becomes widespread, although now much decimated by overgrazing. Similarly, inland from Iquique, Chile, where the watertable comes near the surface, phreatophyte *Prosopis (chilensis* and *tamarugo)* form bizarre open woodlands in an otherwise almost lifeless landscape. The Humboldt Current keeps temperatures in the Coastal Lowlands rather cool throughout the year. At Arica, Chile, summer highs usually oscillate around 27°C and lows keep near 16°C, while in winter minima rarely fall below 9°C and maxima range around 17°C. Coastal Lowland sites personally sampled include (fig. 1) Laredo near Trujillo, Peru, Lambayeque at Chiclayo, Peru, and the Lluta (fig. 2), Azapa, and Camarones valleys of north Chile.

2. *Foothills.* With a median altitude of 1,000 meters, these are drier and warmer than the Coastal Lowlands, because fog generated nightly by the

Humboldt Current here dissipates by 10:00, even in winter (fog often persists until 13:00 along the coast and at Lima, Peru, usually remains all day throughout the winter months). Only north of Chiclayo, Peru, are the Foothills covered by a sparse vegetation of grasses, spiny shrubs, and cacti. Otherwise, they are lifeless outside of river valleys. Near Lima, Peru, the upper slopes of Foothill valleys still support a few giant cacti but by north Chile there is so little rain that vegetation grows only on the valley floors. Foothill localities studied are Olmos north of Chiclayo, Peru; Simbal near Trujillo, Peru; Cupiche, Santa Eulalia, and Palle near Lima; as well as higher parts of the Lluta (Molinos), Azapa (Pampa del Algodonal), and Camarones (Taltape) valleys in north Chile (fig. 1).

3. *Degraded Cloud Forest.* With a median altitude of 1,500 meters, this life zone receives much rain in summer and has dry winters characterized by cool nights and warm, sunny days. It is limited to the northern part of the desert but has some relict forms as far south as Arica, Chile (e.g., the ichneumonid genus *Cyclaulus* and the rosacean tree *Polylepis*). In its typical form, this life zone has medium-sized trees covered with large epiphytic bromeliads but the community more often is represented by narrow bands of shrubs and herbs along streams in deep quebradas. Typical Cloud Forest localities examined are Samne near Trujillo, Peru, and a patch of relict woodland at 33 kilometers east of Olmos along the road to Jaén, Peru (figs. 1 and 3).

4. *Prepuna.* Located mostly above 2,000 meters, this is characterized in much of Peru by shrubby growth along streams and grass on drier sites. Typically, it has mild, moderately rainy summers and dry, nocturnally cold winters with some frost. At the southern end of the desert, in Chile's Tarapacá Province, this biome occurs only in rudimentary form, and is best defined by an endemic giant, spreading cactus, *Cereus candelaris*. Precipitation in the Tarapacá Prepuna averages less than 50 millimeters annually and daytime temperatures reach 22-30°C, although light frosts may fall on winter nights. Some of the main Prepuna localities studied during my research are Matucana at 2,389 meters near Lima and Codpa and Timar at 2,000 meters in north Chile (fig. 1; the Chilean localities of Codpa and Timar are too close to one another for designation by separate symbols on a map of this scale).

5. *Puna.* This extends between 3,000-4,000 meters and is an Andean Desert with grasses, small cacti, and other resistant herbs. In North Chile, where I have been able to study this biome with some care, the Puna seems to receive 50-150 millimeters of rain yearly and experiences summer temperatures whose maxima range between 18-22°C with minima of 4-12°C plus an invernal thermic regimen that includes highs between 12-20°C and lows from 0.0-8°C. Scant oxygen, brutal ultraviolet radiation, and violent winds are

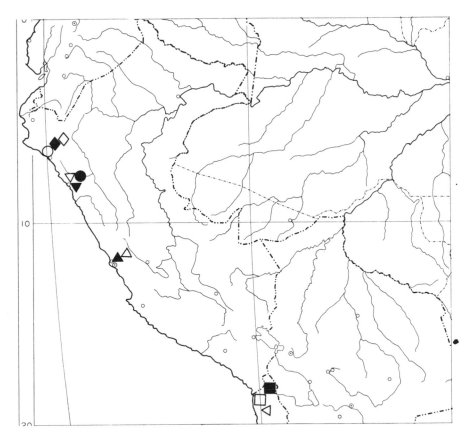

FIG. 1.   Peru and north Chile, showing localities where mesostenines were sampled
during July 1974 and 1975.

1. 33 kilometers west of Olmos, Peru. ◇
2. Olmos, Peru. ◆
3. Lambayeque, Peru. ○
4. Samne, Peru. ●
5. Simbal, Peru. ▽
6. Laredo, Peru. ▼

7. Matucana, Peru. △
8. Cupiche, Sta. Eulalia,
   and Palle, Peru. ▲
9. Chapiquiña, Chile. ■
10. Valle de Lluta, Chile. □
11. Codpa, Chile. ◁

other important abiotic limiting factors in this harsh environment. Chilean
Puna vegetation consists of profuse and quite uniform grasses, some endemic
cacti, herbaceous and arbustive *Baccharis* (Compositae), the urticating vine
Cajophora (Loasaceae), and of elfin *Polylepis* (Rosaceae) woods, which grow
only in the most humid and sheltered quebradas. Puna localities sampled in
north Chile include Chapiquiña, Belén, Socoroma, and Putre (fig. 1).

6. *Altiplano.* This reaches up from 4,000 meters to the snow line. It supports a desolate steppe, somewhat resembling the Puna but with greater precipitation (up to 500 millimeters per year) and lower temperatures (lows of -10°C at almost any time of year). The only Altiplano locality visited was Chungará at nearly 5,000 meters on the Chilean-Bolivian border, slightly northeast of Chapiquiña, Chile (as indicated on fig. 1). No ichneumonids were collected here, but the region does have some characteristic species *(Trachysphyrus venustus* and *Coccygomimus oropha)*, whose adults seem active only in summer.

The above synopsis shows that under present-day climate, the Puna and Altiplano provide a continuous band of vegetation all along the upper fringes of the Peruvian Desert, from Ecuador to north Chile, but that the other life zones except in the northern half or third of the desert become fragmented into widely scattered river valleys. Consequently, cold-adapted animals have a high corridor by which they can range freely the length of the desert. On the other hand, populations of warm-adapted, low-altitude species generally are isolated from one another by the stretches of absolute desert between rivers.

ZOOGEOGRAPHY OF COASTAL DESERT ICHNEUMONIDAE

Ichneumonids are actively flying wasps, most of which parasitize immature stages of holometabolic insects, especially Lepidoptera. Many will take any host of proper size in a particular spatial niche (e.g., pupae in soil, leaf litter and leaf rolls, in herbaceous stems, suspended from the branches of trees or shrubs, etc.). Indeed, few ichneumonids are restricted to a single host genus and even these almost always can attack several species within that genus. The family thus shows good dispersal potential with regard to vagility and trophic requirements. On the other hand, ichneumonids need to drink often and mostly prefer humid, shady places. Even species which inhabit thorn scrub and desert are restricted there to sites with permanent water. Desert ichneumonids thus usually belong to relict populations left behind in humid refugia dating from wetter climatic epochs. Not one of the 355 Latin American ichneumonid genera is endemic to the Coastal Desert and in all the Neotropics there are only 11 genera that appear to have evolved in semiarid or arid habitats (Porter, 1980, pp. 24-26). Consequently, the Coastal Desert ichneumonid fauna is depauperate, concentrated in abnormally humid places, and consists of genera whose evolutional centers lie elsewhere. These facts can be appreciated by reference to Table 1, which lists the ichneumonid genera of the Coastal Desert and indicates the number of species by which they are represented there, their approximate life zone and latitudinal ranges within the desert, and their distribution outside the desert.

FIG. 2.   Valle de Lluta near Arica in Tarapacá Province of north Chile. Here rainfall averages 0.5 millimeters per year. Thornscrub vegetation is restricted to river valleys with permanent water. The slopes above the rivers are devoid of life. (Photograph by Charles C. Porter, August 1975.)

Ichneumonids are concentrated toward the northern half of the Coastal Desert, doubtless because humid refugia are more widely available northward. Of the 81 genera I have recorded from the desert, 34 reach north Chile, 21 more attain the latitude of Lima, Peru, and 26 have been collected only in the far north between Trujillo, Peru, and the Ecuadorian border. For example, the Tribe Mesostenini has only *Trachysphyrus, Mesostenus,* and *Cyclaulus* in north Chile, 9 genera *(Biconus, Cyclaulus, Basileucus, Acerastes, Messatoporus, Trachysphyrus, Mesostenus, Derocentrus,* and *Compsocryptus)* in the Rimac and Santa Eulalia valleys near Lima, and 15 genera in the Trujillo-Chiclayo area.

Thirty-one of the 81 genera reported belong to the Neotropic zoogeographical category, as defined in my recent distributional analysis of Latin American Ichneumonidae (Porter, 1980d, pp. 11-24). In the Tribe Mesostenini, 9 of the 14 desert genera are Neotropical *(Biconus, Cyclaulus, Diapetimorpha, Basileucus, Lymeon, Acerastes, Polycyrtidea, Messatoporus,* and *Agonocryptus)*. A tenth genus, the Oriental and Latin American *Baltazaria,* may be included here, since its New World species show a Neotropic distributional pattern. The Neotropic mesostenine ichneumonid radiation, comprising 52 genera and thousands of species, has major evolutionary centers in the humid Brazilian highlands, the Andean cloud forests, and the mountains of Middle America. However, most of its genera are widely distributed and 31 range all the way from Argentina or Brazil to Mexico, with 14 attaining the southeastern United States. These wasps prefer subtropical or tropical humid forests but some adaptable genera have a few species that reach drier and/or cooler habitats than those sought by the majority. Six of the 10 Coastal Desert genera also attain the southeastern United States as well as central Argentina *(Diapetimorpha, Lymeon, Acerastes, Polycyrtidea, Messatoporus,* and *Agonocryptus)*. The tribe, like many ichneumonid taxa, thus possesses a nucleus of hardy and wide-ranging genera which enter unfavorable habitats almost anywhere but which, nonetheless, are represented in such marginal areas by only 1 or a few species, while they may have dozens or even hundreds of species in optimally humid and mild places. Of the 4 other Coastal Desert Neotropic mesostenines, *Biconus* and *Cyclaulus* are Andean cloud forest elements, *Basileucus* ranges widely in subequatorial South America with a tendency to enter dry regions (e.g., the Argentine Chaco and Subandean Desert), and *Baltazaria* occurs from Mexico to north Argentina but otherwise apparently is restricted to wet forests.

At the specific level, most Coastal Desert Neotropic mesostenines seem to be endemic, although this idea may be modified when we attain better knowledge of the west Ecuadorian rain forest and Andean cloud forest faunas. Within the desert, some species are restricted to the more humid northern half, while others inhabit every fertile area from Ecuador to north Chile. The Coastal Desert in its current super-arid state is so new geologically (a result of Pleistocene climatic events), that the existence of endemic species in individual river valleys would seem precluded. On the other hand, this region has been semiarid since well back in the Tertiary, so that its ichneumonid fauna had much time to evolve as a discrete unit and give rise to endemic species. Thus the precinctive *Cyclaulus eremia* (Porter, 1976b) occurs disjunctly along 1,500

Fig. 3. Relict cloud forest on the western slopes of the Andes 33 kilometers east of Olmos between Chiclayo and Piura in northern Peru. The taller trees, epiphytic bromeliads, and rich herbaceous undergrowth are cloud-forest elements, while the large cacti are invaders from surrounding thorn scrub and desert. (Photograph by Charles C. Porter, July 1975.)

kilometers of coast from Trujillo, Peru, to Arica, Chile, while species of *Messatoporus* and *Acerastes* have been collected from Lima north to Trujillo or Chiclayo.

Several other major ichneumonid groups parallel the mesostenines with regard to richness of the Neotropic distributional component in the Coastal

Table 1.   Ichneumonid Genera of the Coastal Desert

Genus	No. species	Range in desert	Range outside desert
1. *Erythroscambus*	1	Degraded Cloud Forest near Trujillo	*Neotropic, Nearctic:* western U. S. to Argentina
2. *Calliephialtes*	1	North Chile: Coast to Prepuna	*Neotropic, Neantarctic, Nearctic:* U. S. to Chile
3. *Tromatobia*	1	Lima to north Chile	*Neotropic, Neantarctic, Holarctic, Ethiopian*
4. *Zaglyptus*	1	Lima: Foot Hills	*Cosmopolitan:* throughout Neotropic S. America
5. *Clistopyga*	4	Northern south to Lima: Coast to Prepuna	*Cosmopolitan:* Neotropic and Neantarctic S. America
6. *Zonopimpla*	1	Degraded Cloud Forest near Trujillo	*Neotropic:* Mexico to Argentina
7. *Dreisbachia*	1	Degraded Cloud Forest near Trujillo	*Disjunctly Cosmopolitan:* Ecuador and Peru in S. America
8. *Zatypota*	1	Degraded Cloud Forest near Trujillo	*Disjunctly Cosmopolitan:* Neotropic S. America
9. *Itoplectis*	3	Generally distributed, all life zones	*Cosmopolitan:* in Neotropic S. America
10. *Coccygomimus*	6	Generally distributed, all life zones	*Cosmopolitan:* in Neotropic and Neantarctic S. America
11. *Theronia*	2	Trujillo northward	*Cosmopolitan:* best developed in tropics, Neotropic S. America
12. *Netelia*	1	General, all life zones	*Cosmopolitan:* Neotropic and Neantarctic S. America
13. *Macrogrotea*	1	Degraded Cloud Forest near Trujillo	*Neotropic* and *Neantarctic:* avoids lowland rain forest
14. *Brachycyrtus*	2	Trujillo area, north Chile	*Cosmopolitan:* Neotropic S. America
15. *Brachedra*	1	Trujillo area, Degraded Cloud Forest	*Neotropic:* montane
16. *Isdromas*	1	Probably general, north Chilean Puna	*Neotropic, Neantarctic, Ethiopian*
17. *Gelis*	1	Degraded Cloud Forest near Trujillo	*Cosmopolitan:* best developed in Holarctic
18. *Hemicallidiotes*	2	North Chilean Puna, probably more general	*Neotropic* and *Neantarctic*
19. *Biconus*	1	Degraded Cloud Forest, Foot Hills, south to Lima	*Neotropic:* Andean Cloud Forest
20. *Cyclaulus*	1	General, Degraded Cloud Forest, Foot Hills	*Neotropic:* Andean Cloud Forest

Genus	No. species	Range in desert	Range outside desert
21. *Diapetimorpha*	3	Northern: Coastal Lowlands, Degraded Cloud Forest	*Neotropic, Nearctic:* E. U. S. to Argentina
22. *Basileucus*	4	South to Lima: Coastal Lowlands, Degraded Cloud Forest	*Neotropic:* subequatorial S. America
23. *Lymeon*	1	Northern: Coastal Lowlands	*Neotropic, Nearctic:* E. U. S. to Argentina
24. *Acerastes*	1	South to Lima: Coastal Lowlands, Degraded Cloud Forest	*Neotropic, Nearctic:* E. U. S. to Argentina
25. *Polycyrtidea*	1	Northern: Coastal Lowlands, Degraded Cloud Forest	*Neotropic, Nearctic:* S.E. U. S. to Argentina
26. *Messatoporus*	2	South to Lima: Degraded Cloud Forest, Prepuna	*Neotropic, Nearctic:* U. S. to Argentina
27. *Agonocryptus*	1	Northern: Coastal Lowlands at Chiclayo	*Neotropic, Nearctic:* E. U. S. to Argentina
28. *Baltazaria*	1	Degraded Cloud Forest near Trujillo	*Neotropic, Oriental:* in New World from N.E. Mexico to Argentina
29. *Trachysphyrus*	14	General, Coastal Lowlands to Altiplano	*Neotropic, Neantarctic, Nearctic:* U. S. to Argentina and Chile
30. *Mesostenus*	1	Probably general, Trujillo to north Chile, Degraded Cloud Forest, Puna	*Neotropic, Holarctic:* U. S. to Argentina in New World
31. *Derocentrus*	1	Lima, Foot Hills, probably more general	*Neotropic, Sonoran:* E. U. S. to Argentina
32. *Compsocryptus*	1	South to Lima: Coastal Lowlands to Prepuna	*Sonoran, Neotropic:* E. U. S. to Argentina, disjunct outside Sonoran Region
33. *Toxophoroides*	1	Coastal Lowlands, at Chiclayo	*Neotropic, Nearctic:* E. U. S. to Argentina
34. *Eudeleboea*	1	Probably general, Azapa Valley of Chile	*Neotropic, Nearctic:* E. U. S. to Argentina
35. *Campoplex*	1	North Chilean Puna, probably general	*Cosmopolitan*
36. *Venturia*	1	Degraded Cloud Forest near Trujillo, probably general	*Cosmopolitan*
37. *Casinaria*	2	General up to Puna	*Cosmopolitan*
38. *Campoletis*	1	General up to Puna	*Cosmopolitan*
39. *Dusona*	1	South to Lima, at least up to Prepuna	*Cosmopolitan*

TABLE 1. (Continued)

Genus	No. species	Range in desert	Range outside desert
40. *Cymodusa*	1	North Chilean Puna, probably general	*Neotropic, Holarctic, Oriental*
41. *Phobocampe*	1	North Chilean Puna, probably general	*Neotropic, Holarctic, Oriental*
42. *Hyposoter*	1	North Chilean Puna, probably general	*Cosmopolitan*
43. *Prochas*	1	Trujillo northward, Degraded Cloud Forest	*Neotropic:* at least Trinidad to Argentina
44. *Microcharops*	1	Probably general south to Lima, up to Prepuna	*Neotropic, Nearctic:* U. S. to Argentina
45. *Cryptophion*	1	Northern: Degraded Cloud Forest near Trujillo	*Neotropic:* Mexico to Paraguay
46. *Pristomerus*	1	Probably general, Azapa Valley in North Chile	*Cosmopolitan*
47. *Eiphosoma*	1	General south to Lima and up to Prepuna	*Neotropical, Nearctic:* E. U. S. to Argentina
48. *Trathala*	1	Probably general, north Chilean Puna	*Cosmopolitan*
49. *Ophion*	1	Probably general, north Chilean Coastal Lowlands	*Cosmopolitan*
50. *Alophophion*	1	Probably general, north Chile	*Neotropic, Neantarctic*
51. *Enicospilus*	1	Probably general, north Chilean coast to Prepuna	*Cosmopolitan:* most diverse in wet tropics
52. *Mesochorus*	1	Probably general, north Chilean Puna	*Cosmopolitan*
53. *Trieces*	1	Trujillo northward, Foot Hills	*Cosmopolitan*
54. *Triclistus*	1	Lima north, Foot Hills	*Cosmopolitan*
55. *Leurus*	1	Trujillo north, Degraded Cloud Forest	*Neotropic, Nearctic:* U. S. to Argentina
56. *Anomalon*	1	Trujillo north, Foot Hills	*Cosmopolitan*
57. *Blapticus*	1	North Chilean Puna, probably general	*Cosmopolitan*
58. *Orthocentrus*	1	North Chilean Puna, probably general	*Cosmopolitan*
59. *Homotropus*	2	North Chilean Puna, probably general	*Cosmopolitan:* Neotropic and Neantarctic in S. America
60. *Syrphoctonus*	1	North Chilean Puna, probably general	*Neotropic, Neantarctic, Holarctic,* and *Oriental*
61. *Diplazon*	1	General	*Cosmopolitan*

Genus	No. species	Range in desert	Range outside desert
62. *Phaeogenes*	1	North Chilean Puna, probably general	*Cosmopolitan*
63. *Lusius*	1	Trujillo north, Foot Hills	*Neotropic, Oriental, Madagascan:* N.E. Mexico to Argentina in N.W.
64. *Oedicephalus*	1	Trujillo north, Degraded Cloud Forest	*Neotropic:* N.E. Mexico to Argentina
65. *Matara*	1	Lima north, Foot Hills, Degraded Cloud Forest	*Neotropic:* Mexico to Argentina
66. *Lobaegis*	1	Lima north, Foot Hills, Degraded Cloud Forest	*Neotropic, Nearctic:* U. S. to Argentina
67. *Eurydacus*	1	Degraded Cloud Forest near Trujillo	*Neotropic:* N.E. Mexico to Coastal Peru
68. *Tricholabus*	1	Coastal Lowlands near Trujillo	*Cosmopolitan*
69. *Carinodes*	3	General up to Puna	*Neotropic, Neantarctic, Nearctic:* Texas and Florida to Argentina and Chile
70. *Limonethe*	1	Lima north: Foot Hills, Degraded Cloud Forest	*Neotropic, Nearctic:* S.E. U. S. to Argentina
71. *Trogomorpha*	1	Lima north: Coastal Lowlands, Foot Hills, Degraded Cloud Forest, Prepuna	*Neotropic:* S.E. U. S. to Argentina
72. *Conopyge*	1	Lima north: Foot Hills, Degraded Cloud Forest	*Neotropic:* McAllen, Texas to Brazil
73. *Hemihoplis*	1	Trujillo north, Degraded Cloud Forest	*Neotropic, Nearctic:* E. U. S. to Argentina
74. *Hoplismenus* (?)	1	North Chilean Puna	*Cosmopolitan:* S. American species probably represent 1 or more new genera
75. *Setanta*	1	Trujillo north: Foot Hills, Degraded Cloud Forest	*Cosmopolitan*
76. *Diphyus*	1	Lima north: Degraded Cloud Forest, Foot Hills, Prepuna	*Cosmopolitan*
77. *Thymebatis*	3	Probably general, mostly Prepuna and Puna but down to Coastal Lowlands in north Chile	*Neotropic, Neantarctic:* Mostly montane or temperate, few spp. in tropical forests
78. *Dilopharius*	1	Northern: Coastal Lowlands at Chiclayo	*Neotropic, Nearctic:* Texas to Argentina

TABLE 1. (Continued)

Genus	No. species	Range in desert	Range outside desert
79. *Diacantharius*	1	Probably general, low to moderate altitudes: Prepuna near Lima	*Neotropic, Neantarctic, Nearctic:* Texas to Argentina and Chile
80. *Platylabus*	2	General: Degraded Cloud Forest to Puna	*Cosmopolitan*
81. *Ichneumon*	1	Degraded Cloud Forest near Trujillo	*Cosmopolitan*

Desert. Most notable is the Subfamily Ichneumoninae, which has 20 desert genera. Eleven show strict Neotropic affinities *(Carinodes, Conopyge, Eurydacus, Hemihoplis, Limonethe, Lobaegis, Matara, Trogomorpha, Diacantharius, Dilopharius,* and *Oedicephalus).* One *(Lusius)* has a Neotropic distribution in the New World but turns up again in the Palaeotropics. One *(Thymebatis)* is of Neantarctic or Temperate South American extraction (Porter, 1980a, p. 22). The other 7 genera (some of dubious taxonomic position) appear Cosmopolitan *(Ichneumon, Diphyus, Hoplismenus* (?), *Setanta, Tricholabus, Platylabus,* and *Phaeogenes).* Most ichneumonine genera occur from Lima northward, but *Phaeogenes, Carinodes, Hoplismenus* (?), *Thymebatis,* and *Platylabus* attain north Chile, while *Eurydacus, Hemihoplis, Setanta, Tricholabus,* and *Ichneumon* have not yet been collected south of Trujillo, Peru.

The second distributional element represented among Coastal Desert Ichneumonidae is the Holarctic. This has only 4 genera: *Tromatobia* (Ephialtinae), *Trachysphyrus* and *Mesostenus* (Mesostenini), and *Syrphoctonus* (Diplazontinae). All these genera seem to have entered South America along the Andes from the north and otherwise have numerous relatives in temperate parts of the Northern Hemisphere (Porter, 1980d, p. 27). All 4 genera are common in the Coastal Desert and seem to range throughout its extent, especially or at least along elevations beyond 2,000-3,000 meters. *Trachysphyrus,* with 14 local species, is the most diverse Coastal Desert ichneumonid genus and the one with the greatest number of endemic elements. As presently interpreted, *Trachysphyrus* has about 200 South American species plus several in Middle and North America. Its closest relatives are Holarctic and its South American distribution is suggestive of a genus with northern affinities. It is a temperate-adapted group best developed in the Andean and Neantarctic regions, as well as in other cool, high, and/or semarid habitats. On the other hand, *Trachysphyrus* only enters the fringes of rain forests and has not been reported from the Amazon Basin.

Holarctic mesostenine species in the Coastal Desert seem mostly endemic. Only 5, *Trachysphyrus huascar, T. venustus, T. lasius, T. cleonis,* and *Mesostenus cuzcensis,* have been reported from other regions and these are high-altitude forms that range widely in the central Andean Puna with some spillover into similar habitats on the western slopes. On the other hand, 10 species appear restricted to the study area *(T. metallicus, T. carrascoi, T. escomeli, T. weyrauchi, T. diplatys, T. violaceipennis, T. paitensis,* and at least 3 undescribed species). Within the desert, 5 of these species have extensive ranges and 5 seem more restricted distributionally. *T. metallicus* extends from Ecuador to north Chile, *T. carrascoi* and *T. weyrauchi* from Lima to north Chile, *T. violaceipennis* from Trujillo, Peru, to north Chile, and *T. paitensis* from near the Ecuadorian border to Arequipa, Peru. On the other hand, *T. diplatys* and a new species have been taken only in the Rimac Valley near Lima, Peru, *T. escomeli* appears restricted to the area around Arequipa, Peru, *T.* n. sp. nr. *escomeli* is known from 2 localities in north Chile, and there is another undescribed north Chilean species.

The previously mentioned vast distributions of certain high-altitude *Trachysphyrus* are not surprising. At altitudes above 3,000 meters, the Puna life zone provides an unbroken "green belt" from Ecuador to Tarapacá. Less easy to explain is the altitudinal tolerance of species such as *T. paitensis* and *T. violaceipennis,* which have been captured in all zones from the Coastal Lowlands to the Puna. Perhaps, the cooling effect of the Humboldt Current has permitted some high-altitude forms to follow rivers down to sea level. At any rate, certain other insects show similar distributions in the desert. For example, the eumenids *Hypodynerus andeus* and *Pachodynerus peruensis* are common, at least in north Chile, from sea level to more than 3,000 meters.

The third zoogeographic category represented among desert ichneumonids is the Sonoran (Porter 1980d, p.25). The only Coastal Desert Sonoran ichneumonids are the endemic mesostenines, *Compsocryptus fuscofasciatus* and *Derocentrus xerobates.* Sonoran mesostenines are moderately xerophilic taxa, which evolved in the southwestern United States and northern Mexico during the orogeny and progressively drier climates of the later Tertiary. The Sonoran element still is centered in its place of origin, but has some representatives elsewhere in America. *Compsocryptus* not only has *fuscofasciatus* in coastal Peru but also *C. melanostigma* in more or less semiarid parts of north Argentina, as well as *C. fasciipennis* isolated in Cuba and south Florida. Within the Coastal Desert, *Derocentrus xerobates* so far has been found only near Lima (Porter, 1974, p. 36) but *Compsocryptus fuscofasciatus* ranges from Lima at least as far north as Chiclayo, Peru, and has been found in every life zone from the Prepuna to the Coastal Lowlands.

The Neantarctic or Temperate South American biota includes numerous endemic genera conspicuous in central and south Chile plus a much smaller, relict component that occurs, often disjunctly, over much of South America. Some of these widely ranging Neantarctic taxa have radiated into cloud forests and rain forests but the majority prefers higher, cooler, and often more arid habitats than those frequented by most other ichneumonids. Three Neantarctic genera inhabit the Coastal Desert: *Macrogrotea* (Labiinae), *Alophophion* (Ophioninae), and *Thymebatis* (Ichneumoninae). *Macrogrotea* (with many but rare species in Ecuador, Peru, Bolivia, Brazil, and Neotropic Argentina, as well as with several abundant forms in Chile south of the desert) enters the Coastal Desert only in Degraded Cloud Forest habitats from Trujillo northward. *Alophophion* has been recorded in the desert only from north Chile, but may be expected to range more widely. Otherwise, its distribution resembles that of *Macrogrotea*. *Thymebatis,* whose over-all range parallels that of the 2 previously mentioned genera, has at least 2 described species that occupy most north Chilean life zones (Porter, 1980b) plus several more that extend the length of the desert and show preference for altitudes above 2,000 meters.

The final and largest distributional element represented in the Coastal Desert is the Cosmopolitan. This heterogeneous assemblage has 41 local genera and is composed in considerable part of generally adapted and aggressive ichneumonids that have invaded both favorable and unfavorable environments on all or many of the world's major landmasses. Most of these taxa occur, or are likely to be found, throughout the Coastal Desert, wherever vegetation persists. Indeed, 23 of the 34 ichneumonid genera cited from north Chile, where aridity and thermic factors become most extreme, belong to the Cosmopolitan group: *Itoplectis, Coccygomimus, Netelia, Brachycyrtus, Isdromas, Campoplex, Casinaria, Campoletis, Cymodusa, Phobocampe, Hyposoter, Pristomerus, Trathala, Ophion, Enicospilus, Mesochorus, Blapticus, Orthocentrus, Homotropus, Diplazon, Phaeogenes, Hoplismenus* (?), and *Platylabus.*

Paradoxically, the Coastal Desert, although located in the Neotropic Biogeographic Region, possesses an ichneumonid fauna that contains only 39 percent Neotropic genera, as opposed to 51 percent Cosmopolitan elements. This reflects the adaptive versatility of the Cosmopolitan series and the basically sylvan nature of the true Neotropic radiation. It is a pattern repeated in other Latin American deserts, such as the Argentine "Subandino," where 46 percent of the ichneumonid genera are Cosmopolitan and 42 percent Neotropic (Porter, 1975a, p. 188). In Latin American wet forests, the relationship between Neotropic and Cosmopolitan genera is reversed. For example, the rich subtropical rain forests of northeast Argentina (eastern Corrientes, Misiones) are inhabited by about 65 percent Neotropic genera and only 27 percent Cosmopolitan genera (Porter, 1975a, p. 189).

Ecology of Ichneumonids in the North Chilean Puna

Thanks to enthusiastic cooperation from the Universidad del Norte at Arica and to the superbly maintained roads which reach and traverse the highlands of north Chile, especially intensive fieldwork could be done in the Puna of Tarapacá Province. Some results of this research, including analysis of Malaise Trap samples, are provided in the following account.

Of all the north Chilean biotic provinces, the Puna enjoys the most benign climate and has the most ubiquitous and complexly structured vegetation. Since ichneumonids flourish best in humid environments with a lush flora, it is not surprising that the austere but still comparatively verdant Puna has the largest ichneumonid fauna of any north Chilean life zone. Of the 353 specimens and 49 species obtained to date from the whole region, 198 specimens and 32 species were collected in the Puna. Furthermore, 23 species so far have been recorded from the Puna alone, although future collecting surely will reduce the number of endemics. Malaise traps accounted for 140 specimens and 30 species, while 58 specimens and 10 species were taken by hand. Our trap worked uninterruptedly for 7 months, whereas hand collecting was restricted to July. This mainly accounts for the predominance of Malaise material but a contributing factor may be the capricious Puna weather. High winds and snow or rain squalls may spring up at any moment (perhaps several times daily in summer), so that flying insects often have brief activity periods. Traps cover all sunny intervals but the human collector depends on meteorological fortuity.

DIVERSITY

With only 32 ichneumonid species, this fauna is almost uniquely meager. Even the climatically rigorous Argentine Subandean Desert has at least 167 species and any Neotropic wet forest will provide more than 1,000 species (Porter, 1975a). The Puna ichneumonids also are deviant in equitability, since none of the species is common and 11 have been captured only once during 4 years of sampling. Perhaps they live in an "L" selective context, emphasizing "mechanisms for surviving unfavorable periods" and "reproductive rates that may or may not be high" (Whittaker, 1975, p. 51). On the other hand, the cryptic existence of many Puna species (e.g., concealed in bunch grass) makes them hard to collect with traps or hand nets and specialized sampling methods eventually might reveal some of these species to be at least seasonally abundant.

Noteworthy also is the mode of apportionment of species among genera. Twenty-three of the Puna genera have 1 species, while *Coccygomimus, Hemical-*

lidiotes, and *Homotropus* have but 2 each and only *Trachysphyrus,* with 8, shows moderate diversity. This pattern characterizes other deserts (e.g., the Argentine Subandiño, Porter, 1975a, p. 177) and, again, reflects the fact that Ichneumonidae prefer humid forests (I visited subtropical wet forests in Corrientes and Misiones Provinces of northeastern Argentina for 2 weeks in November 1969 and obtained 214 species and 84 genera, of which 4 genera had 4 species, 3 had 5 species, 1 had 6 species, 2 had 10, 1 had 12, 2 had 13, and 1 was represented by 19 species).

HABITATS

The Chapiquiña trap was installed from July 1976 to January 1977 across a small, permanent stream bordered by high bunch grass and, at some distance, by alfalfa patches and *Eucalyptus* groves. Ichneumonids of certain genera (e.g., *Coccygomimus, Trachysphyrus, Carinodes,* etc.) pass the frigid nights deep within the grass clumps and find drinking water in the stream; and such stream-side vegetation also is good for hand collecting, which may yield such species as *Coccygomimus aeolus, Trachysphyrus carrascoi, T. metallicus, T. weyrauchi,* and *Carinodes fulgor.*

Other profitable collecting localities are alfalfa and oregano fields, especially near irrigation ditches. All 4 *Trachysphyrus, Campoletis* sp. 1, *Diplazon laetatorius,* and *Hoplismenus* (?) sp. 1 appeared among these crops. Alfalfa and oregano, at least during winter, are the best source of Puna Hymenoptera, yielding some ichneumonids plus hundreds of Aculeata, such as eumenids (e.g., *Hypodynerus andeus, H. nigricornis*), sphecids (e.g., *Prionyx,* Ammophila, and *Podagritus*) and apoids (e.g., *Colletes, Megachile,* countless halictines, and *Xylocopa viridigastra*). Puna alfalfa, untreated with insecticides, grows more lushly and flowers more profusely than that raised in the rigorously sprayed Prepuna and coastal fields. Perhaps this results in part from the ease with which native parasites and predators invade the unpoisoned alfalfa fields and attack alfalfa pests.

PHAENOLOGY

Table 2 shows that the Chapiquiña trap only could be changed at irregular intervals and disappeared in January, victim of a mountain flood. Nonetheless, it can be seen that Malaise records gradually increase through the spring and reach a maximum in January, the warmest but also the wettest summer month. Again, this bespeaks ichneumonids' hygrophily and vulnerability to dessication. Hand-collecting data, however, modify the above scheme, because they show a fairly diverse and abundant fauna still to be active during July. Although precipitation during this month is rare or nonexis-

TABLE 2. Taxonomic Composition, Diversity, and Phaenology of the Ichneumonid Fauna in the Arican Puna

Species are listed in order of decreasing abundance. Numbers in parentheses denote hand-collected specimens.

Species	Quantity	Distribution of specimens by month						
		Jul.	Aug.	Sept.	Oct.	Nov.	Dec.	Jan.
1. *Cymodusa* sp. 1	36	–	–	4	1	4	–	27
2. *Trachysphyrus carrascoi*	28	(27)	–	–	–	–	–	1
3. *Phobocampe* sp. 1	17	–	–	4	4	4	–	5
4. *Carinodes fulgor*	16	(6) 2	2	–	–	–	–	6
5. *Campoletis* sp. 1	10	(1)	–	5	–	2	–	2
6. *Netelia* sp. 1	9	–	–	–	–	–	–	9
7. *Hemicallidiotes* sp. 1	8	–	2	–	–	–	–	6
8. *Trachysphyrus metallicus*	8	(7)	1	–	–	–	–	–
9. *Trachysphyrus weyrauchi*	7	(5) 1	–	1	–	–	–	–
10. *Casinaria* sp. 1	7	–	–	1	–	6	–	–
11. *Phaeogenes* sp. 1	6	2	2	–	–	–	–	2
12. *Isdromas* sp. 1	5	1	–	1	–	1	–	2
13. *Diplazon laetatorius*	5	1	–	1	–	3	–	–
14. *Coccygomimus tarapacae*	4	1	–	1	1	–	–	1
15. *Coccygomimus aeolus*	4	4	–	–	–	–	–	–
16. *Mesostenus cuzcensis*	4	–	2	–	–	–	–	2
17. *Syrphoctonus* sp. 1	4	–	–	–	–	–	–	4
18. *Blapticus* sp. 1	4	–	–	–	–	–	–	4
19. *Campoplex* sp. 1	3	–	–	1	–	2	–	–
20. *Hyposoter.* sp. 1	2	–	–	–	1	–	–	1
21. *Hoplismenus* (?) sp. 1	2	(1)	1	–	–	–	–	–
22. *Hemicallidiotes* sp. 2	1	–	–	–	–	1	–	–
23. *Trachysphyrus* ca. *paradeisus*	1	1	–	–	–	–	–	–
24. *Trachysphyrus violaceipennis*	1	–	–	–	–	–	–	–
25. *Trathala* sp. 1	1	–	–	1	–	–	–	–
26. *Mesochorus* sp. 1	1	–	–	1	–	–	–	–
27. *Orthocentrus* sp. 1	1	–	–	–	1	–	–	–
28. *Homotropus* sp. 1	1	–	–	–	–	1	–	–
29. *Homotropus* sp. 2	1	–	–	–	–	–	–	1
30. *Thymebatis hypsista*	1	–	–	–	–	–	–	1
31. *Trachysphyrus venustus*	1	–	–	–	–	(1)	–	–
32. *Trachysphyrus lasius*	1	(1)	–	–	–	–	–	–
Total spp./month		13	6	11	5	10	–	16
Total specimens/month		61	10	21	8	25	–	74

tent, most vegetation stays green and many flowers continue to bloom, since the soil still holds water from fall rains and the days are mostly sunny. Under the cool, less desiccating winter sun, ichneumonids continue active, fly more often in the open, and thus fall prey more easily to the hand collector than to Malaise Traps in shady sites (I obtained similar data in my survey of south Texas mesostenine ichneumonids, Porter, 1977, p. 84).

Another egregious feature of Puna ichneumonid phaenology is the short daily flight period. At least in July, profitable collecting begins around 1000 and lasts until 1400 or 1500. Before 1000, temperatures still are near freezing and after 1500 a stiff breeze starts up and ichneumonids plummet, as if fulminated, groundward to seek shelter in vegetation or under stones.

Such phaenologic cycles differ radically from those I have observed in low- and mid-altitude Neotropic wet forests. Here seasonal maxima occur either in spring and fall (e.g., north Argentina) or during mid-winter (Santa Cruz, Bolivia) and almost always the summer is a poor season for Ichneumonidae. Daily cycles in these forests, during warmer parts of the year, frequently involve morning and evening peaks; during winter in the subtropics, however, maximum ichneumonid abundance usually is attained between 1300 and 1600.

GEOGRAPHIC DISTRIBUTION

The north Chilean Puna has no endemic ichneumonid genera. On the contrary, most Puna genera have vast geographic distributions and obviously invaded this habitat from other ecologically more favorable regions. Thirteen Puna genera are Cosmopolitan *(Coccygomimus, Netelia, Campoplex, Casinaria, Campoletis, Hyposoter, Trathala, Mesochorus, Blapticus, Orthocentrus, Homotropus, Diplazon, and Phaeogenes);* 1 *(Mesostenus)* is Neotropic and Holarctic; 3 occur in the Neotropic, Holarctic, and Oriental *(Cymodusa, Phobocampe, and Syrphoctonus);* 1 is Neotropic, Neantarctic, and Ethiopian *(Isdromas);* 4 are Neotropic and Neantarctic but with a bias toward higher, cooler, and drier habitats than those favored by most ichneumonids *(Hemicallidiotes, Trachysphyrus,* a new genus of Ichneumoninae, and *Thymebatis);* while only 1 *(Carinodes)* is Neotropic in the most typical sense (with many species in tropical wet forests, a few in the Neantarctic, and some in other temperate, lofty, or arid environments).

At the specific level, information is scant because only 10 percent of the Latin American ichneumonid species is described and because not enough collecting has been done to establish geographic ranges with confidence. Nonetheless, the described north Chilean Puna ichneumonids show an interesting pattern that suggests considerable endemism. Five species have yet to be recorded outside the area *(Coccygomimus tarapacae,* 2 undescribed *Trachysphyrus,*

Carinodes fulgor, and *Thymebatis hypsista).* As already noted, 4 additional *Trachysphyrus (metallicus, carrascoi, weyrauchi,* and *violaceipennis)* are confined to the West Puna from north Chile well up into Peru or even Ecuador. Evidently, the Altiplano, with its incredibly harsh climate, poses a barrier to interchange of ichneumonids between the West Puna and similar habitats scattered among the interandean valleys and on the upper east slopes of the Andes. This barrier probably has been opened and closed repeatedly during the last half of the Tertiary and, even more so, during Pleistocene glacials and interglacials. The result is that the modern West Puna, from Ecuador through Peru to extreme northern Chile, has considerable specific endemism but, concurrently, harbors such more widely distributed forms as the Cosmopolitan *Diplazon laetatorius* and others quite amply distributed in South America's Andes, such as *Mesostenus cuzcensis* (Arica to central Peru at Cuzco and north as far as Trujillo), *Trachysphyrus lasius* (highlands of north Chile to northwest Argentina at altitudes of 2,000-4,000 m), and *T. venustus* (north Chile, Altiplano and Puna of southern Peru and Bolivia, altitudes above 3,000 m in northwest Argentina).

Conclusions

Spread of cold-adapted Holarctic, Neantarctic, and Cosmopolitan elements into and through the Coastal Desert can be explained in part by present-day geography and climate. The Puna and Altiplano supply a temperate to almost subarctic corridor for entrance of cold-tolerant biota into central western South America, and the western Puna still is a suitable habitat for such species, some of which have followed river valleys to the sea. To account for the Neotropic and Sonoran elements in the desert, however, as well as to analyze fully the distribution of Holarctic and similar species therein, we must ask how the area was affected by Pleistocene and late Tertiary climatic events.

In the early Tertiary, wet forest grew in what is now the Coastal Desert (Axelrod, 1960, p. 259). As the Andes became higher during the middle Tertiary, a rain shadow was created and the wet forest seems gradually to have been replaced by a thorn scrub vegetation (similar to the Argentine Chaco), which, in turn, may have yielded "by the Pliocene" to "a semidesert-type vegetation" (Solbrig, 1976, p. 38). During the Pleistocene, the Humboldt Current probably assumed its present course, adding its rain shadow to that of the Andes and, during interglacial periods, helping to convert the Coastal Desert from a semiarid to an almost lifeless environment. On the other hand, throughout Pleistocene glacial maxima the rain shadow effect would have been mitigated by increased precipitation and lowered temperatures in the

Andes (Solbrig, 1976, p. 29, Bartlett and Barghoorn, 1973, p. 205). Evidently, temperatures at those times averaged 7-8°C lower than during interglacials, the snow line may have reached down to 1,300 meters, and the innumerable coastal rivers that now are dry must then have been raging torrents.

Increased cold and glaciation at higher altitudes would have set a barrier between eastern and western Andean biota. This is why some cold-tolerant ichneumonids, such as *Trachysphyrus,* have endemic species in the western Puna that now coexist there with relatives presently centered on the interandean Puna but which must have been displaced farther east during glacial episodes.

Greater precipitation, moreover, would have depressed coastward the relatively verdant biomes which now occupy higher and often disjunct distributions. Thus, both Andean and subtropical vegetation would have expanded greatly on the coast and lower western slopes, proliferating in gallery along the then-existing network of rivers and interconnecting streams. Even in parts of the Pleistocene (and certainly during long segments of the Tertiary), genuine cloud forest probably reached as far south as Lima and Degraded Cloud Forest might have attained north Chile, permitting spread through the desert of both wet-adapted and mildly xerophilous Neotropical ichneumonids. The varied Neotropic mesostenine ichneumonid assemblage (6 genera) taken by me in July 1975 at Samne, Peru, in Degraded Cloud Forest; the occurrence of such humid forest mesostenine genera as *Biconus, Basileucus, Cyclaulus,* and *Messatoporus* near Lima, Peru, *(Messatoporus* reaches 2,389 m at Matucana in the Rimac Valley); and the surprising reappearance of the wet-adapted *Cyclaulus* in the Lluta Valley of north Chile, all constitute evidence that suggests that the Coastal Desert was not always as dry as in the present interglacial period. Many other animal and plant distributions support this thesis. The rosacean tree, *Polylepis,* grows in a few wet quebradas along the lower edge of the Puna at 3,200-3,500 meters above Arica, Chile. This far south, *Polylepis* is the only tree but northward it often forms the top stratum of cloud forests. Among Hymenoptera, such Coastal Desert endemics as *Itoplectis phoenogaster* (Ichneumonidae), *Pachodynerus peruensis* (Eumenidae), *Polistes weyrauchorum* (Vespidae), and *Sphex peruanus* (Sphecidae) provide further examples of ranges which end in north Chile and reach north to Lima or beyond. Today, all these species are fragmented among isolated river valleys but the isolation surely is recent, since the local populations do not show even subspecific differences. I thus infer that Pleistocene glacial maxima increased available water in the Coastal Desert enough so that even the Neotropic Ichneumonidae of this region evolved as a unit, rather than as a series of discrete faunules isolated in scattered fertile refugia. I also suspect that the presently depauperate lowland Neotropic desert ichneumonid assemblage was more seriously decimated by late Tertiary and Pleistocene interglacial aridity than by the depressed temperatures of Pleistocene glacial peaks. Most Neotropic biota (from plants to insects and even some reptiles) is surprisingly cold-tolerant, as shown by its massive extension into scarcely frostless southeast Brazil, its ample representation in the mountains of northeast Mexico, and its significant occurrence in the eastern United States south of 40° N. lat. (Porter, 1980d, pp. 18-20).

The Sonoran element also must have dispersed and evolved in response to Pleistocene and late Tertiary events. The driest periods allowed some of these thorn scrub and deciduous forest genera to spread south from Mexico into South America. At such times they would have spread widely, but would not have entered extreme deserts, such as interglacial western Peru. During wet epochs, humid forests expanded and probably pushed Sonoran species into the Coastal Desert and other drier areas, which by then had become suitable refugia, being semiarid rather than almost lifelessly arid.

The Peruvian Coastal Desert emerges as a coherent, sharply isolated geographic and ecological unit, whose ichneumonid fauna includes wide-ranging Neotropic, Holarctic, Sonoran, Neantarctic, and Cosmopolitan genera. It has no endemic genera but, in response mostly to Pleistocene climatic fluctuations, has evolved a largely endemic set of species. This desert thus resembles other Neotropic arid zones, such as the Argentine Subandino (Porter, 1975a) and the Lower Río Grande Valley of south Texas (Porter, 1977). Indeed, 36 of the 70 ichneumonid genera known from the Subandino occur likewise in the Peruvian Coastal Desert while 46 of those that inhabit the Coastal Desert (including the 36 previously mentioned as reaching northwest Argentina) range also north to the Lower Río Grande area. More specifically, 9 of the 11 mesostenine genera known from the Subandino are present in the Coastal Desert (*Trachysphyrus, Compsocryptus, Diapetimorpha, Basileucus, Polycyrtidea, Mesostenus, Derocentrus, Messatoporus,* and *Agonocryptus*), and 9 of the 16 genera of the same tribe known from south Texas also turn up in Coastal Peru (*Compsocryptus, Diapetimorpha, Lymeon, Polycyrtidea, Acerastes, Mesostenus, Derocentrus, Messatoporus,* and *Agonocryptus*). Moreover, all of these mesostenines (except *Basileucus,* which is limited to Neotropic subequatorial South America) have an over-all geographic distribution that, disjunctly or uniformly, embraces the bulk of the Neotropical realm, from the southern United States to north Argentina. Throughout the Neotropics, therefore, the same environmental factors have worked upon essentially the same wide-ranging material to produce desert ichneumonid faunas whose generic composition is notably similar but which, at the species level, show abundant endemisms.

REFERENCES

AXELROD, D. I.
1960.   The evolution of flowering plants.   Pp. 227-305 *in* "Evolution after Darwin," vol. 1, S. Tax, ed.   Univ. Chicago Press.
BARTLETT, A. S., and BARGHOORN, E. S.
1973.   Phytogeographic history of the Isthmus of Panama.   Pp. 203-299 *in* "Vegetation and Vegetational History of Northern Latin America," A. Graham, ed.   Elsevier Scientific Publishing Company, Amsterdam.
PORTER, C. C.
1974.   New species and records for the genus *Mesostenus* in South America.   Acta Zoologica Lilloana, vol. 31, pp. 27-46.
1975a.   Relaciones zoogeográficas y origen de la fauna de Ichneumonidae en la provincia biogeográfica del monte del Noroeste Argentino.   Acta Zoologica Lilloana, vol. 31, pp. 175-252.
1975b.   A revision of the Argentine species of *Epirhyssa*.   Acta Zoologica Lilloana, vol. 31, pp. 125-158.
1975c.   New records for *Zethus* from Texas.   Florida Entomologist, vol. 58, pp. 303-306.
1975d.   A new Floridian *Polycyrtidea* with comments on zoogeography of Florida Mesostenini.   Florida Entomologist, vol. 58, pp. 247-255.
1975e.   Argentine *Xorides*.   Rev. Chilena de Ent., vol. 9, pp. 51-56.
1975f.   Notas sobre sinonimia y ecología de dos *Trachysphyrus* sudamericanos.   Rev. Chilena de Ent., vol. 9, pp. 169-170.
1976a.   *Prosthoporus,* a new Bolivian genus of the subtribe Lymeonina.   Psyche, vol. 83, pp. 271-276.
1976b.   *Cyclaulus* in the Peruvian Coastal Desert.   Florida Entomologist, vol. 59, pp. 353-360.
1976c.   A new Argentine genus of Theriini.   Psyche, vol. 83, pp. 185-191.
1976d.   New records for *Thyreodon* from south Texas.   Psyche, vol. 83, pp. 304-309.
1977.   Ecology, zoogeography, and taxonomy of the Lower Río Grande Valley Mesostenini.   Psyche, vol. 84, pp. 28-91.
1978a.   A revision of the genus *Epirhyssa*.   Stud. Ent., vol. 20, pp. 297-412.
1978b.   *Periceros* in Mexico, with comments on insect distribution in the northern Neotropics.   Florida Entomologist, vol. 61, pp. 69-74.
1978c.   Ecology and taxonomy of Lower Río Grande Valley *Zethus*.   Florida Entomologist, vol. 61, pp. 45-53.
1978d.   Ecological notes on Lower Río Grande Valley Sphecini.   Florida Entomologist, vol. 61, pp. 54-63.
1979.   Ichneumonidae de Tarapacá. I. La subfamilia Ephialtinae.   Idesia, vol. 5, pp. 157-187.
1980a.   A new *Thyreodon* from south Texas.   Florida Entomologist, vol. 63, pp. 242-246.
1980b.   Joppini of Tarapacá.   Florida Entomologist, vol. 63, pp. 226-242.
1980c.   *Bicyrtes* in the Lower Río Grande Valley of Texas and in northeast Mexico.   Florida Entomologist, vol. 63, pp. 281-285.

1980d. Zoogeografía de la fauna latinoamericana de Ichneumonidae. Acta Zoologica Lilloana, vol. 36, pp. 5-46.

1981a. Ecological notes on Lower Río Grande Valley *Xylocopa*. Florida Entomologist, vol. 64, pp. 175-182.

1981b. *Certonotus,* an Australian genus newly recorded in South America. Florida Entomologist, vol. 64, pp. 235-244.

1981c. New records for *Monobia* in south Texas and northeast Mexico. Florida Entomologist, vol. 64, pp. 260-267.

SOLBRIG, O.

1976. The origin and floristic affinities of the South American temperate deciduous and semidesert regions. Pp. 7-49 *in* "Evolution of Desert Biota," D. Goodall, ed. Univ. of Texas Press, Austin.

TOWNES, H. K.

1966. A catalog and reclassification of Neotropic Ichneumonidae. Mem. Amer. Ent. Inst., vol. 8, pp. 1-367.

WHITTAKER, R. H.

1975. Communities and ecosystems, 385 pp. MacMillan, New York.

CHARLES C. PORTER

Ecology and Social Structure of the Rufous Elephant-Shrew

Principal Investigator: Galen B. Rathbun, University of Nairobi, Nairobi, Kenya; and Office of Zoological Research, National Zoological Park, Smithsonian Institution, Washington, D. C.[1]

Grant Nos. 1349 and 1589.   For a study of the social behavior and ecology of the rufous elephant-shrew *Elephantulus rufescens.*

Elephantulus is the most widespread of the four Macroscelidea genera (Corbet and Hanks, 1968). Most of the elephant-shrew literature deals with this genus, yet this is the first study of the ecology and behavior of a free-living member of the taxon. Sauer (1973) observed the behavior and ecology of *Macroscelides* in the Namib Desert of southwestern Africa and my previous work (1980) dealt with *Rhynchocyon* behavior and ecology. To date 3 of the 4 genera have therefore been studied; only *Petrodromus* is not well known. There are 9 species of *Elephantulus* distributed in Africa from Morocco south to the Cape and from central Africa to the east coast. *Elephantulus rufescens* (fig. 1) is restricted to eastern Africa in dry bushlands and woodlands.

This project was designed as a work comparable to the *Rhynchocyon chrysopygus* study carried out in Kenya during 1971 and 1972 (Rathbun, 1979). The elephant-shrews' social structure, feeding and reproductive habits were studied using marked, free-living individuals, captives, and a small series of snap-trapped specimens.

All of the fieldwork for this study was carried out between March 1974 and October 1976 at Bushwhackers Safari Camp, 20 kilometers northeast of Kibwezi, Kenya, on the bank of the Athi River. The habitat was densely wooded bushland interspersed with game trails and grassy glades. The principal study area was located within the 17-hectare (42-acre) camp.

Elephantulus was captured by means of drop traps placed over well-used elephant-shrew trails (see below). Animals were color ear-tagged and toe-clipped and then released where captured. I subsequently watched the free-ranging animals with the aid of binoculars from tripod towers 4 to 5 meters

---

[1] Currently with Sirenia Project, U. S. Fish and Wildlife Service, Gainesville, Florida.

high. Toward the end of the study some elephant-shrews were fitted with self-powered luminous "Betalight" ear tags, which enabled me to observe them at night without using a spotlight. Because the animals' activities were restricted to their trail networks, sooted-card tracking (Justice, 1961) provided a very quick and easy method of determining the distribution of each individual. During the 12-month study more than 4,000 tracked sooted cards were analyzed, and in over 560 hours of watching for free-ranging *Elephantulus,* approximately 130 hours of actual observations were accumulated.

During the August 1974 dry season 8 specimens were snap-trapped, and an additional 10 were collected in the December 1974 wet season. The stomachs from these specimens were analyzed to determine the proportion of different food items eaten, and the reproductive tracts were preserved for later analysis. Leaf litter invertebrates were sampled during the periods of trapping to determine food availability.

Individual Activity

Based on both direct observation and a treadle-activated events recorder placed on different elephant-shrew trails, the Bushwhackers animals were polycyclic; peaks of activity occurred at dawn and dusk and the least activity occurred during the heat of midday. A tabulation of activity at first sighting for a female and male during early morning and late afternoon gave an estimate of the animals' activity budget over a one-month period (fig. 2).

Elephantulus stretched, yawned, and face-washed in a manner similar to that of most small mammals. It sandbathed by rolling onto its sides; there was no dorsal or ventral component to the rolling action.

The trails built and used by the rufous elephant-shrews were both continuous paths and discontinuous patch tracks that honeycombed the leaf-, grass-, and twig-littered ground. The animals often foraged within one meter of their trails, but rarely went farther afield. They spent a relatively large portion of their daylight activity cleaning trails. While walking along they used a forefoot to sweep away accumulated leaf litter, while small twigs and grasses were usually bitten in two before being swept away. There was some indication that males spent a greater proportion of time trail cleaning than females; neither sex trail cleaned during the night. The importance of the trail system to the elephant-shrews in escaping speckled sand snakes, *Psammophis punctulatus,* was well demonstrated on three occasions during the study.

While resting or sleeping (I never saw an elephant-shrew close its eyes, even when all other indications were that it was sleeping), an animal would choose a spot on a trail that was fairly open, but shaded, and would lie down

FIG. 1.   Adult *Elephantulus rufescens*.

with its rear legs under its body and its head resting on its forefeet. At the slightest foreign sound or motion the animal would jerk to attention. If further disturbed it raced away down a trail. I never observed captive or free-living animals build or use a burrow or nest, even at parturition.

Feeding Habits

Elephantulus foraged by probing about in the litter with its nose and licking up invertebrate prey with its long tongue. The animals also broke open termite foraging tunnels on the surface of the ground and licked up the insects as they came out or ingested them by sticking their long noses into the tunnels. During the study I observed seven instances of female rufous elephant-shrews setting up small (ca. 30 square meters) foraging territories within their home ranges for one or two days. The boundaries of these small territories corresponded to the borders of the termite-foraging activity. Conspecifics and birds trying to feed on the termites were promptly chased away.

The common bush *Premna resinosa* fruited during the wet seasons and *Elephantulus* was seen eating the 4-millimeter diameter drupes when they fell to

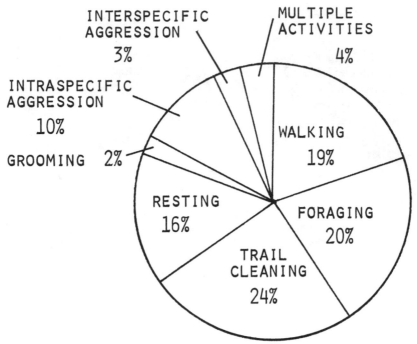

FIG. 2   Diurnal activity budget for *Elephantulus rufescens*.

the ground. An analysis of 18 stomach contents indicated, as tabulated below, that termites were the principal food item eaten and that plant matter was not eaten to any great extent:

Food Item	Percent Contribution
Termites	79.0
Ants	14.0
Beetles	3.0
Cockroaches	0.3
Spiders	0.2
Centipedes	0.2
Other invertebrates	0.3
Plant matter	3.0
	100.0

Considering the elephant-shrews' feeding behavior, the density of invertebrates in the leaf litter, and the stomach contents, the rufous elephant-shrew was probably selecting for termites in its diet.

Social Structure

When the observations and tracking loci for each individual elephant-shrew were plotted on a study area map, the animals were found to be paired on home ranges that varied from 0.16 to 0.52 hectares (0.4 to 1.3 acres) with a mean of 0.31 hectares. The habitat was not saturated with home ranges, but all were contiguous with the home range of at least one other pair. Contiguous home ranges only joined in two or three locations, where the trail networks of each pair came together. These areas of contiguity were usually in a small clearing or on a camp road and both pairs used the 4- to 5-meter-diameter areas. Opposite individuals of a contiguous pair seldom met on a border area, but if they did, an aggressive encounter resulted (I saw this six times). Inter-pair territorial aggression was sex specific, the females chased females most often and the males chased males most often. The home range (i.e., territory) boundaries were not stable over time, but showed changes as individuals disappeared and were replaced by new animals.

Although the elephant-shrews were paired for life (until one animal died or disappeared), they showed few pair bond characteristics. They rarely interacted peacefully and most often the female dominated the male. There was no allogrooming and they slept and foraged separately.

Both sexes rubbed a well-developed sternal gland on the substrate as they walked about on their trail networks. There was no site specificity in the sternal gland marking. About half of the 67 instances I observed occurred around border areas and the other half were well inside the home ranges. The animals also marked with a perineal drag, but I observed this only six times. Dung piles were formed at specific sites along territorial borders as well as inside the home ranges. These dung piles served as static-optic markers; an individual visiting a border area would go to a dung pile and sniff any new contributions before depositing five or six pellets of its own.

Reproduction and Ontogeny

I observed ten sexual encounters, where a male followed a female and attempted to mount her. No copulations were seen, so only estimates of the gestation period can be made. Of the 17 births that were well documented, 7 were considered to be consecutive from the same females. The mean interval for the 7 births was 61 days with a range of 59 to 65 days. This indicates, along with observed sexual behavior after births, that a postpartum estrus may occur. Females produced either one or two young per litter and they bred all year. The young were weaned when about 30 days old and by the 40th day, parental-young aggression began and increased in intensity until the offspring were finally driven from the parental home range. This usually occurred by the time the next litter was born. A survivorship curve based on the 17 young born during the study shows two dips, one reflecting a high postpartum death rate and the other a possible increased death rate related to the forced dispersal of the young. I estimate the rufous elephant-shrew may attain an age of two and a half or three years.

Capture and Handling

In preparation for a study of pair-bonding behaviors in captive *E. rufescens* at the National Zoological Park, Washington, D. C., specimens were live-trapped in Kenya using a drop trap (Rathbun, 1981; Rathbun, Beaman, and Maliniak, in press). The trap was constructed of a 20-centimeter-square steel-rod frame with two layers of fine bird mist-netting stretched across it. This frame was placed over an elephant-shrew trail with one side propped up, so that an elephant-shrew could walk under it along its trail. A trigger mechanism was made by bolting a small wood mouse trap to a steel stake, which was driven into the ground next to the prop. When an elephant-shrew walked under the steel frame it activated the trap by disturbing a cotton thread trip-line, which led to the mouse trap bait treadle. When the treadle was wiggled, the mouse trap snapped and pulled the prop out from under the steel frame, thus pinning the elephant-shrew to the ground. As compared to all other conventional small mammal traps, this worked very well. The major drawback was that someone had to stay near the trap while it was set, as the elephant-shrews were prone to damage themselves when caught. Considerable assistance was received from Mr. Tom Huels, Ms. Christine Ryan, and Dr. Jack Frazier.

The elephant-shrews were sent via a Pan American direct flight from Nairobi to New York, which took about 21 hours. The animals were put in individual cotton cloth bags (20 by 40 centimeters) and then tied to the inside wall of a 30-centimeter-diameter stiff, woven, natural-fiber basket for shipment. No food or water was included with the animals. On arrival in New York they were met and immediately given food and water and then driven to the National Zoological Park in Washington, D. C. This shipping technique worked well. Of the 24 animals shipped (14 females, 10 males), only two deaths (1 female, 1 male) occurred and in both cases the animals were noted to be in poor condition before shipment.

Two methods of acclimatizing the elephant-shrews after capture at Bushwhackers were tried. The attempt to maintain *Elephantulus* in Nairobi for 2 to 3 weeks before shipment resulted in a 40-percent mortality. The best success was obtained by feeding the elephant-shrews milk and termites during the 1- to 3-day trapping operation and then shipping them immediately. No animals were lost during the acclimatization period at the National Zoological Park.

REFERENCES

CORBET, G. B., and HANKS, J.
  1968.   A revision of the elephant-shrews (Macroscelididae).   Bull. British Mus. Nat. Hist. (Zool.), vol. 16, pp. 47-112.
JUSTICE, K. E.
  1961.   A new method for measuring home ranges of small mammals.   Journ. Mammal., vol. 42, pp. 462-470.
RATHBUN, G. B.
  1979.   The ecology and social structure of elephant-shrews.   Zeitschr. Tierpsychol., Advances in Ethology Supplement, vol. 20, pp. 1-76.
  1980.   Ecology of the golden-rumped elephant-shrew (*Rhynchocyon chrysopygus*) of Kenya.   National Geographic Society Research Reports, 1971 Projects, vol. 12, pp. 573-578.
  1981.   Pedal scent-marking in the rufous elephant-shrew, *Elephantulus rufescens*. Journ. Mammal., vol. 62, pp. 635-637.
RATHBUN, G. B.; BEAMAN, P.; and MALINIAK, E.
  _____.   Capture, husbandry and breeding of rufous elephant-shrews, *Elephantulus rufescens*.   International Zoo Yearbook, vol. 21. (In press.)
SAUER, E. G. F.
  1973.   Zum sozialverhalten der Kurzohrigen elefantenspitzmaus, *Macroscelides proboscideus*.   Zeitschr. Saugetierk., vol. 33, pp. 65-97.

GALEN B. RATHBUN

Biosystematic and Evolutionary Studies of
Salvia Subgenus *Calosphace*

Principal Investigator: James L. Reveal, University of Maryland, College Park, Maryland.

Associate Investigator: Kathleen M. Peterson, University of Maryland, College Park, Maryland.[1]

Grant No. 1388:   In support of preliminary research on the biosystematics, evolution, and phytogeography of the entirely New World mint genus *Salvia* subgenus *Calosphace*.

The mint genus *Salvia* L. subgenus *Calosphace* (Benth.) Benth. in Benth. & Hook. is entirely of New World distribution. The subgenus ranges from the midwestern and southern United States southward through Middle America to southern South America. In addition, species occur on several Caribbean islands. Approximately 500 species comprise the subgenus, and the center of greatest species diversity is in the tropical highlands of Mexico, with secondary areas of high diversity in the Andean chain and in the grasslands, or *campos,* of Brazil and in the Gran Chaco of Paraguay, Uruguay, and Argentina.

Originally circumscribed by Bentham (1876), the subgenus *Calosphace* was last revised by Epling (1939). Epling's work on *Salvia* was primarily morphologically oriented, and he suggested a list of numerous characters, mostly of the corolla and stamens, which made possible the placement of species within rather natural sections. These 91 sections represented groupings based not only upon morphological characteristics, but upon phytogeographical considerations as well.

Epling's descriptions of his sections and species were for the most part meticulously and accurately presented. However, a major problem encountered by later botanists with Epling's work relates to the fact that the keys to sections and species and descriptions of all taxa are written in Latin. His key to sections is presented in rather ponderous paragraph fashion. Thus, quick and sure identifications are difficult.

During the 1950's, Epling began a revision of his 1939 treatment of subgenus *Calosphace;* unfortunately, he died in 1968 before he could finish the

---

[1] Currently at Department of Botany, University of Montana, Missoula, Montana.

project. His handwritten manuscript exists and will be used as the basis of a new revision of the subgenus.

That the subgenus *Calosphace* is in need of taxonomic revision is evidenced by consideration of the following points. First, the last-published major taxonomic revision of the subgenus was presented in 1939. Since that time, several important taxonomic tools have been applied successfully to other plant groups and have helped to elucidate concepts of species and other taxonomic categories. These techniques include chromosome counts, hybridization studies, phytochemistry, statistical analysis of morphological characters, pollination biology, and electron microscopy, as well as refinement of traditional areas of study. To date, none of these techniques has been applied on a large scale basis to the subgenus *Calosphace.*

That the subgenus has been "neglected" in terms of biosystematic research is no surprise, given the size of the group and its Pan-American distribution. Even at an alpha-taxonomic level, the synonymies and typification problems associated with many species have proven to be complex and have acted as a deterrent to biosystematic workers who would otherwise be interested in pursuing problems in the subgenus.

Second, the species list continues to grow as botanical expeditions are made into previously unexplored territory, especially in the New World tropical highlands. Many of these species are as yet not formally described, because few botanists since Epling have considered themselves sufficiently knowledgeable of the subgenus *Calosphace.*

Third, recently undertaken large-scale floras, such as *Flora Neotropica* and *Flora of the Chihuahuan Desert* will include the treatment of many species of *Salvia,* most of which are in the subgenus *Calosphace.* Additional knowledge of this group and the species which comprise it is needed in order to provide reasonably accurate descriptions of taxa and to assess the affinities between taxa.

Finally, the rapid destruction of neotropical ecosystems and habitats due to agricultural practices demands that the biota of these areas be studied immediately, before severe reduction in habitat size and/or extinctions occur. Investigations of the biota of such places must include intensive fieldwork in order to provide an accurate assessment.

Funding from the National Geographic Society was provided for the initial field studies of our research which will lead to an eventual revision of the subgenus *Calosphace.* Preliminary fieldwork, principally in Mexico, has proceeded along two lines of investigation. The first of these involved the collection of all *Salvia* species seen in the field. Numerous dried herbarium specimens were made for each population studied, and these specimens have been identified and distributed to major world herbaria. When available, young inflorescences were collected and preserved for cytological studies of chromosome number. In addition, detailed notes were taken as to locality and habitat characteristics for each population of plants studied.

The second line of investigation was Peterson's field studies of the section *Farinaceae* (Epling) Epling. The 15 species which comprise this section and their affinities to each other were the subject of her doctoral dissertation. Peterson's studies have represented a pilot project in which biosystematic tools were applied in an effort to resolve taxonomic problems within section *Farinaceae*. These tools included chromosome counts, pollen stainability, pollination biology, pollen exine ultrastructure, and statistical analysis of character variation.

The selection of a topic for biosystematic studies involves the satisfaction of certain criteria. Given the length of time usually allotted for a doctoral study, the large number of species in subgenus *Calosphace* prohibits even a broad overview of the entire subgenus. Because most of Epling's (1939) sections of the subgenus are well-defined, natural sections, it was decided to choose a section which would be amenable to the type of study which had been envisioned. Such a section would have to contain a relatively small number of species, be primarily of North American distribution in order to make field-work financially feasible, and contain several species which had been the source of taxonomic confusion. The section *Farinaceae* met all of the above-mentioned requirements.

The section *Farinaceae* consists of a group of species which are mostly perennial herbs in habit, although plants may attain heights of three meters. The leaves vary from linear to ovate and these conditions may even be observed within one species. The flowers are bilabiate, are quite colorful, and range from purple with white accents to deep cerulean blue, or white. Often the calyx is blue pigmented and equally as attractive as the corolla.

The section includes chiefly Mexican plants which exhibit highest species diversity in the central Mexican volcanic cordillera region, but species also occur in Baja California Sur. Two species occur in South America in the grass-lands of Brazil and in the Gran Chaco region. In addition, three species are native to the midwestern, southeastern, and southwestern United States.

There are five species assemblages within section *Farinaceae* which have been the source of taxonomic confusion. Each of these complexes exhibits continuous morphological variation for certain critical characters, and this variation is often correlated with geographical distribution.

Of the five assemblages, perhaps the most infamously problematic is *Salvia azurea* Michx. ex Lam. This species has the widest geographical distribution of any in the section: it extends westward from Georgia and Florida through the Gulf Coast states to Texas and northward into the Great Plains, and Epling (1939) described a disjunct subspecies in Nuevo León, Mexico. Epling divided the species into four subspecies, based upon geographical distribution and rather subtle pubescence characteristics of the leaves and stems. Three of these subspecies occupy a broad range extending from Texas and the midwestern plains eastward through the Gulf Coast states to the Atlantic coastal plain. They exhibit a pattern of continuous morphological intergradation, especially with regard to vegetative characters such as leaf shape and pubescence type. Examination of herbarium specimens and subsequent fieldwork soon proved that Epling's division of this assemblage into three subspecies was by no means adequate to account for all of the morphological variants.

The second complex is the *Salvia reptans* Jacq. (=*S. leptophylla* Benth.) assemblage. These plants are primarily distributed in south-central Mexico, ranging from Jalisco eastward through Michoacán, Puebla, and Hidalgo, and southeastward to Oaxaca, Chiapas, and adjacent Guatemala. Throughout this range the plants vary considerably for vegetative characters. In addition, a disjunct, glabrous variant occurs in southwestern Texas. Epling (1939) stated that *S. reptans* is closely allied to another species, *S. heterotricha* Fern., and the two species occupy the same geographical range. In his unpublished manuscript (see References), Epling placed *S. heterotricha* in synonymy with *S. reptans*. An added complication here is that both these superficially resemble a linear-leaved subspecies of *S. azurea*.

A third problematic assemblage again includes *Salvia reptans*, but in question here is the possible relationship between this species and *S. scoparia* Epling, a Brazilian species. These two species resemble each other in their narrow, fascicled cauline leaves.

A fourth group includes four species: *Salvia similis* Brandegee and *S. amissa* Epling, from Baja California Sur and Arizona, respectively, and *S. pallida* Benth. and *S. pseudopallida* Epling, from the Gran Chaco in South America and from Coahuila, Mexico, respectively. It is interesting that Epling (1939) speculated that these four species may form a cluster, each member of which is separated geographically, but which together may represent one polymorphic disjunct aggregate.

The fifth source of confusion in the section concerns *Salvia farinacea* Benth., which ranges from eastern Texas westward to eastern New Mexico and into adjacent northern Mexico. This species exhibits continuous morphological variation with regard to vegetative characters, the extremes being quite distinct from each other, but with a highly variable group of intermediates separating them.

Field Studies

During July and early August, 1974, fieldwork was begun by Peterson in eastern Mexico along the Sierra Madre Oriental southward to Mexico, D.F. Plants were collected and pressed for later use as herbarium specimens. In addition, immature flowers were gathered and preserved for chromosome studies. Species of section *Farinaceae* observed in the field included *Salvia reptans* and *S. azurea*. Additionally, specimens of other *Salvia* species were collected. Among these is a probable new species, a red-flowered sage from the slopes of Mt. Popocatépetl in Puebla.

During October and November, 1976, we conducted extensive field studies in Mexico, along with C. Rose Broome, of the University of Maryland, and Raymond M. Harley, Royal Botanic Gardens, Kew, England. During this trip we explored an isolated region of southwestern Mexico in the state of Guerrero. We traveled for five days during October along a recently opened logging road approximately 100 miles long, and extending from the town of Milpillas southwestward over the crest of the Sierra Madre del Sur to the coastal town of Atoyac. Along this road we encountered a multitude of vegetation zones and habitats, ranging from rather dry chaparral zones, to higher elevation oak-pine forests at about 2000 meters elevation, to cloud forests at the 3500-meter crest of the Sierra, to dense tropical forests on the seaward slope of the mountains. We collected many species of *Salvia* along the road, and several represent new species which are as yet undescribed. Because this region had been little explored botanically, we also collected specimens of many other plants, in addition to cytological material and wood samples. Seeds which were collected were taken to England by Harley and many of these species are now in cultivation at the Royal Botanic Gardens.

Upon our return, we sent specimens from this foray to specialists in various plant groups for identification. The net result was that one new genus and at least a dozen new species were found. In addition, several new state records were established for Guerrero and we also were able to collect a few species which had been collected only once or twice by botanists before us. Among the new taxa were new species of *Hansteinia* and *Justicia* (Acanthaceae), three new species of the sunflower family (Asteraceae), *Montanoa revealii* H. Robinson, *Rumsfordia revealii* H. Robinson, and *Sinclairia broomeae* H. Robinson, two new grasses (Poaceae), including one bamboo *(Chusquea)*, a new Mariposa lily *(Calochortus)*, two new members of the figwort family (Scrophulariaceae), and surprisingly, a new species of the insectivorous genus *Utricularia*. A popular-interest article describing the Guerrero expedition was presented in a University of Maryland publication (Broome et al., 1977).

Subsequent to the botanical foray in Guerrero, fieldwork on the 1975 trip to Mexico was conducted separately by Reveal and Harley for two weeks, and by Peterson and Broome for five more weeks. Peterson and Broome collected intensively in the states of Jalisco, Michoacán, Mexico, and in the Sierra Madre Oriental. During this period *Salvia reptans, S. heterotricha,* and *S. farinacea,* of section *Farinaceae,* were collected and studied. Information gathered about *S. reptans* was presented in an article in *Curtis's Botanical Magazine* (Peterson and Harley, 1978), in which this species has been colorfully illustrated and described, along with a description of its value as a cultivated plant.

Studies of pollination biology of *Salvia reptans* were also commenced during this trip. Behavior of insect visitors was observed and photographed, and representative specimens of all insect visitors were collected. Data obtained from this trip and subsequent field trips indicate that the principal legitimate pollinators of section *Farinaceae* are long-tongued bees of the insect family Apidae. Commonly, these bees are bumblebees (*Bombus* spp.), and in the case of *S. reptans,* Euglossine bees of the genus *Eulaema.* Nectar thieves were also commonly observed in association with the species of section *Farinaceae,* and these insects are principally hesperiid skippers (Lepidoptera).

Conclusions

As a result of our field studies funded by the National Geographic Society and other agencies we have been able to amass a very large inventory of *Salvia* specimens which will be used in the future for detailed morphological studies. This base of recently collected specimens, along with those from future field trips, will be invaluable to us as we proceed on our revision of the subgenus *Calosphace.* Field study and subsequent identification of *Salvia* specimens has also enabled us to become familiar with most of the sections in the subgenus, such that we are now aware of several groups which are strongly in need of immediate taxonomic re-evaluation.

Chromosome counts will soon be available for many of the species which were collected in the field, and it is hoped that chromosome number data will prove to be as useful a tool in elucidating species delineations as it has been for species within section *Farinaceae.*

A taxonomic revision of section *Farinaceae* has been completed by Peterson (1978) and results of this study will be submitted for publication within the year. While data obtained from studies of pollination biology and scanning electron microscope examination of pollen exine ultrastructure were useful in and of themselves, they shed little light upon the taxonomic problems associated with the section.

Chromosome counts were obtained for all species of section *Farinaceae* studied in the field. Other than detailed analyses of morphological characters, chromosome counts proved to be a most useful character for circumscribing taxa. For *Salvia azurea* the chromosome number is $n = 10$ throughout the United States range of this species. However, the disjunct Mexican subspecies, ssp. *mexicana* Epling, proved to have a chromosome number of $n = 6$. The chromosome number of *S. reptans* is $n = 7$, for both the central Mexican populations and for the widely disjunct glabrous populations from western Texas. Additionally, *S. farinacea* populations uniformly have a chromosome number of $n = 10$, despite the wide range of morphological variation in this species.

In summary, section *Farinaceae* is best treated as consisting of 15 species, and these species have been grouped into three more or less discrete assemblages of closely related species. The polymorphic *Salvia azurea* consists of two subspecies, ssp. *azurea* and ssp. *pitcheri* (Torr. ex Benth.) Epling. The Mexican subspecies is given status as a distinct species, based upon differences in chromosome number and certain morphological features. *Salvia farinacea* exhibits a geographically continuous pattern of variation in leaf form, such that no infraspecific taxa can be clearly delineated. *Salvia reptans* consists of two geographically disjunct varieties.

Acknowledgments

Our appreciation is expressed to Raymond M. Harley, Royal Botanic Gardens, Kew, England, for providing identifications of many *Salvia* species, and to the National Science Foundation for providing additional funding in the form of Grant No. DEB 75-23324 under the Grants for Improvement of Doctoral Dissertations Program.

REFERENCES

BENTHAM, G.
  1876.   *"Salvia."*   Vol. 2, pp. 1194-1196 *in* "Genera plantarum," by G. Bentham and J. D. Hooker.
BROOME, C. R.; REVEAL, J. L.; and PETERSON, K. M.
  1977.   Exploring the green frontier.   University of Maryland Graduate School Chronicle, vol. 10, pp. 3-6.
EPLING, C.
  1939.   Revision of *Salvia* subgenus *Calosphace*.   Repert. Spec. Nov. Regni Veg. Beih., vol. 110, pp. 1-383.
  _____.   Untitled manuscript of a tentative and unfinished revision of *Salvia* subgenus *Calosphace*. Xerox copy in the Department of Botany, University of Maryland, College Park, Maryland. (Unpubl.)

PETERSON, K. M.
    1978.   Systematic studies of *Salvia* L. subgenus *Calosphace* (Benth.) Benth. in
             Benth. & Hook. sect. *Farinaceae* (Epling) Epling (Lamiaceae).   Ph.D.
             dissertation, University of Maryland, College Park, Maryland (Unpubl.)
PETERSON, K. M., and HARLEY, R. M.
    1978.   Tab. 751. *Salvia reptans*. Labiatae.   Curtis's Bot. Mag., vol. 182, part
             1, pp. 13-16.

KATHLEEN M. PETERSON
JAMES L. REVEAL

The Ecology of Lions in the Kitengela Conservation Unit, Kenya

Principal Investigator: Judith A. Rudnai, Nairobi, Kenya.

Grant No. 1293: For a study of the ecology of lions in the Kitengela Conservation Unit adjoining Nairobi National Park, Kenya.

This study was carried out between November 1974 and November 1975 in that part of the Athi-Kapiti Plains known as the Kitengela Conservation Unit (KCU) adjoining Nairobi National Park's (NNP) southern boundary (fig. 1). The KCU contains 568 km²; the study area covers approximately 450 km². The aims were to assess the area's role in the continued welfare of the NNP lion population, which was shown in previous studies (Rudnai, 1973a) to migrate to and from the Park both on a short- and a long-term basis.

After a few months it became evident that the most fruitful line of inquiry was to concentrate on the relationship between the lions and the pastoral Masai in the Kitengela to the south as well as the ranches to the east of the Park. Thus attention was focused on all those aspects of the lions' predatory habits that affect livestock-keeping in the areas surrounding NNP.

The area is *Acacia* woodland and grassland, with *Pennisetum mezianum*, *Themeda triandra*, and *Setaria incrassata* the most frequently occurring grasses. In the lightly wooded areas *Acacia drepanolobium* is the dominant tree, while along the rivercourses various species of *Acacia* occur.

Methods

In all, 594 visits were made to 71 bomas or Masai homesteads and numerous other trips to farms and ranches bordering the KCU and NNP to gather information and investigate reports.

All remains of lions were collected for age and sex determination. A record was kept of all other carcasses found.

Rain gauges set up were made useless by constant interference. Data used are from five East African Meteorological Department stations as indicated on figure 1.

All wild animals were counted monthly in 10 blocks including the three main habitat types, *Acacia drepanolobium* wooded grassland, grassland, and

565

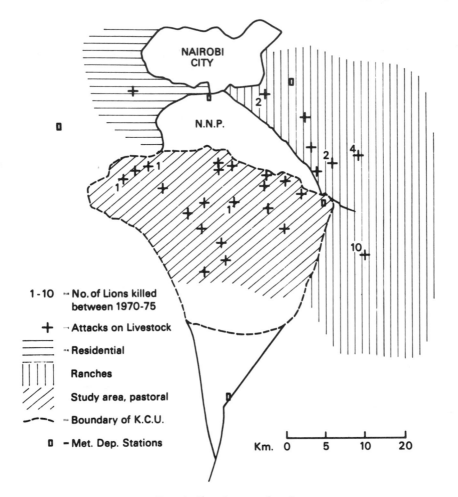

FIG. 1. Sketch map of study area.

riverine strips. In addition, all herds of over 50 head of zebra and wildebeest were recorded at all times.

Results

The herbivore population.   Animal numbers per km² averaged 51.1, ranging from 21.0 to 92.9, with highest numbers in February, July, and August, the end of the dry seasons (fig. 2). This is the same pattern as that prevailing

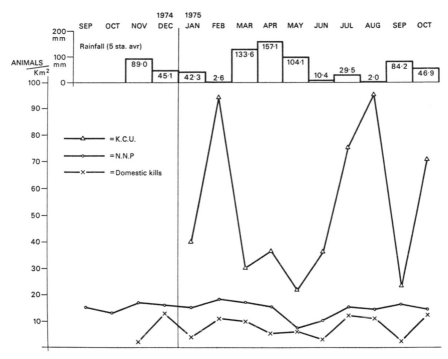

FIG. 2. Numbers of domestic stock killed by month, prey animal density, and monthly rainfall during study period.

in NNP although during 1975 it was far less pronounced than during previous years.

NNP Ungulates

Year	Min. no. km²	Max. no. km²	Increase	Source
1972	29.84	117.04	3.9 fold	Rudnai, 1974
1975	6.9	18.2	2.6 fold	NNP monthly censuses

To test for seasonal fluctuations in numbers of wildebeest and zebra, the most important ungulates in the KCU, all herds of over 50 animals recorded were divided into four categories and values assigned to each herd size. When numbers were totaled for each month significantly more animals were found present in the dry season (precipitation below 45 mm).

The fact that both in NNP and in the KCU numbers are low during the rains and increase during the dry season indicates that the animals leaving the Park migrate beyond the KCU, farther to the east and south.

Predation.   Forty-five carcasses were classified as lion kills on the basis of injuries, lion footprints around the carcasses, or other indications that lions had fed on them. Numbers were too low for establishing seasonal patterns; however, striking differences with prey killed in NNP, as recorded during my previous study, were evident (Rudnai, 1974).

The kongoni (hartebeest) population in the study area is only between 0.4 and 1.8/km^2 while in NNP between 1968 and 1972 it averaged 20.4/km^2. Warthog occur only at a density of 0.2/km^2, while in NNP this figure was 1.4/km^2 (Rudnai, 1973). Both species are virtually absent from lion kills in the KCU while in NNP they constituted almost 45 percent of all kills (Rudnai, 1974).

No preferential selection for either zebra or wildebeest, constituting almost 90 percent of kills found, was evident. Selection for males was highly significant in wildebeest. Zebra carcass numbers were too low to be tested for sex selection.

Presence of lions.   Contact was made on ten occasions with an average of 1,242.5 km traveled between encounters; this was clearly unrewarding. Thus most data are based on indirect evidence. Sightings by others were accepted if proof was adduced or another independent witness supported the report.

To test for seasonality in the presence of lions, all records including sightings, footprints, and kills were tabulated by month, each presence taken as one regardless of number of lions in a group. The results showed significantly more lions during the dry months, thus contradicting the generally voiced opinion of the pastoralists that lions were more numerous during the rains in years past.

As ungulate numbers were also significantly higher in the dry season we may infer that the presence of lions is positively correlated with presence of ungulates.

Raids on livestock.   Data on damage to livestock were collected for the years 1970-75 from areas outside the study area as well. This includes some residential sections adjacent to the west of NNP and ranches to the east and southeast of the Park, thus embracing all areas into which lions may penetrate (fig. 1).

Estimates of livestock density are 35 cattle and 35 sheep and goats per km^2, considerably higher than wild-ungulate density (51.1/km^2).

Fifty-eight head of livestock were killed during the study period. Losses ranged from 0.05-0.07 percent in the pastoral area to 0.5-2.8 percent on the ranches. No seasonal trend was evident, and no relationship was found to number of ungulates present either in NNP or in the KCU.

Lion mortality.   Remains of nine lions were collected. With the help of Dr. G. L. Smuts sex and age were determined on the basis of skull measurements and tooth wear. Of nine remains five were 3 years old or younger and two were over 8. Lions between 4 and 8 years can be considered in their prime, while those between 2 and 3 are inexperienced, having left their mothers at about the age of 2, and are therefore at a greater risk, as are also those past their prime over 8.

Known cases of mortality are summarized below:

```
Lions shot, 1970-75 ............................... 19
Lions speared, 1974-75 ........................... 2
Died of unknown causes........................... 9
                                                ──
                                                30
Adult male died in NNP 1974.................... 1        31
Annual increment (6) of NNP population                 ──
   (Rudnai, 1973b) for 1970-75 (6 x 6)                 36
                                                        ──
                                                         5
```

These figures account for all but five of the lions that should have been added to the NNP population, which, however, had remained stable during this period, i.e., 27 in 1969, 30 in 1972, and 29 in 1975, according to E. Norris's report on predators in NNP (1975, unpubl.).

Discussion

There is no evidence of an appreciable resident population of lions in the KCU, which acts as a dispersal area for the subadults from NNP who leave their prides (Rudnai, 1973b). Apparently few of these animals settle down in the KCU.

Many of the lion sightings were of animals coming from or returning to NNP; some others were recognized as Park residents.

A lion census using recordings lent by Dr. G. L. Smuts resulted in only two sightings during four nights, supporting the contention that there are very few resident lions in the KCU. If their numbers were comparable to those in NNP there should be 110 animals ($4km^2$/lion).

To evaluate whether the KCU is prime or marginal lion habitat we must consider three main factors—prey availability, cover, and disturbance by man.

Prey density at an average of $51/km^2$ is comparable to the highest yearly average in NNP between 1962 and 1972 (Rudnai, 1974) and the lowest monthly figure, 21/km², is only slightly lower than the minimum monthly numbers in NNP, 24.65 for the period 1968-72 (*ibid.*). During this study monthly figures were consistently higher than those for NNP.

As availability of prey is as important as numbers present, adequate cover for hunting is also an important factor. Even in this respect the study area must be considered good lion range, with its large areas of *Acacia drepanolobium* woodland shown to be the favored hunting habitat for lions in NNP (Rudnai, 1973a).

The reason for the lack of a sizable resident population must therefore be attributed to the presence of the pastoralists.

While traditional lion hunts by groups of young Masai warriors account for only a few deaths, frequent harassment and disturbance by the resident pastoralists constitute a factor in the scarcity of lions in the KCU.

My records for 1970-75 show most lions destroyed to have been in the ranching areas (fig. 1). Of the two lions listed as speared one was killed within an enclosure in the act of stockkilling; circumstantial evidence indicates the other to have been killed during a traditional lion hunt.

The seasonal fluctuation of lion sightings shows that lions are attracted to the area by the game concentrations especially during years of very low prey availability in NNP.

The contention that lions were more troublesome in all areas surrounding the Park during the rainy season was not borne out by my findings.

Decreased fluctuation of game availability together with an over-all very low level of ungulate populations in NNP during 1974-75 as compared with former years caused lions to make more regular excursions to the surrounding areas. Many sightings during this study were of lions coming from NNP early in the evening or returning there after sunrise. In 1968-69 during 42 nights of following lions in NNP they were only once seen leaving the Park area (Rudnai, 1973a).

The NNP lion population remained stable (as shown above), but ungulate numbers had greatly decreased by large-scale die-off during the 1973-74 drought. This necessitated an increase in the hunting areas of the resident groups. As shown by Rudnai (1973a) the areas used for hunting by night and those where prides spend the daylight hours do not coincide; thus even while groups remained resident in the Park during this study, they may have included part of the outlying area within their hunting domain.

The pastoral Masai have traditionally tolerated wildlife, but this attitude is rapidly changing. The ranches along the eastern boundary of NNP are organized along commercial lines, and their owners are even less willing to suffer losses by predation without compensation. While these losses may be low in statistical terms, resentment engendered by even a few kills may be out of proportion with real damage suffered, since individuals feel they do not benefit from game in general and predators in particular, yet have to bear the brunt of the damage inflicted by wild animals.

Even though compensation payment for livestock killed by lions is on the books, in practice it is virtually unavailable because of a cumbersome administrative procedure.

As the survival of wild animals, including predators, depends ultimately on their acceptance by the people who must share their habitat, recommendations for a streamlined procedure for compensation payment have been put before the Kenya Government, as a result of this study. These recommendations laid down guidelines for the conditions under which such compensation should be paid, for the manner of assessing damages, and for processing the claims (Rudnai, 1979). It is hoped that the acceptance of such a scheme will help to make the presence of these predators more acceptable to the pastoralists and ranching inhabitants of the areas surrounding NNP and thus assure the survival of the NNP lion population.

REFERENCES

RUDNAI, JUDITH A.
   1973a.   The social life of the lion, 122 pp., illus.   MTP Medical and Technical Publishing Co., Lancaster, England.
   1973b.   Reproductive biology of lions (*Panthera leo massaica* Neumann) in Nairobi National Park.   Afr. Wildl. Journ., vol. 11, pp. 241-253.
   1974.   The pattern of lion predation in Nairobi National Park.   Afr. Wildl. Journ., vol. 12, pp. 213-225.
   1979.   Ecology of lions in Nairobi National Park and the Kitengela Conservation Unit in Kenya.   Afr. Journ. Ecol., vol. 17, pp. 85-95.

JUDITH A. RUDNAI

Spatial and Temporal Pattern of Calling Sites in *Coturnix* Quails

Principal Investigator: Wolfgang M. Schleidt, University of Maryland, College Park, Maryland.

Grant No. 1350:   For a study of calling behavior patterns of *Coturnix* quails.

This study is part of a continuing effort to determine the role of the male's "wet-my-lips" call in the behavior and ecology of the Eurasian migratory quail (*Coturnix coturnix coturnix* L.). This report summarizes the results of field observations within the breeding range of this species made near the town of Neusiedel, Burgenland, Austria (lat. 16°50′E., long. 47°55′N.). The calls were recorded at an array of three microphones by use of a stereophonic tape recorder between May 13 and June 12, 1974. Subsequently the tapes were analyzed in the laboratory in order to determine the number of different individuals detectable during the observation period, the dates on which they were present, and the location from which each was calling. The methods used are described in detail elsewhere (Schleidt, 1973; Magyar, Schleidt, and Miller, 1978). In this particular study we used a simplified version, recording on a stereophonic UHER 4200 Report IC with one microphone on one track, and on the second track the second and third microphone were alternated after a call series had started. In other words, the arrival time difference between microphones 1 and 2 was measured at the beginning of a call sequence, and the arrival time difference between microphones 1 and 3 was measured at the end of the same call sequence.

Although the quail has been a popular game bird in Europe since antiquity, and is known for its calling during the mild nights of spring and early summer (hence the poetic and onomatopoeic rendering of the call in English as "wet-my-lips"), very little is known about the behavior in its natural habitat and about its ecology. This bird is very inconspicuous, secretive, and rarely visible in the tall cover of spring meadows and fields. Its presence is inferred solely from the male's call, in a habitat presumably suitable for breeding, and from hunting, when birds are lured by caged calling males or flushed by bird dogs.

It was generally assumed that the quail, as other migratory birds, arrives in spring at the breeding grounds, establishes a territory, raises one or several broods of young, and in fall leaves for the winter quarters in the subtropical

573

and tropical areas of Africa. This simplistic view was questioned when bird-banding studies showed that individuals that were captured and banded within what was assumed to be a breeding population with established territories were recaptured a considerable distance away only few days or weeks later (Warga, 1931). This finding infers that at least a part of the population migrates throughout the breeding season, searching for particular and still unknown features of the habitat. Only if particular requirements are met will a bird settle for a few weeks, raise a brood, and then continue its gypsy life (see Moreau and Wayre, 1968; Glutz von Blotzheim, 1973).

One potential drawback of the bird-banding studies, which have led to the revised picture of the quail's life, is that the individuals captured and banded might have been disturbed by the handling and might have left the area because they considered it unsafe for them. Therefore, a method of field observation that minimizes the disturbance of the animals was used in this study. In the laboratory we established that the rhythm of the "wet-my-lips" call, especially the intervals between the "wet-my" syllables and the "my-lips" syllables, is quite variable within a population of quail, but highly stereotyped for each individual (Schleidt and Shalter, 1973; Schleidt, 1982). This feature of the call can be used to determine *how many individuals* are calling within a particular area. When such calls are recorded simultaneously with at least three microphones spaced out at a known distance and location, the *location* of each calling bird can be estimated with some accuracy. By combining these two methods, the *identity, location,* and *time* of calling can be determined for all calling males in the area without ever having to touch or even to see the particular individuals.

During spring and summer of 1972, we used this method to sample the calling quails at intervals of about 10 days throughout the breeding season, starting when the first migrants arrived and ending when calling had ceased, the fields were cut, and coveys consisting of juveniles and adults were observed. During this period, at least 40 different individuals were recorded calling within the area under observation (approximately 1 square kilometer), but nearly all were recorded only during one single recording night. In other words, 10 days later a different set of males was calling.

In order to fill in the gaps between the samples taken at 10-day intervals, the microphones were left in place continuously during a 2-week period of favorable weather in the spring of 1974, and recordings were attempted every night. Of the 13 males detected during this period, only one was recorded over several successive nights (from May 13 to May 21), while the other 12 birds had evidently left the area within 24 hours after their first detection. This result is consistent with the earlier bird-banding studies, and with my own results of the 1972 season, and indicates that the vast majority of the quails calling in this area are not resident holders of territories but migrants searching for suitable habitat.

The migratory quail is the only member of the order Galliformes known to be migratory in the strict sense; that is, this bird is crossing on its flights continents and large bodies of water (e.g., the Mediterranean Sea) and as such is an oddity among its relatives. Although there seems to be a tendency within this order to be "opportunistic" in an ecological sense, that is, to move into suitable habitat and respond to favorable conditions with high fecundity, and consequently show considerable fluctuations in their numbers in space and time ("r selected"), the migratory quail has apparently evolved into an extreme case in connection with its high mobility. The crepuscular and nighttime calling of the males, as well as certain acoustical features of the call itself, allows the migrants to detect during their nocturnal flights the presence of conspecific males in potentially suitable habitats over a considerable distance (the call carries at night under favorable conditions over 1 kilometer. During the following day, they can explore the particular habitat for food and mates, and engage in courtship or aggressive interactions with resident or migrant conspecifics. Depending on the result of their exploration, they can settle down and attempt to raise a brood, or continue migration.

In order to corroborate this hypothesis further, it is necessary to find whether the abundance of food has an effect on the number of successive nights during which newcomers stay in a particular location. Also, it should be tested whether the playback of quail calls has an effect on the presumed resident male(s) in a particular area, either by eliciting a higher rate of calling over an extended period of the night (provoking a male already mated and therefore presumably not vocalizing to call in response to the presumed intruder), or by repelling newcomers and preventing them from settling in the proximity of the "territory" claimed by the loudspeaker.

REFERENCES

GLUTZ VON BLOTZHEIM, U. N., ed.
    1973.   Handbuch der Vögel Mitteleuropas, vol. 5, 700 pp., illus. Akademische Verlagsgesellschaft, Frankfurt am Main.
MAGYAR, I.; SCHLEIDT, WOLFGANG M.; and MILLER, B.
    1978.   Localization of sound-producing animals using the arrival time difference of their signals at an array of microphones. Experientia, vol. 34, pp. 676-677.
MOREAU, REGINALD E., and WAYRE, P.
    1968.   On the Palaearctic quails. Ardea, vol. 56, pp. 209-227.

SCHLEIDT, WOLFGANG M.
　　1973.　　Localization of sound producing animals by means of arrival time differ-
　　　　　　ences of their signals at an array of microphones.　　The Noisy Channel,
　　　　　　vol. 1, no. 2, pp. 1-6. University of North Dakota, Grand Forks.
　　1982.　　Stereotypes feature variables are essential constituents of behavior pat-
　　　　　　terns.　　Behaviour, vol. 79, pp. 230-238.
SCHLEIDT, WOLFGANG M., and SHALTER, M. D.
　　1973.　　Stereotypy of a fixed action pattern during ontogeny in *Coturnix coturnix
　　　　　　coturnix*.　　Zeitschr. für Tierpsych., vol. 33, pp. 5-37.
WAGRA, K.
　　1931.　　Maszse von *Coturnix coturnix*.　　Aquila, vol. 36/37, pp. 138-142.

WOLFGANG M. SCHLEIDT

The Ethnomedicine of the Torres Strait Islanders

Principal Investigator: George J. Simeon, Brown University, Providence, Rhode Island.

Grant No. 1286:   For a study of native diseases and cures among islanders of the Torres Strait south of New Guinea.

The Torres Strait Islands were brought to the attention of the scientific community through the Cambridge Expedition of the last decade of the 19th century and the subsequent publication of their research. In this century, however, very little anthropological fieldwork has been centered in the Torres Strait area.[1] My own research for a 6-month period in 1974 was in the area of ethnomedicine. I define ethnomedicine as the investigation, from an anthropological perspective, of disease and injury; that is, disturbed bodily states in contrast to psychosomatic or psychological ones among societies utilizing non-Western medical techniques.

The primary goal of my research was to delineate the present situation in regard to the state of ethnomedicine in the Torres Strait, but not to reconstruct the past. Of course, any recollections, reminiscences, and data referring to no-longer-extant medical practices were recorded—even those narratives that I considered of historical and ethnographic significance but that did not refer, either directly or indirectly, to medicine were duly recorded or noted down.

Any anthropologist working in the Torres Strait, whatever his field of inquiry, has to contend with the fact that the "pure" or "unadulterated" Torres Strait version or practice of any custom, whether historic or contemporary, will be difficult, if not impossible, to uncover. This is because the Torres Strait islanders, in addition to their indigenous culture, have been influenced from the time of their first settlement, and in varying degrees on the different islands, by the peoples with whom they came into contact. The main sources of culture contact were from Papua New Guinea, Aboriginal Australia, Mela-

---

[1] The only other professional anthropologists that I am aware of as having done in-depth field research in the Torres Strait Islands are Dr. Jeremy Beckett of Sydney University, Australia, and Dr. Wolfgang Laäde of the University of Zürich, Zürich, Switzerland. I wish to thank both of these scholars for their helpful suggestions in regard to fieldwork in the Torres Strait Islands.

nesia, and Polynesia. Thus I found that various flora and their uses have been introduced from these sources. Furthermore, aspects of sorcery relating to native medicine have also been introduced to the Torres Strait especially from Papua New Guinea and the Cape York Peninsula.

Cultural and personality differences among the Torres Strait islanders are recognized by the people themselves, since they are aware that various cultural influences have affected the islands in different ways. Geographical and ecological factors affecting migration and settlement patterns have been the main force behind the differences. However, the basic cultural and geographic divisions coincide to give four main island groups—viz., the Eastern, Western, Central, and Northern.

Early on in my research it became evident that belief in sorcery was a major factor in indigenous concepts of disease etiology. However, the Torres Strait islanders themselves divided the sorcery into two types: *puripuri* and *maid*. The origin of the former term is obscure although it may possibly be Papua New Guinean or Indonesian, but the practice itself derives from coastal Papua and Aboriginal Australia, especially the Cape York Peninsula. The *puripuri* of the Torres Strait falls into both the "transitive" and "intransitive" forms of sorcery as described by Cawte (1974, p. 88). Transitive forms are those in which the active intervention of a sorcerer is identifiable while intransitive forms are those in which no such activity is evident.

Maid is the term for the traditional Torres Strait sorcery, practitioners of which are found only in the Eastern Islands, but the victims may belong to any of the island groups. Although manifesting elements common to sorcery found elsewhere, *maid* represents what Cawte (p. 76) defines as the regional superstructure, that is, "the set of assumptions that characterize the disease concepts of a community and distinguish it from others." *Puripuri,* on the other hand, represents a variety of the common infrastructure (ibid.) of primitive concepts of disease.

In regard to the spatial relationships of sorcery (ibid., p 102), the Torres Strait manifestations divide into three spatial categories: near, intermediate, and far. *Puripuri,* which represents the borrowed forms of sorcery, operates at all three spatial distances. For example, someone may believe that something malevolent has been done directly to his body, albeit unknown to the victim; or it may be that the sorcerer was some distance away but on the same island, that is, within walking distance; finally, the sorcerer might be hundreds, or even thousands of miles away. *Maid,* however, is usually effective either within the close or middle spatial relationships. It is both important and interesting to point out that there is no remedy which may be utilized to counter, stop, or diminish the effects of *maid.*

Certainly the Torres Strait Islands are not as sorcery-ridden as are some societies in Papua New Guinea and Aboriginal Australia. This is recognized by many of the islanders themselves, especially those who have visited or worked in other areas. By "sorcery-ridden" I mean that a constant, all-pervading fear of being victimized by a sorcerer is present. One Torres Strait islander, who had served as a schoolteacher at an Australian Aboriginal settlement, related how the Aborigines living there would be afraid to leave a cup of drinking water unguarded, even briefly, lest someone should poison them via the water.

For the general and commonplace illnesses and injuries that occur, natural causes such as poor nutrition, God, or accident are evoked as the primary culprits. More and more, especially when an ailment is serious and/or incapacitating, people turn for treatment to their island dispensary or to the hospital on Thursday Island. Household remedies, which usually involve the administration of plants, are applied for minor and non-debilitating illnesses and injuries. The plants are obtained and prepared either by the individual himself, a knowledgeable member of the household, or an outsider skilled in plant remedies. However, the knowledge and use of medicinal plants is gradually declining especially with the facile and free access to scientific medicine. Coupled with this is the lack of interest in plant medicine by the younger generation, and the sometimes difficult, and always time-consuming, task of securing the necessary plants. In addition, the increase of building and construction has also resulted in the destruction of the flora itself and the obliteration of the soil where it grew naturally.

Many of the plant remedies are the specialized knowledge of individual families who will not reveal the process of preparation or the plants involved. However, someone outside the circle of relatives who requests a cure will have it readily offered without any charge or fee. Some families have a reputation of knowing several such special remedies and individuals will turn to them for help. The knowledge of plant cures varies from individual to individual, but today there are virtually no specialists in this aspect of curing. Even in the past, from what older informants told me, the use of medicinal plants was basically a family affair. Only a few specialists, but certainly none who earned their livelihood in this manner, probably ever practiced.

I collected approximately 200 specimens of plants together with some shells and coral used for medicine and/or food. Photographs, which numbered about 225, included the flora and fauna, informants, dwellings, and scenery in general. Some movie films, depicting scenery, various island activities, coconut grinding, and the uses of medicinal plants were also taken. As of this writing I do not know if any of the plant specimens collected will prove of value to science, since they are now in the process of being identified and catalogued.

I interviewed informants of both sexes, of various ages, and with different backgrounds in regard to the knowledge of medicine and plants. The informants were interviewed formally, that is, by asking previously prepared questions as well as informally, that is, by letting them speak spontaneously. Stories, recollections, detailed narratives, and songs were also tape recorded.

The project base was on Thursday Island, and I also visited or lived on the following islands: Hammond, Horn, Murray, Coconut, Yam, York, and Banks. The only island group that I could not visit was the northern one.

Although the plant and other specimens collected are representative of the various islands visited, the bulk of my written and taped data comes from Eastern Islands informants, especially Murray and Darnley. This is due to the factors of time spent, the availability of informants, and above all the quality of the informants.

The goals stated in the original research proposal were met as follows: (1) to determine what diseases occur, their causes and treatment by both empirical and magico-religious agents and means, and to delineate the native concepts of disease and curing: this part of the project was fulfilled and indeed forms the bulk of my study; (2) to tape record pertinent oral material: this goal was also met; (3) to film materials (such as medicinal plants) and methods (such as curing ceremonies) that are important to illness and curing: medicinal plants were photographed, but with the lack of medical specialists and the dwindling use of indigenous forms of treatment it was not possible to film any practitioner actually administering to a patient.

A great deal of basic ethnographic research in all areas of anthropology remains to be carried out in the Torres Strait Islands. I particularly would advocate and emphasize an intensive study of one village on one island, focusing, for example, on topics such as: the amount and type of land owned by family groups; the amount of this land that is under cultivation; the means of cultivation; the crops grown; the income from these crops; other occupations, in addition to agriculture, engaged in by the family; the amount of man-hours spent in all subsistence activities; and the inheritance patterns in regard to land ownership.

After my data has been analyzed and the plants and other specimens identified, I plan to publish a monograph in which I will compare and evaluate the results of this research in relation to other similar studies in adjacent geographical areas and with my own previous fieldwork in the New Hebrides and Melville Island, Australia. I have also published an article in *Acta Ethnographica*.

In conclusion I wish to thank the National Geographic Society for the opportunity to carry out fieldwork in the Torres Strait. Ever since I was an undergraduate student in anthropology, I have been very interested in these islands and have always cherished the desire to conduct research there in the footsteps of the famed Cambridge Expedition.

REFERENCES

CAWTE, JOHN
    1974.   Medicine is the law: Studies in psychiatric anthropology of Australian tribal societies, xxiv+260 pp.   University Press of Hawaii, Honolulu.

HADDON, ALFRED C.
    1901-1935, 1971.   Reports of the Cambridge Anthropological Expedition to Torres Straits.   Cambridge University Press, 1901-1935; Johnson Reprint Corporation, New York, 1971.

SIMEON, GEORGE J.
    1972.   Some goals for ethnomedicine.   Ethnomedizin, vol. 2, no. 1/2, pp. 155-156.
    1976.   Ethnomedicine in the Torres Strait.   Acta Ethnographica, vol. 25, no. 3/4, pp. 398-400.

GEORGE J. SIMEON

Archeological Excavations of the Vaito'otia and Fa'ahia Sites on Huahine Island, French Polynesia

Principal Investigator: Yosihiko H. Sinoto, Bernice P. Bishop Museum, Honolulu, Hawaii.

Grant Nos. 1352,   For excavation of the Archaic habitation site on Huahine, So-
1512, 1779.   ciety Islands, 1974-1975, and 1977.

I am most grateful for the financial support from the National Geographic Society, and also for the generous donations from Ben Deane and James Deane, who have helped us financially since the beginning of the excavations in 1973. Without the support of the Deanes, commencement and continuation of the fieldwork would not have been possible. I gratefully acknowledge also those who assisted and cooperated in many ways with the project: Richard Soupene, Bali Hai architect, for his interest and efforts in protecting the exposed artifacts and the sites during hotel construction, enabling us to start excavations and subsequent fieldwork; Hugh Kelley, owner of the Bali Hai Hotel Huahine, for his permission to excavate; Tim Drost and Mike Kelley, Bali Hai managers; Jacques Drollet and Denis Capitaine, French Government officials who granted the excavation permit and temporary export permit for the artifacts; and Dr. and Mrs. Henri Lavondes, O.R.S.T.O.M., for their help in obtaining the export permit. I express my appreciation also to Dr. Yoshio Kondo, Dr. Alan C. Ziegler, Dr. Dennis M. Devaney, and Dr. Patrick V. Kirch, B. P. Bishop Museum, for identification of land snails, hermit crabs, and bones from the midden. Figures 2 and 5 are reprinted here with the permission of the Institute for Polynesian Studies, Brigham Young University, Hawaii Campus.

The Vaito'otia site, located northwest of Fare, capital of Huahine, was discovered accidentally in 1972 when a pond was dredged during construction of the Hotel Bali Hai Huahine (fig. 1). One whalebone hand club, similar to the *patu* of the New Zealand Maori, was recovered from the dredging. A collagen date of A.D. 850±70 (GAK-4629) was obtained on a dredged whale rib, and preliminary test excavations in August 1973 confirmed that cultural deposits were still intact at the site.

Preliminary excavations revealed that the site is unique in central Polynesia. The waterlogged cultural layer contained much vegetal material—coconut, pandanus keys, and wood. Typologically early Tahitian adzes,

583

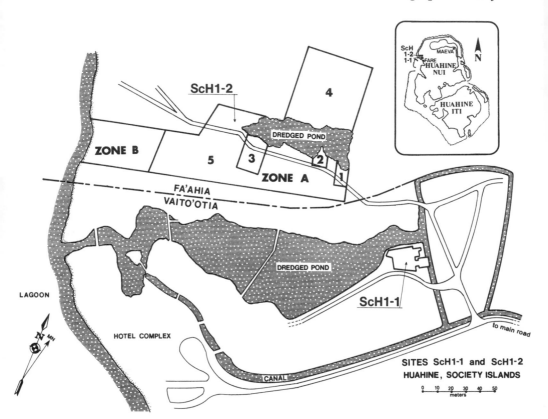

FIG. 1.   Location of excavated areas in the Vaito'otia (ScH1-1) and Fa'ahia (ScH1-2) sites, Huahine Island.

bonito-lure shanks, fishhooks, and wooden structural posts led us to believe that the site was the earliest habitation site so far known in the Society Islands, justifying an extensive expansion of the site excavation.

The second phase of excavation, September to November 1974 (Sinoto and McCoy, 1975), yielded artifactual, faunal, and floral materials. Particularly noteworthy were a number of wooden artifacts, including hand clubs and a canoe paddle. Other significant finds were floorboards and posts of habitation or storage structures, with enough evidence to postulate reconstructions.

Before the structural remains could be examined the rainy season began, and we had to rebury the remains and postpone fieldwork. The third phase of excavation, September to October 1975 (Sinoto, 1976), yielded additional structural remains, as well as wooden artifacts including a bow, four adz handles, and a fragment of a ceremonial spear.

In March 1977, Mr. Soupene notified us that wooden hand clubs and beaters had been recovered from the dredging of a new pond at Fa'ahia, the land division adjacent to Vaito'otia (fig. 1). In response to our urgent request, the National Geographic Society granted funds for archeological salvage excavations. Fieldwork was carried out from July to September 1977. The artifacts recovered at Fa'ahia obviously belonged to the same cultural context as those from the Vaito'otia site. The material culture assemblages and site features from the two areas may represent different segments of one large settlement complex.

Site Environment

Located on the grounds of the Hotel Bali Hai Huahine, the site complex is situated on a flat coastal plain about 300 meters inland from the beach and opposite Ava Moa Pass, an opening in the fringing reef. The beach has been modified for hotel guests. Judged from undisturbed areas nearby, however, it originally was more sandy and level to the south toward Fare, with a higher, storm-built ridge of coral extending east. This part of the island, built up by natural deposition of coral and other debris, completely blocked the lagoon that forms Fauna Nui Lake toward the east. The area northeast of the site is low and swampy, and there are many brackish pools.

The environmental setting of the site can be reconstructed from present conditions and from results of the excavations. The locality is well situated for exploitation of the sea, and taro could have been cultivated easily in the nearby swampland, without terracing. The thick soil deposit, visible near the foot of the hill about 500 meters inland, could have been utilized at one time for cultivation of crops such as yam. At the time of initial occupation, the ground level of the site area may have been lower than that of the surrounding area. In general, the ground was damp, and perhaps even flooded after heavy rains. High tide would also have influenced the ground water level.

The Vaito'otia site comprises five stratigraphic layers overlying sterile Layer VI, which is found at ca. 70 centimeters below present ground surface. Layer V is dark, organic, silt-mixed, and waterlogged and is the main cultural layer; all others were naturally deposited, but the top of Layer IV was occupied again in contemporary times. In Fa'ahia three layers overlie sterile Layer IV, which is reached at ca. 40 centimeters below surface. Layers II and III are equivalent to Layers IV and V, respectively, of Vaito'otia. The stratification of Section 3 (fig. 1) is different, however. Under the fill, the dark, humus-mixed

POND

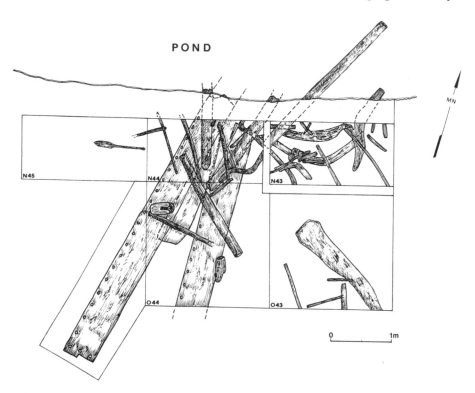

FIG. 2.   Plan view of wooden objects in situ in Layer III, Section 3, Zone A, Fa'ahia site. Excavation of this area in 1981 revealed that Section 3 was a stream, and that objects and debris were washed into the streambed and lodged there.

overburden, Layer I, is thicker than in other sections, and there is no equivalent of Layer II. There is a very dark humus lens (IIIa) with sporadic deposits of grass, *Costa* sp. (Zingiberraceae) on top. This lens is submerged, and is approximately 25 centimeters lower than the top of Layer II in Section 2. Under IIIa is the deep, convex Layer III; we did not reach the bottom of this layer because of heavy water seepage, but it extends at least 1.10 meters below IIIa. Large wooden objects were found in this thick deposit, and many of them were still intact (fig. 2). According to Yoshio Kitagawa, geologist from the Historical Museum of Hokkaido, Japan, the subsidence of Layer V under the present high-water level could be the result of slight tilting of this portion of the island. A recent study of sea-level change in the Tuamotuan Archipelago (Salvat, 1970) indicated that the sea level subsided as much as 3 meters in the

FIG. 3.   Stone adzes, a whalebone dagger, and a pearl-shell scraper in situ in the Vaito'otia site.

past 3,000 years; if this is true, Kitagawa's hypothesis is one explanation for the waterlogged nature of the cultural layer throughout the site complex.

Microtopographic examination by Kitagawa also revealed that large waves or *tsunami* entered from the lowest elevation in the Fa'ahia side, pushing the water toward Vaito'otia. The scatter pattern of debris, such as coconut husks, pandanus, and pieces of wood, clearly shows the direction of the water force.

In general, it appears that the site area was once drier and that subsidence occurred sometime after the end of occupation. Several piles of over a hundred *Turbo* shells, with some shells containing remains of complete hermit crabs (*Coenobita* cf. *perlata*), were found in the bottom layer of the site, indicating that these shell piles were once on open dry land.

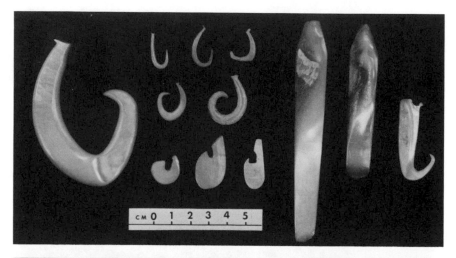

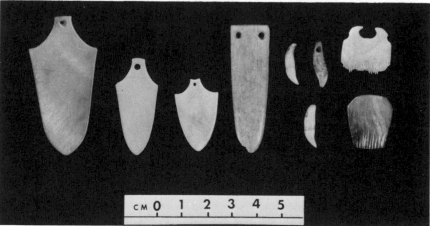

FIG. 4.   Shell and bone artifacts from the Vaito'otia site. *Top,* One-piece pearl-shell fishhooks, fishhook blanks, bonito-lure hook shanks, and a compound-shank hook; *bottom,* three pearl-shell pendants, bone pendant, fish-tooth pendants, and pearl-shell tattooing combs.

Artifacts

Portable artifacts from Vaito'otia consist of numerous stone scrapers and choppers, basalt and shell adzes, *Terebra*-shell chisels and pecking tools, a *Cassis*-shell chisel, turtle-bone and pearl-shell scrapers, pearl-shell graters, whalebone daggers, pearl-shell one-piece fishhooks, compound shank hooks,

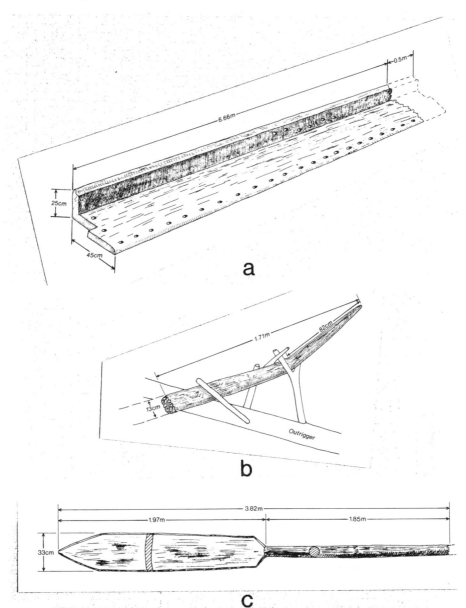

FIG. 5. Wooden artifacts from Section 3, Fa'ahia site: a, Side-board planks, for lashing to canoe hull; b, part of an outrigger boom; c, steering paddle. The boards were previously thought to be the planks for the double canoe platform (Sinoto, 1979).

FIG. 6.   Hand clubs *(patu)* from the Vaito'otia site. *Top,* Wooden club from excavation; *bottom,* whalebone club from dredging.

and bonito-lure shanks (figs. 3, 4). Curiously, not a single bonito hook point was found from the excavations. Abraders of branch coral (*Acropora* sp.), pearl-shell pendants of a type so far known only from the early Marquesas, fish- and porpoise-tooth ornaments, shaped whale-tooth pendants, a cloak pin, a mallet and a harpoon head of whalebone, and pearl-shell tattooing combs were recovered.

Some of the significant discoveries in 1977 were: (1) parts of canoes and canoe accessories—a boom for an outrigger (fig. 5b), two 23-foot-long side boards from a canoe (fig. 5a), a large steering paddle (fig. 5c), a spreader, paddles, and a bailer; (2) two types of wooden handles for adzes; (3) a grooved wooden tapa beater that was associated with a possible stone anvil from Section 4; (4) whalebone and wooden hand clubs *(patu);* and (5) long wooden clubs.

All the above Vaito'otia and Fa'ahia artifacts could be included in the Marquesan Phases I and II material culture inventories (Sinoto, 1970). Present in the Marquesan inventory but missing from Vaito'otia is pottery. On the other hand, some artifacts found in Vaito'otia and Fa'ahia are not found in the Marquesan inventory. These include hand clubs (fig. 6), unfinished adz handles (fig. 7,bottom), a piece of a bow (fig. 7,top), a spear, and other wooden objects such as those related to canoes, a hanging hook, and structural lumber and posts. It is quite possible that these objects existed in the Marquesas and have not been found only because site conditions have not permitted their preservation.

Thus, when the Vaito'otia and Fa'ahia assemblages are considered as a whole, they can be classified into the same cultural assemblage as the Marquesan material, even though these two places are geographically far apart.

Structural Remains

The posts and floorboards found in the Vaito'otia excavations represent four structures. These buildings originally stood on low stilts. Three stone pillars indicate that height from the ground to the floor was about 30 centimeters. Five wooden floorboards, each measuring 4 meters long, 25 centimeters wide, and 4 centimeters thick, were found in association with two stone and one wooden supporting posts, two main gable post-bases, and one wooden floor girder (fig. 8). Gable framing was suggested by the inward tilt of the large post base and by a slightly curved post found nearby. The structures probably measured about 4 to 6 meters long, 1.5 meters wide, and 2.5 meters tall (fig. 9). Discoveries of sennit, used for tying house frames, and of coconut and pandanus material, indicate that the structures were thatched.

It is probable that the structures were used for storage. They are located away from the main area of activity, as indicated by the distribution pattern of portable artifacts. In addition, no fireplaces or evidence of cooking facilities were found near the structures. What was stored in them is still not known; yam is a possibility. It may be possible to find and identify intracellular crystals (calcium oxalate) from the soil samples to identify the root crops that were stored. If the structures were in fact used as storehouses, we may surmise that agriculture was extensive enough to produce a surplus.

Midden

The principal components of the midden are mammal, fish, reptile (turtle), bird, shell, and vegetal material. Although fragmented fish bones are the most common midden material, bones of green and other marine turtles are

FIG. 7. Wooden artifacts: *Top*, Unfinished adz handle; *bottom*, bow fragment.

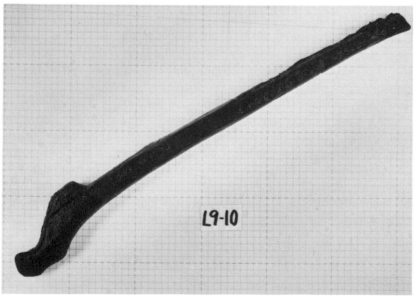

TABLE 1.   Identified Land-snail Shells from Site ScH-1-1

Shells were identified by Dr. Yoshio Kondo, malacologist, B. P. Bishop Museum. Identifications are to nearest species.

Species	Layer			
	II	III	IV	V
Mautodontha parvidens (Pease)*	x		x	x
Lamellaxis gracilis (Hutton)*	x	x	x	x
Subulina octona (Bruguiere)	x			
Assiminea nitida (Pease)	x			x
Omphalotropis huaheinensis (Pfeiffer)	x			
Georissa parva (Pease)	x	x		x
Helicina decolorata Schmeltz	x			
Truncatella guerini Villa	x	x	x	x
Liardetia samoensis (Mousson)		x	x	x
Lamellidea oblonga (Pease)	x		x	x
Lamellidea pusilla (Gould)		x	x	x
Tornatellinops variabilis (Odhner)		x	x	x
Tornatellides oblongus (Anton)			x	x
Gastrocopta pediculus (Shuttleworth)		x		x

*Recent name changes, corrected by Dr. Carl Christensen, B. P. Bishop Museum.

also common. The basic Polynesian domestic animals of dog, pig, and possibly chicken are present. Bones of marine mammals—whale and dolphin—were also found.

Midden quantity suggests that the excavated site area was not directly related to preparation and consumption of food. However, such activities might have been centered in the area of the dredged pond in Vaito'otia or, more likely, in Section 4 of Fa'ahia. The variety of midden materials, however, indicates active exploitation of marine resources and horticulture with domestic animals. A number of important local plant resources are indicated by the recovery of coconut trunks and husks, pandanus fruits, gourds, and 'ava *(Piper methysticum)*.

Land Snails

By using a flotation method, we found small land snails in the deposits from all layers. These snails were identified by Dr. Yoshio Kondo, Bishop Museum malacologist, and are listed in Table 1. According to Dr. Kondo, they live on debris on the ground surface; this may indicate that all the layers were once exposed for some time before the next layer was deposited. This interpretation is made with some caution, however, particularly because of the evidence for flooding of the·site area and the consequent possibility that at least some of the snails may represent a secondary deposition.

Although no attempt has been made yet to analyze in detail the quantitative sample collections of land snails recovered from the Vaito'otia site, the patterns of distribution of land snails throughout the Pacific are interesting and have relevance for interpreting man's settlement of Polynesia.

Lamellidea oblonga, usually associated with lowland food plants, is widely distributed, probably owing to "the frequent voyages of the Polynesians, who transported food plants on their travels, especially between islands only a few hundred miles apart" (Cooke and Kondo, 1960, p. 201). *L. oblonga* was found in the Marquesan Hane site with *Gastrocopta pediculus* and *Elasmias* spp., and was probably in the Marquesas at least by the end of the Settlement Period (Kirch, 1973, p. 29).

Dates for the Site Complex

The radiocarbon age dates (ranges in calendar years, adjusted: Ralph et al., 1973) for the Vaito'otia site are A.D. 870±80 (whalebone), A.D. 865±80 (wood from Layer V), A.D 1180±85 (coconut shell from Layer V), and A.D. 1180±90 (charcoal from Layer IV). The date for whalebone is reasonable, even though bone from arctic marine mammals tends to produce dates that are up to 300 years earlier than the true date (Tauber, 1976). Nevertheless, this early date is supported by two dates from the Fa'ahia site—A.D. 830±90 and A.D. 805±90—for charcoal samples from Layer III, the equivalent of the Vaito'otia Layer V. While the dates for occupation of the site complex between A.D. 850 and 1200 may not be far off, typological comparison of the cultural assemblages with those from the Marquesas indicates that the beginning of the occupation of Vaito'otia and Fa'ahia may have been earlier than the radiocarbon dates obtained.[1] The Marquesan dates are A.D. 300 to 600 for Phase I and A.D. 600 to 1300 for Phase II. Comparison of adzes indicates that the Vaito'otia and Fa'ahia sites are probably older than the Maupiti site, which yielded a collagen date of A.D. 860±85 (GX-0207) (Emory and Sinoto, 1964). In both the Marquesas and Society Islands it has been well demonstrated that

---

[1]The subsequent excavations in Fa'ahia in 1980 and 1981 indicated that the occupational period continued to A.D. 1100 or A.D. 1200, as attested by the typological changes in stone adzes, closer to those of the later period. It is, of course, possible that the nuclear tests in French Polynesia had some effect on the carbon that we sampled.

FIG. 8.   Fallen floorboards of storage house, with stone posts restored in
position.

tanged adzes became the basic form only during the late period and that untanged adzes are characteristic of West Polynesia and also of archaic Central
and East Polynesian assemblages. From the Hane site, Uahuka Phases I and
II, 92 percent of the adzes are untanged, from Vaito'otia and Fa'ahia, 91 percent are untanged, and from Maupiti, 73 percent are untanged. Although the
sample of Maupiti adzes is smaller than those of the other two sites, the data
may well suggest that the Vaito'otia and Fa'ahia sites are closer to the early
phases of the Hane site than to the Maupiti site.

Cultural assemblages after A.D. 1350 in the Society Islands show marked
differences from the earlier assemblages. It is not clear when reversed-triangular adzes first appeared in the Society Islands, but certainly they existed by
A.D. 1350. The discovery of a reversed-triangular adz in the Bellows Field and
018 sites, Oahu, Hawaii, has some implications for dating the appearance of
these adzes in the Society Islands. The Hawaiian adz was associated with ra-

diocarbon and volcanic-glass hydration-rind dates between A.D. 900 and A.D. 1100 (Kirch, 1974; Pearson et al., 1971; Cordy and Tuggle, 1976). No reversed-triangular adzes were found at Vaito'otia and Fa'ahia, indicating that these sites pre-date the appearance of this form. In addition, no stone pounders were found in the Vaito'otia and Fa'ahia sites; pounders are not found in the inventory of New Zealand material culture, and the accepted radiocarbon date for initial occupation of New Zealand is A.D. 1000 (Simons, 1973). When all these factors are considered, there is convincing evidence that the Vaito'otia and Fa'ahia sites were occupied initially before A.D. 850, then the population increased and the activity areas were expanded.

Conclusion

The excavation of the Fa'ahia site revealed that the site complex is spread out over the entire Vaito'otia and Fa'ahia areas. The designation of two sites, then, does not represent a cultural separation but rather is a recording convenience based on the present land divisions. However, there are activity clusters in both sites and it seems that the occupational activities continued for a slightly longer period of time in Fa'ahia than in Vaito'otia. Based on the distribution pattern of the artifacts and features, it is most likely that there was also a main activity area in Vaito'otia that was destroyed by the pond dredging. The land area could have been drier than it is now, but probably it was quite wet or even flooded, particularly after rain. The location is favorable for cultivation of wetland taro and deep-sea fishing is accessible through the pass. The area is close to the foot of the hill where there are at least two wells available as sources of fresh water. These combined factors demonstrate that the area was favorable for habitation.

Exploitation of suitable stone for tools was also practiced. Numerous flake knives and choppers were found, as well as the raw material (mugearite) used for their manufacture. The nearest and probably the only place on the island where mugearite is found is in Maeva, about 7 kilometers east of the site.

A rather sophisticated life-style is suggested, through the recovery of remains of important plants, of *'ava,* used for a ceremonial drink, and of artifact types that persisted in later cultural assemblages. These include a spear, which is probably a mourner's staff, and a bow similar in size to ones that Captain Cook collected.

The excavations demonstrated that storage houses and a fishhook manufacturing area were in Vaito'otia, and that the habitation area and adz and canoe manufacturing area were in Fa'ahia. It is now much clearer than originally thought that the occupation of the sites was not a short one. The storage

FIG. 9.   Postulated reconstruction of storage house.

houses indicate that there were surplus foods, and the clusters of manufacturing areas imply the presence of craftsmen specializing in various tasks. Based on these findings, one can assume that there was an organized society.[2] The objects related to large canoes revealed that the people were making and utilizing such ocean-going vessels. We are now witnessing the actual canoes referred to in the Polynesian legends of long voyages between island groups.

This somewhat complex material culture was most likely brought in from the Marquesas, rather than developed in Huahine; the assemblage is nearly identical to those of the early Marquesan period, although pottery culture had already been dropped in the Marquesas. The presence of hand clubs, made and used at the Huahine site, rather than imported from New Zealand in historic times, establishes strong evidence of settlement patterns from the Marquesas to the Society Islands and then to New Zealand.

The Vaito'otia and Fa'ahia sites were encountered in 1973, 13 years after the Bishop Museum started extensive archeological investigations in the Society Islands. The area's significance is that of the preserved perishable material

---

[2]The 1981 excavation in Fa'ahia revealed a stone foundation for a chief's house, known from the historical evidence in the Society Islands.

culture inferring the existence of such artifacts in the Marquesas (so far no comparable materials have been found elsewhere in Oceania), as well as in later periods in the Society Islands. The Maupiti site belongs to the later part of the same settlement period. There is still a missing gap, however, in evidence for the cultural sequence for the Society group; at some time between A.D. 1100 and 1350 the characteristic, historically known Tahitian culture began to evolve.

REFERENCES

COOK, C. MONTAGUE, JR., and KONDO, YOSHIO
    1960.   Revision of Tornatellinidae and Achatinellidae (Gastropoda, Pulmonata). B. P. Bishop Mus. Bull. 221, 303 pp.

CORDY, ROSS H., and TUGGLE, H. D.
    1976.   Bellows, Oahu, Hawaiian Islands: New work and new interpretation. Archaeol. and Phys. Anthrop. Oceania, vol. 11, no. 3, pp. 207-235.

EMORY, KENNETH P., and SINOTO, YOSIHIKO H.
    1964.   Eastern Polynesian burials at Maupiti. Journ. Polynesian Soc., vol. 73, no. 2, pp. 143-160.

KIRCH, PATRICK V.
    1973.   Prehistoric subsistence patterns in the northern Marquesas Islands, French Polynesia. Archaeol. and Phys. Anthrop. Oceania, vol. 8, no. 1, pp. 24-40.
    1974.   The chronology of early Hawaiian settlement. Archaeol. and Phys. Anthrop. Oceania, vol. 9, no. 2, pp. 110-119.

PEARSON, RICHARD; KIRCH, PATRICK V.; and PIETRUSEWSKY, MICHAEL, JR.
    1971.   An early prehistoric site at Bellows Beach, Waimanalo, Oahu, Hawaiian Islands. Archaeol. and Phys. Anthrop. Oceania, vol. 6, no. 3, pp. 204-234.

RALPH, E. K.; MICHAEL, H. N.; and HAN, M. C.
    1973.   Radiocarbon dates and reality. MASCA Newsletter, vol. 9, no. 1, pp. 1-20.

SALVAT, BERNARD
    1970.   L'histoire des atolls recontée par leur faune. Science Progrès Découverte no. 3423, pp. 17-23. Paris.

SIMONS, D. R.
    1973.   Suggested periods in South Island prehistory. Rec. Auckland Inst. and Mus., no. 10, pp. 1-58.

SINOTO, YOSIHIKO H.
    1970.   An archaeologically based assessment of the Marquesas as a dispersal center in East Polynesia. Pp. 105-130 *in* "Studies in Oceanic Culture History," vol. 1, R. C. Green and M. Kelly, eds. Pacific Anthropological Records, Department of Anthropology, Bernice P. Bishop Museum, Honolulu.
    1976.   Final phase of the excavation of an archaic habitations site on Huahine, Society Islands. Preliminary Report on the 1975 excavations, submitted to the National Geographic Society. (Unpublished.)

1979. Excavations on Huahine, French Polynesia. Pacific Studies, vol. 3, no. 1, pp. 1-40.

1982. A brief report on the 1981 excavations of Sections 3 and 5, Zone A, Fa'ahia Site, Huahine Island, French Polynesia. (Unpublished.)

SINOTO, YOSIHIKO H., and McCOY, PATRICK C.

1975. Report on the preliminary excavation of an early habitation site on Huahine, Society Islands. Journ. Soc. Océanistes, vol. 31, no. 47, pp. 143-186. Musée de l'Homme, Paris.

SINOTO, YOSIHIKO H., and HAN, TONI

1981. Report on the Fa'ahia site excavations, Zone "A"—Section 5, Fare, Huahine, Society Islands, French Polynesia (1980 excavations). (Unpublished.)

TAUBER, HENRIK

1976. C-14 activity of Arctic marine mammals. Carbon-14 Dating Laboratory, Copenhagen, Denmark. (Abstract.)

YOSIHIKO H. SINOTO

Ecological and Physiological Investigations of Alpine Cushion Plants

Principal Investigators: George G. Spomer and Dana S. Dawes, Department of Biological Sciences, University of Idaho, Moscow, Idaho.

Grant No. 1387: For ecological and physiological investigations of alpine cushion plants.

Certain plants found in various parts of the world assume a very compact, flattened to mounded growth form. Such plants are referred to as cushion plants. Cushion plants, in contrast to more open mat plants, form a vegetative surface that is almost impenetrable except by sharp objects. This growth habit seems to be an adaptation to habitats characterized by high winds and frequent cold temperatures. Consequently, cushion plants are most abundant in polar and subpolar alpine habitats, high arctic habitats, and cold desert habitats, such as in the northern Great Plains region.

The cushion habit results when there is an extensive branching of shoots combined with little or no stem elongation. The result is a compact mound of miniature rosettes formed at the end of the many branches. The extreme branching seems to be the result of conversion of the apical meristem of most of the branches each year from vegetative to reproductive growth, i.e., from continuous leaf production to a terminal flower or inflorescence (as suggested by Dr. Sterling B. Hendricks, pers. comm.). Because the embryonic tissues are then "used up," new vegetative growth must originate from lateral buds, which then produces branching. In essence, each branch seems to function like a biennial, except that it may require more than two seasons to flower. (It is of interest that many if not most of the tundra forbs have rosetted growth habits.)

It has often been observed, however, that when cushion plants from tundra habitats are transplanted to lowland sites, they rapidly lose their compact cushion form through stem elongation. Such growth is sometimes observed also in protected tundra sites. (In contrast, lowland species that form cushions seem to be inherently fixed in form.) The question then arises, What differences in habitats bring about this change, or what are the significant environmental differences between habitats above and below timberline relative to the plants? This question was the subject of the investigations here reported.

601

Several factors have been proposed as causing stunting of plants in the alpine—cushion plants included. Lack of water is one such factor. Indeed, alpine tundras have been described as cold deserts, and the exposed cushion-plant habitats are among the driest tundra sites. Yet observations during years when soil moisture was ample revealed no noticeable changes in growth of cushion plants, so that it is not likely that this is an important factor.

Cushion habitats are also characterized by extreme winds, as previously mentioned, and this condition has also been suggested as the factor controlling growth. But in some limited studies done previously (Spomer, 1964) wind reduction did not seem to alter growth. Similarly, there are indications from these same studies that neither high light nor ultraviolet radiation intensities play a role in suppressing growth, as has been suggested by some workers.

Most of the evidence points to low heat levels as the principal cause of stunting and cushion formation. But this is usually inferred (Daubenmire, 1954) from correlations between tundra occurrence and *air* temperature conditions, which average 10°C. or less above timberline, while studies have now shown that shoot tissue temperatures commonly range from 20°-35°C. during the day in the alpine plants (Salisbury and Spomer, 1964). Nonetheless, in one study (Spomer, 1964) using controlled environment chambers, stem elongation was significantly reduced by lower *ambient* temperatures (less than 18°C.). Temperatures higher than 18°C. caused a reduction of vigor and eventual death. Consequently, it was thought that soil (root) temperatures might be the primary factor in regulating cushion-plant growth.

Studies have subsequently been conducted in alpine areas throughout the Northwest and in controlled environment facilities at the University of Idaho to determine if this were indeed the case.

At the same time we undertook a study of the hormonal mechanisms involved. This, we felt, would not only help to confirm any conclusions reached in the environmental studies but also might help us to understand how it is that lowland cushion species maintain their form. There are at least four possible explanations as to why stem growth of cushion plants is inhibited under alpine conditions: (1) Gibberellins (GA), which are usually necessary for stem elongation, may be reduced in the stems owing to low soil temperatures as GA is thought to be produced or converted to active forms in the roots of many plants; (2) levels of abscissic acid (ABA), a growth inhibitor associated with dormancy and hardening, may occur in relatively high concentrations in the shoots due to increased stress—particularly due to cold conditions in the soils; (3) supraoptimal levels of auxin may accumulate in shoot tissues owing to decreased transport or metabolism in the roots due to cold conditions; or (4) cytokinin (CK) levels may be too low to promote elongation in the stems due to reduced production in the cold roots. CK is usually required as well as GA to promote stem elongation. It may be, of course, that a combination of these effects is occurring or that some other mechanism is involved, but based upon the literature and previous experience these seemed most plausible.

Two basic approaches were used to investigate the various possibilities described above: First, as a part of field studies, various hormones and combinations of hormones were applied to plants during the growing season; second, attempts were made to extract hormones and determine the levels of activity in the tissues.

Field Studies

The principal site of field studies was on the northern edge of the Beartooth Plateau located in southwest Montana. The elevation of accessible portions of this plateau ranges from 3,050 to 4,000 meters. Other observations and measurements were variously made in the alpine regions of the Lemhi Mountains of southern Idaho, the Wallow Mountains in northeast Oregon, and the Enchantment Lake region of Mount Stuart in the northern Cascades of Washington. Limited observations were also made in a few subalpine locations including the summit of Mount Jumbo just outside of Missoula, Montana, along the river bluffs of the Columbia River gorge near Vantage, Washington, and the high plains south of Casper, Wyoming.

All the sites in which cushion plants were found were characteristically exposed and windy. Alpine sites were also generally characterized by low soil temperatures in the rhizosphere (10-15-centimeter depth). Typically temperatures seldom exceeded 15°C. during the growing season and were often lower except on a "marginal" alpine site on Mount Howard in the Wallows. Here temperatures were about 18°C. Soil temperatures in lowland sites except Mount Jumbo were not measured, but other studies of soil temperatures in these regions indicated that they typically exceed 20°C. at comparable depths.

The Mount Jumbo site, despite its relatively low elevation of 1,350 meters, was more similar to alpine sites since soil temperatures were 14°-15°C. during the period of maximum growth and blooming. This site was investigated because a specimen of moss campion (*Silene acaulis* L.), which is normally found only in polar or alpine tundras, had been collected from this area a number of years ago and put into the Stillinger Herbarium at the University of Idaho. The Mount Jumbo population, which we subsequently discovered near the summit of this "grassy bald," had a looser growth form, somewhat intermediate between a cushion habit and a mat. In addition, the flower stalks were much elongated, and the leaves had a fleshier appearance and were darker in color. It is likely that this population represents a distinct ecotype and may actually be a separate species. We were not able to ascertain how extensive the population was in this area of the Sapphire Mountains.

Another somewhat unusual site we discovered was that on the tailings of an old chromium mine on the Beartooth Plateau. The cushions, which must have become established in the area about 1946 when the mine was abandoned, were considerably larger in diameter, by three to five times, than cushions of the same species in adjacent areas. But in other respects the cushions of this site were similar to "normal" cushions.

In contrast to the low alpine soil temperatures recorded, shoot tissue temperatures measured with an infrared radiometer in several locations varied between 20° and 32°C. during the day. This seems to confirm the notion that alpine cushion plants may experience temperature conditions considerably different from those indicated by air temperatures.

To verify results of previous studies of the effects of light and wind on cushions growing in the field, several individuals were shaded by one or two layers of window-screen material arched over the plants and supported by two wires so that air could freely circulate under the screen dome. This shading reduced the light levels to 50 and 75 percent, respectively. Shoot tissue temperatures under the screens were reduced 2°-7°C. on clear days but were essentially the same on cloudy days. Other plants were shielded downwind with wedges of clear hardware cloth about 15 centimeters high supported by wire stakes at the ends and apex. These shields reduced wind speeds by 50-100 percent over the surface of cushions inside.

Neither alteration of environmental factor produced significant changes in stem or leaf sizes. This seems to verify the results and conclusions drawn from previous studies.

In an attempt to alter levels of hormones, several cushions were sprayed with various solutions in late June 1975 and again in late July. Solutions used included giberellic acid (GA_3), zeatin (a CK), a combination of GA_3 and zeatin, 2, 4-dichloroanisol (an "anti-auxin"), and distilled water as a control. In several cases the area of a single cushion could be divided into four parts and different treatments given to each since previous studies indicated that hormones are not appreciably translocated. This permitted contrasting effects of different treatments on genetically identical plant material thereby eliminating any potential differences due to genetic variation.

Again, no significant responses were elicited by these treatments. Assuming these results are accurate, one could conclude that stunting might still be due to accumulations of ABA.

Controlled Environmental Studies

In controlled environment studies we primarily used individuals of the moss campion because it was readily available and is nearly ubiquitous throughout the northern alpine and polar tundra. Plants were obtained in the dormant state from the Beartooth Plateau and transported to the University of Idaho where they were potted in sand in plastic disposable mouse cages. These were then placed in controlled environment units (Spomer, 1976) that contained a cold plate at −19°C. to create vertical temperature gradients in the soils. Air temperatures were at room temperatures, and shoot temperatures were generally around 20°C. when the lights were on. Light was provided for a 16-hour period each day by two 150-watt GE Coolbeam lamps and a GE RS-sunlamp (to provide near-UV), covering an area of about 1.8 square meters. Soil temperature was varied by regulating the distance from the soil surface to the cold plate. We had intended to compare growth in two soil temperature conditions—cold, with temperatures of 0°-7°C. from 10 centimeters to the surface, and warm, with 16°-18°C. at comparable depths. But we inadvertently created an intermediate state of 2°-14°C. in a few of those supposedly in the cold treatment.

After growing the plants in these conditions for a month, we measured stem length and diameter and leaf length on at least 10 branches on each cushion. The following results were obtained:

Treatment	Average stem length (mm.)	Average stem diameter (mm.)	Average leaf length (mm.)
Cold	1.5	1.1	17.4
Intermediate	6.8	1.1	13.3
Warm	6.5	0.9	13.1

There were no statistical differences between plants grown in the warm and intermediate conditions. There were also no statistical differences between stem diameters in cold soils and in the warmer soils. This latter result implies that CK is probably not involved, since deficiencies in this hormone are generally associated with smaller stem diameters. Stem and leaf lengths in the cold soil conditions, however, were considerably less than those in warmer soils, which seems to confirm the proposition that soil temperature is an important factor in cushion-plant growth.

Two points are in evidence in these results that suggest that soil temperatures generally are not the total answer. First, even with soil temperatures lower than those encountered in the field, elongation was *not* totally suppressed—unlike that in plants growing in the field. And second, temperatures near the surface seem more important than those deeper in the soil since the temperatures at 5 centimeters and deeper were more comparable in the cold and intermediate conditions than between intermediate and warm conditions.

It is also possible that diurnal fluctuations in the shoots, and possibly at the soil surface, might be acting in concert with low soil temperatures to produce the compact cushion form normally found in the field. These temperatures frequently fluctuate between 25°-35°C. in the day and 1°-2°C. or lower at night. So an additional experiment was initiated to test the effects of diurnal fluctuations. Cushions in this case were subjected to shoot temperatures of about 20°-25°C. during the day and about 5°-7°C. during the night (the lower limit of the growth chamber capabilities). Soil temperatures were maintained in the previous colder range for all plants. With this treatment stem elongation was completely arrested. Unfortunately, no warm soil controls were included and the number of plants used was limited, and so the results must be viewed as tentative at best.

Taken in toto the environmental studies suggest that surface or subsurface (upper 2 centimeters) soil temperatures and temperature fluctuations perhaps combined with fluctuations in shoot temperatures are the critical factors determining growth form in these plants.

Hormone Analysis

Because of the inherent limitations and ambiguities associated with knowing if and how much of a hormonal solution actually penetrates the tissues of a plant, we had hoped to follow up by analyzing the endogenous levels of hormones. Since much of the evidence points to ABA as the most likely mediator of growth in cushion plants, our efforts have been largely concentrated on analysis of ABA activity in the tissues under field and various controlled environmental conditions. We soon discovered, however, that most techniques for assaying hormonal levels have been developed for studies in which considerably more tissue is available than we could obtain (for various reasons). As a consequence, we have not been able to determine if in fact a high level of ABA is the principal cause of stunting under field conditions.

Our efforts might, however, lead to some significant progress in the area of assay. We originally started with the barley half-seed bioassay coupled with thin-layer chromatography but soon found this to be inadequate. This was followed with a rather lengthy and intensive effort to develop suitable gas-liquid chromatographic techniques (with flame ionization detection) for ABA analysis. But after a considerable investment of time and effort we found that the technique was marginally sensitive at best. We feel, however, that the development of a competitive immunological assay (e.g., radioimmunoassay or competitive enzyme-linked assay) offers the best chances for measuring ABA in this and other ecologic investigations. Toward this end we have developed a specific antibody serum to ABA but have not completely developed the methods for a quantitative assay.

Conclusions

While we seem to have made some progress in determining the environmental factors involved in controlling the growth form of alpine cushion plants, several questions are left unanswered, including the precise nature of how low heat levels or fluctuating temperatures regulate stem and leaf elongation. Also does this mechanism operate in the cushion plants or other tundra, for example those of the Andean páramo, which is characterized by a profusion of enormous cushion plants? Nonetheless, it has been an exciting excursion to date, one in which we have developed a deeper appreciation and fascination with the complexities and mysteries of native plant species.

REFERENCES

DAUBENMIRE, REXFORD
  1954.   Alpine timberlines in the Americas and their interpretation.   Butler Univ. Bot. Stud., vol. 11, pp. 119-136.
SALISBURY, FRANK B., and SPOMER, GEORGE G.
  1964.   Leaf temperatures of alpine plants in the field.   Planta, vol. 60, pp. 497-505.
SPOMER, GEORGE G.
  1964.   Physiological ecology studies of alpine cushion plants.   Physiol. Plantarum, vol. 17, pp. 717-724.
  1976.   Simulation of alpine soil temperature conditions.   Arctic and Alpine Res., vol. 8, pp. 251-254.

GEORGE G. SPOMER

Southeastern Mediterranean (Levantine Basin-Nile Cone) Sedimentation and Evolution

Principal Investigator: Daniel Jean Stanley, Smithsonian Institution, Washington, D. C.

Co-Investigator: Andrés Maldonado, C.S.I.C., University of Barcelona, Spain.

Grant No. 1337: In support of a study of recent Nile Cone history based on sediment core and sub-bottom analysis.

A series of studies was undertaken to detail the Late Quaternary lithofacies patterns and history of the eastern Mediterranean and, in particular, the Nile Cone. The Cone, largest of the Mediterranean submarine fans, has accumulated in the Levantine Basin, a relatively small, elongate enclosed sea (cf. Carter et al., 1972). Detailed petrologic and chronostratigraphic examination was made of 74 piston and gravity cores and of drill cores from Sites 130 and 131 of the 1970 Deep-Sea Drilling Project Leg 13 (fig. 1). Petrologic techniques utilized X-radiography, size analysis, total carbonate and organic matter, scanning electron microscope (SEM), compositional analysis of the clay and sand fraction of more than 170 core samples, and radiocarbon dating. Data are presented in published papers by Maldonado and Stanley (1975, 1976, 1978, 1981), Stanley and Sheng (1979), Stanley and Maldonado (1977, 1979), and Stanley et al. (1979). The petrologic methods used in this investigation and the results obtained may be applicable to the stratigraphic study of older eastern Mediterranean sections and other small oceans.

The term "Nile Cone" is applied to the entire arcuate submarine bulge off the Egyptian Shelf. The name "Rosetta Fan" is applied to the region seaward of the Rosetta Branch of the Nile (RF in fig. 1); the area off the Damietta Branch of the Nile is the "Levant Platform" (cf. Ross and Uchupi, 1977). The sector east of the Levant Platform off Sinai, Israel, and Lebanon is termed the distal continental margin. Other important features on or contiguous with the Cone are the Herodotus Basin plain and the Eratosthenes Seamount and Basin plain. The arcuate Mediterranean Ridge abuts the northern edge of the Herodotus Basin and Nile Cone (MR in fig. 1).

The study area, about 600 kilometers wide, lies between the Egyptian Shelf and the Mediterranean-Cyprus Ridge (a distance of about 220 km) in the

609

eastern Mediterranean. The Nile River, draining a region of about 3 million square kilometers, has formed an extensive subaerial delta covering an area of about 22,000 square kilometers. Prior to the construction of the Aswan High Dam in 1964, it had a discharge in excess of 12,000 cubic meters per second and carried about 120 to 140 million tons of sediment per year that was mostly fine-grained. The Egyptian Shelf refers to the broad (about 40 to 65 km wide) seismically tranquil platform between the Nile delta and the slope; it is the most extensive shelf bordering the Levantine Basin (Summerhayes et al., 1978; Coleman et al., 1981).

Particular attention is paid to the Rosetta Fan, which has a gentle to hummocky relief except on its distal, lower fan area where salt tectonics have deformed the Plio-Quaternary cover. The lower fan merges with the Herodotus Basin plain, whose depth exceeds 3,000 meters. The Fan covers an area of about 70,000 square kilometers and is broader than it is long. A narrow, relatively low gradient slope, extending from the shelf edge to depths of 300 to 600 meters merges with the uppermost fan. The Nile Cone surface is not intensely dissected except in the Levant Platform ridge-and-valley sector and in the region comprising a network of low relief channels on the lower Rosetta Fan. The concave-up surface does not display a marked suprafan or fan lobe physiography. The slope above the Fan is relatively smooth, and only one large valley, the Alexandria Canyon (AC in fig. 1), appears to cross the slope and upper fan seaward of the Rosetta Branch.

We thank the National Science Foundation-Deep-Sea Drilling Project, University of Miami School of Marine and Atmospheric Science, Lamont-Doherty Geological Observatory of Columbia University, and Woods Hole Oceanographic Institution for generously providing core samples. Additional funding for the study was given by Smithsonian Research Foundation grants and the Consejo Superior de Investigaciones Científicas.

General Depositional Patterns

The Plio-Quaternary development of the Nile Cone is closely related to the evolution of the Nile River, which has served as its major terrigenous sediment source. Seismic surveys of the Cone (Ross and Uchupi, 1977) show that the unconsolidated Plio-Quaternary sedimentary section of the Cone has an average thickness of 2,000 meters and in places exceeds 3,000 meters. This depositional cover is locally absent above some salt diapirs in the Levant Platform. Our preliminary investigations revealed the remarkable lithological variety of Nile Cone sediment types and their cyclic nature (Maldonado and Stanley, 1975, 1976); moreover, certain core transects on the Cone show a gradual downslope transition from characteristic prodeltaic units to more typical distal facies (Stanley and Maldonado, 1977). Subsequent studies (Maldonado and Stanley, 1978) defined regional lithofacies distribution patterns during six different periods, from about 60,000 years B.P. to the present, and called attention to significant changes in the transport mechanisms during the recent formation of this large submarine fan. Stanley and Maldonado (1979) then showed the degree to which slope and base-of-slope lithofacies patterns represent a direct response to the overprint of regionally important climatic cycles and eustatic oscillations. Gravity-controlled deposits alternate with suspensite (hemipelagic-sapropel) sediments as a result of transport in a quasi-enclosed silled basin, a setting where the interplay of climate, physical oceanography, and biogenic versus terrigenous input factors is particularly critical.

Submarine fan deposition during the past 60,000 years was favored on the Rosetta Fan sector of the Cone, reflecting enhanced sediment input from the Rosetta Branch of the Nile, particularly during lowered sea level stands. The fluctuations of fine-grade sediment input are related to the shifting of Nile prodeltaic depocenters across the shelf and changes in Nile headwater migration. Concomitantly, marked alteration of physical oceanographic parameters, including stratification and possible reversal of currents, has resulted in the distinct depositional patterns of the Rosetta Fan (fig. 2). The Late Quaternary fan, which exemplifies one fan model, is characterized by (a) deposition of a thick (2,000 to 3,000 m) underlying wedge of Plio-Quaternary sediment in a region of relatively low structural mobility; (b) the absence of well-developed fan lobes, the presence of a shallow channel network on the lower fan surface, and a generally smooth surface configuration; and (c) accumulation of sediment successions consisting of thick sand pods (restricted to lower sectors of the fan), T_{c-e} and $T_e t$ turbidite sequences, well-developed sapropel layers, and relatively important proportions of suspensite as well as gravitative deposits.

Most of the Rosetta Fan surface has been influenced by fan deposition during the Late Quaternary, thereby suggesting that sediments, transported across a broad sector seaward of the Rosetta Branch, were moved downslope over wide areas of the slope—that is, materials were not strictly channelized as they are in most of the fans studied to date. There is no clear-cut lithofacies distinction between prodeltaic sections on the outer shelf to slope and those comprising thin-bedded turbidites farther seaward on the fan; although transitions between these two facies are gradational, transport processes involved may be different.

Two contrasting depositional patterns are apparent on the Nile Cone: a broad, essentially downslope-trending belt consisting largely of gravity-

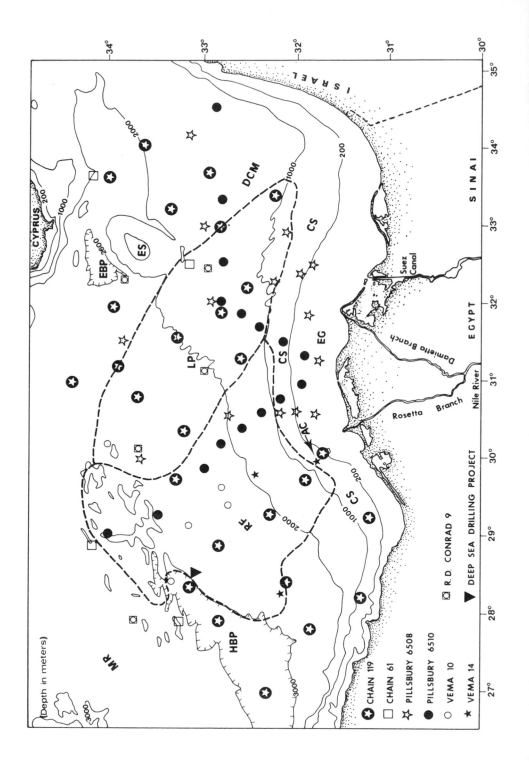

induced deposits that cover much of the Rosetta Fan (fig. 2); a wide east-west zone, comprising largely suspensite facies, that occupies much of the remaining Cone. Water mass stratification appears to have modified the movement of suspensites and may have been of importance in concentrating thick, rapidly deposited units on the slope seaward of important areas of Nile River input and of shelf-edge erosion, primarily off the Rosetta Branch. Distal turbidite types recovered throughout much of the Nile Cone may have accumulated as a result of several factors: low-density turbid flows initiated at a time of reduced sediment supply, deposition triggered by shelf-edge spillover and by overbank sheet flow, as well as deposition at increased distances away from the point of major sediment entry. Thus, the terms *proximal* and *distal* as applied to turbiditic sequences on the Cone describe specific lithofacies types rather than distance from input sources or paleobathymetric conditions.

Rosetta Fan Development and Cyclic Sedimentation

The major factors controlling the Rosetta Fan depositional patterns on the Nile Cone in the Late Quaternary are (a) the structural framework and associated physiography, and (b) sediment input; other factors, (c) climatic control and related eustatic oscillations and (d) physical oceanographic parameters, also are important. Although these latter have played a somewhat subsidiary role, they nevertheless were influential in determining specific transport processes, the nature of sediment types, and the facies distribution (cf. Maldonado and Stanley, 1978).

The interplay of the above controlling factors has given rise to the specific Cone spatial and temporal depositional patterns. The (a) higher input of finer-grained terrigenous material transported onto (b) a structurally rather tranquil and morphologically smooth margin, (c) the absence of a well-developed canyon-fan valley system and the reduced importance of downslope channelization, and (d) the imprint of climatic and eustatic oscillations of sediments accumulating in a closed silled basin account for the overall characteristics of the Rosetta Fan, where lobe development is not apparent. This is in contrast

---

FIG. 1.   Chart of the southeastern Mediterranean showing the location of cores examined in this study. Symbols and numbers refer to ship cruises. Letter codes refer to major physiographic provinces (depth in meters): RF=Rosetta Fan; LP=Levant Platform; DCM=distal continental margin; CS=continental slope; EG=Egyptian Shelf; AC=Alexandria Canyon; HBP=Herodotus Basin plain; ES=Eratosthenes Seamount; EBP=Eratosthenes Basin plain; MR=Mediterranean Ridge. (From Stanley and Maldonado, 1979.)

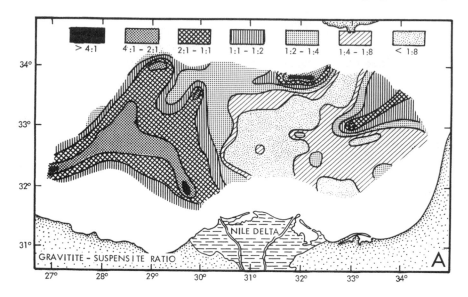

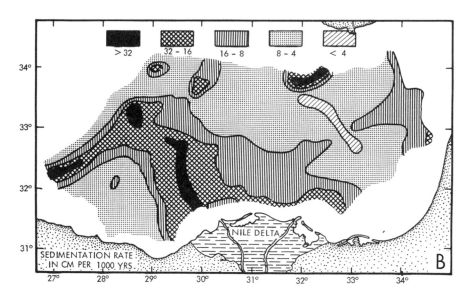

Fig. 2. Late Quaternary sediment facies in the southeastern Mediterranean based on analysis of cores shown in Figure 1. Chart A shows gravitite to suspensite ratio, and chart B depicts sedimentation rates (in cm/1000 years) for the period from about 58,000 years B.P. to the present. (Modified after Maldonado and Stanley, 1978.)

to many fans studied to date. These latter typically respond to (a) more limited sediment supply, consisting of enhanced proportions of coarse-grained input, transported onto (b) a structurally active and physiographically complex margin, (c) the well-developed canyon-fan valley system and importance of downslope channelization, and (d) the role of bottom currents.

Moreover, the Quaternary sections revealed in cores are formed by regionally extensive repetitions of sediment sequences (*cyclothems* s.l.) showing a successive orderly arrangement of sediment types (Maldonado and Stanley, 1976). Detailed lithofacies analysis reveals the recurrence of three basic terms in many cores (fig. 3): a basal olive-gray hemipelagic mud and turbidite sequence; a middle sapropel sequence; and an upper yellowish-orange hemipelagic sequence, including calcareous ooze, and a turbiditic sequence. This cyclic sedimentation closely reflects the Quaternary dynamics. For example, the alternation of sapropel with well-oxidized, bioturbated deepwater hemipelagic mud records phases of basinwide stratified water mass and associated anaerobic conditions that periodically alternated with phases of vertical mixing, as at present.

That the cyclothems are correlatable between cores over a wide region indicates a consistent and major change of environmental factors affecting most of the Levantine Basin. Analysis of the uppermost cyclothem (fig. 3) can be made in the light of the late Quaternary (Würm-Holocene) dynamics. The middle term, the sapropel, is perhaps the most useful parameter for evaluating these large-scale, essentially climatic factors. The sapropel layer, dated at between about 7,500 and 9,000 years B.P., accumulated during the warming trend of the climatic curve in the Early Holocene (Ryan, 1972). We agree with those workers who relate the anaerobic conditions under which these organic layers accumulated with water mass stratification. Whether this stratification is the result of increased outflow of low-salinity waters from the Black Sea into the Eastern Mediterranean coupled with decreased evaporation rates, or surface-water warming, or excess inflow of fresh water from rivers and melting ice and associated current reversals at the straits of Gibraltar and Sicily is not determined. It is apparent, however, that both stratification and related stagnation were basinwide phenomena.

The upper term of the cyclothem (hemipelagic sequence and calcareous ooze) is essentially post-glacial, and spans the time from about 7,500 years B.P. to present. The lower term of the cyclothem (gray hemipelagic mud and turbidites) includes the entire basal Holocene and probably Late Pleistocene, when the eustatic sea-level stands were considerably lower and higher volumes of terrigenous sediments could bypass the shelf and be transported into the deeper parts of the basin. The base of this lower term is as yet undated by us.

In summary, our lithofacies analysis shows that the Nile Cone is more complex than many "classic" fans that are formed essentially of turbidites and hemipelagic mud (Maldonado and Stanley, 1979). Quaternary cyclothem development resulted from sedimentation in a quasi-enclosed silled basin, a setting particularly sensitive to the interplay of climatic, physical, oceanographic, and biogenic versus terrigenous input factors. The Nile Cone, including the Rosetta Fan, serves as one type of submarine fan formed by cyclic sedimentation.

Correlation with Paleoclimatic and Eustatic Oscillations

The availability of numerous radiocarbon dates and detailed sedimentological analyses enables us to identify more precisely the lithostratigraphic units that comprise the three uppermost Late Quaternary cycles in the Levantine Sea. It can be demonstrated that these units, covering a period of time from approximately 55,000 years B.P. to the present, are correlatable across the study area shown in Figure 1. The changes of lithofacies with time are determined quantitatively by using multivariate and univariate analyses of eight sediment types and sedimentation rates (Stanley and Maldonado, 1978). A statistical treatment that includes cluster and principal component analyses allows definition of two major assemblages of cores: pelagic (suspensite) and mass flow (gravitite) types. An attempt is made to relate the evolution in time of sedimentary patterns with major climatic and eustatic changes affecting the eastern Mediterranean. All data considered here indicate that each complete cycle correlates with a major eustatic change, and that differences in successive cycles coincide broadly with variations in successive paleoclimatic trends (fig. 4). Cycles 1 (Late Wisconsin to Holocene) and 3 (Middle to Late Wisconsin), display comparable sedimentary patterns and record a general warming-rise in sea level. In contrast, Cycle 2 (Late Wisconsin), lithologically distinct from the former, is a response to a major cooling-eustatic lowering trend.

Cycle 1 (about 17,000 yr. B.P. to present) was deposited during the phase of sea level rise in the Late Wisconsin to the Holocene. Sedimentation rate and the proportion of gravitite sediment types decreased markedly during this time span as the North African coastline retreated landward. This phase coincides with a filling of the fluvial valleys and deltaic deposition on the shelf. Sediment types forming this cycle in sectors seaward of the shelf-edge comprise largely fine-grained lithologies, including turbiditic mud as well as hemipelagic deposits.

Cycle 2 (about 28,000 to 17,000 yr. B.P.), associated with the Late Wisconsin regression, accumulated primarily during a phase of pronounced sea

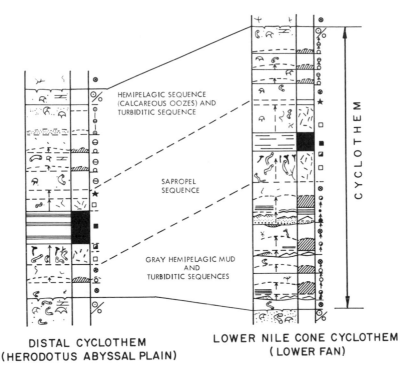

FIG. 3.   Idealized logs of deep-sea cyclothems, showing three major lithofacies terms
on the lower Nile Cone and in the Herodotus Basin plain.   (From Maldonado and
Stanley, 1976.)

level lowering (to 125 m or somewhat greater depths below present mean sea
level). Lithofacies forming Cycle 2 are generally more terrigenous (i.e., include larger proportions of sand and silt turbidites than those of Cycles 1 and
3). Clean, coarse-grained sands, prominent in the lower division of Cycle 2,
are possibly reworked from coastal and/or shallow marine environments.
These materials were subsequently displaced downslope by mass flow mechanisms (Maldonado and Stanley, 1978) as sea level first began to drop.

   During the development of Cycle 2 sedimentation rates and percentage of
gravitite sediment types increased in the suspensite core assemblage, and decreased in the gravitite core assemblage. The increased rates and proportions
of gravitite types in the suspensite core assemblage record the progressive seaward migration of the Nile delta and associated coastline to a position close to
the shelf-edge. As sea level lowered, enhanced amounts of material were transported by both suspensite and gravitite mechanisms onto the slope and Nile
Cone beyond the Egyptian Shelf.

The decreased percentages of gravitive sediment types and rates in the gravitite core assemblage during the maximum lowered sea level phase (time of layers S_3 to C_2 in fig. 4) is not so readily explained. One possible hypothesis is that during the maximum eustatic low stand, large volumes of sediment were temporarily stored on the outer shelf and not shed downslope; it appears that large-scale failure and the downslope transport of significant volumes of material occurred primarily as sea level began to rise once again (at the beginning of Cycle 1). In this view, it is assumed that the initial rise in sea level would induce failure of the metastable shelf edge-upper slope sediment wedge.

An alternative hypothesis that cannot be totally rejected is that enhanced volumes of sediment were transported during the early, not the late, phase of sea lowering. This may record major river incision and increased flow as a result of climatic changes in the Nile headwater regions and along the Nile River valley. The suspensite core assemblage trends, however, do not clearly record enhanced sediment transport during the early phase of Cycle 2 development. The available information tends to favor the former hypothesis as the more rational explanation of this apparent anomaly.

The lithofacies patterns in Cycle 2 suggest that, in general, there are two major periods when large proportions of gravitites were shed seaward off the Egyptian Shelf: when sea level first begins to drop (beginning of Cycle 2), and when sea level begins to rise (beginning of Cycle 1).

Cycle 3 (about 55,000 to 28,000 yr. B.P.) was deposited during the Middle to Late Wisconsin, a period during which several large-scale sea level fluctuations are recorded (eustatic curve in fig. 4). The prevailing sediments forming this cycle are fine-grained and included both gravitite and suspensite types. Calculated sedimentation rates during this phase do not indicate a clear-cut change with time. This may be an artifact due to the limited core information available and to the uncertainty of the age of key horizon C_4. The significant decrease in the percentage of gravitite sediment types in the different core assemblages is comparable to the trend in Cycle 1.

The correlation between Cycle 3 and the generalized eustatic sea level curve is not obvious. In this respect, it should be recalled that variations in the percentage of gravitite and other sediment types in cycles are independent of the age assigned to the different key horizons. This fact and the observed facies similarities between Cycles 3 and 1 indicate that Cycle 3 records a general rise in sea level. As in the case of Cycle 1, decreased sedimentation rate of Cycle 3 is related to a general landward migration of the Nile delta and its associated coastline, although several eustatic fluctuations may have occurred during this period.

A complete major climatic oscillation as envisioned comprises a eustatic maximum high–to low–to high stand. On this basis, each of the three cycles examined constitutes one half of a climatic event, and each complete sedimentary cycle essentially develops either during a phase of eustatic rising, or low-

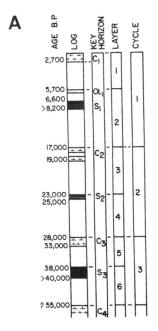

FIG. 4. Idealized Levantine Sea-Nile Cone stratigraphic sections based on core analysis. A, Complete section showing dated Late Quaternary key stratigraphic horizons (C=calcareous ooze; S= sapropel; OL=oxidized layer) used for regional correlation, six lithostratigraphic layers, and three uppermost cycles. B, Lithostratigraphic section in A correlated with generalized eustatic and paleoclimatic curves. Cycle 1 correlates with a warming-eustatic rise, and Cycle 2 with a cooling-eustatic lowering of sea level. (For detailed explanation and listing of references, see Stanley and Maldonado, 1979.)

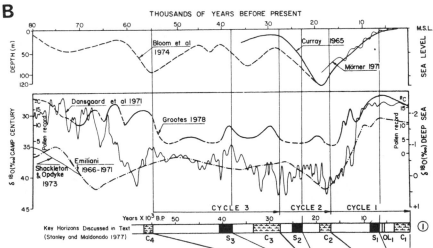

ering, of sea level. The asymmetrical nature of the paleoclimatic-eustatic curves is suggested on the basis of the distinct lithological character of each cycle which, as recorded in this study also reflects asymmetry. Each successive

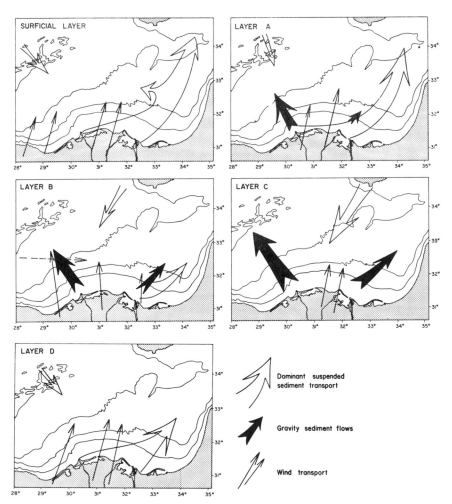

FIG. 5.   Dominant clay mineral dispersal patterns in the southeastern Levantine Basin interpreted for the uppermost (=Surficial) and four underlying stratigraphic horizons. Layer A=5,700 yr. B.P. to present; Layer B=12,000 to 5,700 yr. B.P.; Layer C=18,000 to 12,000 yr. B.P.; and Layer D=23,000 to 18,000 yr. B.P. Arrows show dispersal of sediment by suspensite transport, downslope mass gravity flows, and eolian processes; arrow size reflects relative importance of these deposition mechanisms.   (From Maldonado and Stanley, 1981.)

warming (sea level rise) or cooling (sea level lowering) has resulted in the variable lithostratigraphic development of successive cycles. The lithostratigraphic asymmetry within a cycle is due to the fact that the initial point of a cycle begins at a maximum low climatic/eustatic event and terminates at a maximum high, or vice-versa.

Clay Mineral Studies and Depositional Evolution

It is widely accepted that clay mineral assemblages transported onto and beyond continental margins provide a record of conditions imprinted in source terrains and, in particular, alteration induced by climate and weathering. The role of depositional process or clay mineral distribution, however, is generally neglected. The availability of stratigraphically well-defined cores in the southeastern Levantine-Nile Cone sector provides a more precise means to assess the relative importance of the climatic versus the sedimentary process imprint on the clay mineral assemblages (Maldonado and Stanley, 1981). The clay distribution patterns during the time interval from about 23,000 years B.P. to the present in the upper sediment sequences of the southeastern Levantine Sea and Nile Cone area do not correlate with Late Quaternary climatic changes. Instead, temporal and spatial variations of clay assemblages are closely related to sedimentary processes. The latter involve fluctuations in dispersal from the Nile River, the main input of sediment, and the interplay of water mass circulation patterns, gravitational transport of sediment downslope, and wind that carries substantial amounts of dust-size material into the basin.

Smectite, the main clay mineral carried by the Nile, is abundant on the Nile Cone in sectors where mass-gravity deposition prevails, while kaolinite coincides with areas of predominant hemipelagic deposition. High concentrations of smectite off Lebanon reflect the transport of suspensites east from the Nile delta by surface waters. Kaolinite, a largely wind-blown component, is most abundant in the west, away from the east-moving smectite-rich plume of surface water. The higher percentages of kaolinite observed at present and prior to 18,000 years B.P. reflect the decreased importance of deposition by mass gravity processes. Illite and clorite also are abundant in areas of hemipelagic deposition, but have a different source from the kaolinite. They come mainly from a northern Levantine Sea provenance, and may record more extensive dispersal by water mass circulation, which at present extends across the eastern Mediterranean as a counter-clockwise gyre.

Predominant clay mineral dispersal patterns and the relative importance of suspended sediment, gravity flow and wind transport mechanisms are depicted schematically in Figure 5. In conclusion, the vertical fluctuations in mineral assemblages at any one core locality in the Levantine Sea study area primarily record changes in the predominant type of sedimentary processes rather than fluctuations in climatic conditions and diagenesis per se. Moreover, it is apparent that the interpretation of paleoclimatic conditions by the study of clay sequences in individual cores should be approached cautiously in relatively small ocean basins such as the Mediterranean.

As an outgrowth of clay study of core sections from the Nile Cone and the southeastern Levantine Sea we discovered the mineral trona, or urao (Stanley and Sheng, 1979). This natural sodium bicarbonate [$Na_3H(CO_3)_2 \cdot 2H_2O$] occurs with trace amounts of thenardite, a sodium sulphate (Na_2SO_4). These minerals, noted in some cores collected between the Egyptian Shelf and Herodotus Basin plain (fig. 6), normally form in arid terrestrial environments, generally shallow saline lakes. No recorded examples of trona have been recorded earlier in deep marine environments in the modern Mediterranean or elsewhere.

The occurrence of trona in relatively restricted areas of the Nile Cone and during specific time intervals (about 19,000 to 23,000 yrs. B.P.; about 5,000 to 6,000 yrs. B.P.; and about 2,500 to 3,000 yrs. B.P.) precludes an artifact or wind-blown origin. It is more likely that trona-containing deposits of terrestrial origin were carried to the shelf-edge by the various branches of the paleo-Nile and then transported downslope, primarily toward the northwest, along with terrigenous sediments by mass gravity processes. Resedimentation would have prevailed during the phase of accelerated Nile Cone progradation at the time of the eustatic low stand, and we postulate that preservation of some evaporites would be related to the short transit time and almost immediate burial within turbidite silts and muds. Trona in younger Nile Cone sections may in some way record the large-scale tectonic activity in the Upper Holocene. Structural displacement may have triggered slumps and downslope movement of outer shelf evaporite series during this recent time span. We suspect that redeposited evaporites disseminated and preserved in recent deep-sea sediments are probably more common than is generally recognized.

Nile Cone Petrology and Origin of the Southern Mediterranean Ridge

The Mediterranean Ridge, the broad arcuate swell in the eastern Mediterranean extending from the Ionian Sea to the eastern Levantine Basin, constitutes a distinct topographic and tectono-stratigraphic province between the seismically active southern European and more stable Nile Cone-North African margin (Finetti, 1976). The characteristic hummocky ridge-and-swell to-

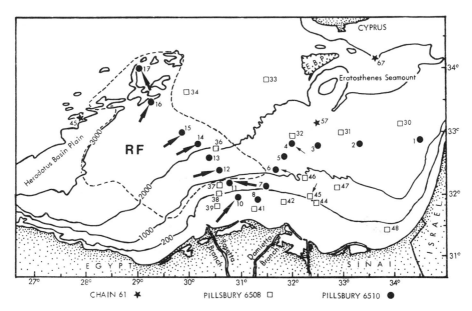

Fig. 6.   Chart showing location of cores examined for clay minerals. Heavy arrows depict cores with moderate to significant amounts of trona; light arrows denote cores with trace amounts of trona. RF=Rosetta Fan.   (From Stanley and Sheng, 1979.)

pography of the Ridge is the surface expression of what appears, in seismic profiles, as a folded and faulted sediment complex. The contact between deformed sedimentary units of the southern part of the Ridge and the more gently stratified Plio-Quaternary series forming the western Nile Cone (Ross and Uchupi, 1977) tends to be well-defined and delineates the northwestern margin of the Herodotus Basin plain (fig. 1).

All hypotheses pertaining to the Ridge invoke important, large-scale tectonic displacement in the late Tertiary to the present, and one should expect that evidence of these geologically recent events would be recorded in sedimentary sequences deposited in this area. One aspect of our Levantine Sea investigation (Stanley et al., 1979) focuses on the provenance of terrigenous sand layers of Pleistocene age on the southern part of the Ridge at the approximate midpoint between the more obvious potential sources of sediment: Nile delta, Crete, Cyprus, and the Eratosthenes Seamount. This sector has more specifically been termed the Hellenic Outer Ridge (Stride et al., 1977). Pleistocene and possibly Upper Pliocene core sections recovered in this part of the Ridge in 1970 at DSDP Site 130 (fig. 7) have been interpreted as distal Nile

Cone deposits which were uplifted 1 million years ago and subsequently deformed (Ryan et al., 1973). Arguments in support of this scheme are based partly on regional correlation of sub-bottom reflectors of probable Messinian and post-Miocene age, but more specifically on mineralogical comparisons between DSDP Sites 130 and 131 at the base of the Nile Cone and on the pollen content in Pleistocene samples at Site 130. These studies all emphasize the North African, largely Nile, affinity of the southern Ridge deposits. The difference in relative percentages of the dominant heavy minerals (primarily an amphibole-pyroxene-epidote-opaque mineral suite) between Nile Cone and Ridge samples is attributed by Ryan and other (1973) to differences in grain size and to marked changes of source terrain drained by the Nile River during the Quaternary.

Observed regional differences indicate a more complicated provenance-dispersal of Pleistocene sediment on the southern part of the Mediterranean Ridge than previously envisioned. This is based on heavy and light minerals from terrigenous sand layers, mostly turbidites, in DSDP Site 130 and 131 cores and in *Pillsbury* 6508 and 6510 and *Vema* 10 piston and gravity cores on the outer Egyptian Shelf, Nile Cone and Herodotus Basin plain, and on shallower marine reworked deposits in *Chain* 119 grab samples on the inner to middle Egyptian Shelf in front of the Nile delta (fig. 7).

Although composition of the probable lower to middle Pleistocene sands at DSDP Site 130 and Pleistocene sand in *Pillsbury* core 6510-17 is broadly similar to the Nile-derived sediment on the Nile Cone, our investigation recognizes some significant mineralogical differences on the southern part of the Ridge. We believe that the distinct suite of mineral species in the Ridge samples indicates input from a more proximal source terrain in addition to the Nile-derived sands. The much higher proportion of amphiboles in southern Ridge cores is not, as previously suggested, due only to a finer grain size in this more distal sector; examination of comparable textural grades in Nile Cone DSDP Site 131 and *Vema* 10-53, 55, and 57 core samples all show substantially lower proportions of amphiboles than in DSDP Site 130 and *Pillsbury* 6510-17 core samples (fig. 7). Furthermore, the greater proportion of angular grains of both heavy and light components (apatite, serrated pyroxenes, quartz, feldspar), an increased percentage of unaltered feldspar grains, apatite and brown hornblende, the presence of glaucophane grains, angular quartz overgrowth on euhedral and subhedral quartz grains, a radiating crack pattern within some euhedral quartz and feldspar grains, and a generally lower proportion of solid inclusions in quartz grains identify a mineralogical assemblage distinct from that in the modern to pre-Quaternary main Nile, Nile delta, and Nile coastal deposits.

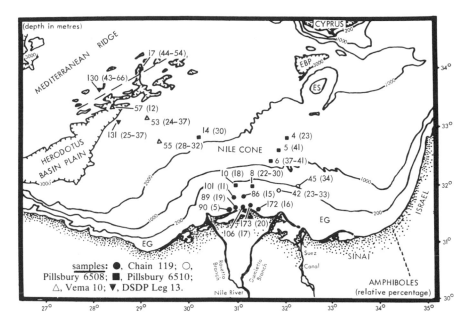

FIG. 7.   Chart showing the relative percentage of sand-sized amphiboles in the heavy mineral assemblages on the Egyptian Shelf (EG), Nile Cone, and southern part of the Mediterranean Ridge. ES=Eratosthenes Seamount; EBP=Eratosthenes Basin plain. Note increased amphibole content in the southern Ridge samples. (From Stanley et al., 1979.)

The angular, serrated, and non-altered state of various mineral species in the Ridge samples records minimum weathering-abrasion effects; this is in contrast with the reworked, subangular to rounded, and often altered grains on the Egyptian Shelf and Nile delta that invariably show considerable effect of one or multi-cycle fluvial or eolian (or both) transport. The immature mineral fraction in DSDP Site 130 and *Pillsbury* 6510-17 sands records the introduction of material from more proximal plutonic igneous and possibly also metamorphic sources rather than from distal African terrains. The compositional mix of reworked Nile-derived material and "fresh" components would imply the addition of new sediment at some point between the Nile delta-Egyptian Shelf sector and the southern Ridge core localities. As most of the sands examined in cores DSDP Site 130 and *Pillsbury* 6510-17 were emplaced by turbidity currents and associated gravity induced mass-flow processes, we are required to consider some modification of the direct downslope southeast to northwest dispersal path that has prevailed in this sector during the Late Quaternary (fig. 2) and described earlier in this report.

Where did the fresh sedimentary material enter the transport system? The extensive seismic survey of the Nile Cone by Ross and Uchupi (1977) does not reveal basement series at or near the surface between the Nile delta and the Ridge, and we exclude a southerly position for the introduction of fresh minerals. Transport from a northern Hellenic Arc-Crete source is precluded on the basis of the heavy mineral composition which is significantly different in that sector. Cyprus and the Eratosthenes Seamount, located approximately 300 kilometers northeast and east of the sample sites, while not excluded, seem to be unlikely source areas. We invoke a two-phase dispersal pattern: (a) transport downslope of recycled African sand on the Nile Cone surface in a direction away from the Nile delta to an area north of the present Herodotus Basin plain during a first stage of Nile Cone progradation, and (b) then a remobilization and subsequent short-distance transport of this Nile-derived material, to which a distinct igneous and metamorphic fraction has been added in the Ridge area. The topographically complex configuration of the Ridge is of geologically recent origin, and it is possible that some resedimentation occurred during the Pleistocene in the area where transport would not be possible on the present Ridge surface.

Immature mineral assemblages in Pleistocene sands of the short *Pillsbury* 6510-17 core, about 90 kilometers northeast of the much older Pleistocene DSDP Site 130 locality, strengthens the hypothesis of yet undefined igneous-metamorphic sources in the south-central Ridge area. The possibility of a surface or near-surface exposure of sub-sedimentary basement on the Ridge should not be readily dismissed although no specific evidence for this has been provided by gravity measurements or seismic profiles. Our findings, consistent with structural compressive thrust-belt (Finetti, 1976) and decollement reconstructions, suggest the possibility of some movement of the basement, perhaps as part of an allochthonous slice. The petrographic evidence indicating local input should be considered in developing an interpretive scheme for the Mediterranean Ridge.

In summary, petrology is clearly an essential tool to resolve the complex interplay between sedimentation and tectonics and to interpret the recent origin of the eastern Mediterranean.

REFERENCES
(See Maldonado and Stanley citations below for more comprehensive citation lists).

CARTER, T. G.; FLANAGAN, J. P.; JONES, C. R.; and others
    1972.   A new bathymetric chart and physiography of the Mediterranean Sea.   Pp. 1-23 *in* "The Mediterranean Sea—A Natural Sedimentation Laboratory," D. J. Stanley, ed.   Dowden, Hutchinson and Ross, Stroudsburg, Pa.

COLEMAN, J. M.; ROBERTS, H. H.; MURRAY, S. P.; and SALAMA, M.
  1981.   Morphology and dynamic sedimentology of the eastern Nile delta shelf.
          Mar. Geol., vol. 42, pp. 301-326.
FINETTI, I.
  1976.   Mediterranean Ridge: A young submerged chain associated with the
          Hellenic Arc.   Boll. Geofisica Teorica Applicata, vol. 18, pp. 31-65.
MALDONADO, A., and STANLEY, D. J.
  1975.   Nile Cone lithofacies and definition of sediment sequences.   Proc. IX
          Intern. Congr. Sediment., vol. 6, Nice, pp. 185-191.
  1976.   The Nile Cone: Submarine fan development by cyclic sedimentation.
          Mar. Geol., vol. 20, pp. 27-40.
  1978.   Nile Cone depositional processes and patterns in the Late Quaternary.
          Pp. 239-257 *in* "Sedimentation in Submarine Canyons, Fans, and
          Trenches," D. J. Stanley and G. Kelling, eds.   Dowden, Hutchinson
          and Ross, Stroudsburg, Pa.
  1979.   Depositional patterns and Late Quaternary evolution of two Mediterra-
          nean depositional processes in the Southeastern Levantine Sea.   Sedi-
          mentology, vol. 28, pp. 21-32.
ROSS, D. A., and UCHUPI, E.
  1977.   The structure and sedimentary history of the southeastern Mediterranean
          Sea-Nile Cone area.   Amer. Assoc. Petrol. Geol. Bull., vol. 61, pp.
          872-902.
RYAN, W.B.F.
  1972.   Stratigraphy of late Quaternary sediments in the eastern Mediterra-
          nean.   Pp. 149-169 *in* "The Mediterranean Sea—A Natural Sedimen-
          tation Laboratory," D. J. Stanley, ed.   Dowden, Hutchinson and Ross,
          Stroudsburg, Pa.
RYAN, W.B.F.; HSU, K. J.; and others
  1973.   Initial reports of the Deep Sea Drilling Project, 13.   U. S. Govt. Print.
STANLEY, D. J., and MALDONADO, A.
  1977.   Nile Cone: Late Quaternary stratigraphy and sediment dispersal.   Na-
          ture, vol. 266, pp. 129-135.
  1979.   Levantine Sea–Nile Cone lithostratigraphic evolution: Quantitative
          analysis and correlation with paleoclimatic and eustatic oscillations in
          the Late Quaternary.   Sediment. Geol, vol. 23, pp. 37-65.
STANLEY, D. J., and SHENG, H.
  1979.   Trona in Nile Cone Late Quaternary sediments: Probable redepositional
          origin.   Mar. Geol., vol. 31, pp. M21-M28.
STANLEY, D. J.; SHENG, H.; and KHOLIEF, M. M.
  1979.   Sand on the southern Mediterranean Ridge: Proximal basement and dis-
          tal African-Nile provenance.   Nature, vol. 279, pp. 594-598.

STRIDE, A. H.; BELDERSON, R. H.; and KENYON, N. H.
    1977.   Evolving miogeanticlines of the East Mediterranean (Hellenic, Calabrian
            and Cyprus outer ridges).   Philos. Trans. Royal Soc. London, vol. 284,
            pp. 255-285.
SUMMERHAYES, C. P.; SESTINI, G.; MISDORP, R.; and others
    1978.   Nile delta: Nature and evolution of continental shelf sediments. Mar.
            Geol, vol. 27, pp. 43-65.

DANIEL JEAN STANLEY

Relic Ports on the West African Grain Coast

Principal Investigator: William R. Stanley, University of South Carolina, Columbia, South Carolina.

Grant No. 1374:   In partial support of a geographic investigation of relic ports in West Africa.

Investigation of relic ports along West Africa's Grain Coast has been under way for several years; this report summarizes findings derived from research supported by the National Geographic Society during the first six months of 1975. Following are basic definitions for the terminology used: *Grain Coast* refers to the coastal portions of Liberia and eastern Sierra Leone, with the western boundary at Sherbro Island, Sierra Leone. Historically, it was along this stretch of coast beginning in the late 15th and early 16th centuries that European seafarers noticed an abundance of grains of the malagueta pepper, a much-sought-after product and one probably exceeded in demand only by gold and ivory. *Relic port* denotes a coastal settlement or site of a former trading nexus where ship-to-shore commerce took place. This trade either has fallen to a trickle of its former importance or has ceased altogether.

Two separate investigations are emphasized. First was fieldwork in West Africa at or near the actual port sites. Secondly, public and private archives in Europe, especially in Hamburg, were examined in order to gain a perspective of West African trade through the eyes of shipowners. This report concerns itself primarily with results of investigations conducted in West Africa of the Liberian portion of the Grain Coast.

Evolving transport technology has caused many of these once flourishing coastal trading centers to revert to backwashes; particularly significant was the construction in 1898 of the Sierra Leone Government Railway, a line penetrating eastward and roughly paralleling the coast, and the building in 1947 of a modern deep-water port at Monrovia, Liberia. The practical result of both developments has been the channeling (first in Sierra Leone and later in Liberia) of each nation's import-export commerce primarily into their capital cities, which now serve as the main interfaces between sea and land transport. What the railroad did for Sierra Leone, roads did for Liberia.

In Sierra Leone, the Government Railroad not only opened up hitherto undeveloped export-oriented agricultural areas, it also attracted traders away from the coastal settlements to railside. Commodities such as piassava, palm

629

Fig. 1.   Abandoned house in Marshall. The style is typical of 19th-century coastal
    Liberia and is similar also to many of the trading stores of the time, where the trad-
    er lived in the upper story and the shop occupied the ground-level floor.

kernels, and coffee, formerly head-loaded or sent by riverboat to the coast—
time-consuming and difficult passages under the best of conditions—were re-
directed to the railroad, often in the opposite direction. In time, roads were
hacked from the bush to link the railroad to choice agricultural areas; these
had the effect of expanding the railroad's zone of influence at the expense of
the coastal settlements. Bonthe, on Sherbro Island, had approximately one-
half of Sierra Leone's export tonnage in 1900 and ranked just below Freetown
as the country's leading port. Today it handles but a few hundred tons of commerce and is conspicuous for the number of large, once-active trading stores
long abandoned and falling into decay. Sulima, near the Liberian border, was
formerly the second leading piassava-exporting port. Today, it has no export
commerce whatsoever and contains a population probably smaller than before
the Age of Discovery.

    Whereas Liberia lacks a general goods-carrying railroad, and Monrovia
did not effectively dominate the country's foreign commerce until after World
War II, the development of a port there immediately led to a major development scheme to link the city to the interior. Road construction annually has

FIG. 2. Aerial view of the commercial core of River Cess. The Cestos River, lower portion of picture, enters the Atlantic Ocean, upper portion of picture, a few hundred feet to the left. Trade stores still stand at 'A' and 'B'; the one remaining wharf in town is at the rear of 'B' and is situated to take advantage of the protected waters of the river. A Kru fishing village, 'C', typifies a housing arrangement considerably different from that developed by the Americo-Liberians for their community.

had a significant portion of the national budget. The interior of the country was "opened-up," and each new mile of road drew still more commerce into Monrovia's orbit and away from the smaller coastal settlements. Even trading sites near the mouths of the great rivers were affected; to move goods by road to Monrovia was easier than to move them downstream, often where distances by water were significantly less than by road. Shipping firms in Europe and, to a lesser extent, in the U.S.A. began making the capital city the only port-of-call in this country rather than stopping at the numerous coastal settlements formerly served. Then, too, ships had grown in size and the economics of the situation favored one or two stops where large tonnages of goods might be handled. As in Sierra Leone, the Lebanese traders, who came to dominate the handling of foreign trade after World War I and who were to be found in practically every coastal settlement of consequence, were deserting the coast in order to locate at more advantageous sites along the newly built road net-

FIG. 3.   Robertsport (Cape Mount) had, in World War II, a temporary respite from
its decline into obscurity. Lacking a road connection to the rest of the country until
1973, Robertsport's strategic coastal site had led to its being chosen in 1941 by
Pan American Airways for its first marine airport in Africa, to serve the trans-
Atlantic Clipper Ships. Later, a land airstrip was built for use by the Army Air
Corps. The metal fence seen here is constructed of pieces of "Marsden Matting,"
steel strips placed on the sand for aircraft to land on. These fences serve as the only
visible reminder of this former temporary flurry of activity.

work. Many of these Levantine traders still can remember their fathers' shops
in the coastal settlements and can even remember when the move inland took
place. Their assistance was invaluable in helping to identify ruins of former
stores, once the sites of relic ports were determined.

To the European seafarer the Grain Coast likely represented a unity hardly
existing on the shore. Several distinct and often hostile groups peopled this
coastal region, a complexity that only increased with the advent of Creole society in Sierra Leone and of the Americo-Liberians in Liberia. There was, however, a major difference in the manner in which these two peoples related to
the host societies. Creoles were largely restricted to the peninsula where Freetown is located; when Creole traders entered indigenous tribal areas, they generally did so with the permission of the people. Americo-Liberians, however,
not only built several widely separated settlements along the entire stretch of

Fig. 4.   New iron-ore exporting port at Lower Buchanan. The mouth of the St. John River, upper center of picture, was the site of the first Americo-Liberian settlements in the area; Edina on the right bank and Upper Buchanan on the left bank. Silting of the river's entrance led to the development of Lower Buchanan, seen in the bend of the coastline. All commercial functions in the area now are concentrated in Lower Buchanan.

what is now Liberia, they also created whatever government was to be recognized by Europeans—if not diplomatically, then at least commercially. Because of the need for excise revenue, it was the Americo-Liberian settlements that first were declared "ports of entry." Nevertheless, indigenous settlements had trade with the Europeans and many of them were regular ports-of-call. To deny them the ability to conduct trade with the Europeans, even if this were possible, was to invite armed retaliation. Americo-Liberian society of the time was simply too fragile to risk instability of such possible magnitude.

Traders in both Creole and Americo-Liberian settlements built their shops as close to the water's edge as possible; these were to become the nuclei of present-day business sections. Then, too, in Liberia, the sites for settlements were chosen primarily because of topography; access to but protection from the sea became foremost considerations in a settler society maintaining

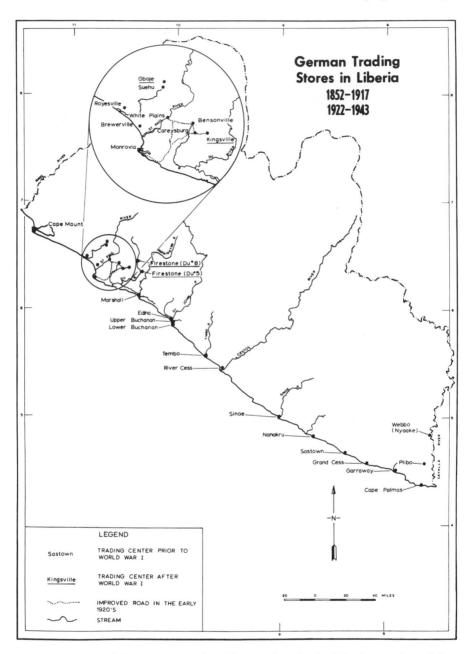

**German Trading
Stores in Liberia
1852–1917
1922–1943**

Gboje
Suehu
Royesville
White Plains
Brewerville
Bensonville
Careysburg
Kingsville
Monrovia

Cape Mount

Firestone (Du*8)
Firestone (Du*5)

Marshall

Edina
Upper Buchanan
Lower Buchanan

Tembo
River Cess

Sinoe

Webbo
(Nyaake)

Nanakru
Sastown
Grand Cess   Plibo
Garraway
Cape Palmas

–N–

LEGEND

Sastown	TRADING CENTER PRIOR TO WORLD WAR I
Kingsville	TRADING CENTER AFTER WORLD WAR I
·····•········	IMPROVED ROAD IN THE EARLY 1920'S
∿∿	STREAM

20   0   20   40   MILES

FIG. 5. Sites of German-operated trading stations in the Liberian portion of the
Grain Coast. German firms dominated Liberia's external commerce until World
War I; note the relative absence of sites in the interior.

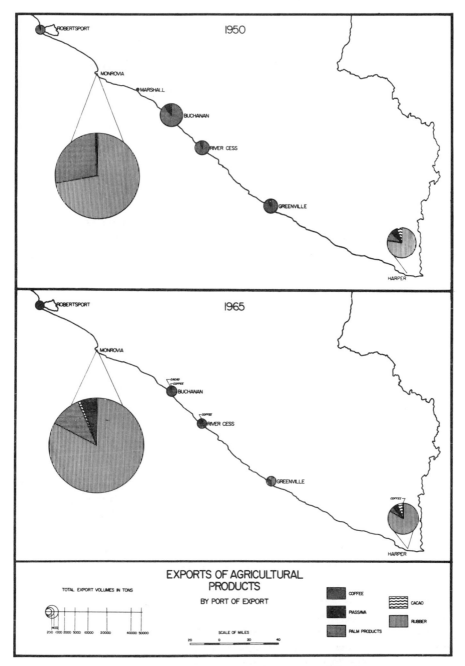

FIG. 6.   Agricultural exports in 1950 and 1965.

close maritime commercial ties to the land from which they emigrated. On the other hand, indigenous villages were conspicuous by their location along straight stretches of beach. Here, ability to draw fishing canoes from the water up onto the beach was of critical importance. Trade stores might be anywhere in the area although they were usually located outside of the native housing compounds. Whatever the setting, the European trader probably lived in the second story of a sometimes crudely constructed two-story building. (See fig. 1.) Trade was carried on in the ground floor. He likely was unmarried and was the representative of a European firm that often had its own fleet of ships. The trader obtained agricultural produce and sold manufactured items. Intricate barter arrangements often were developed, and the arrival offshore of his firm's ship set in motion a transfer of goods between ship and shore, usually by means of surf boats which, in many ports, were used to carry the goods ashore.

Aside from identifying sites of relic ports, the research sought also to identify those ports that have continued to carry on commerce and, where possible, the nature of their trade. How has the sequence of port abandonment been related to emergence of alternate transport technologies and, in Liberia, to external stimuli? In selected sites, evidence was collected to assist in reconstructing physical layouts of the trading zone. Trade stores, because of their seminal role in commerce at the settlements, were selected as a significant focus of investigation. So were the traders themselves who, while lacking meaningful historical continuity, do provide a means of identifying some of the changes that have occurred over the past 50 years. (See figs. 2, 3, and 4.)

Our travel to the relic ports was by plane, boat, car, and by foot. Air travel was especially valuable since many of the settlements still lack surface links to the rest of the country. Planes also permitted some low-level photography, which proved useful in establishing the parameters for later ground reconnaissance.

One method for transmitting to the reader the results of these and earlier investigations is the map. A measure of the magnitude of commercial decline at many coastal settlements best fitting the category of relic port may be deduced from a comparison of two figures: One (fig. 5) depicts the distribution of German-national-operated trading stores through the early 1940's, while the other (fig. 6) identifies the volume and composition of agricultural exports by port of export for two sample years since World War II. No export commerce is recorded for most of the coastal stations having had an expatriate German trader only a few years earlier; these years coincide with expansion of the road network into the Interior and with construction of a modern port at Monrovia. Of course, few German traders returned to these outstations after the war. The merchant fleets that served these firms had been destroyed, and economic opportunities were perceived to be more advantageous in the larger settlements. Penetration into the interior led to many nonagricultural development projects. Their magnitude, especially for extractive minerals,

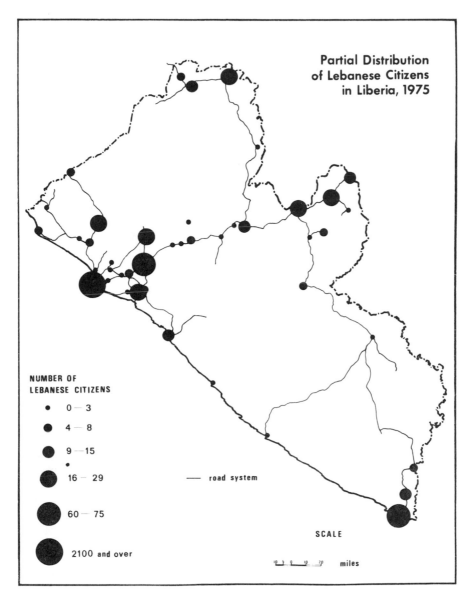

FIG. 7.   Lebanese in Liberia.

mandated use of a deep-water port and at the same time caused a fundamental change in the activities traders believed to have the best economic potential. Thus, the era of small-scale agricultural exports from a number of locations was changing in favor of both agricultural and nonagricultural tonnages from only a few ports.

Retail trade and the exporting of agricultural produce at most of these smaller locations soon passed into the hands of the Lebanese. Of those settlements having exports, all fall under the shadow of Monrovia's expanding commercial hinterland. Furthermore, were it not for the smaller of Firestone's natural-rubber plantations in Liberia being a few miles inland from Harper (Cape Palmas) in southeast Liberia, then it is doubtful whether the relatively large export tonnages at this port would have been recorded. Only the Americo-Liberian settlements depict export commerce; the transformation from a series of fragile settler bridgeheads in an alien land to a political unit with strong centralized control has taken place.

By far the most revealing measure of the decline of the coastal trading settlements, however, was through identification of the distribution and density of Lebanese nationals, a task completed during the fieldwork of 1975. One should keep in mind that these people have replaced the Germans as the principal expatriate trading group and, unlike the Germans at an earlier period, are to be found in Liberia in substantial numbers, in excess of 3,000. Relatively few of the smaller coastal settlements had Lebanese at the time of these investigations; they were located mainly in Monrovia, Buchanan, Harper, or at inland locations along the newly expanding road system. (See fig. 7.)

As a rule, the stronger the Americo-Liberian presence in a coastal settlement, the greater the likelihood of finding the structure housing the original expatriate trading store. In many of the smaller, indigenous villages, no trace could be found of the former expatriate trading establishment. In part, this is due to the normal ravages of time in a tropical climatic zone. It may also be attributable to the use of temporary facilities, one of the implications being that traders posted to some of the more remote relic ports maintained a lifestyle in some respects only slightly removed from that practiced by the indigenous population.

A compilation of a series of village plats identifying the location of individual trading stores has been completed.

REFERENCES

BEAZLEY, CHARLES RAYMOND
    1906.   The dawn of modern geography . . . c. A.D. 1260-1420, vol. 3, 638
             pp., illus.   Clarendon Press, Oxford.

BLAKE, JOHN W.
   1937.   European beginnings in West Africa, 1454-1578, 212 pp.   Longmans, Green, London.
CLARKE, JOHN I., ed.
   1966.   Sierra Leone in maps, 120 pp., illus.   University of London Press, London.
EANNES DE ASURARA, GOMES
   1899.   The chronicle of the discovery and conquest of Guinea, translated by Charles Raymond Beazley and Edgar Prestage, vol. 2, pp. i-cl, 129-362, illus.   Hakluyt Society, London.
HARLEY, GEORGE N.
   1939.   Roads and trails in Liberia.   Geogr. Rev., vol. 29, no. 3, pp. 447-460, illus.
JOHNSON, HARRY H.
   1906.   Liberia, vol. 1, 520 pp., illus.   Hutchinson & Co., London.
LAWRENCE, A. W.
   1964.   Trade castles and forts of West Africa, 390 pp., illus.   Stanford University Press, California.
POPULATION CENSUS OF SIERRA LEONE
   1965.   1963 population census of Sierra Leone, vol. 1.   Central Statistics Office, Freetown.
STANLEY, WILLIAM R.
   1970.   The Lebanese in Sierra Leone: Entrepreneurs extraordinary.   African Urban Notes, vol. 5, pp. 157-174.
   1973.   Transport expansion in Liberia.   Pp. 87-103 *in* "Transport and Development," 230 pp., illus., B.S. Hoyle, ed.   Barnes & Noble, New York.
   1974.   Economic study of a proposed Liberia-Sierra Leone highway link: The Mano River Bridge.   Unpublished report for African Development Bank, 70 pp.   Abidjan, Ivory Coast.
UNITED STATES HYDROGRAPHIC OFFICE
   1974.   H.O. No. 134, Sailing Directions, 1972. Single sheet.   U. S. Government Printing Office, Washington, D. C.
VAN DER LAAN, H. L.
   1975.   The Lebanese traders in Sierra Leone, 385 pp.   Mouton, The Hague.
WINDER, R. BAYLY
   1961-62.   The Lebanese in West Africa.   Comparative Studies in Sociology and History, vol. 4, pp. 300-303.

WILLIAM R. STANLEY

Studies on the Lemurs of the Comoro Archipelago

Principal Investigator: Ian Tattersall, American Museum of Natural History, New York, New York.

Grant No. 1305:   In support of a study of the ecology and behavior of the ruffed lemur, *Varecia variegata,* in Madagascar.

As the discrepancy between the title of this report and that of the grant suggests, it was not my original intention to study the Comorian lemurs. Conditions in Madagascar, however, prevented my carrying out the study I had originally envisaged and caused me to turn my attention to the Comoros (fig. 1), which are unique outside Madagascar in possessing wild-living natural populations of lemurs. At the time of my study, which lasted from November 1974 to June 1975 and which was the first ever to have been carried out on the Comorian lemurs, the four islands of the Comoro group together constituted an Overseas Territory of France; since then, however, radical political changes have occurred. Three of the islands (Grande Comore, Anjouan, and Mohéli) now form the independent Comoro Republic, while the fourth, Mayotte, has become a Territorial Collectivity of France.

Two lemuroid species, both of the genus *Lemur,* are found on the Comoros: *L. mongoz* on Anjouan and Mohéli and *L. fulvus mayottensis* on Mayotte. Neither species is unique to the Comoros (although the subspecies *L. f. mayottensis* is restricted to Mayotte), and the presence on the islands of both is most likely attributable to relatively recent human activity (Tattersall, 1976a, 1977a). The absence of wild-living lemurs on the largest island of the archipelago, Grande Comore, is presumably due to the lack there of permanent water.

At a time when the lemur populations of Madagascar are severely threatened, the condition of the only other wild-living populations of these animals must be of considerable concern. The results of my surveys show that *L. mongoz* is relatively abundant even in areas of secondary vegetation on Mohéli (290 square kilometers) but is substantially less so in similar areas on the more densely populated Anjouan (424 square kilometers). In the forested highland interior of the latter island, however, the abundance of the species is probably higher than anywhere else in the world.' *L. f. mayottensis* is likewise far from rare: I have made a rough population estimate of 50,000 individuals on an island with an area of only 375 square kilometers (Tattersall, 1976a, 1977a).

641

Neither *L. mongoz* nor *L. f. mayottensis* is at present too greatly threatened by hunting, although the practice is on the increase, especially in Mayotte. The major worry for the future of these animals is habitat destruction, which is proceeding apace. Reports with detailed recommendations for the conservation of the lemurs and of their habitat have been submitted to both the Comorian and the Mayotte authorities; both have expressed a welcome sensitivity to the problem.

Before progressing to further consideration of the Comorian studies, I should note that before leaving Madagascar in 1974 I was able to undertake a survey of lemur distributions in the northern part of Madagascar. To detail the results of this survey (which defy summary) would add inordinately to the length of this report and could add nothing to the versions published elsewhere (Tattersall, 1976b, 1977b).

Lemur mongoz

A previous study in Madagascar of this species (Tattersall and Sussman, 1975; Sussman and Tattersall, 1976) had yielded the unexpected finding that, unlike other members of its genus studied so far, *Lemur mongoz* is (a) nocturnal and (b) lives in pair-bonded "family" groups. In my surveys on Mohéli and Anjouan I was thus particularly concerned to collect further information pertaining to social organization and activity rhythm.

Group composition. Censusing of *L. mongoz* groups was facilitated by the difference in pelage coloration between males and females (fig. 2), whereby females possess white cheeks and throats, and males russet. Juveniles showed the female coloration pattern regardless of their sex (fig. 3) and therefore could not be discriminated. Subadults, probably aged from about 14 to 16 months during the survey (November to January), were not always distinguishable from adults. Table 1 provides a breakdown of the group compositions noted in Madagascar, Anjouan, and Mohéli and shows an intriguing pattern.

The social units of Anjouan *L. mongoz* are clearly most satisfactorily interpreted as "family" groups consisting of an adult male and female together with up to two immature offspring, one in each age-category (ca. 3 months and ca. 15 months). In only one case was a group of five individuals observed; this is most plausibly explained by twinning, which in captive *L. mongoz* runs at about 8 percent of births. One group that was censused contained two females alone; but this group was reliably reported recently to have lost its male through human interference.

In Mohéli, however, not all groups could be interpreted as "families." Even if one were to accept an abnormally high rate of twinning, only 73 percent of groups conformed to a "family" structure. There is some evidence to suggest that on Mohéli there is seasonal variation in group structure (Tattersall, 1976c, 1978), but this is far from certain, and it may be that we are looking here at geographical, interpopulation, variation. Further study at other times of year will be needed to clarify the situation.

Activity rhythm. Malagasy *Lemur mongoz* was observed to be active only at night and to begin and cease activity within very narrow ranges of light intensity (ca. 2-22 lux). In Mohéli a similar pattern was found to hold, although light levels appeared to be rather less critical. But whereas in the warm, seasonal lowlands of Anjouan (where the environment is broadly similar to those surveyed in Madagascar and Mohéli) nocturnality was likewise found to be the rule, in the cool, humid central highlands of that island *L. mongoz* was observed to be active throughout the hours of daylight. Given the clear-cut ecological distinction between the nocturnal and diurnal *L. mongoz* populations, it seems reasonable to propose an environmental effect on activity rhythm: one having to do, perhaps, with thermoregulation.

Lemur fulvus mayottensis

Of the mainland subspecies of *Lemur fulvus*, *L. f. mayottensis* most closely resembles *L. f. fulvus*, from which it was probably derived. Indeed, the two

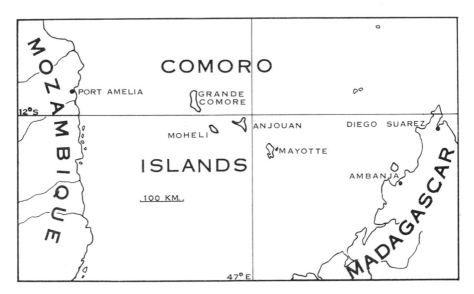

FIG. 1.   Map showing the location and disposition of the Comoros in the Mozambique Channel.

TABLE 1.　Breakdown of Group Compositions of *Lemur mongoz*
in the Various Study Areas

Male	Female	Inf / juv	Number of groups	Percent
MADAGASCAR (1973; N=5)				
1	1		3	60
1	2		1	20
1	2	1	1	20
MADAGASCAR (1974; N=3)				
1	1		1	33
1	1	1	1	33
2	1	1	1	33
ANJOUAN (1974; N=26)				
1	1		6	31
1	2		2	8
2	1		2	8
1	2	1	5	19
2	1	1	4	15
1	1	1	4	15
2	2	1	1	4
	2		1	4
MOHÉLI (1974; N=22)				
1	1		6	27
1	2	1	2	9
1	1	1	3	14
2	2	1	4	18
2	2		4	18
3	2	1	2	9
4	2	1	1	5
	4		1	5

subspecies are distinguished primarily by the extreme variation in pelage coloration found in the Mayotte lemur, which nonetheless centers around a mean close to that of *L. f. fulvus* (fig. 4). One unfortunate consequence of this was that, in the absence of any marked sexual dichromatism, distinguishing between male and female Mayotte lemurs demanded a great deal of practice and even with expertise was not always possible.

The site chosen for intensive study was an area of forest bordering a stream near Mavingoni, a village situated at an elevation of approximately 100 meters on the northern flank of Benara (660 meters), Mayotte's highest mountain. This forest, about 3.8 hectares (ca. 10 acres) in extent, included all three

FIG. 2.   Adult female (above) and male (below) *Lemur mongoz* from the highlands of
Anjouan. Note the differences in pelage coloration.

FIG. 3.   Juvenile female *Lemur mongoz* (aged ca. 6 weeks) from Mohéli. Juveniles of both sexes display the coloration typical of the adult female until the males are over 3 months old.

of the secondary forest types that now characterize most of the northern part of Mayotte. These are: "mixed mango forest," a mixed consociation dominated by the mango tree (*Mangifera indica:* Anacardiaceae); "mango forest," which is composed almost entirely of extremely tall mangoes; and "avocat marron forest," named for its primary component, *Litsea tersa* (Lauraceae). This last forest type is rarely found at an advanced stage of succession and in contrast to the other forest types is of low stature. Importantly for the lemurs, each forest type is characterized by an abundance of lianas (Tattersall, 1977c).

Habituation of the lemurs to observation was relatively easy, and it was usually possible to maintain contact with the subject animals throughout the hours of daylight (approximately 0600-1800 hours). I recorded most observations (a total of 416 hours) using a latitudinal sampling technique. At 5-minute intervals information was entered on a prepared data sheet concerning the number of individuals engaged, at each of the various levels of the forest, in each of these activities: feeding, grooming, resting, moving, travel, and other. "Feeding" observations were accompanied by a note of the item con-

FIG. 4.   Adult male (above) and female (below) *Lemur fulvus mayottensis*. In this lemur there is no sexual dichromatism.

sumed. Collection of data in this way made my observations directly comparable to those made by Sussman (1972, 1974, 1975) on the rufous lemur, *Lemur fulvus rufus,* in southwest Madagascar. Additionally, a journal record was kept, and some 150 hours of "focal animal" time samples were also accumulated. These latter, however, are probably subject to undue bias, and I have preferred to rely wherever possible on the latitudinal data.

The four months (February through May) during which the data were quantified fell during the rainy season. Although rainfall in 1975 was somewhat below average, it was nonetheless very substantial and the vegetation exhibited normal phenology.

Social organization. The rufous lemur (Sussman, 1972, 1974, 1975; all references here to Sussman are to these works) and the brown lemur, *L. f. fulvus* (Harrington, 1975), are known to live in stable groupings of modest size, and so it came as something of a surprise to realize that the social groupings of the Mayotte lemur are fluid and constantly changing in composition. I have thus chosen to use the term "associations" for the social units one sees in the field, for the term "group" implies a level of stability not found here (Tattersall, 1977c). Because I was unable consistently to recognize individuals, I could not determine whether associations in fact represented subgroups of larger, more exclusive groupings. The size of the associations I followed generally fluctuated between about 6 and 16 individuals, and the mean size of 100 associations censused in various parts of Mayotte (but not at Mavingoni) was 9.1 individuals. This mean value is very close to that quoted by Sussman for groups of the rufous lemur (9.4 individuals).

In the 32 *L. f. mayottensis* associations in which all individuals could be identified by sex, the socionomic sex ratio was almost exactly 1:1 (139 males to 135 females). Censusing of the study forest yielded a count of 38 individuals (19 adult-sized males, 16 adult-sized females, 1 juvenile male, 2 juvenile females), grouped into four associations of 7, 9, 11, and 11 individuals, respectively.

Day ranges and population density. Obviously the concept of "home range" is difficult to apply to the Mayotte lemur, and in the absence of stable identifiable groupings it is clearly more useful to speak of population density. The Mavingoni census yielded a count of 38 individuals occupying an area of about 3.8 hectares, and so population density in this forest is approximately 10 individuals/ha. (1000 square kilometers). This density is high but comparable to those given by Sussman for the rufous lemur in southwest Madagascar.

On one day each month the path of association travel was mapped from dawn to dusk. When the association split, the larger number of animals was

FIG. 5.   Adult male *Lemur fulvus mayottensis* in a typical resting posture on a large horizontal branch.

followed. Travel distances ranged from around 1,150 meters (February) to 450 meters (May), with a mean of about 800 meters. Even the shortest of these distances vastly exceeds the average 135 to 150 meters recorded by Sussman for the rufous lemur.

Diet and feeding behavior.   Over the period of the study the Mayotte lemur was observed to exploit over 48 different food resources, consisting of the leaves, flowers, and fruit of at least 32 plant species. However, as many as 29 of these resources each accounted for under 0.5 percent of feeding time, to a total of only 3.7 percent. Over-all, the three most common food items (all fruit) together accounted for about 61 percent of feeding time, and the top six for about 75 percent (items 4-6 were all leaves). In total, the exploitation of fruit occupied 67.4 percent of feeding time, of leaves 27.3, and of flowers (including floral buds), 5.0 percent.

These figures differ dramatically from those provided by Sussman for the rufous lemur. This animal exploited a much narrower range of food items (17 and 16, respectively, at two different forests) and of plant species (a combined total in both forests of 13 species). Even more strikingly, leaves were predominant in the diet of the rufous lemur; the leaves of the tamarind tree (*Tarmarin-dus indica:* Cesalpinaceae) alone accounted for 75 percent of the diet at one forest and for over 50 percent at the other.

The Mayotte lemurs displayed a vast array of feeding postures and techniques, and no potential source of sustenance, whatever its location within the forest, was beyond their reach. Choice of part was very specific; thus in the case of the leaves of the Indian almond (*Terminalia catappa:* Combretaceae) the petiole alone was consumed, while the flowers of the kapok (*Ceiba pentandra:* Bombaceae) were licked for their nectar (and pollen?) content.

Patterns of activity.   Although *Lemur fulvus* has generally been regarded as diurnal, the Mayotte lemur is evidently active on a 24-hour schedule. It is unfortunate that I was unable to undertake observations at night, since the hours of darkness obviously obscure much of this lemur's activity. The highest levels of activity were observed during the first half-hour (0600-0625) and last hour (1700-1800) of observation, while the middle of the day was usually characterized by a major period of resting. Besides the feeding peaks at the beginning and end of the day, another was observed between 0800 and 0825 hours. Feeding activity then decreased through the morning, but after a minimal period between about 1130 and 1330 hours, increased steadily through the afternoon. Subsequent observation, in 1977 and 1980, has confirmed the 24-hour "oiel" activity rhythm (Tattersall, 1982).

The activity:rest ratio of the Mayotte lemur was low, at 0.52; the best corresponding figure for the rufous lemur is 0.79. It may be that the relatively low diurnal activity level of the Mayotte lemur reflects a relatively high level of activity at night; but at the moment this must remain speculation.

Use of the vertical habitat.   Following Sussman, I recognized five different levels in the forest: 1, the ground layer; 2, the shrub layer (up to 2 meters); 3, the intermediate layer, between 2 meters and the canopy; 4, the continuous canopy; and 5, the discontinuous emergent layer. Canopy height varied according to the forest type, and avocat-marron forest differed from the other types in being dominated by level 3, in possessing a discontinuous canopy-equivalent layer, and in lacking level 5.

Sussman noted a clear preference by the rufous lemur for the continuous canopy. At no period of the day did this lemur spend more of its time in the lower levels than in level 4. The Mayotte lemur, on the other hand, did spend substantial amounts of time in the intermediate layer; but this may be attributed to the fact that it passed much of its time in avocat-marron forest, where many of its feeding sites were located. Like the rufous lemur, the Mayotte lemur showed a distinct lack of enthusiasm for the ground.

FIG. 6. Reciprocal grooming between an adult male (left) and female *Lemur fulvus mayottensis*. Most all grooming was concentrated on parts of the body inaccessible to the individual animal, but here the female is grooming the male's hand, having just had hers groomed by the male.

Substrate preferences. During focal-animal sampling a record was kept of the orientation and diameter of the branch supporting the focal individual at each sampling interval. Horizontal supports were clearly preferred (61 percent of time). Vertical supports were largely eschewed (6 percent); oblique branches were used for the remainder of the time. Preferences shown during resting alone were remarkably similar to those for over-all time.

Branches of medium diameter (2.5-10.0 centimeters) comprised the most frequented category (48 percent of time); small ones (1.0-2.5 centimeters) were next most commonly used (33 percent), considerably exceeding the large ones (10.0 centimeters) with 14 percent of time. Fine branches (1.0 centimeters, 5 percent) were the least exploited. The preference of the animals, however, was clearly for horizontal or only moderately sloping medium-to-large branches (fig. 5); the rather low figure for time spent on large branches reflects the facts that orientation is more important than diameter in substrate choice and that horizontal or gently sloping large branches are not very common.

It should be noted, however, that although these substrate preferences are clear, locomotor behavior was very flexible and opportunistic. Regardless of preference, the lemurs would do whatever was necessary to reach a given food source or point in the forest.

Social behavior.   The Mayotte lemur is extremely sociable; some 48 percent of the resting time of individuals was spent in physical contact with other individuals. Grooming occupied 4.3 percent of total time, and of the time devoted to grooming only 35 percent was spent in autogrooming, compared to 65 percent in allogrooming or mutual grooming. Most grooming bouts were reciprocal (fig. 6). I do not have the impression that particular individuals groomed, or were groomed, more than others (although to be sure of this would require better recognition of individuals than I was able to attain) or that one sex more commonly assumed the role of groomer or groomee. No system of dominance relationships was apparent.

An intriguing aspect of social behavior is food-sharing, sometimes seen during consumption of the fruit of the liana *Saba comorensis* (Apocynaceae). This globular fruit was generally detached from the vine and carried elsewhere to be eaten, and on occasion the possessor of the fruit might be approached by another individual with intent to share (but not to deprive). The willingness of individuals to share varied greatly. Sometimes they would permit sharing of the fruit without demur; on other occasions only after prolonged importuning; and on yet others not at all. Successful sharing almost always took place between females; male-female sharing was only once observed; and male-male sharing, never.

Sharing such as this has not previously been reported for lemurs, although I have seen a similar type of behavior (Tattersall, 1977c) in a male-female pair of *Lemur mongoz.*

Anogenital marking was occasionally observed, but since this is a relatively unobtrusive behavior, the observed occurrence probably greatly underestimates the actual occurrence and reliable context is difficult to provide.

Discussion

The results and implications of this study are more fully discussed elsewhere (Tattersall, 1977c), but one or two brief points may be made here.

Many of the substantial differences in behavior between *L. f. mayottensis* and *L. f. rufus* appear to be related to their distinct dietary preferences. The former is a dietary generalist and a frugivore; the latter, a dietary specialist and a folivore. In consequence, the food resources exploited by the Mayotte lemur are more widely scattered, both within the forest as a whole and within each individual tree. This appears to explain satisfactorily why the Mayotte lemur spent more time in "movement," traveled farther daily, and ranged more widely than did the rufous lemur; but it does not account in any clear way for the much more limited amount of time it spent feeding. Similarly, it seems reasonable to assume that the fluid pattern of social organization exhibited by the Mayotte lemur is related in some way to its dietary and foraging strategy; but the nature of this relationship is obscure.

Finally, perhaps the most interesting general aspect of the study is what it adds to our emerging knowledge of the variability in behavior among the lemurs. Far greater than anyone imagined only a few years ago, this variety can only whet our appetites for further knowledge of these fascinating and beautiful creatures.

REFERENCES

HARRINGTON, JONATHAN E.
   1975.   Field observations of social behavior of *Lemur fulvus fulvus* E. Geoffroy 1812.   Pp. 259-279 *in* "Lemur Biology," Ian Tattersall and R. W. Sussman, eds., 365 pp., illus.   Plenum Press, New York and London.
SUSSMAN, ROBERT W.
   1972.   An ecological study of two Madagascan primates: *Lemur fulvus fulvus* Audebert and *Lemur catta* Linnaeus.   Ph.D. dissertation, Duke University.
   1974.   Ecological distinctions in sympatric species of *Lemur*.   Pp. 75-180 *in* "Prosimian Biology," R. D. Martin, G. A. Doyle, and A. C. Walker, eds., 963 pp., illus.   Duckworth, London, and University of Pittsburgh Press.
   1975.   A preliminary study of the ecology and behavior of *Lemur fulvus fulvus* Audebert 1800.   Pp. 237-258 *in* "Lemur Biology," Ian Tattersall and R. W. Sussman, eds.   Plenum Press, New York and London.
SUSSMAN, ROBERT W., and TATTERSALL, IAN
   1976.   Cycles of activity, group composition and diet of *Lemur mongoz mongoz* Linnaeus 1766 in Madagascar.   Folia Primatol., vol. 26, pp. 363-378.
TATTERSALL, IAN
   1976a.   Note sur la distribution et sur la situation actuelle des lémuriens des Comores.   Mammalia, vol. 40, no. 3, pp. 519-521.
   1976b.   Notes on the status of *Lemur macaco* and *Lemur fulvus* (Primates, Lemuriformes).   Anthrop. Pap. Amer. Mus. Nat. Hist., vol. 53, pt. 2, pp. 255-262.
   1976c.   Group structure and activity rhythm in *Lemur mongoz* (Primates, Lemuriformes) on Anjouan and Mohéli Islands, Comoro Archipelago.   Anthrop. Pap. Amer. Mus. Nat. Hist., vol. 53, pt. 4, pp. 367-380.
   1977a.   The lemurs of the Comoro Islands.   Oryx, vol. 13, no. 5, pp. 445-448.

TATTERSALL (continued)

1977b. Distribution of the Malagasy lemurs, part 1: The lemurs of northern Madagascar. Ann. New York Acad. Sci., vol. 293, pp. 160-169.

1977c. Ecology and behavior of *Lemur fulvus mayottensis* (Primates, Lemuriformes). Anthrop. Pap. Amer. Mus. Nat. Hist., vol. 54, pt. 4, pp. 421-482.

1978. Behavioural variation in *Lemur mongoz*. Pp. 127-132 *in* "Recent Advances in Primatology," vol. 3, D. J. Chivers and K. A. Joysey, eds.

1979. Patterns of activity in the Mayotte lemur, *Lemur fulvus mayottensis*. Journ. Mamm., vol. 60, no. 2, pp. 314-323.

1982. The primates of Madagascar. Columbia University Press, New York. (In press.)

TATTERSALL, IAN, and SUSSMAN, ROBERT W.

1975. Observations on the ecology and behavior of the mongoose lemur *Lemur mongoz mongoz* Linnaeus (Primates, Lemuriformes) at Ampijoroa, Madagascar. Anthrop. Pap. Amer. Mus. Nat. Hist., vol. 52, pp. 193-216.

IAN TATTERSALL

Ecology of Primates in Southeastern Peru

Principal Investigator: John Terborgh, Department of Biology, Princeton University, Princeton, New Jersey.

Grant Nos. 1356 and 1450.   To inaugurate a long-term study of the ecology of primates in Peru's Manu National Park. Support covered the first two years in which the research team conducted a census of the primate community and undertook preliminary ecological observations.[1]

Peru's Manu National Park lies in the farthest corner of the Amazon Basin. It includes part of a vast wilderness that forms the headwaters of the Ucayali, Purus, and Madre de Dios rivers. The region is so remote and inaccessible that to this day the indigenous tribes have not been contacted.

It is in this setting that we launched a long-term study of the ecology of several primate species. Our field site is the Cashu Cocha Biological Station in the Manu National Park. To reach it we must travel 250 kilometers from Cuzco on a winding one-way road, and then transfer to a dugout for another 400-kilometer journey, first down the Alto Madre de Dios River and then up the Manu. The trip takes 4 to 5 days from Cuzco. Unfortunately, it is necessary to go to such lengths to study primates in Amazonia because it is only in the most inaccessible portions of the Basin that their populations are not decimated by hunting.

At Cashu Cocha we enjoy the rudiments of a field station in the form of a 4-room thatched-roof house that overlooks an emerald, jungle-rimmed oxbow lake. Here we follow a rustic, do-it-yourself life-style, with minimum comforts but maximum tranquility. One is truly locked away from civilization. No one visits for months at a time. The senses become attuned to the signals of passing life in the surrounding forest. The weather is mild, the sky is blue, and the lake is refreshing. A more sublime spot in which to combine work with companionship and relaxation would be hard to find.

---

[1] The second author, Charles H. Jansen, collaborated in the fieldwork and performed much of the data analysis. He is now at the University of Washington, Seattle, Washington. It is a pleasure to acknowledge the assistance in the field of Debra Moskovits and Grace Russell.

Cashu Cocha is a monkey watcher's paradise. Twelve species inhabit the vicinity, including representatives of most of the New World genera. To a person accustomed to the temperate forest, where one can walk all day and see only an occasional squirrel, the tropical forest is another world. The abundance of animals is truly astonishing. A morning's walk may produce half a dozen species of monkeys, plus scattered agoutis, peccaries, coati mundis, ta-

TABLE 1.   Population Densities and Other Characteristics of Primate Species Found at Cashu Cocha in Peru's Manu National Park

Common name (Scientific name)	Approx. weight (g.)	Population density[1]	Diet[2]	Position in forest[3]	Troop size	Home range area (ha.)
Pygmy Marmoset (*Cebuella pygmaea*)	100	5	S,I,N	U,M	2-8	<1
Goeldi's Marmoset[4] (*Callimico goeldii*)	500	-	?	U,M	2-5?	?
Saddle-backed Tamarin (*Saguinus fuscicollis*)	350	16	F,I,N,S	U,M	2-7	6-40
Emperor Tamarin (*Saguinus imperator*)	400	12	F,I,N,S	U,M	2-5	6-40
Titi Monkey (*Callicebus moloch*)	800	24	F,L	M	2-3	8-16
Night Monkey (*Aotus trivirgatus*)	1,200	20	F,I,N	M	2-5	?
Saki Monkey (*Pithecia monachus*)	1,500	<5	F,?	C	3-6?	?
Squirrel Monkey (*Saimiri sciureus*)	950	50	I,F,N	M,U,C	30-40	>400
White-fronted Capuchin (*Cebus albifrons*)	2,500	35	F,I,N	M,C	10-18	150-200
Brown Capuchin (*Cebus apella*)	3,000	40	F,I,N	M,C	8-14	50-70
Red Howler (*Alouatta seniculus*)	7,000	30	F,L	C	5-8	10-20
Black Spider Monkey (*Ateles paniscus*)	6,500	25	F,N,L	C	variable	?
Smokey Woolly Monkey[5] (*Lagothrix lagothricha*)	7,000	-	F,?	C	10-20	?

[1] Estimated number of individuals per square kilometer.
[2] F=fruit; I=insects and other small animals; L=leaves; N=nectar; S=sap.
[3] C=canopy; M=middle story; U=understory.
[4] Found near Cashu Cocha but not within the censused study area.
[5] Found elsewhere in Manu Park.

manduas (an arboreal anteater), and perhaps one of the many rarer denizens of the forest, not to mention a normal count of squirrels. Every day is different, and each one offers the tantalizing possibility of encountering something rare and memorable, such as a tapir, jaguar, or giant anteater.

What is to account for the enormous variety and abundance of animals? Mainly it is the prodigious supply of fruit, measured in tons per acre, that the forest produces on a year-round basis. There are other important commodities too, such as insects and foliage, but basically it is fruit that fuels the ecosystem of the tropical forest.

Primate Census

Our first task on settling down to work at Cashu Cocha was to census the primate community. The established methods, although reasonably straight-forward conceptually, all entailed practical complications owing to the fact that animals seldom choose to behave in accordance with a set of preordained mathematical assumptions. There are two basic approaches, with variants of each.

In the transect methods an observer walks a measured course and records all the animals detected along the way, noting how far away each was at the instant of detection. At the end of the walk, or better, a series of walks, one has a definite count of animals made in an indefinite area. To convert this into an estimate of the population density, that is, the number of animals per unit area, one must somehow determine the area that was covered in the census. One dimension of the area is known from the length of the walk; the other, the width of the swath within which animals were noticed, must be estimated from the distribution of detection distances. There are various ways of developing the statistics, but that is not the main problem. Difficulties arise from the behavior of the animals. The species differ in their intrinsic detectability. Some (e.g., squirrel monkeys) live in large noisy mobs that are invariably noticed long before the observer arrives on the scene. Others (e.g., marmosets) become excited when they spot a human and often approach noisily to scold. In this case the monkeys have detected the observer, rather than vice versa. And still others (e.g., howlers and titi monkeys) may silently stare from the treetops without moving a muscle. The observer may be lucky enough to spot them, but then he may not. There are other complications too which result from variations in behavior at different times of day, non-random aggregations of monkeys around fruit trees, and distortions introduced by the fact that both the observer and the observed are in motion during the census. Correcting for all these effects requires a good deal of statistical finesse, and even

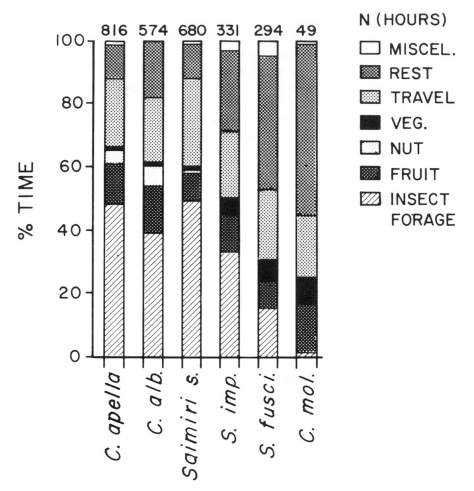

Fig. 1. Time budgets of six primate species at Cashu Cocha. Five omnivorous species are contrasted with one vegetarian species (*Callicebus moloch*). The bars average results from two or more samples.

then there remain unresolvable discrepancies when one compares different variants of the method.

The other basic approach employs the converse tactic of starting with a known area and then trying to estimate the number of animals that live within it. Breeding birds are routinely censused in this way by tallying the number of territorial males that are singing within a measured plot. However, the method is much less satisfactory for monkeys. For one thing, most monkeys don't

sing (though some do), and for another, most monkeys are only casually territorial. By following troops one can gain an impression of how much space they
are using, but as we and others have discovered, ranging patterns may vary
radically with the seasons in accordance with the availability of fruit supplies.
Several troops may congregate in a small area when it contains a concentrated
food source (e.g., a large fig tree) and then disperse when the fruit is exhausted. Neither the highly congregated nor the dispersed state conveys an accurate
impression of the number of troops that are using a particular area. Weeks of
observations may be required to learn how many troops there are, and how
much space each one uses.

In short, neither the transect methods nor the fixed area approach offers
an ideal solution to the problem of censusing primates. We tried them both,
and by applying appropriate corrections and using our seasoned judgment, arrived at a set of estimates for the population densities of 11 species (Table 1).
All told, there are roughly 260 monkeys per square kilometer at Cashu Cocha
which form a combined biomass of 690 kilograms. This appears to be a New
World record, both for the total density of individuals and for the number of
coexisting species.

Ecology

How do so many species succeed in utilizing the same forest without ex-
cessive competition? There is often broad overlap in the kinds of fruits eaten,
yet each species possesses some distinctive habits which apparently allow it to
coexist with the others.

With one exception, all the species obtain a major fraction of their calories from fruit, but most include other categories of food in their diets as well.
Howler and titi monkeys eat leaves and probably obtain most of their protein
from them. However, they eat different sorts of leaves. Howlers exclusively
select flush leaves, tender young ones that are just expanding, generally in the
crowns of large trees. Titis, on the other hand, eat fully expanded leaves, often
of certain vines. The two species also consume markedly different collections
of fruits. When broadly categorized their diets are similar, but on closer scrutiny they are seen to differ greatly in the particular species used.

This would perhaps be true of the spider and saki monkeys as well,
though we know rather little about their dietary habits beyond the fact that
both are highly frugivorous.

We are much better acquainted with the foraging behavior of the smaller
primates, particularly the 5 omnivorous species that have been the focus of our
attentions since 1975. At a superficial level these too seem to have very similar

diets composed of nearly even mixtures of fruit and insects (fig. 1), yet the details of how they obtain their food differ strikingly, sometimes in ways we would not have anticipated.

The two capuchins, *Cebus apella* and *C. albifrons,* at first seemed to employ almost identical repertoires of foraging techniques. Both search through dead leaves, peel bark and break hollow twigs to find insects, and both feed on similar arrays of fruits. Not until we had a chance to observe them in the early part of the dry season, when fruit supplies sink to an annual minimum, did differences become apparent. *Cebus apella,* with its more powerful jaw musculature, was able to crack open palm nuts and to extract long cylinders of pith from the stems of a number of plants. This gave it an abundant, if crude, food supply through the period of fruit deprivation. *Cebus albifrons,* on the other hand, opened palm nuts with considerable difficulty, and virtually ignored the pith-containing plants used by its relative. Instead, the *albifrons* scouted a much larger area, ranging into places we had never known them to go in search of rare fruiting figs. On finding one of these, the troop remained ensconced in the vicinity, making daily or twice daily visits to the tree until the fruit was exhausted. During times of plenty the two *Cebus* species often lead virtually identical lives. They diverge in extremis, when one turns to rough forage that is omnipresent and abundant but normally disdained, and the other becomes semi-nomadic in quest of widely scattered, but highly concentrated, food sources.

The much smaller squirrel monkey *(Saimiri sciureus)* normally eats most of the same fruit species that are used by *Cebus.* In fact, squirrel monkeys persistently join *Cebus* troops to form mixed associations that may last from a few hours to several weeks. When fruit is scarce, squirrel monkeys become even more nomadic than *Cebus albifrons,* traveling linear distances of several kilometers in search of rare fruit trees. But such trees are not always available, and when they are not, *Saimiri* becomes wholly insectivorous. During these periods the animals work unceasingly from dawn until dark, hunting through dead leaves and foliage for pupae, larvae, eggs, and other small-prey items which they capture at a rate of several per minute.

Whether *Saimiri* are able to sustain their weight at these times is not known, but it is an interesting question. The largest exclusively insectivorous birds weigh between 100 and 200 grams. By this measure, *Saimiri* is enormous (800-1,000 g.). Its extra size confers no apparent advantage in increasing either the rate at which prey are captured or the average size of prey. As an insectivore, *Saimiri* must push its energy budget to the limit, and that no doubt accounts for its untiring obsession for foraging when there is no fruit available. It is doubtful that a larger monkey could depend on insects for anything more than a dietary supplement and a source of protein.

Marmosets, the smallest of the New World monkeys, have found a novel kind of refuge from the competition of aggressively dominant larger species. It lies in their preference for a limited number of fruit species which have the common property of ripening piecemeal over extended periods of several weeks to several months. The larger primates obtain nearly all of their fruit from crops that ripen synchronously, usually on rather large trees. Food is plentiful, but the supply lasts only a few days. The trees visited by marmosets, in contrast, offer only a few fruits at a time, but provide a reliable, if paltry, supply for a major portion of the year. The amounts available are too small and scattered to be of interest to large primates which prefer to feed rapidly, but are adequate to meet the much reduced capacities and metabolic demands of the 300-400-gram *Saguinus* species. To harvest such fruits the marmosets follow a "traplining" routine, visiting a number of trees or vines in succession, and returning to individual trees at fairly regular intervals of 3 to 4 days. The intervals presumably allow for ripening of additional fruits.

The traplining habit seems to offer an explanation for two more distinctive features of marmoset behavior: the small size of their troops (2-5, rarely 7 individuals) and their intense territoriality. The number of trees that would have to be visited per day to satisfy the appetite of a troop can be expected to increase linearly with the number of its members. A large troop would have to visit many trees and would thereby have to travel proportionately farther, and patrol a larger area. Thus its efficiency would be less than that of a smaller troop in which the individuals could enjoy larger meals at each stop. *Saguinus* troops at Cashu Cocha are in fact as small as they can be, consisting normally of a breeding pair and their offspring.

Efficiency considerations also suggest that marmosets should be territorial, which they are with a vengeance. If overlap between troop home ranges were tolerated, then no troop could be assured of finding food in any of its regular fruit trees. The unnoticed inroads of neighboring groups would leave food scattered in an unpredictable pattern, a situation that would be to the detriment of all. By defending a definite area, each group is assured of the exclusive use of a known array of food sources, and can organize its activities so as to exploit them with a high level of efficiency.

The ecology of the two *Saguinus* species at Cashu Cocha is complicated by the fact that they form mixed troops comprised of one family of each species. Together the two families form a coalition that exploits and defends a common territory. The factors which motivate this unprecedented relationship are still obscure. However, the fact that the two species travel and feed together has made clear that the vegetable component of their diets is identical. Their ecological differences appear to lie exclusively in the realm of insect foraging, which they do in strikingly distinct ways. *Saguinus imperator* is a vine and branch walker that seeks insects in dense foliage. *Saguinus fuscicollis,* in contrast, locomotes by vertical clinging and leaping (i.e., it grasps vertical trunks and progresses by springing from one to the next). Accordingly, it captures virtually all of its prey on the surfaces of large trunks, limbs, and vines. The spatial overlap of the insect foraging activities of the two species approaches zero, while they seem to defend and share a common pool of fruit resources. This, too, is a result we would never have been able to anticipate at the outset.

Finally, for completeness, we should mention the tiny pygmy marmoset, *Cebuella pygmaea.* This curious little sprite is one of the most specialized of all primates, the mammalian equivalent of a sapsucker. *Cebuella* has a typical marmoset social organization in that it lives in family units. But it obtains the bulk of its food in a most singular fashion by biting small pits in the bark of just two or three trees, and then patrolling the pits to lap up the accumulated exudate. Thus they are trapliners too, but their territories are tiny, no larger than a suburban house lot.

In summary, our studies have led us to the realization that the ecological distinctions between New World primate species depend not so much on the gross features of their diets as upon behavioral differences in the ways they exploit fruit resources, and upon the various last ditch measures they take to tide themselves through the annual nadir of fruit abundance. The marmosets are particularly interesting in having evolved a divergent set of social and behavioral traits that grant them effective competitive isolation from the larger species. And the diminutive *Cebuella,* lowest of all in the interspecific peck order, escapes the competition of even its marmoset relatives by assuming a way of life that is practically unique among mammals.

JOHN TERBORGH
CHARLES H. JANSON

The Evolution of Freshwater Adaptation in Stingrays

Principal Investigator: Thomas B. Thorson, School of Life Sciences, University of Nebraska-Lincoln, Lincoln, Nebraska.

Associate Investigators: Daniel R. Brooks, Department of Zoology, University of British Columbia, Vancouver, British Columbia, Canada, and Monte A. Mayes, Dow Chemical U.S.A., Midland, Michigan.

Grant Nos. 1410, 1581, 1711, 1859.   In support of study of the zoogeographic and evolutionary history of South American freshwater stingrays (family Potamotrygonidae).

Elasmobranch fishes (sharks, skates, and rays) include species inhabiting the full spectrum of environmental salinity, and ranging from fully marine species, through those exhibiting all degrees of euryhalinity, to completely freshwater forms. Their means of dealing with their problems of regulating internal water and salt content (osmoregulation) have been summarized by Smith (1931, 1936); Potts and Parry (1963); Thorson (1967); Hoar and Randall (1969); and Pang, Griffith and Atz (1977). MARINE SPECIES, occurring largely offshore and in fully saline waters (±35 parts per thousand, or ppt) retain sufficient urea and other organic substances to maintain a concentration in body fluids that is hyperosmotic to the environment. Water is drawn in osmotically, providing the water needed for urine production and obviating the need for drinking seawater. A special structure, the digitiform or rectal gland, supplements the kidneys in secreting excess salt in a fluid containing about twice the concentration of NaCl found in the body fluids. EURYHALINE SPECIES are largely shallow-water, inshore forms. They function as marine species when in highly saline water, but when they move into brackish or fresh water, urea retention is relaxed, urea content of body fluids drops to 20-50 percent of marine levels, rectal gland function is reduced or ceases, and massive osmotic uptake of water is balanced by production of copious, dilute urine. Truly FRESHWATER SPECIES, the South American freshwater stingrays of the family Potamotrygonidae, permanently adapted to fresh water, have lost the ability to concentrate urea, although they have the enzymes to produce it, and they have a greatly atrophied and apparently non-functioning rectal gland. They are unable to revert to the ancestral urea retention, even when transferred to

663

sea water, and cannot survive in sea water more concentrated than about 14 ppt salt.

The family Potamotrygonidae consists mainly of one genus, *Potamotrygon* (=*Paratrygon*), with 25 or more named species. Two other genera (*Elipesurus* and *Disceus*), each with only one species, are in an uncertain state (Castex, 1968, 1969; Bailey, 1969). The systematic status of these genera and of the species of *Potamotrygon* is in need of thorough examination. Potamotrygonids are found in the larger drainage systems of South America that flow into the Caribbean and Atlantic, as well as some of the smaller systems. They represent the ultimate in freshwater adaptation in the elasmobranchs. In view of their uniqueness in lacking the otherwise universal elasmobranch characteristics of urea retention and a functioning rectal gland, they have been studied remarkably little and very little is known of their history on the South American continent. There is no fossil record to go by, as the only two references to fossil potamotrygonids are almost certainly invalid (Thorson and Watson, 1975), so evidence must be sought in living rays.

The fact that the full range of salinity preference and/or salt tolerance of elasmobranchs is represented among the various ray species suggested that a comparative study of that group might be a rich source of information bearing on the evolution of freshwater adaptation.

To obtain the desired information, we set out to collect freshwater stingrays from each of the major South American drainage systems in which they occur, as well as coastal species of rays in the vicinity where each system empties into the sea. We concentrated on features of ray biology that might be expected to have undergone change as the transition took place from the marine to the freshwater way of life. The aspects deemed most pertinent were (1) urea content of body fluids in relation to environmental salinity; (2) morphological and functional condition of the rectal gland, also in relation to environmental salinity; and (3) helminth parasite fauna of the gut.

In the hope of understanding better the phenomenon of freshwater adaptation in elasmobranchs in general, the data gathered during the investigation have been directed more specifically to questions regarding the potamotrygonids. These questions concern the physiology of osmoregulation of the freshwater rays, their zoogeographic origin and mode of colonization of their present range, and their phylogenetic history and affinities.

Fieldwork

National Geographic Society grants supported six, three- to six-week collecting trips from 1975 to 1979, on which Thorson was accompanied by asso-

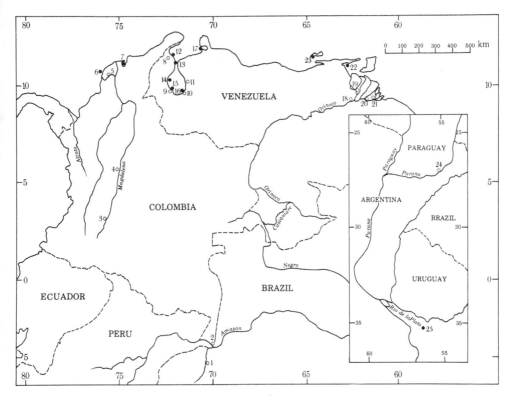

FIG. 1. Collecting sites: Open circles, freshwater rays, closed circles, coastal rays
(for key to locations, see table 1).

ciate investigators, Daniel R. Brooks and/or Monte A. Mayes, as follows:

Summer 1975 (Brooks), to Neiva, La Dorada, San Cristóbal, Quibdó, and Ciénaga
Grande de Santa Marta, Colombia.

Summer 1976 (Brooks and Mayes), to Cartagena, Ciénaga Grande de Santa Marta,
Quibdó, and Leticia, Colombia. We were also accompanied by assistants, Eddie
Parr, Joel T. Thorson, and Richard Cromwell.

Summer 1977 (Mayes), to Lago de Maracaibo and Golfo de Venezuela, Venezuela.

February-March 1978 (Brooks), with the Duke University collecting expedition to
the Orinoco Delta, Venezuela, on the M/V *Eastward,* supported by a National
Science Foundation grant to John G. Lundberg and Jonathan N. Baskin.

Summer 1978 (Mayes), to Lago de Maracaibo, Golfo de Venezuela, Golfo de Paria,
and Isla de Margarita, Venezuela.

Summer 1979 (Thorson only), to Paraná River, Paraguay, Río de la Plata, Uruguay,
and Lago de Maracaibo, Golfo de Venezuela, and Golfete de Coro, Venezuela.

TABLE 1.   Collecting Sites and Species
Taken from Five Drainage Systems (see fig. 1)

Drainage system	Freshwater species	Coastal species
AMAZON		
1. Río Itacuaí	*Potamotrygon circularis*	
2. Leticia	*P. circularis, P. motoro*	
MAGDALENA		
3. Neiva	Unsuccessful	
4. La Dorada	*P. magdalenae*	
5. San Cristóbal	*P. magdalenae*	
6. Cartagena		*Rhinobatos percellens, Narcine brasiliensis, Dasyatis americana, D. guttata, Urotrygon venezuelae, Urolophus jamaicensis, Aetobatus narinari*
7. Ciénaga Grande		*D. guttata, Himantura schmardae, Urotrygon venezuelae*
LAGO DE MARACAIBO		
8. Río Cachirí	*P. yepezi*	
9. El Congo	*P. yepezi*	
10. Bobures	*P. yepezi*	
11. Río Misoa	*P. yepezi*	
12. Golfo de Venezuela		*D. guttata, A. narinari, Rhinoptera bonasus*
13. Bahía de Tablazo		*D. guttata, H. schmardae, Rhinoptera bonasus*
14. Lago de Maracaibo		*D. guttata*
15. Lago de Maracaibo		*D. guttata, H. schmardae*
16. Lago de Maracaibo		*D. guttata, H. schmardae*
17. Golfete de Coro		*Rhinobatos percellens, N. brasiliensis, D. americana, D. guttata, Rhinoptera bonasus, A. narinari*
ORINOCO		
18. Los Castillos	*P. hystrix*[1]	
19. Tucupita	*Disceus thayeri*[1]	
20. El Toro vicinity	*P. reticulatus*	
21. Curiapo vicinity	*P. hystrix*[1]	
22. Golfo de Paria		*D. guttata, Rhinoptera bonasus*
23. Isla de Margarita		*Rhinobatos percellens, N. brasiliensis, D. americana, D. guttata, Gymnura micrura*
PARANÁ-RÍO DE LA PLATA		
24. Hohenau	*P. falkneri*	
25. Off Montevideo		*Myliobatis goodei*

[1] See Materials and Methods section

TABLE 2.   Serum Urea Concentration of Nine Species of
Freshwater Stingrays (Family Potamotrygonidae)

Drainage system species	No. of specimens	Urea concentration (mM/L)		Environ-mental salinity (ppt)	Collecting site
		Average	Range		
MAGDALENA					
Potamotrygon magdalenae	13	0.7	0.3-1.2	<0.01	San Cristóbal
LAGO DE MARACAIBO					
P. yepezi	4	1.6	1.1-2.1	3.4	El Congo, Bobures
P. yepezi	2	0.7	0.6-0.8	1.0	El Tulé (isolated pools)
AMAZON					
P. motoro	4	0.9	0.7-1.1	<0.01	Leticia
P. circularis	2	1.4	1.1-1.8	<0.01	Leticia
P. sp.	1	0.7		<0.01	Leticia
ORINOCO					
P. hystrix[1]	3	1.3	0.7-2.1	<0.01	Curiapo
P. hystrix[1]	1	4.0		?	Los Castillos (isolated pool)
P. reticulatus	5	1.1	0.5-2.0	<0.01	El Toro and Km 82
Disceus thayeri[1]	1	3.7		?	Tucupita
PARANÁ - RÍO DE LA PLATA					
P. falkneri	4	0.8	0.6-0.9	<0.01	Hohenau

[1] See Materials and Methods section

Materials and Methods

Collecting sites are shown in Figure 1 and named in Table 1, which also lists the species taken, by collecting site and drainage system.

We are reasonably confident of our identifications, except in one case. According to R. M. Bailey (pers. comm.), the specimens upon which one species (*Potamotrygon hystrix*) was erected may represent as many as three species and, depending on the resolution of the problem, our specimens may be *P. humboldti*. We refer to them throughout the following pages as *P. hystrix*. The specimens are on deposit at the U. S. National Museum of Natural History.

The identity of *Disceus thayeri* is not in question, but the controversy referred to leaves its correct name temporarily in doubt. In the absence of a decision by

TABLE 3.   Serum Urea Concentration in *Dasyatis guttata*
Taken From a Wide Range of Environmental Salinity

Urea concentration (mM/L)	Environmental salinity (ppt)	Urea concentration (mM/L)	Environmental salinity (ppt)
509	35.5	269	7.0
509	35.5	258	7.0
464	35.0	243	5.5
464	35.0	243	5.0
383	27-32	225	0-5
336	25.0	214	0-5
304	25.0	213	0-5
344	22.0	204	0-5
310	22.0	195	0-5
299	17.0	193	0-5
286	16.0	193	3.5
275	16.0	186	3.5
243	16.0	142	3.5
295	13.0	201	2.8
284	13.0	191	2.8

TABLE 4.   Serum Urea Concentration in Relation to Environmental Salinity
in Nine Species of Coastal Stingrays and the Potamotrygonidae

Species	No. of specimens	Urea concentration (mM/L)		Salinity range (ppt)	
		Average	Range	Specimens tested for urea	All specimens collected
Rhinobatos percellens	2	464	442-485	35	27-35.5
Narcine brasiliensis	13	285	269-377	27-35	27-35.5
Dasyatis americana	3	455	449-461	27-35	27-35.5
Dasyatis guttata	30	282	142-509	2.8-35.5	2.8-35.5
Himantura schmardae	3	208	186-249	4-25	4-25
Gymnura micrura	2	493	472-514	35	35
Urotrygon venezuelae	3	447	409-489	27-32	27-32
Aetobatus narinari	1	373	373	27-32	27-35.5
Rhinoptera bonasus	4	294	260-308	14-18	14-35.5
Potamotrygonidae	40	1.1	0.7-4.0	0-3.5	0-3.5

the International Commission on Zoological Nomenclature, we use the traditional binomial, to avoid confusion.

We had little trouble obtaining rays through Colombian, Venezuelan and United Nations fishery agencies; commercial fishermen and professional collectors; sport fishermen; local and visiting ichthyologists; and both volunteer and hired help. Specimens were taken on baited hook and line; gigs, harpoons and pointed sticks; by throw nets; two-man seines; long beach seines operated by crews of a dozen men or more; long gill nets operated from small boats; a small, homemade otter trawl on a 30-foot launch; commercial otter trawlers; and by the use of rotenone. One crew from whom we purchased coastal rays used dynamite.

For urea determinations, blood was taken by cardiac puncture from rays fresh enough so the heart was still beating. The blood was either spun in a field centrifuge or allowed to clot and the plasma or serum was frozen on dry ice. Samples were taken to the University of Nebraska-Lincoln or analyzed in a field laboratory. Urea concentrations were determined by Sigma kit, which employs the diacetyl monoxime method of Crocker (1967).

Rectal glands were removed from freshly caught rays. Some were preserved whole or in slices in Bouin's fluid (later changed to 70 percent ethyl alcohol), or neutral buffered formalin, for light microscopy. Some were cut in sections less than one millimeter thick and placed in glutaraldehyde for electron microscopy. Others were frozen on dry ice for enzyme assay.

Parasites were removed from the spiral valve, stomach, gills, and nasal membranes of freshly caught rays. The parasites were processed with standard procedures, stored in appropriate preservatives in vials, and returned to the home laboratories for study.

Results

UREA IN RELATION TO ENVIRONMENTAL SALINITY

Previous reports of low urea content in potamotrygonids have been restricted to *Potamotrygon motoro, P. circularis,* and species of uncertain or unspecified identity. Those of known origin were entirely from the Amazon drainage; others obtained from aquarium fish dealers were probably, although not necessarily, from the Amazon.

Table 2 shows the urea concentration of serum of 40 freshwater rays of nine species, from five major drainage systems, together with salinities in which they were taken.

Salinity of all flowing streams tested was near zero. At El Tulé, rays were taken from ponds below the El Tulé Dam, in the bed of the Río Cachirí, dur-

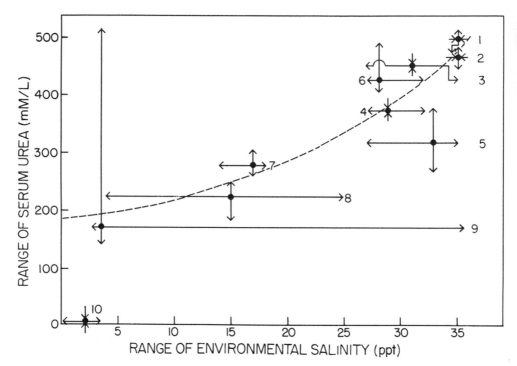

FIG. 2.   Range of serum urea concentration (vertical axis) in relation to environmental salinity (horizontal axis) in South American freshwater and coastal stingrays. Salinity ranges are only for those rays for which serum levels were determined (Table 4). Species numbered as in Figure 3. Dotted line indicates urea levels of *Dasyatis guttata* taken from the full range of environmental salinity.

ing a period of drought. The ponds had been subject to evaporation with no intake for many months and salinity was about one part per thousand. El Congo and Bobures are at the south end of Lake Maracaibo, where the salinity of collecting sites was more than three ppt. Such an environmental salinity places little stress on the osmoregulatory mechanisms, and, in view of the laboratory observation that potamotrygonids do not respond to elevated salinities by urea retention, no significance can be attached to slight differences in urea content. All are very low, even the slightly higher urea content of one *P. hystrix* and one *Disceus thayeri*, both taken from unknown salinities. At most, the urea levels are in the low range of mammalian urea concentrations and within the general range of those reported in potamotrygonids by Thorson (1970), by Thorson, Cowan, and Watson (1967), by Gerst and Thorson (1977), and by Griffith et al. (1973).

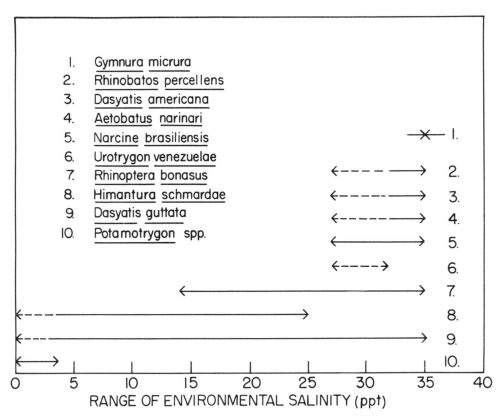

FIG. 3. Relative degree of euryhalinity of South American freshwater and coastal stingrays in terms of environmental salinity of all rays collected.

Although changes in urea content in relation to changed ambient salinity have been reported under experimental conditions in various elasmobranchs, the difference in urea content has never been documented for a single species over the whole range of environmental salinity. Table 3 provides such documentation for *D. guttata*. Urea concentration was determined in 30 individuals for which the environmental salinity was also known. Urea ranged from 509 millimoles per liter (mM/L) in 35.5 ppt to an average of ca. 183 (as low as 142) in 2.8 and 3.5 ppt.

Table 4 shows the urea concentration related to environmental salinity of *D. guttata* and eight additional species of coastal rays plus the family Potamotrygonidae. In most cases, too few specimens are involved to indicate the full range of tolerance and response to different salinities. Nevertheless, Table 4

TABLE 5.   Ratio of Rectal Gland Weight to Body Weight in Five Species of
Freshwater Stingrays of the Family Potamotrygonidae

Drainage system species	No. of specimens	Rectal gland weight/ body weight ratio (units per million)	
		Average	Range
LAGO DE MARACAIBO			
Potamotrygon yepezi	3	8.0	6-10
AMAZON			
P. circularis	3	20.7	15-26
P. sp.	1	8.0	
ORINOCO			
P. hystrix[1]	2	10.5	7-14
PARANÁ-RÍO DE LA PLATA			
P. falkneri	2	20.0	18-22

[1] See Materials and Methods section

indicates in a general way something of the degree of euryhalinity (or stenohalinity) of the species involved. Figure 2 shows graphically, for each species in Table 4, the range of urea concentration in relation to the range of environmental salinity from which all specimens tested for serum urea concentration were taken. The complete environmental salinity ranges from which all collected specimens were taken are shown in Figure 3 for the same species.

RECTAL GLAND IN RELATION TO ENVIRONMENTAL SALINITY

The presence of a rectal gland in elasmobranchs has been known since at least 1785 (Munro, 1785, Structure and Physiology of Fishes, cited by Crawford, 1899), but its function was unknown until Burger and Hess (1960) discovered that it served as a supplementary salt excretory organ. Oguri (1964) noted that the gland was larger in marine bull sharks (*Carcharhinus leucas*) than in the same species taken in fresh water of the Lake Nicaragua-Río San Juan System. The glands of the latter also showed some retrogressive histological features, as might be expected in an environment that calls for salt conservation rather than excretion. The discovery (Thorson, Cowan and Watson, 1967; Junqueira, Hoxter and Zago, 1968) that the freshwater stingrays of

TABLE 6. Ratio of Rectal Gland Weight to Body Weight in Seven Coastal Species of Stingrays, *Carcharhinus leucas* and the Family Potamotrygonidae

Species	No. of specimens	Rectal gland weight/ body weight ratio (units per million)		Environmental salinity (ppt)
		Average	Range	
Rhinobatos percellens	3	86	67-98	35
Narcine brasiliensis	3	76	74-79	27-35
Dasyatis americana	2	105	95-115	35
Dasyatis guttata	7	53	45-73	16-25
Dasyatis guttata	8	24	15-41	3-7
Gymnura micrura	1	67		35
Urotrygon venezuelae	6	107	82-138	27-32
Rhinoptera bonasus	1	300		30
Rhinoptera bonasus	5	157	135-171	18-22
Potamotrygonidae	11	14	6-26	fresh water
Carcharhinus leucas	1	78		"high," but not known
Carcharhinus leucas	4	28.5	19-44	fresh water

South America (Potamotrygonidae) had lost the ability to concentrate urea, as marine elasmobranchs do, raised the question of the status of the rectal gland, which would seem to be of no further use to elasmobranchs that live perpetually in fresh water. A minor controversy over this subject was settled when Thorson, Wotton and Georgi (1978) demonstrated the presence of a rectal gland in *Potamotrygon motoro* and *P. circularis,* albeit a much reduced one, and probably without secretory function.

The present investigation was aimed at observing the difference in size and activity of the rectal gland in relation to salinity of the habitat and to compare the structure in various species of freshwater rays from all the major South American drainage systems. This was done by determining the ratio of the weight of the gland to the total body weight and, in some cases, by histological examination of sections of the gland by light and/or electron microscopy.

Details of the microscopic examination are not yet available, but the weight ratios are reported in Table 5 (for five species of freshwater rays) and Table 6 (for coastal species of rays, the Potamotrygonidae and, for comparison, the bull shark *Carcharhinus leucas*).

The rectal gland weight/body weight ratio in relation to environmental salinity of all specimens for which that ratio was determined is shown graphically in Figure 4, which is based on the data in Table 6.

HELMINTH PARASITE FAUNA

During this investigation, we examined 237 freshwater and coastal sting-rays, representing 22 species, collected from 25 localities. From coastal rays, we collected 32 species of helminths, and from freshwater rays, 21 species, mostly cestodes in both cases. These account for nearly 50 percent of all hel-minth species known from South American elasmobranchs. Of the collected species, 35 were previously undescribed and 3 new genera were erected to ac-commodate some of them. About 20 papers will eventually have been pub-lished on our collections. (See all references listed for Brooks, Buckner, Deardorff, Fusco, and Mayes.)

No species of helminth occurred in both freshwater and marine sting-rays, although some species parasitized a variety of either marine or freshwater rays. Species occurring in freshwater rays comprised monophyletic groups in all cases. *Paravitellotrema overstreeti,* a digenetic trematode, and *Megapriapus ungriai,* an acanthocephalan, represent the only parasites of these two groups known from potamotrygonids. They are both more closely related to parasites of freshwater bony fishes than they are to parasites of elasmobranchs. The oth-er 20 species of helminths known from potamotrygonids clearly are most closely related to groups parasitizing marine elasmobranchs.

We also collected helminth parasites from a variety of freshwater bony fishes. No species were found infecting both potamotrygonids and any bony fish. Cestodes representing the order Proteocephalidea exhibit their greatest diversity in South American siluriform fishes, but no proteocephalidean oc-curred in potamotrygonids. Similarly, 13 species of tetraphyllidean and one species of trypanorhynchan cestodes, characteristic of marine elasmobranchs, parasitize potamotrygonids and none occurs in siluriforms.

REPRODUCTION AND DEVELOPMENT

Incidental to the findings presented in this report related specifically to freshwater adaptation, extensive data were recorded on various other aspects of the biology of South American stingrays. Foremost among these were their re-production and development. Observations were made on male and female re-productive systems; various other reproductive parameters were observed and recorded; developing young were preserved; and proportional measurements were made of several fetal and postnatal stages, through sexual maturity. The findings on reproduction and development of *Potamotrygon circularis* and *P. motoro* have been prepared for publication elsewhere (Thorson, Langhammer, and Oetinger, 1983) and will not be presented here.

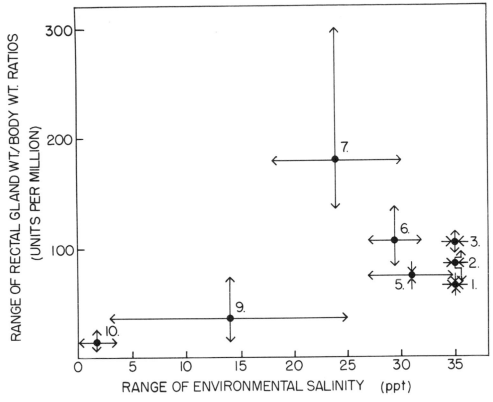

Fig. 4. Range of rectal gland weight/body weight ratio (vertical axis) in relation to environmental salinity (horizontal axis). Salinity range given only for those rays for which the ratio was determined (Table 6). Species numbered as in Figure 3.

Discussion and Conclusions

Full strength sea water is approximately a molar solution (1000 mM/L) of a mixture of solutes, mostly inorganic ions. An elasmobranch acclimated to this external medium adjusts its internal solute content (especially by urea retention) to a level slightly hyperosmotic to that of sea water. This results in a moderate osmotic uptake of water, just sufficient in volume to provide for metabolic needs. Overloading with salt is prevented by excretion of the excess by the kidneys and by an active rectal gland. If the same animal were transferred to water of progressively lower salinity, without any internal adjustment of solute level, or reduction of rectal gland secretion, osmotic uptake of water would increase until the volume was so massive that urine production could not balance the uptake, salts would be reduced below tolerable levels, and the animal would inevitably die from overhydration or salt depletion. This is in fact what has happened in most laboratory attempts to transfer elasmobranchs taken from sea water into fresh water, unless the subjects were promptly returned to higher salinities. There has been no successful attempt to acclimate elasmobranchs to completely fresh water except in species mentioned earlier which enter fresh water in nature. The reason for the failure is quite simply the use of species that are incapable of making the necessary osmoregulatory adjustments, especially (1) by sufficiently lowering the urea level, thus limiting the influx of water to a tolerable rate, and (2) by reducing and eventually stopping salt loss by damping and finally shutting off the rectal gland.

These two capabilities would appear to be absolute prerequisites for complete freshwater adaptation of elasmobranchs. The comparative data we have accumulated on these two subjects from our series of stingrays are discussed separately.

UREA RETENTION

If the transition of the Potamotrygonidae to fresh water were a recent phenomenon, still in progress in some members of the family, it would seem reasonable that a gradient of urea retention might be found in those members occurring in geographic situations where the transition was facilitated by a broad zone of gradually changing environmental salinity. Such an interface between marine and fresh water exists in the Orinoco Delta, where a vast network of channels with a very slight elevation gradient provides a fluctuating salinity gradient determined primarily by tides and seasonal rainfall. Perhaps an even more ideal interface is provided by the Gulf of Venezuela and Lake Maracaibo, where salinity ranges from full strength sea water (or even hypersaline conditions) in the Gulf, through varying intermediate salinities, to fresh water at the south end of the lake, at least during rainy seasons and around river mouths. During the times we were present (always during the months of July and August), salinities on the south shore of the lake were from 2.8 to 3.5 ppt, but salinities at all points are highly variable and dependent upon seasonal rainfall and other physical factors.

No evidence can be found in Table 2 to demonstrate a urea gradient within the Potamotrygonidae related to distance from the sea. The stingrays taken closest to the sea (*Potamotrygon hystrix* at Curiapo in the Orinoco Delta, and *P. yepezi* at El Tulé, in the northern part of the Maracaibo Basin) had urea ranges essentially identical with those of *P. motoro* and *P. circularis* from the upper Amazon (ca. 3400 km from the sea). Furthermore, the ranges within the various drainage systems overlap one another. The process of suppression of urea retention appears to have been completed in all living species of potamotrygonids tested. However, urea-producing enzymes are present and urea is still a major excretory product in the family (Goldstein and Forster, 1971; Gerst and Thorson, 1977).

Potamotrygonids represent the ultimate in freshwater adaptation among elasmobranchs. They have not only abandoned urea retention as an osmoregulatory mechanism, but are incapable of calling upon this ancestral strategem effectively even when transferred experimentally to higher environmental salinities. They have a very narrow range of urea concentrations, and have never been reported in salinities greater than 3.4 ppt in nature (this study). They are normally found only in water with a salinity of near zero (Table 2, figs. 2 and 3).

Next to potamotrygonids, the three elasmobranchs best adapted to fresh water, of all those studied, are (1) *Dasyatis garouaensis,* a stingray of the Benue River in Nigeria and Cameroon (Thorson and Watson, 1975); (2) *Pristis perotteti,* the largetooth sawfish of the Lake Nicaragua-Río San Juan System (Thorson, 1982); and (3) *Carcharhinus leucas,* the bull shark of the Lake Nicaragua-Río San Juan System (Thorson, 1976). After weeks, months, or even years in fresh water, their urea concentrations may decline to a level of about 212 mM/L for *D. garouaensis* (Thorson and Watson, 1975), approximately 100 for *P. perotteti* (Thorson, unpublished data), and around 170 for *C. leucas* (Thorson, Cowan, and Watson, 1973). In these and every other elasmobranch species reported to have been tested in reduced salinities (other than potamotrygonids) the urea level was reduced by as much as 50-80 percent below the typical marine urea level, but in no case did it drop below some minimal level where it was maintained regardless of how long the animals remained in the reduced salinity.

The stingray species that inhabit the inshore waters of the Caribbean Sea along the northern South American coast include illustrations of several stages between the fully marine degree of urea retention and those of the three species mentioned above. Their relative degree of euryhalinity is shown in terms of urea retention and environmental salinity of collecting sites *of those tested for urea* in Figure 2 (based on Table 4) and solely in terms of environmental salinity *of all rays collected* in Figure 3 (also based on Table 4). *Gymnura micrura* (1) was collected only in full strength sea water and both specimens taken had among the highest levels of urea. It appears to be the most restricted to salt water of all species taken. *Rhinobatos percellens* (2), *Dasyatis americana* (3), *Aetobatus narinari* (4), *Narcine brasiliensis* (5), and *Urotrygon venezuelae* (6), are all inshore, relatively shallow water forms, taken in waters of several collecting sites varying from 27-32 ppt to full strength sea water (35 or 35.5 ppt).

Whereas *G. micrura* is relatively stenohaline (at the marine end of the spectrum), species 2-6 have a wider tolerance to saline conditions (are more euryhaline), but also tend to prefer areas of relatively high salinity. *Rhinoptera bonasus* (7) has a still wider range of salinity tolerance, having been taken from waters of 14-35.5 ppt. Urea was tested only in specimens from 14-18 ppt salinity, and urea values are therefore relatively low, but would probably rise to the usual marine levels if specimens from full strength sea water were tested. The species is migratory, passing long distances through the open sea, so is clearly capable of dealing with high salinities for protracted periods, as well as intermediate salinities.

Himantura schmardae (8) and *Dasyatis guttata* (9) were taken in all the major coastal collecting sites that had relatively low salinities (ranging down to completely fresh water in river mouths). These sites were in Lake Maracaibo, Venezuela, and Ciénaga Grande, Colombia, as well as the mouths of the Río San Juan-Río Colorado, Costa Rica). Occurrence of *H. schmardae* was limited to salinities of 0.0 ppt up to 25 ppt, and it was never taken in the sea in the long beach seines and gill nets with which most of our coastal collections were made. *D. guttata,* on the other hand, was taken in the same places where *H. schmardae* was found, but was also taken in all major collecting sites in the sea, including the same waters where species 1-7 were taken, with salinities up to 35 and 35.5 ppt. Bigelow and Schroeder (1953) state that nothing whatever is known of the habits of *D. guttata* and they make no mention of its occurrence in low salinities. Our findings show that *D. guttata* is clearly the most euryhaline of all ray species studied, occurring in the complete range of environmental salinities and having a broad range of urea levels, correlated clearly with the environmental salinities of collecting sites (dotted line in fig. 2, based on data in table 3). *H. schmardae* has also been treated in the literature as a marine ray. Bigelow and Schroeder (1953) mention no preference for fresh or brackish water, but remark that nothing is known of their habits. Their references to collecting sites are not explicit enough to indicate the environmental salinity. Castro-Aguirre (1978) reports the species in two coastal, brackish water lagoons in Mexico. Our observations indicate that both the range of salinity tolerance and the range of urea levels of *H. schmardae* clearly characterize it as a brackish water form, preferring intermediate to low salinities. We took both *H. schmardae* and *D. guttata* near river mouths, where the salinity might be virtually zero, but we have taken neither species above the mouth of any river. Nevertheless, of all species studied that do not actually penetrate fresh water regularly or for prolonged periods, these two species appear to be closest to having sufficient osmoregulatory versatility to do so.

The degree of euryhalinity of an elasmobranch stems in large part from the range of its ability to respond to changes in environmental salinity by raising or lowering the levels of urea in its body fluids. It is reasonable to speculate that, assuming a marine ancestry for the Potamotrygonidae (see discussion below), the present-day forms of that family are the end product of a progression in the range of this response to salinity levels from (1) the STENOHALINE, MARINE condition such as found in *G. micrura* (and undoubtedly most elasmobranchs in deep water or the open sea); through (2) the EURYHALINE BUT RELATIVELY HIGH SALINITY condition of species 2-6; (3) EURYHALINITY EXTENDED TO INTERMEDIATE SALINITIES, as in *R. bonasus;* (4) the FULLY EURYHALINE condition of *D. guttata;* (5) EURYHALINITY RESTRICTED TO INTERMEDIATE AND LOW SALINITIES, as in *H. schmardae;* (6) EURYHALINITY SUCH AS THAT OF *C. leucas,* ALLOWING LONG PERIODS IN FRESH WATER, BUT REPRODUCTION STILL TAKING PLACE IN COASTAL, BRACKISH WATER; (7) EURYHALINITY OF *P. perotteti,* ALLOWING MANY YEARS, POTENTIALLY THE COMPLETE LIFE CYCLE, IN FRESH WATER, INCLUDING REPRODUCTION; and eventually (8) THE END POINT, THE POTAMOTRYGONIDAE, in which the unique elasmobranch osmoregulatory feature, urea retention, has been completely suppressed. They are highly stenohaline, at the freshwater end of the spectrum, functioning essentially as do the freshwater bony fishes.

RECTAL GLAND

As is true for urea retention, the excretion of salt by a rectal gland has also been totally suppressed in the Potamotrygonidae. Both would be counterproductive for a fish living in fresh water. The rectal gland persists in potamotrygonids, but is greatly reduced in size. The tubules that secrete salt in marine elasmobranchs are still in evidence, but are sparsely distributed in much connective tissue (Thorson, Wotton, and Georgi, 1978). The glands have no known function in fresh water. They are apparently incapable of secreting salt, even when the rays are gradually transferred to salt water. When environmental salinity is experimentally increased beyond ca. 10-15 ppt, the concentration of salts builds up in the body fluids and death ensues (Thorson, 1970; Griffith et al., 1973; Gerst and Thorson, 1977; Bittner and Lang, 1980).

Five species of *Potamotrygon,* from four drainage systems, vary little among themselves in relative size of rectal gland, as indicated by the ratio of rectal gland weight to body weight (Table 5).

In previous work it has been found that the gland is much more prominent in marine elasmobranchs than in euryhaline or freshwater species and that potamotrygonids have the smallest rectal glands of all chondrichthyans (Thorson, Wotton, and Georgi, 1978). This is borne out in Table 6 and Figure 4, where relative rectal gland size is given for 7 species of coastal rays, the potamotrygonids of Table 5, and *Carcharhinus leucas* from Table 6. Figure 4 indicates that, except for *Rhinoptera bonasus* (No. 7), the relationship of rectal gland size to environmental salinity is much the same as that of urea concentration (fig. 2). The inshore, shallow water species, Nos. 1-6, (here lacking No. 4, *Aetobatus narinari*), had a somewhat higher rectal gland weight to body weight ratio than the highly euryhaline *Dasyatis guttata* (specimens taken from relatively low salinities). This same group of species was clustered somewhat similarly as regards urea concentration (fig. 2), i.e., they all had relatively high urea content as well as rectal gland size, and were restricted to relatively high salinities. *D. guttata* has a very wide salinity tolerance and its urea retention varies directly with salinity throughout the whole salinity range. However, its rectal gland size was determined only from specimens taken from salinities up to 25 ppt, so we can only surmise that the gland is larger in the specimens taken from full-strength sea water.

Rhinoptera bonasus is the only species that does not fall into the pattern of the others. Its relative rectal gland size is distinctly greater than that of the others. As noted, the cownose ray is migratory and must be equipped to deal with high salinity for long periods. However, the species taken along the shores of Isla Margarita (*G. micrura, R. percellens, D. americana,* and *N. brasiliensis*) are also in full strength sea water virtually continuously, since the island is semiarid and there is seldom much runoff into coastal waters. The day we arrived there was a rare heavy rain and parts of the island were flooded, but water at all collecting sites contained no less than 35 ppt salt. *R. bonasus* is a thick-bodied, heavy ray, and those used for Figure 4 were far larger than any of species 1-5. However, within a species, large (older) individuals tend to have smaller rectal glands than the small (young) ones, so on that basis *R. bonasus* would be expected to have a relatively smaller rectal gland rather than a larger one. An examination of the histology of the glands and of the intensity of their secretory activity may disclose that the glands of species 1-5 are more efficient or sustain more intense activity than in *R. bonasus*. Burger (1972) found that *Dasyatis sabina,* a highly euryhaline ray found in inshore waters of the Atlantic Coast of the United States, had a rectal gland/body weight ratio of 240 units per million, as compared with *Squalus acanthias* whose ratio was 600 (both from full strength sea water). The volume of rectal gland fluid secreted was also smaller than that of *S. acanthias,* but its chloride concentration was greater, so the total chloride output of the two species was nearly equal, in spite of the disparity of rectal gland size.

The relative size of the rectal gland not only differs between species in different salinities, but also changes within a species that can tolerate a wide range of salinity. This was shown for the completely euryhaline *Carcharhinus leucas* by Oguri (1964) and was confirmed by our own rectal gland weight to body weight ratios (Table 6). Ratios of four adult *C. leucas* from fresh water averaged 28.5 units per million and one from coastal water was 78 (salinity relatively high but not measured). The same general relationship is found in the fully euryhaline *D. guttata*. Seven individuals from salinities of 16-25 ppt had ratios from 45 to 73 (average 53), while 8 from salinities of 3-5 ppt had 15 to 41 (average, 24). It should be noted that several of both the freshwater *C. leucas* and *D. guttata* had ratios in the upper range of those of *Potamotrygon*. In a third species, *R. bonasus*, the cownose ray, which migrates long distances through the open sea, 5 specimens taken in salinities from 18 to 22 ppt had ratios of 135-171 (average, 157), while a single specimen taken in 30 ppt had a considerably larger gland (ratio of 300).

Again assuming a marine ancestry for the family Potamotrygonidae, its rectal gland must also have progressed, in its full adaptation to fresh water, through all degrees of salt-excreting capability, as illustrated in living forms by the following five stages:

(1) ESSENTIALLY STENOHALINE, MARINE *(Squalus acanthias* of other studies).   The spiny dogfish may at times enter moderately brackish water, but it does not normally enter fresh water (Bigelow and Schroeder, 1948), and has never been successfully acclimated to salinities substantially reduced from full strength sea water. No information is available on the rectal gland function of any pelagic or deep water elasmobranchs. Therefore, inshore, relatively shallow water species like *S. acanthias* are the only elasmobranchs available to use as examples having essentially a fully marine rectal gland. Presumably such a gland would be a relatively large one, packed with active secretory tubules incapable of turning down their activity sufficiently to conserve salt in fresh water or moderately low salinities. The rectal gland of *S. acanthias* satisfies the first two conditions: Its rectal gland weight to body weight ratio has been reported as 444 (Bonting, 1966) and 600 (Burger, 1972), higher than ratios of any species reported in the present study; and various studies have demonstrated that *S. acanthias* has a rectal gland containing a mass of solidly packed secreting tubules (e.g., Bulger, 1963). However, no rectal gland studies on *S. acanthias* or any other marine species have proceeded far enough in reduced salinities to demonstrate a damping down of rectal gland activity in salinities low enough to be critical. Burger (1965) studied rectal gland secretion in *S. acanthias* transferred to salinities of 60-92 percent sea water. In such an external medium, the concentration of salts in the rectal gland secretion was only slightly reduced, while the volume increased, so total salt excretion probably increased. The animals became overhydrated, as indicated by lowered hemat-

ocrit readings. If Burger's suggestion is correct, that the stimulus for activating the rectal gland includes a volume component, this might explain the continued (and increased) production of rectal gland fluid and would suggest that in lower and lower environmental salinities, the problem would become more and more acute, and, unless salt loss could be stopped, death would certainly result from a combination of water and solute imbalances.

(2) EURYHALINE, WITH PREFERENCE FOR RELATIVELY HIGH TO INTERMEDIATE SALINITIES (species 1-7 of this study; *Hemiscyllium plagiosum* of others). Judging from their positions in Figures 3 and 4, species 1-7 should satisfy the hypothetical requirements of a rectal gland suited for this stage: A moderately large gland, well-supplied with secretory tubules sufficient to accommodate the need for excess salt secretion, but possessing a limited ability to regulate such secretion in reduced salinities. The size (fig. 4) and secretory capabilities of the rectal glands of these species apparently satisfy this characterization, as attested by the species' ranges of environmental salinity tolerance (fig. 3). However, we made no study of the volume and composition of the rectal gland fluid itself, and we can only assume that failure to shut off secretion by the rectal gland of these species is probably a factor in their absence from waters of low salinities, as appears to be the case in *H. plagiosum* studied by Wong and Chan (1977). These investigators kept *H. plagiosum* in 50 percent sea water for 6 days of acclimation plus various experimental periods. After acclimation to 50 percent sea water, the volume of rectal gland fluid (per unit of weight and time) remained the same as in 100 percent sea water, while the urine output increased by 278 percent. The concentration of Na^+ and Cl^- in the rectal gland fluid (mM/L) dropped by about 40 percent. After acclimation, however, the body weight of the sharks had increased by 26 percent. Allowing for this added water, the actual output of rectal gland fluid (rather than volume per unit of weight and time) increased by 26 percent, so the 40-percent decline in concentration of salts represented only a 25-percent reduction in actual quantity of salt excreted. We see then that in half strength sea water, the rectal gland of *H. plagiosum* continues to function almost at its rate in full-strength sea water. The rate of salt loss is somewhat reduced, but the difficulties of overhydration seen in half strength sea water are compounded when environmental salinity is further reduced. Chan and Wong (1977) reported experiments in which *H. plagiosum* were subjected to gradual dilution of the external medium to a salinity of about 12 percent sea water (ca. 4 ppt). Throughout the period of study the animals continued to gain weight (water) to a maximum of ca. 30-40 percent; plasma volume almost doubled and intramuscular fluid space expanded appreciably; hematocrit declined by more than 50 percent; and plasma concentration (total osmolarity) of electrolytes (Na^+,

K^+, and Cl⁻) all declined a little more or less than 50 percent. By the time the dilution had reached ca. 20-percent sea water (7 ppt), the bodies became stiff and blanched, and death occurred at 12 percent (4 ppt). They very likely passed their lethal limit well before the 20-percent level. They were caught in coastal waters of Hong Kong in salinities of 25-34 ppt. The species makes brief excursions into less saline waters to feed but probably are restricted (for permanent residence) to the cited salinities. Rectal gland secretion was not studied at these extended dilutions, but it is probable that *H. plagiosum* is incapable of "shutting off" its rectal gland; neither it nor the kidneys appear to be designed for life in low salinities.

(3) FULL EURYHALINITY, BUT NOT ORDINARILY OCCURRING IN FRESH WATER *(Dasyatis guttata* of this study; *D. sabina* of others).   It was seen that *D. guttata* tolerates the full range of salinity, from fresh water to full-strength sea water; its urea content varies accordingly, through the full range of urea concentration found in other elasmobranchs, except Potamotrygonidae; and its rectal gland is relatively small. However, glands were only weighed in specimens taken from salinities of 25 ppt or less and it is almost certain that specimens taken in full-strength sea water would have relatively larger rectal glands. *D. sabina,* a species of very similar habits and similarly broad range of salinity tolerance, had (in specimens from sea water) rectal glands with a relative weight of 240 units per million (Burger, 1972). This is more than twice the relative size of glands in species 1-6, and it is within the range of those of *Rhinoptera bonasus.* In the absence of information on rectal gland function of *D. guttata,* some findings of various studies on *D. sabina* are presented. Burger's (1972) study concerned glands functioning in an external medium of undiluted sea water (salinity not specified). The rate of chloride secretion by the rectal gland in this medium was similar to that of *Squalus acanthias.* There is no question that this fully euryhaline species osmoregulates completely effectively in its marine phase. Studies of *D. sabina* in different salinities have been reported by de Vlaming and Sage (1973) and by Beitz (1977). The latter compared the rays in two salinities, 29-32 ppt (about 90% sea water) and 34-40 ppt (ca. 110%) and confirmed that the species has a rectal gland that performs well in sea water, but tells nothing about what happens to it in substantially lower salinities. The study of de Vlaming and Sage did not specifically concern the rectal gland, except by implication. These investigators transferred *D. sabina,* after 7 days' acclimation in a medium of 805 mM/L, to 322 mM/L (about 1/3 full-strength sea water) for 1, 3, 6, and 12 days. They found that body weight (water content) increased slightly, but reached its maximum in one day and returned to its original value by 3 days and then stabilized; muscle water increased very slightly in 24 hours, but then dropped

back a little and stabilized; hematocrit dropped slightly in 24 hours but returned to its original value by 3 days and then stabilized; plasma sodium dropped within 24 hours but then remained on a plateau; and urea dropped from 352 mM/L to 245 in one day, to 214 by 3 days, then remained relatively stable. In brief, in salinity reduced to 1/3 sea water (11 ppt), *D. sabina* functions very effectively, including, by implication, its rectal gland. Unfortunately, the only evidence in salinities lower than 11 ppt for either *D. guttata* or *D. sabina* is that provided by the fact that they both are known to be taken in water that is completely fresh (our observations for *D. guttata;* Gunter (1938) for *D. sabina*). The oldest (largest) *D. guttata* tend to be found in water of lower salinities in Lake Maracaibo. In several of these large ones, the rectal glands appeared to be wasting away and in some cases were difficult or impossible to find. There appears to be a progression, within the life cycle, from an active, morphologically well-developed rectal gland in the very young, through gradually reduced stages, to an atrophied, probably nonfunctioning gland in old age.

(4) FULLY EURYHALINE, ABLE TO PENETRATE FRESH WATER FOR LONG PERIODS *(Carcharhinus leucas).* Oguri (1964), Gerzeli et al. (1969), Thorson, Wotton, and Georgi (1978) and this study have shown that the size of the rectal gland is appreciably smaller in bull sharks taken from fresh water than in those taken from the sea. Oguri also reported that the freshwater glands have undergone regression, with relatively fewer tubules and a greater proportion of connective tissue. The gland remains prominent throughout life, however, and no tendency has been observed for older (larger) ones to favor fresh water more than in earlier life. The evidence available for the ability of bull sharks to turn off their rectal glands when in fresh water consists only of the implied evidence of their survival for long periods in fresh water. Tagging records indicate repeated catching of individual bull sharks in Lake Nicaragua (as many as five times) over a period of 4 or 5 years (Thorson, unpublished data). These might conceivably have returned to the sea between captures, but sharks found in Lake Bayano, a freshwater impoundment in Panama created by a dam four years earlier, were barred from returning to the sea during that time (Vásquez and Thorson, 1982). Further evidence can be inferred from studies that have been made on various aspects of the osmoregulation of *C. leucas* in fresh water compared with the same or other species in the sea (Thorson, 1962; Urist, 1962; Thorson and Gerst, 1972; Thorson, Cowan, and Watson, 1973). In composite, these studies indicate the following: Freshwater *C. leucas* has urea reduced by about 55 percent from marine levels; electrolyte concentrations are reduced by 15-20 percent; hematocrit is maintained, in fact is slightly higher in freshwater sharks; total body water is virtually identical in

fresh water and saline water; plasma volume is about the same, or slightly less in fresh water. There can be no doubt that *C. leucas* is well equipped for effective osmoregulation in fresh water as well as in sea water, which would have to include a rectal gland that can accommodate completely to both media. *Pristis perotteti* likewise can function well in both media, but the Lake Nicaragua-Río San Juan population probably spends most or all of its life in fresh water (Thorson, 1982). Its rectal gland, as in *D. guttata,* appears to undergo pronounced reduction after its immature years. *Dasyatis garouaensis* appears to spend its whole life in fresh water and reproduces there (Thorson and Watson, 1975). However, there is uncertainty as to whether or not it is restricted to fresh water and whether or not it can tolerate transfer to salt water. It has a rectal gland, but nothing is known of its ability to secrete Na^+ and Cl^-.

(5) THE END POINT, THE POTAMOTRYGONIDAE, in which the rectal gland has atrophied and its function has been suppressed and cannot be "turned on."

PROPOSED ANSWERS TO QUESTIONS CONCERNING THE PHYLOGENETIC AND ZOO-GEOGRAPHIC HISTORY OF THE POTAMOTRYGONIDAE

Cladistic analysis of the helminth parasites collected from both freshwater and coastal species of stingrays has been presented elsewhere. Only a brief summary of the findings is included here. Readers who are interested in a more detailed discussion and support for the conclusions are referred to the original paper by Brooks, Thorson and Mayes (1981).

We propose the following answers to a series of questions concerning the potamotrygonids, based on parasitological and/or physiological data:

(1) ARE THE POTAMOTRYGONIDAE A MONOPHYLETIC OR POLYPHYLETIC GROUP? Species of helminths infecting freshwater rays comprise, or are members of, relatively highly derived, monophyletic taxa in all cases, strongly suggesting a monophyletic origin for potamotrygonids. Consistent with this view are (a) the fact that all potamotrygonid species studied have completely lost their urea retention capability and there are no demonstrable differences between species in urea retention nor are urea gradients in evidence within species; (b) the finding that the rectal gland is approximately equally atrophied in all species studied; and (c) the presence in all known potamotrygonid species of a long, slender, prepelvic process, which is not found in any of the most closely allied batoid families (Dasyatidae, Gymnuridae, and Urolophidae).

(2) WERE THEY DERIVED FROM FRESHWATER OR MARINE ANCESTRY? Although we have proceeded on the commonly held assumption that the freshwater rays descended from marine ancestry, questions have

been raised as to whether they may have arisen from freshwater elasmobranch ancestors that arose in, and never left fresh water (see discussion in Thorson, Wotton, and Georgi, 1978). The potamotrygonid helminth fauna comprises species whose closest relatives occur almost exclusively in marine elasmobranchs rather than in freshwater bony fishes, suggesting for potamotrygonids a common ancestry with some marine stingray stock. A marine origin is also indicated by the presence, in all species studied, of a vestigial rectal gland, which is a well developed and functioning salt-secreting structure in all other elasmobranchs, both marine and euryhaline.

(3) WERE THEY DERIVED FROM ATLANTIC OR PACIFIC ANCESTRY? The usual assumption is that, since all drainage systems of South America inhabited by potamotrygonids empty into the Atlantic, those drainage systems were colonized by invasion by marine stingrays from the Atlantic. However, with few exceptions, the closest genealogical relatives of parasite taxa whose members infect potamotrygonids have a circum-Pacific distribution pattern, suggesting that geographic affinities are Pacific rather than Atlantic.

(4) WHAT IS THE SISTER GROUP? No helminth parasite species found in potamotrygonids has also been found in any marine elasmobranch species. However, 5 genera of close genealogical relatives are found in a variety of coastal stingray species. All 5 genera are found in *Urolophus* (one, *Eutetrarhynchus,* only in *Urolophus*) and 11 of the 16 species have *Urolophus* as a host. By contrast, only 1 species is known from the genus *Aetobatus,* 2 from *Myliobatis,* 2 from *Himantura,* and 3 from *Dasyatis.* This suggests that at least some urolophids and the potamotrygonids harbor parasites derived from a common ancestral helminth fauna which may have occurred in a common ancestral host, suggesting a close phylogenetic relationship between urolophids and potamotrygonids. It should be noted that the distribution of the urolophids is, with the exception of one species, exclusively Pacific.

(5) HOW DID POTAMOTRYGONIDS COLONIZE THEIR PRESENT GEOGRAPHIC RANGE? If we reject (as we have) the origin of potamotrygonids from ancestors that had no marine history, the common assumption would be that the family occupied South American fresh waters either by invasion of each drainage system individually by different marine stingrays, or by one major invasion of one system followed by dispersal into all systems presently inhabited by the family. Our parasitological findings have rejected both possibilities and replaced them with the proposal that the family Potamotrygonidae arose from Pacific urolophids that became entrapped by Andean orogeny in what was originally Pacific sea water, but gradually became brackish, was entirely cut off from the Pacific, and eventually became the freshwater drainage systems of the present time.

(6) WHAT WAS THE TIME SCALE FOR THE EVOLUTIONARY HISTORY OF POTAMOTRYGONIDAE? Reliable time markers of evolutionary history, ordinarily provided by fossils, are entirely lacking for potamotrygonids. Two references to fossil potamotrygonids (Larrazet, 1886; Arambourg, 1947) have found their way into the literature, but both are now considered highly questionable (see Thorson and Watson, 1975). Although we have no specific time markers of any kind, several lines of evidence are at hand to support the passage of a very long period of time for the complete adaptation of potamotrygonids to life in fresh water: (a) The extent of speciation. At least 25 species of potamotrygonids have been described and named in South American fresh waters. Even though some of these may prove on closer study to be ill-founded, the group has obviously been present long enough for extensive evolution to occur. (b) Rectal gland atrophy. The present study shows that the great reduction in size of the rectal gland and number of secretory tubules and the loss of salt-secreting function reported previously for *Potamotrygon motoro* and *P. circularis* (Thorson, Wotton, and Georgi, 1978) have also occurred in all other species studied. The morphological reduction of the gland and the complete suppression of its function in a group whose marine and euryhaline relatives so universally employ the gland in their osmoregulation suggest a long history in fresh water. (c) Suppression of urea retention. It was seen in Table 2 that freshwater rays of all species studied, from all of the five major South American drainage systems, definitely share the complete lack of urea concentration reported by earlier workers in *Potamotrygon motoro* and *P. circularis*. The complete abandonment of urea retention, without even a vestigial ability to call on this response in elevated salinities, with no gradient of the phenomenon in evidence within a species or within the family, and occurring as it does in a group in which urea retention is otherwise so universally found, argues strongly for a long existence of the Potamotrygonidae in fresh water. They probably all lost their capability for urea retention essentially before (or perhaps early in the process of) occupation of their present ranges.

On the basis of our cladistic analysis of the helminth fauna of South American stingrays, we have hypothesized a chronology of the history of potamotrygonid evolution from Pacific, urolophid ancestry. We believe it to be consistent with the geological history of South America and the evolution of South American freshwater habitats (based primarily on Kummel, 1962; Harrington, 1965; and Putzer, 1969). Although the additional data presented in this report do not provide direct evidence for a specific time scale, they are entirely compatible with the time frame as set forth by Brooks, Thorson, and Mayes (1981, pp. 168-170), concerning the attainment by potamotrygonids of their present existence:

By the beginning of the Cretaceous, *Urolophus*-like ancestral stingrays comprised part of a coastal stingray fauna occurring along the west coast of South America. By the mid to late Cretaceous, Andean orogeny had created a shallow saline inland body of water communicating with the Pacific in the north, which was to remain open until the Miocene. From later Cretaceous to Miocene, continuing orogeny and fresh-water runoff resulted in progressive desalination of the inland water and sediment subduction along the western edge of the emerging Andes. During this period a number of batoid elasmobranchs which occurred sympatrically with the urolophid ancestors disappeared from the area, leaving the incipient potamotrygonids as the only remnant of that portion of the ancestral elasmobranch fauna.

Paleocene to Miocene geographic changes in South America produced isolated fresh-water habitats beginning in the southern part of the continent (Paraná drainage) and proceeding northward. Potamotrygonids and their parasites were isolated by those same geographic changes; the Paraná-Paraguay system was probably isolated in the Paleocene. The Amazon basin became a separate eastward-flowing entity in the Miocene. Terminal Andean orogeny in the Pliocene-Pleistocene along with eustatic drops in sea level produced, as fresh-water habitats, the Magdalena River system, the Orinoco River system, and the Maracaibo area. Since the Paleocene, there has been apparent post-isolation dispersion by potamotrygonids and their parasites from fresh-water isolated areas of greater age to those of lesser age, such as from the Paraná to the Amazon or the Amazon to the Orinoco. Some cases of apparent dispersion may also be the result of isolation without speciation. In either case, the "noise" produced by plesiomorphic or convergent dispersion has not overshadowed the "signal" of evolution consistent with the geographical evolution of South America since the beginning of the Cretaceous.

Acknowledgments

We appreciate financial support provided by the National Geographic Society; grants from the University of Nebraska-Lincoln Research Council; and permission to accompany the R/V *Eastward* on a collecting cruise in the Orinoco Delta financed by a National Science Foundation grant to John G. Lundberg and Jonathan N. Baskin.

For help in all stages and aspects of our investigation, we are indebted to far too many individuals and institutions to mention, but for major aid in obtaining stingrays and providing facilities, we must mention the following: In VENEZUELA, Dr. Francisco Mago Leccia, Antonio Rios, Héctor Barrios, José Moscó M., Alfredo Gómez G., Donald G. Taphorn, Craig and Maria Lilyestrom, Harold and Lynn Longaker, Dr. Emery, Caroline and Eric Sutton, and the owner, captain, and crew of the trawler *Dantjole;* in COLOMBIA, Orlando Mora Lara, Augusto Samper M., Alvaro Boada Guarín, Guillermo Quiñones

González, Adolfo Barón Porras, Alberto Villaneda, Dr. James M. Kapetsky, Dr. David A. Conroy, Hans Heinrich, Mike Tsalickis, William Mackay, and Dean Hendrickson; in PARAGUAY, Dr. Hernando Bertoni, Minister of Agriculture and Livestock, Antonio Torres, Juan Pío Rivaldi, Phil and Peg Myers, Ana Aurora Galli, Erik Raynears, Philippe Legris, Wilfredo Richter, and Bruno Ruggero Fornells; in URUGUAY, Dr. Raúl Vaz-Ferreira, Dr. Hebert Nion, Alex Schwed Olin, and the owner, captain, and crew of the trawler *Carla;* in the UNITED STATES, Drs. Reeve M. Bailey, C.J.D. Brown, Eugenie Clark, Perry W. Gilbert, the late Carl L. Hubbs, Robert L. Martin, Phillip W. Myers, Stewart Springer, Jeffrey M. Taylor, and Jamie E. Thomerson.

REFERENCES

ARAMBOURG, C.
  1947.   Mission scientifique de l'Omo (1932-1933), vol. 1, pp. 469-471.   Muséum National d'Histoire Naturelle, Paris.
BAILEY, REEVE M.
  1969.   Comments on the proposed suppression of *Elipesurus spinicauda* Schomburgk (Pisces). Z.N. (S.) 1825.   Bull. Zool. Nomencl., vol. 25, pts. 4/5, pp. 133-134.
BEITZ, BARRY E.
  1977.   Secretion of rectal gland fluid in the Atlantic stingray, *Dasyatis sabina.* Copeia, 1977, no. 3, pp. 585-587.
BIGELOW, HENRY B., and SCHROEDER, WILLIAM C.
  1948.   Fishes of the western North Atlantic: Part 1, Lancelets, Cyclostomes, Sharks.   Yale Univ., Mem. Sears Found. Mar. Res. no. 1, pp. 1-576.
  1953.   Fishes of the western North Atlantic: Part 2, Sawfishes, guitarfishes, skates and rays.   Yale Univ., Mem. Sears Found. Mar. Res., no. 1, pp. 1-514.
BITTNER, A., and LANG, S.
  1980.   Some aspects of the osmoregulation of Amazonian freshwater stingrays *(Potamotrygon hystrix)* – I. Serum osmolality, sodium and chloride content, water content, hematocrit and urea level.   Comp. Biochem. Physiol., vol. 67A, pp. 9-13.
BONTING, SJOERD L.
  1966.   Studies on sodium-potassium-activated adenosinetriphosphatase-XV. The rectal gland of the elasmobranchs.   Comp. Biochem. Physiol., vol. 17, pp. 953-966.
BROOKS, DANIEL R.
  1976a.   *Neodeuterobaris pritchardae* gen. et sp. n. (Digenea : Microscaphidiidae) in a sideneck turtle, *Podocnemis lewyana* Dumeril, 1852, from Colombia. Journ. Parasitol., vol. 62, pp. 426-428.
  1976b.   Five species of platyhelminths from *Bufo marinus* L. (Anura : Bufonidae) in Colombia with descriptions of *Creptotrema lynchi* sp. n. (Digenea : Allocreadiidae) and *Glypthelmins robustus* sp. n. (Digenea : Macroderoididae).   Journ. Parasitol., vol. 62, pp. 429-433.

BROOKS, DANIEL R. (continued)

1977a.   A new genus and two new species of trematodes from characid fishes in Colombia. Trans. Amer. Microsc. Soc., vol. 96, pp. 267-270.

1977b.   Six new species of tetraphyllidean cestodes, including a new genus, from a marine stingray *Himantura schmardae* (Werner, 1904) from Colombia. Proc. Helminthol. Soc. Wash., vol. 44, pp. 51-59.

BROOKS, DANIEL R., and DEARDORFF, THOMAS L.

1980.   Three proteocephalid cestodes from Colombian siluriform fishes, including *Nomimoscolex alovarius* sp. n. (Monticelliidae : Zygobothriinae). Proc. Helminthol. Soc. Wash., vol., 47, pp. 15-21.

BROOKS, DANIEL R., and MAYES, MONTE A.

1978.   *Acanthobothrium electricolum* sp. n. and *A. lintoni* Goldstein, Henson and Schlicht, 1969 (Cestoda : Tetraphyllidea) from *Narcine brasiliensis* (Olfers) (Chondrichthyes : Torpedinidae) in Colombia. Journ. Parasitol., vol. 64, pp. 617-619.

1980.   Cestodes in four species of euryhaline stingrays from Colombia. Proc. Helminthol. Soc. Wash., vol. 47, pp. 22-29.

BROOKS, DANIEL R.; MAYES, MONTE A.; and THORSON, THOMAS B.

1979.   *Paravitellotrema overstreeti* sp. n. (Digenea : Hemiuridae) from the Colombian freshwater stingray *Potamotrygon magdalenae* Dumeril. Proc. Helminthol. Soc. Wash., vol. 46, pp. 52-54.

1981a.   Systematic review of cestodes infecting freshwater stingrays (Chondrichthyes : Potamotrygonidae) including four new species from Venezuela. Proc. Helminthol. Soc. Wash., vol. 48, pp. 43-64.

1981b.   Cestode parasites in *Myliobatis goodei* Garman (Myliobatiformes : Myliobatidae) from Rio de la Plata, Uruguay, with a summary of cestodes collected from South American elasmobranchs during 1975-1979. Proc. Biol. Soc. Wash., vol. 93, pp. 1239-1252.

BROOKS, DANIEL R., and THORSON, THOMAS B.

1976.   Two tetraphyllidean cestodes from the freshwater stingray *Potamotrygon magdalenae* Dumeril, 1852 (Chondrichthyes : Potamotrygonidae) from Colombia. Journ. Parasitol., vol. 62, pp. 943-947.

BROOKS, DANIEL R.; THORSON, THOMAS B.; and MAYES, MONTE A.

1981.   Freshwater stingrays (Potamotrygonidae) and their helminth parasites: Testing hypotheses of evolution and coevolution. Pp. 147-175 *in* "Advances in Cladistics: Proceedings of the First Meeting of the Willi Hennig Society," V. A. Funk and D. R. Brooks, eds. New York Botanical Garden, New York.

BUCKNER, RICHARD L., and BROOKS, DANIEL R.

1980   Occurrence of *Quadrigyrus torquatus* Van Cleave, 19⁻⁰ (Acanthocephala) in North-central Colombia. Proc. Helminthol. ⸱   Wash., vol. 47, pp. 139-140.

BULGER, RUTH E.

1963.   Fine structure of the rectal (salt-secreting) gland of the spiny dogfish, *Squalus acanthias*. Anat. Rec., vol. 147, pp. 95-127.

BURGER, J. WENDELL
  1965.   Roles of the rectal gland and the kidneys in salt and water excretion in the spiny dogfish. Physiol. Zoöl., vol. 38, pp. 191-196.
  1972.   Rectal gland secretion in the stingray, *Dasyatis sabina*. Comp. Biochem. Physiol., vol. 42A, pp. 31-32.
BURGER, J. WENDELL, and HESS, WALTER N.
  1960.   Function of the rectal gland in the spiny dogfish. Science, vol. 131, pp. 670-671.
CASTEX, MARIANO N.
  1968.   *Elipesurus* Schomburgk, 1843 (Pisces): Proposed suppression under the plenary powers. Z.N. (S.) 1825. Bull. Zool. Nomencl., vol. 24, pt. 6, pp. 353-355.
  1969.   Comment on the objections forwarded by R. M. Bailey to the proposed suppression of *Elipesurus spinicauda* Schomburgk (Pisces). Z.N. (S.) 1825. Bull. Zool. Nomencl., vol. 26, pt. 2, pp. 68-69.
CASTRO-AGUIRRE, JOSÉ LUIS
  1978.   Catálogo sistemático de los peces marinos que penetran a las aguas continentales de México con aspectos zoogeográficos y ecológicos. Dirección General del Instituto Nacional de Pesca, Serie Científica, no. 19, pp. 1-298.
CHAN, D.K.O., and WONG, T. M.
  1977.   Physiological adjustments to dilution of the external medium in the lipshark *Hemiscyllium plagiosum* (Bennett). I. Size of body compartments and osmolyte composition. Journ. Exp. Zool., vol. 200, pp. 71-84.
CRAWFORD, J.
  1899.   On the rectal gland of the elasmobranchs. Proc. Royal Soc. Edinb., vol. 23, pp. 55-61.
CROCKER, C. L.
  1967.   Rapid determination of urea nitrogen in serum or plasma without deproteinization. Amer. Journ. Med. Technol., vol. 33, pp. 361-365.
DEARDORFF, THOMAS L.; BROOKS, DANIEL R.; and THORSON, THOMAS B.
  1981.   A new species of *Echinocephalus* (Nematoda : Gnathostomidae) from neotropical stingrays with comments on *E. diazi*. Journ. Parasitol., vol. 67, pp. 433-439.
DE VLAMING, VICTOR L., and SAGE, MARTIN
  1973.   Osmoregulation in the euryhaline elasmobranch, *Dasyatis sabina*. Comp. Biochem. Physiol., vol. 45A, pp. 31-44.
FUSCO, ALAN, C., and BROOKS, DANIEL R.
  1978.   A new species of *Spirocamallanus* Olsen, 1952 (Nematoda : Camallanidae) from *Trachycorystes insignis* (Steindachner) (Pisces : Doradidae) in Colombia. Proc. Helminthol. Soc. Wash., vol. 45, pp. 111-114.
GERST, JEFFERY W., and THORSON, THOMAS B.
  1977.   Effects of saline acclimation on plasma electrolytes, urea excretion, and hepatic urea biosynthesis in a freshwater stingray, *Potamotrygon* sp. Garman, 1877. Comp. Biochem. Physiol., vol. 56A, pp. 87-93.
GERZELI, G.; GERVASO, M. V.; and DE STEFANO, G. F.
  1969.   Aspetti della ghiandola rettale e della regolazione osmotica in Selaci marini e d'acqua dolce. Bol. Zool., vol. 36, pp. 399-400.

GOLDSTEIN, LEON, and FORSTER, ROY
  1971.   Urea biosynthesis and excretion in freshwater and marine elasmo-
           branchs.   Comp. Biochem. Physiol., vol. 39B, pp. 415-421.
GRIFFITH, R. W.; PANG, P.K.T.; SRIVASTAVA, A. K.; and PICKFORD, G. E.
  1973.   Serum composition of freshwater stingrays (Potamotrygonidae) adapted
           to fresh and dilute sea water.   Biol. Bull., vol. 144, no. 2, pp. 304-
           320.
GUNTER, GORDON
  1938.   Notes on invasion of fresh water by fishes of the Gulf of Mexico, with
           special reference to the Mississippi-Atchafalaya River system.   Copeia,
           1938, no. 2, pp. 69-72.
HARRINGTON, H. J.
  1965.   Geology and morphology of Antarctica.   *In* "Biogeography and Ecolo-
           gy in Antarctica," J. Van Miegham, P. Van Oye, and J. Schell,
           eds.   W. Junk, The Hague.
HOAR, W. S., and RANDALL, D. J.
  1969.   Fish physiology: Vol. 1, Excretion, ionic regulation and metabolism,
           465 pp.   Academic Press, New York.
JUNQUEIRA, L.C.U.; HOXTER, G.; and ZAGO, D.
  1968.   Observations on the biochemistry of fresh water rays and dolphin blood
           serum.   Rev. Bras. Pesquisas Med. Biol., vol. 1, pp. 225-226.
KUMMEL, B.
  1962.   History of the earth: an introduction to historical geology, 707
           pp.   W. H. Freeman and Co., San Francisco.
LARRAZET, M.
  1886.   Des pièces de la peau de quelques sélaciens fossiles.   Bull. Soc. Geol.
           France, ser. 3, vol. 14, pp. 255-277.
MAYES, MONTE A., and BROOKS, DANIEL R.
  1981.   Cestode parasites of some Venezuelan stingrays.   Proc. Biol. Soc.
           Wash., vol. 93, pp. 1230-1238.
MAYES, MONTE A.; BROOKS, DANIEL R.; and THORSON, THOMAS B.
  1978.   Two new species of *Acanthobothrium* Van Beneden, 1849 (Cestoidea : Te-
           traphyllidea) from freshwater stingrays in South America.   Journ. Para-
           sitol., vol. 64, pp. 838-841.
  1981a.   Two new tetraphyllidean cestodes from *Potamotrygon circularis* Garman
           (Chondrichthyes : Potamotrygonidae) in the Itacuai River, Brazil.
           Proc. Helminthol. Soc. Wash., vol. 48, pp. 38-42.
  1981b.   *Potamotrygonocotyle tsalickisi* gen. et sp. n. (Monogenea : Monocotylidae)
           and *Paraheteronchocotyle amazonensis* gen. et sp. n. (Monogenea : Hexa-
           bothriidae) from *Potamotrygon circularis* Garman (Chondrichthyes : Pota-
           motrygonidae) in northwestern Brazil.   Proc. Biol. Soc. Wash., vol.
           94, pp. 1205-1210.
OGURI, MIKIO
  1964.   Rectal glands of marine and freshwater sharks: Comparative histology.
           Science, vol. 144, pp. 1151-1152.
PANG, P.K.T.; GRIFFITH, R. W.; and ATZ, J. W.
  1977.   Osmoregulation in elasmobranchs.   Amer. Zool., vol. 17, pp. 365-
           377.

POTTS, W.T.W., and PARRY, GWYNETH
  1963.   Osmotic and ionic regulation in animals, 423 pp. Pergammon Press, Oxford.

PUTZER, H.
  1969.   Überblick über die geologische entwicklung Südamerikas. Pp. 1-24 *in* "Biogeography and Ecology in South America," E. J. Fittkau, J. Illies, H. Klinge, G. H. Schwabe, and H. Sioli, eds. W. Junk, Publ., The Hague.

SMITH, HOMER W.
  1931.   The absorption and excretion of water and salts by elasmobranch fishes: I. Fresh water elasmobranchs. Amer. Journ. Physiol., vol. 98, pp. 279-295.
  1936.   The retention and physiological role of urea in Elasmobranchii. Biol. Rev., vol. 11, pp. 49-82.

THORSON, THOMAS B.
  1962.   Partitioning of body fluids in the Lake Nicaragua shark and three marine sharks. Science, vol. 138, pp. 388-390.
  1967.   Osmoregulation in freshwater elasmobranchs. Pp. 265-270 *in* "Sharks, Skates, and Rays," P. W. Gilbert, R. G. Mathewson and D. P. Rall, eds. Johns Hopkins Press, Baltimore.
  1970.   Freshwater stingrays, *Potamotrygon* spp.: Failure to concentrate urea when exposed to saline medium. Life Sci., vol. 9, pp. 893-900.
  1976.   The status of the Lake Nicaragua shark: An updated appraisal. Pp. 561-574 *in* "Investigations of the Ichthyofauna of Nicaraguan Lakes," T. B. Thorson, ed. School of Life Sciences, University of Nebraska-Lincoln.
  1982.   Life history implications of a tagging study of the largetooth sawfish, *Pristis perotteti*, in the Lake Nicaragua-Río San Juan system. Env. Biol. Fish., vol. 7, pp. 207-228.

THORSON, THOMAS B.; COWAN, C. MICHAEL; and WATSON, DONALD E.
  1967.   *Potamotrygon* spp.: Elasmobranchs with low urea content. Science, vol. 158, pp. 375-377.
  1973.   Body fluid solutes of juveniles and adults of the euryhaline bull shark *Carcharhinus leucas* from freshwater and saline environments. Physiol. Zoöl., vol. 46, pp. 29-42.

THORSON, THOMAS B., and GERST, JEFFERY, W.
  1972.   Comparison of some parameters of serum and uterine fluid of pregnant, viviparous sharks *(Carcharhinus leucas)* and serum of their near-term young. Comp. Biochem. Physiol., vol. 42A, pp. 33-40.

THORSON, THOMAS B.; LANGHAMMER, JAMES K.; and OETINGER, MADELINE I.
  1983.   Reproduction and development of the South American freshwater stingrays, *Potamotrygon circularis* and *P. motoro*. Env. Biol. Fish., vol. 8, no. 4 (in press).

THORSON, THOMAS B., and WATSON, DONALD E.
  1975.   Reassignment of the African freshwater stingray, *Potamotrygon garouaensis*, to the genus *Dasyatis*, on physiologic and morphologic grounds. Copeia, 1975, no. 4, pp. 701-712.

THORSON, THOMAS B.; WOTTON, ROBERT M.; and GEORGI, TODD A.
    1978.   Rectal gland of freshwater stingrays, *Potamotrygon* spp. (Chondrichthyes: Potamotrygonidae).   Biol. Bull., vol. 154, pp. 508-516.

URIST, MARSHALL R.
    1962.   Calcium and other ions in blood and skeleton of Nicaraguan fresh-water shark.   Science, vol. 137, pp. 984-986.

VÁSQUEZ MONTOYA, RAFAEL, and THORSON, THOMAS B.
    1982.   The bull shark *(Carcharhinus leucas)* and largetooth sawfish *(Pristis perotteti)* in Lake Bayano, a tropical man-made impoundment in Panama.   Env. Biol. Fish., vol. 7., pp. 341-347.

WONG, T. M., and CHAN, D.K.O.
    1977.   Physiological adjustments to dilution of the external medium in the lipshark *Hemiscyllium plagiosum* (Bennett). II. Branchial, renal and rectal gland function.   Journ. Exp. Zool., vol. 200, pp. 85-96.

THOMAS B. THORSON
DANIEL R. BROOKS
MONTE A. MAYES

Prehistoric Demography of Coastal Ecuador

Principal Investigator: Douglas H. Ubelaker, U. S. National Museum of Natural History, Smithsonian Institution, Washington, D. C.

Grant No. 1330:   In support of excavations yielding skeletal remains and information on burial customs of the prehistoric populations of the coast of Ecuador.

In 1973 I directed the excavation of a large cemetery in Guayas Province, southern coastal Ecuador, which dates from the Late Integration Period. This excavation produced 54 large ceramic urns containing several hundred human skeletons and consequently a wealth of information about prehistoric mortuary customs and skeletal biology of that time and place (Ubelaker, 1981). With support from the National Geographic Society, I returned to coastal Ecuador to augment this sample with comparative information from other, preferably earlier, sites and cultures.

Following a short visit to archeological sites producing skeletal materials in eastern Mexico, I arrived in Quito, Ecuador, on May 31, 1974. There I discussed the project with local archeologists and received an official excavation permit from the antiquities commission. After arriving in Guayaquil on June 10, I was joined by other members of the expedition: Fernando Luna Calderón of the Museo del Hombre Dominicano, Dominican Republic, and Wilfrido Zuniga Silva from Guayaquil. They were augmented later in the season by Maruja Andrade from Quito and Tim Seaver and Wade Edris from Pennsylvania.

On June 17 the owner of Hacienda Ayalán (location of previous excavation) notified me that because of unforeseen local problems, he could not permit us to resume work at the original site. Consequently, I contacted the owners of land adjacent to Hacienda Ayalán for permission to search for sites on their properties. Thanks to the fine cooperation received, a test excavation on June 26 located a cemetery largely of the Jambeli culture in the northeast corner of the town of San Lorenzo on Hacienda Soledad, less than 12 kilometers north of the Ayalán site. This culture relates to the Regional Development Period, estimated to date about 500 B.C.-A.D. 500. Since a cemetery of this culture had never been excavated systematically and since this one offered the much-needed time depth to my study of prehistoric biology, I terminated the survey and arranged to excavate there for a period of two months.

FIG. 1. Feature 50, a young adult female buried on her back with legs flexed to the right.

FIG. 2. Feature 23, an adult buried in the sitting position.

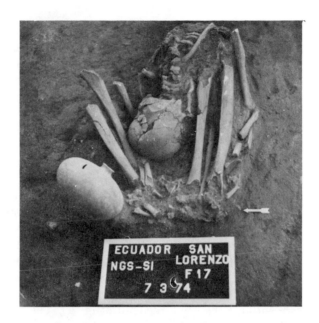

FIG. 3. Feature 17, an adult buried in the sitting position, with a ceramic vessel offering.

FIG. 4. Feature 32, an old adult male buried on his left side with offerings of ceramic vessels, plates, and bowl-shaped lime deposits.

Test excavations revealed that the cemetery was concentrated in an area 30 by 50 meters on a hilltop, while evidence of habitation extended around the surrounding hillsides. With the help of 8 to 10 hacienda workers, we excavated an area 30 by 30 meters and secured 106 skeletons, many with associated cultural offerings.

The mortuary customs at this site turned out to be quite varied (table 1). Nine percent of the burials were secondary, implying that immediately after death the bodies were placed in a different location until the flesh decomposed, and then the bones were transferred to the cemetery. Eighty-four percent of the skeletons were articulated, implying they were buried immediately after death. Of these articulated skeletons, the following positions were recorded: 2 percent on the back with legs extended; 6 percent on back with legs flexed to the left; 9 percent on back with legs flexed to right (fig. 1); 19 percent in sitting position (figs. 2, 3); 10 percent on left side (fig. 4); 10 percent on right side; 10 percent face down with legs extended; 12 percent on back with legs flexed up over chest (fig. 5); and 6 percent on back with lower legs flexed inward (fig. 6). One female skeleton was found on her left side within a shallow ceramic urn (fig. 7). The remaining 7 percent of the skeletons had been disturbed by recent construction or by natural erosion prior to our excavation. Table 1 also shows that this variability was not restricted to any age or sex category. These findings contrast with the uniform mortuary practice of the subsequent Late Integration Period as observed at the cemetery on Hacienda Ayalán.

All ages were represented in the recovered burials. Adults over the age of 20 years predominated (73 percent). Of the 28 individuals younger than age 20, 18 (64 percent) were between birth and 5 years old, reflecting the usual high rate of infant mortality in prehistoric times. Sex could be determined only for 34 of the 78 adult skeletons, but among these, males and females were about equally represented.

Table 2 indicates that the skeletons most often were oriented with the skulls to the southwest; however, other orientations were found in high frequencies, again documenting the variability in the mortuary customs.

Twenty-nine of the crania were sufficiently intact to allow observations on artificial cranial deformation. Of these, all but two (93 percent) displayed marked vertical occipital flattening. The two exceptions were undeformed, one a female and the other an adult of undetermined sex.

Mortuary offerings were found with 37 percent of the skeletons. As table 3 shows, offerings were associated with adults more often than subadults and with males more often than females. Only one (6 percent) of the 18 infants had associated offerings, in contrast to 10 (67 percent) of the 15 adult males. The data suggest that the type of offering varied with age: ceramic urns from birth to 5 years; earrings from 5 to 10 years; no artifacts from 10 to 15 years; and ceramic plates from 15 to 20 years. Artifacts associated exclusively with females were metates (grinding stones), spindle whorls (small ceramic objects used in spinning thread), and ceramic urns. Artifacts associated exclusively with males were carved-shell spatulas and small bowl-shaped masses of lime. The lime masses probably represent deposits originally within perishable gourd containers. Both the spatulas and lime deposits reflect the practice of chewing coca, and document the male association of this custom. Ceramic vessels, plates and compoteras (fig. 8), metal earrings, shell beads, and dog skeletons were found with both sexes.

The average depth of the skeletons was about 17 centimeters (measured from the present ground surface to the highest bone). Infants and children were about 5 centimeters deeper than adults. Adult males and females were found at about equal depths (13-14 centimeters). The original depth of the skeletons could not be determined because the hilltop has undergone considerable erosion since the time of Indian occupation, especially on the periphery where a shell layer was exposed. In the center of the hilltop, the shell layer was covered with 20 centimeters of topsoil. Most of the skeletons were found within that shell layer or slightly above it.

Some spatial variability was noted within the cemetery. Subadults tended to be concentrated in the eastern third, whereas adults occurred mostly in the center and western thirds. No segregation of the sexes was detected, but individuals buried in certain positions tended to occur together. For example, most of the skeletons lying face down with legs extended were concentrated in the extreme eastern part of the cemetery. Most of the skeletons buried in the sitting position were concentrated in a 10-by-10-meter area in the north-central part. All secondary (nonarticulated) burials were found in a 5-by-5-meter area in the northwestern part.

Following completion of the excavation on August 20, I went to Quito for several days to deliver a lecture on the fieldwork and to secure final permission to export the small artifacts and skeletons for study. All the ceramic fragments and complete vessels remained in Ecuador for analysis by a team of Ecuadorian archeologists. Following study, these specimens will be deposited in the proposed new archeological museum of the Banco Central in Guayaquil, where they will constitute the first collection from the Jambeli culture.

I returned to Washington, D. C., by way of Mexico City in order to attend the XLI International Congress of Americanists. At one of the sessions I presented a report of the summer's work. When I arrived in Washington on September 10, I found that all the collection already had been received. I plan

FIG. 5. Feature 85, an adult male buried on his back with the legs flexed up over the chest area.

FIG. 6. Feature 35, an adult buried on its back with the lower legs flexed inward.

FIG. 7. Feature 37, an adult female buried on her left side within a shallow ceramic urn.

FIG. 8. Feature 69, an adult in the sitting position buried with two ceramic vessels and a double compotera.

TABLE 1.   The Correlation of Burial Position With the Age and Sex of the Skeleton

Position	Sex indeterminable										Male		Female		Totals	
	0-5 yrs.		5-10 yrs.		10-15 yrs.		15-20 yrs.		20+ yrs.		20+ yrs.		20+ yrs.			
	no.	%	no.	%	no.	%	no.	%	no.	%	no.	%	no.	%	no.	%
Indeterminable																
Disturbed	4	22	–	–	–	–	–	–	3	7	–	–	–	–	7	7
Secondary	1	5	–	–	–	–	–	–	8	18	–	–	–	–	9	9
Supine																
Legs extended	–	–	–	–	–	–	–	–	2	4	–	–	–	–	2	2
Legs left	3	17	–	–	–	–	–	–	1	2	1	7	1	6	6	6
Legs right	3	17	–	–	–	–	–	–	5	11	1	7	1	6	10	9
Legs up	–	–	–	–	–	–	–	–	9	20	2	13	2	11	13	12
Legs in	4	22	–	–	–	–	–	–	1	2	1	7	–	–	6	6
Sitting	1	6	–	–	1	100	–	–	7	16	5	33	6	33	20	19
Left side	–	–	3	50	–	–	–	–	3	7	3	20	2	11	11	10
Right side	–	–	2	33	–	–	1	33	3	7	1	7	4	22	11	10
Prone	2	11	1	17	–	–	2	67	3	7	1	7	2	11	11	10
Totals no. (%)	18	(17)	6	(6)	1	(1)	3	(3)	45	(42)	15	(14)	18	(17)	106	(100)

TABLE 2. Compass Direction of the Skull Relative to the Postcranial Skeleton by Age and Sex

Age and sex	Compass direction																		Total
	N		NE		E		SE		S		SW		W		NW		?		
	no.	%	no.	%	no.	%	no.	%	no.	%	no.	%	no.	%	no.	%	no.	%	no.
Sex indeterminable																			
0-5 years	1	6	3	17	1	6	2	11	1	6	4	22	1	6	2	11	3	17	18
5-10 years	1	17	1	17	–	–	1	17	–	–	–	–	1	17	2	33	–	–	6
10-15 years	1	100	–	–	–	–	–	–	–	–	–	–	–	–	–	–	–	–	1
15-20 years	–	–	–	–	1	33	–	–	–	–	2	67	–	–	–	–	–	–	3
20+ years	4	9	4	9	3	7	3	7	3	7	13	29	3	7	3	7	9	20	45
Male 20+ years	4	27	1	7	1	7	0	0	1	7	5	33	2	13	1	7	0	0	15
Female 20+ years	4	22	2	11	1	6	1	6	0	0	3	17	1	16	4	22	2	11	18
Totals no.(%)	15	(14)	11	(10)	7	(7)	7	(7)	5	(5)	27	(25)	8	(8)	12	(11)	14	(13)	106

TABLE 3. Occurrence of Mortuary Offerings by Age and Sex

Age and sex		Offerings present		Offerings absent		Total
		no.	%	no.	%	
Sex Indeterminable						
	0-5 years	1	6	17	94	18
	5-10 years	2	33	4	67	6
	10-15 years	–	–	1	100	1
	15-20 years	1	33	2	67	3
	20+ years	18	40	27	60	45
Male	20+ years	10	67	5	33	15
Female	20+ years	7	39	11	61	18
Totals No. (%)		39	(37)	67	(63)	106

to study the skeletal material and small artifacts in an attempt to document firmly the mortuary customs, morphology, pathology, and demography of the population buried at this site. My research, combined with that of the Ecuadorians, should yield for the first time a view of trends in mortuary customs and human biology for an extended period of coastal Ecuadorian prehistory.

REFERENCE

UBELAKER, DOUGLAS H.
1981. The Ayalán cemetery a late integration period burial site on the South Coast of Ecuador. Smithsonian Contributions to Anthropology, no. 29.

DOUGLAS H. UBELAKER

Crab Predation and Shell Architecture in High Intertidal Snails

Principal Investigator: Geerat J. Vermeij, University of Maryland, College Park, Maryland.

Grant No. 1290: In aid of a study of crab predation and shell architecture in high intertidal snails.

During the summer of 1974, funds from the National Geographic Society allowed me to initiate studies on the methods and effectiveness of predation by various crabs on intertidal shelled gastropod mollusks. This work is part of a larger effort designed to explain striking differences in shell architecture among snails living in physically comparable conditions in the several shallow-water tropical marine biogeographic regions. For example, open-surface rocky-shore gastropods in the low intertidal and shallow subtidal in the tropical Pacific and Indian Oceans possess shells that have lower spires, narrower apertures, more toothed apertures, and a greater development of shell sculpture than their counterparts in the tropical Atlantic.

It was initially intended to compare crab predation on high intertidal snails in Guam and the Philippines, since the snails in these two areas differ in the degree of development of shell features believed to be adaptations against predation by crabs; but political conditions in the southern Philippines and the relative paucity of experimental snails in Guam led to an emphasis on the study of predation by low intertidal to subtidal crabs on the numerous gastropods living on the reef flat at Pago Bay, adjacent to the University of Guam Marine Laboratory on the windward shore of the island.

Attention was focused on four species of crabs—the xanthids *Eriphia sebana* Shaw and Nodder, *Carpilius maculatus* L., and *C. convexus* L. and the parthenopid *Daldorfia horrida* (L.). Specimens of each of these were kept in plastic aquaria in recirculating sea water together with a variety of potential prey gastropods and hermit crabs. Sea water was changed daily, and dead or consumed prey were removed as soon as detected. Each potential prey snail was identified, its length measured, and, if its shell was crushed, the shell thickness measured at points of fracture. The time between introduction of a prey item into the aquarium and its removal was noted, and all eaten and un-eaten prey were labeled and kept for later analysis. The primary question to be

705

answered was, What size does a particular prey species need to achieve to become immune from predation by a crab of given carapace width?

Eriphia, a fairly nimble crab with red eyes and strikingly dimorphic claws, can readily move about out of the water. With its massive master claw (either the right or the left claw), this crab often attempts first to break the lip of a shell. With species whose shells have a broad aperture, such as *Nerita albicilla,* soft parts are removed by the crab without damage to the shell. If the lip cannot be broken, as in the case of species such as *Morula granulata* with strong teeth bordering the aperture, the crab often attempts to break off the shell's spire. In this way a crab 49 millimeters in carapace width can successfully prey upon *Cerithium columna* up to 32 millimeters long (the species in Guam attains a shell length of 34 millimeters. *Eriphia* individuals studied were never successful in crushing species of *Conus, Cypraea,* and *Drupa,* all of which have low spires and long or obstructed apertures. Young individuals of *Trochus niloticus* up to about 28 millimeters in shell diameter can be broken by inserting the claw into the aperture and fracturing the base; larger specimens (maximum diameter about 80 millimeters) are immune from predation by *Eriphia.* Most species of *Morula* are also immune from predation by this crab, except at young stages when the outer lip of the aperture is still thin. *Eriphia* appears to take hermit crabs inhabiting dead snail shells, and living gastropods, indiscriminately.

The slow tanklike *Carpilius maculatus,* which can attain a carapace width of 15 centimeters, was the largest crab studied. Like *Eriphia,* it is characterized by strongly dimorphic claws, the right chela normally being the extremely massive master claw. This species probably cannot move easily when out of water. Mollusks successfully consumed by *C. maculatus* up to 112 millimeters in width include *Drupa ricinus* (25 millimeters), *D. morum* (28 millimeters), *Cerithium columna* (32 millimeters), *Trochus niloticus* (36 millimeters), *Cypraea caputserpentis* (32 millimeters), *C. moneta* (24 millimeters), *C. depressa* (33 millimeters), *Vasum turbinellus* (29 millimeters), *Conus* spp. (26 millimeters), *Chicoreus adustus* (36 millimeters), and *Cantharus undosus* (28 millimeters). Many species in this list, including *T. niloticus, Conus* spp., *Drupa* spp., *V. turbinellus,* and *C. undosus,* achieve immunity from crab predation upon reaching a critical size; this is also the case with *Turbo setosus, Morula* spp., and *Cerithium nodulosum.* Strongly spinose species such as *Drupa* spp., *C. nodulosum,* and *V. turbinellus* often have individual spines removed by *Carpilius* and are often given up in favor of more available shells. Species such as these, which generally also possess narrow or obstructed apertures, can be broken successfully only by breaking the spire or, when the spire is very short, by removing the left dorsal wall of the shell. *Trochus* is taken in much the same way as is done by *Eriphia*. Attempts to break the lip of a shell usually follow rather than precede attempts to slice the spire of such species as *C. columna* and *Cantharus undosus*. Cowries (*Cypraea*) are broken by removing the dorsal wall of the shell, usually leaving the base together with the strongly toothed narrow aperture intact.

The smaller *Carpilius convexus*, which attains a width of 79 millimeters, is similar in its method of predation to *C. maculatus*, though it more often resorts to lip-cutting. An adult individual of this species broke several cowries but could not break the shell of any *Conus* or *Morula granulata*.

Daldorfia horrida is an exceedingly quiescent crab with slightly dimorphic but not otherwise impressive claws. Nonetheless, this cryptic species slices the spires or removes the dorsal wall of all sizes of *Cerithium columna*, *Cypraea moneta*, *Cantharus fumosus*, and *Nerita albicilla*. A crab 69 millimeters in width was less successful with *Vasum turbinellus* (19 millimeters), *Drupa ricinus* (17 millimeters), and *Trochus niloticus* (23 millimeters) and was unable to injure even small *Cerithium nodulosum*, *Cypraea depressa*, *C. caputserpentis*, and *Conus* spp. Lip-cutting is rarely employed by this crab, nor could soft parts be extracted from any species without shell damage.

All these crabs are likely to be important predators on living shelled gastropods and on hermit crabs inhabiting abandoned shells. While more direct evidence is required, the abundance of damaged shells in the field exhibiting features like those of shells broken by crabs in the laboratory suggests that crab predation is an important source of mortality and selective pressure on shelled gastropods and hermit crabs. Of the four species of crab studied, only *Eriphia* is potentially a predator of middle to high intertidal prey. All species possess strong chelae with a molariform basal tooth used for shell crushing. In general, such shell features as low spires, strong sculpture, teeth bordering the aperture, and a narrow aperture are effective antipredatory devices against crabs and undoubtedly also against fishes. Species such as *Trochus niloticus* and *Cerithium columna* lacking well-developed morphological antipredatory features may achieve immunity from crushing predation either by achieving large size or by maintaining high reproductive rates and short generation times.

The work initiated with the help of the National Geographic Society is continuing with the support of the National Science Foundation and will be expanded to include further studies in Guam and in the Caribbean region.

REFERENCES

VERMEIJ, GEERAT J.
   1976.   Interoceanic differences in vulnerability of shelled prey to crab preda-
            tion.   Nature, vol. 260, pp. 135-136, illus.
   1978.   Biogeography and adaptation: Patterns of marine life, 332 pp.
            Harvard University Press, Cambridge.
   1979.   Causes of death and shell architecture of Micronesian reef-associated
            snails.   Evolution, vol. 33, pp. 686-696.
ZIPSER, EDITH, and VERMEIJ, GEERAT J.
   1978.   Crushing behavior of tropical and temperate crabs.   Journ. Exp. Mar.
            Biol. Ecol., vol. 31, pp. 155-172.

GEERAT J. VERMEIJ

The Bronze Age Eruption of Santorini (Thera) and the Demise of Minoan Civilization

Principal Investigators: Dorothy B. Vitaliano, U. S. Geological Survey, Bloomington, Indiana, and Charles J. Vitaliano, Indiana University,
Bloomington, Indiana.

Grant No. 1347:   For an attempt to determine the precise dating of the Bronze
Age eruption of Santorini Volcano, Aegean Sea.

Background

The Bronze Age eruption of Santorini (Thera) Volcano has been suggested as the cause of the abrupt downfall of the Minoan civilization on Crete and various Aegean islands (Marinatos, 1939) in ca. 1450 B.C. (according to archeological dating). While we did not doubt that the eruption was the blow that had weakened the Minoans and allowed control of their dominions to pass into the hands of the Myceneans, we published a paper in the *Acta* of the First Scientific Congress on the Volcano of Thera (Vitaliano and Vitaliano, 1971) in which we suggested that although the effects of the eruption on Crete and elsewhere must have been quite serious, they alone could not account for all aspects of the general destruction on Crete in 1450 B.C.

One of the major purposes of that first Thera Congress was to ascertain what stretch of time was represented by the thickness of tephra (lump pumice and pumiceous volcanic ash) burying the Minoan ruins on Santorini, in which no artifacts that could be dated to much later than ca. 1500 B.C. have been found. An unforeseen problem was presented, therefore, when the volcanologists at the Congress were unanimously of the opinion that the tephra did not represent an interval of several decades but rather was deposited in a matter of days or weeks or, at most, months.

In this light, if the eruption was the blow that caused the downfall of Minoan civilization in 1450 B.C., then it became difficult to explain why the very prosperous settlement on Santorini was apparently abandoned for several decades before that; whereas, if the settlement was abandoned because of an impending eruption in ca. 1500 B.C., that eruption could not have been the immediate cause of the demise of Minoan civilization in 1450 B.C.

In an effort to pin down the time of the eruption as closely as possible relative to the stages of Minoan culture, we spent some time on Crete in 1971 at the invitation of the late Prof. Spyridon Marinatos (then inspector general of antiquities for Greece and personally directing excavations on Santorini), collecting samples of soils from natural or artificial exposures and, wherever possible, from Minoan ruins.

Subsequent examination of those samples under the petrographic microscope showed undeniable traces of volcanic ash from the Santorini Bronze Age eruption (distinguishable from volcanic glass shards from any other potential source by its refractive index)[1] in the soils of Crete, which confirmed the evidence of deep-sea sediment cores (Ninkovich and Heezen, 1965), which indicated that at least the eastern end of Crete was covered by fallout from that eruption; and in samples collected from crevices in Minoan ruins, from various archeologically dated levels. But there was only one site where we had been able to collect samples from the crucial Late Minoan I A (1500 B.C.) level, where its presence would mean that the eruption occurred in ca. 1500 B.C., and its absence that it occurred in ca. 1450 B.C.

To our surprise, traces of the Minoan tephra were present in the 1500 B.C. level, suggesting that the earlier date was the correct one. But even though the layer from which the samples were collected was thought by the archeologists at the dig to have been sealed after a local destruction in ca. 1500 B.C. and had been freshly dug at the time of our visit (thus ruling out the possibility of contamination), the implications were too important to justify drawing definite conclusions on the basis of the evidence at this one site. In the published results of that study (Vitaliano and Vitaliano, 1974) we stressed the need for additional evidence from other sites.

The Melos Project

As a direct result of that publication we were invited by Prof. A. C. Renfrew, director of the excavations at Phylakopí on Melos under the aegis of the British School at Athens, to visit Melos in the summer of 1974 to collect additional samples from the trenches at that dig, where good sections through the whole Bronze Age occupancy were exposed. The grant from the National Geographic Society together with one from the American Council of Learned Societies enabled us to accept the invitation.

Despite unforeseen difficulties occasioned by the political crisis in Greece just the day after we arrived in Athens, we were able to get to Melos to collect

---

[1] Details of the technique of sample preparation and microscopic examination are published in Vitaliano and Vitaliano (1974) and in an appendix to the Phylakopi excavation report for 1974-75 (Vitaliano and Vitaliano, in press).

samples in several sections exposed in different trenches while the dig was being closed (under orders from Athens, as were all foreign digs that summer). Back in the laboratory, shards of Santorini Bronze Age tephra were found in several of the samples. But this was not the end of the work stemming from our grant. Armed with the results of our study of the 1974 samples and having witnessed our sampling technique, Professor Renfrew was able to collect many additional samples in the 1975 season, concentrating on a narrower stratigraphic interval including the levels in which ash particles had already been found. Those were subsequently examined by us, and many more traces were revealed.

Results

As at Kato Zakro on Crete, there are unmistakable traces of the Minoan tephra in the dig at Phylakopí on Melos. Although the pottery yielded by the levels in which they were found has not permitted as precise dating as hoped, the earliest particles definitely appear before the Late Bronze I destruction level (correlated with the 1450 B.C. level on Crete). The time interval between their appearance and the destruction, according to Professor Renfrew, was enough for "at least one floor renewal." This corroborates our earlier findings that the eruption and the 1450 B.C. destruction were not simultaneous and reinforces the conclusion that the eruption could not have been the direct cause of the collapse of Minoan civilization.

J. V. Luce (1976) has suggested that the eruption and destruction on Crete both occurred in ca. 1470 B.C., arguing that the Marine Style pottery on the basis of which the Late Minoan I B stage (1500-1450 B.C.) is distinguished does not represent a separate time interval but is contemporaneous with the Late Minoan I A. This suggestion is incompatible with our finding that there is a definite time break between the eruption and the general destruction on Crete.

C. Doumas (1974) has suggested that the eruption occurred in 1500 B.C., but the caldera collapse did not take place until 1450 B.C., when it was triggered by an earthquake. In this view, the settlement on Santorini was abandoned in 1500 B.C. just before it was buried in the tephra, and the general destruction on Crete was caused by the combination of destructive sea waves generated by the collapse and the earthquake which triggered that collapse. Though the postponement of the collapse for about 50 years might be questioned on geologic grounds, this idea at least is fully consistent with our findings.

These results were presented orally in an invited paper given in the symposium on "Explosive Volcanism in the Quaternary" during the 10th Congress of the International Quaternary Association (INQUA) in Birmingham, England, in August 1977, and are included in two papers to be given orally at the Second International Scientific Congress "Thera and the Aegean World" to be held in Greece in August 1978: one by Vitaliano and Vitaliano (1978?) and the other by A. C. Renfrew (1978); both are published in the *Acta* of the Congress. In addition, a detailed description of the technique of sampling and studying the samples will be published as an appendix to a forthcoming Phylakopí excavation report (Vitaliano and Vitaliano, in press).

Since this report was written, a visible layer of the Minoan tephra was found in a Minoan dig at Trianda, on Rhodes, well below the destruction level. This layer is up to 10 cm thick, and its context "suggests that the tephra fall did not cause any significant break in the life of the settlement." (See Doumas and Papazoglou, 1980; and Keller, 1980.)

REFERENCES

DOUMAS, CHRISTOS
  1974.   The Minoan eruption of the Santorini Volcano.   Antiquity, vol. 48, pp. 110-114.
DOUMAS, C., and PAPAZOGLOU, L.
  1980.   Santorini tephra from Rhodes.   Nature, vol. 287, pp. 322-324.
KELLER, JÖRG
  1980.   Did the Santorini eruption destroy the Minoan world?   Nature, vol. 287, p. 779.
LUCE, J. V.
  1976.   Thera and the devastation of Minoan Crete: A new interpretation of the evidence.   Amer. Journ. Archaeol., vol. 80, pp. 9-16.
MARINATOS, SPYRIDON
  1939.   The volcanic destruction of Minoan Crete.   Antiquity, vol. 13, pp. 425-439.
NINKOVICH, DRAGOSLAV, and HEEZEN, BRUCE C.
  1965.   Santorini tephra.   Colston [Research Society] Pap., vol. 17, pp. 413-453.
RENFREW, A. C.
  1978.   Phylakopí and the Late Bronze I period in the Cyclades.   Pp. 403-421 *in* "Thera and the Aegean World," vol. 1 (Papers presented at the Second International Scientific Congress, Santorini, Greece, August 18-25, 1978.)
VITALIANO, CHARLES J., and VITALIANO, DOROTHY B.
  1974.   Volcanic tephra on Crete.   Amer. Journ. Archaeol., vol. 78, no. 1, pp. 19-24.
  1978.   Laboratory investigation of samples collected from the Phylakopí excavations, 1974 and 1975 (appendix to excavation report by A. C. Renfrew). (In press.)

VITALIANO, DOROTHY B., and VITALIANO, CHARLES J.
1971.   Plinian eruptions, earthquakes, and Santorin—a review.   Pp. 88-108 *in* Acta of the 1st Scientific Congress on the Volcano of Thera, Greece, September 15-23, Athens, 1969.
1978.   Tephrochronological evidence for the time of the Bronze Age eruption of Thera.   Pp. 217-219 *in* "Thera and the Aegean World," vol. 1 (Papers presented at the Second International Scientific Congress, Santorini, Greece, August 18-25, 1978.)

DOROTHY B. VITALIANO
CHARLES J. VITALIANO

Distribution of Shallow-water Marine Mollusca, Yucatán Peninsula, Mexico

Principal Investigator: Harold E. Vokes, W. R. Irby Professor of Earth Sciences, Emeritus, Tulane University, New Orleans, Louisiana.

Grant No. 1378:   For transportation and boat hire, permitting collection from otherwise inaccessible areas of mangrove swamp environment along the Yucatán peninsular coasts.

Early in his archeological studies of Yucatán Mayan sites the late E. Wyllys Andrews IV became aware of the fact that the sea had played a most significant role in the lives of these ancient people. Almost every offertory cache and tomb contained marine elements, usually molluscan, and much of the jewelry and artifacts found had been contrived from molluscan shells. In addition, the numerous coastal shell middens attested to the fact that fish and mollusks were important in their diet. Early in the 1950's it occurred to him that a knowledge of the present distribution of these forms might afford clues to possible ancient trade routes. Accordingly, he began making collections from sites along the coast from the vicinity of Belize northward around the peninsula and westward as far as Ciudad del Carmen and Zacatal, Campeche. He maintained a carefully documented and annotated catalogue that, at the time of his death in 1971, occupied five volumes and included records of some 580 species from 56 localities. One result was the publication in 1969 [1970] of "The Archaeological Use and Distribution of Mollusca in the Mayan Lowlands."

It was while engaged in the preparation of this monograph that Dr. Andrews became most aware of the inadequate level of present knowledge of the marine molluscan faunas of the Yucatán area. At that time (1969) only three short papers had listed faunas from local areas: Baker, 1891, mentioning 112 species from two localities on the north coast, Silam (= Dzilam Bravo) and Progresso, and Campeche on the west; Weisbord (1926) mentions 103 species from Progresso and five localities along the Campeche coast southward from Campeche itself; Jaume (1946) lists 136 species from the northeastern coast between Isla Cancun and Cabo Catoche and also cites 65 species reported by Weisbord (1926) that were not found in the Cabo Catoche area.

The obvious need for broader coverage of the faunal area led Andrews to begin the preparation of an annotated checklist that would detail the composition and distribution of the shallow-water faunas all around the Yucatán Pen-

715

insula. His initial studies had been concerned primarily with the larger species that had been utilized by the Maya; with the new emphasis, however, it became necessary to secure collections of the smaller forms in order to present a truly significant picture of the entire fauna. The collection and identification of these fauna had only been started when Andrews became afflicted with the illness that led to his death. When it became evident that the illness was terminal, the present writers promised to see the project through to completion. They had first become acquainted with Andrews and his molluscan studies in 1964 and subsequently had spent many days in the field and laboratory assisting him in the collection and identification of the species present.

The assumption of this task involved the revisiting of previously collected localities to secure representatives of smaller species and, incidentally, to attempt to add to the collections of the larger forms. In addition, as new access roads were opened it became possible to add new sites for more complete coverage. By early 1974 the collections had been increased to include 635 species from 68 localities.

By this time, however, it was obvious that extensive areas of coastal swamps made the adjacent shorelines inaccessible except from boats working along the coast. Since these swampy areas present differing ecologic environments than do the sand and rock beaches it was essential that they also be collected in order to prepare a truly comprehensive view of the shallow-water faunas. Four major areas so isolated included: (1) the northern coast of the State of Campeche from a point immediately north of the city of Campeche to the northern end of the state near the city of Celestún, Yucatán; (2) the central portion of the northern Yucatán Coast between Dzilam Bravo on the west and San Felipe on the east; (3) the northeastern corner of the peninsula, essentially between El Cuyo, Yucatán, to the west and Isla Contoy on the east, especially including, however, the offshore barrier island of Isla Holbox and the area about Cabo Catoche, Quintana Roo; and (4) the southeastern part of the State of Quintana Roo, especially the area between Bahía de la Ascensión and the Belize/Mexico border south of the village of Xcalak.

In 1974 a grant from the Committee for Research and Exploration of the National Geographic Society made possible the hiring of boats and guides and the eventual completion of the collections needed. It had been hoped that these sites could be collected during December 1974, but a number of storms made this impossible and the fieldwork was continued during the summer and winter seasons of 1975.

The collections now contain 826 species from 97 localities. Included are 577 species of Gastropoda, 232 of Bivalvia (Pelecypoda), 10 Polyplacophora, 5 Scaphopoda, and 2 Cephalopoda.

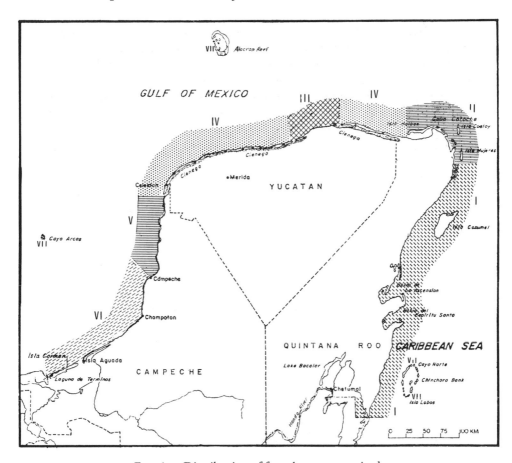

FIG. 1.   Distribution of faunal areas recognized.

The Yucatán Peninsula is of particular interest in that its eastern coast fronts on the Caribbean Sea while the northern and western coasts are on the Gulf of Mexico. The rather striking differences between the faunas of these areas, however, seem to be more the result of the exceedingly differing ecologic environments present than of the purely geographic distributional factors. Most notable is the fact that the east coast drops steeply into deep waters—the 10-fathom line being about one mile offshore—and is margined by a relatively continuous series of long-shore barrier coral reefs, while the north and west coasts are marked by shallowed seas—the 10-fathom line being about 19 to 20 miles offshore on the north coast and more than 40 miles out from the west coast near Campeche. This is an expression of the greatly shallowed waters over the Yucatán Bank; an area of sand and lime-mud deposition with coral growth, when present, primarily only in the more distant offshore reaches. These differences reveal themselves even in the colors of the seawaters: those off the eastern shore being characteristically deep blue in color while those of the north and west coasts, especially in the Gulf of Campeche area, have a "milky" green hue, reflecting not only the shallowness of the sea but also the rather high content of suspended lime-mud.

Within these various areas there are varieties of coastal types of ecologic significance insofar as the molluscan faunas are concerned. The northern half of the east coast is fault-block controlled, apparently by a northward extension of the Río Hondo fault zone of northern Guatemala, western Belize, and southern Quintana Roo (Lake Bacalar and Chetumal area). The northernmost part of this area appears to have been less intensely uplifted than that to the south and the offshore islands of Cancún, Mujeres, and Contoy represent remnants of sand dune deposits formed on a wave-cut terrace during a Pleistocene lowered stand of sea level, while the present coastal lands were built up by subsequent accretion and cementation of migrating beach and dune ridges. Southward from Cancún to and beyond Tulum to the coast is controlled by the fault blocks and the barrier reefs, with a shoreline marked by sea cliffs and intermediate back-reef calcareous sand beaches. Farther to the south from the region of Bahía de la Ascensión to the Belize border area near Xcalak the present shoreline consists for the most part of raised beach ridges that are immediately adjacent to the inner side of the barrier reefs and which pass inland into low-lying swamplands.

In contrast, the north coast throughout most of its extent is a greatly elongated barrier beach formed of shoreward migrating sands with a narrow hypersaline lagoon (called a "cienega") behind it. (The salt obtained from this cienega was of major significance to the ancient Maya of Yucatán, who carried on an extensive trade with other areas of Mexico and Central America. Salt is still being produced by a large factory near Los Colorados, Yucatán.) Although occasional groins and concrete piers have permitted some rock clinging forms to migrate into the area, essentially the only interruption to the long sand beaches of the northern coasts occurs near the center of the area from Punta Yalkubul eastward to and slightly beyond Isla Cerrito. Here a small outcrop of limestone has been added to by materials from Mayan ruins, particularly at and near Isla Cerrito; the result is to form the only relatively hard-bottom area of any extent along that coast.

With the above single exception, the area of sand beaches and cienegas extends from the vicinity of Cabo Catoche on the northeast corner of the peninsula westward rounding the northwest corner and passing southward to Punta

Ninum south of Celestún. From Punta Ninum southward for about 50 miles, to the city limits of Campeche, the immediate coast is marked by mangrove swamps. A small sandbar area about 10 miles from Punta Ninum is occupied by the fishing village of Isla Arenas, constituting the only significant settlement along the coast. Southward from the city of Campeche to the vicinity of Champotón, the coast transgresses an uplifted fault block of Eocene limestones that has been deeply eroded by subsequent solution and weathering, resulting, along the shore, in a series of rocky headlands with intermediate bays having sandy beaches.

Southwestward from Champotón the coast consists of a long sand beach occasionally marked by small areas of beach rock and/or jetty piles.

For convenience roman numerals, as follows, were assigned to the various collecting areas; these designations are used on the map (fig. 1) and in tables 1 and 2.

I. East coast area (Isla Cancún to Belize border).
II. Northeast corner area where the Caribbean and Gulf of Mexico faunas intermix (Isla Mujeres to west end of Isla Holbox).
III. Rocky area of north coast (Punta Yalkubul to coast east of Isla Cerrito).
IV. North coast sand and cienega facies (El Cuyo to Punta Ninum, excluding rocky area of list III, above).
V. Northwest coastal mangrove area (Punta Ninum south to city of Campeche).
VI. Southwestern coast from city of Campeche to Ciudad del Carmen and Zacatal, Campeche).
VII. Offshore reefs (Cayos Arcas, off west coast; Arrecife Alacranes, off north coast; and Cayos Norte and Lobos of the Banco Chinchorro off southeast coast).

TABLE 1. The Number of Shelled Molluscan Species in the Collections from Each of the Areas

Molluscan Class	I	II	III	IV	V	VI	VII	Total
Gastropoda	353	409	222	324	200	320	271	577
Pelecypoda	128	154	87	141	93	144	94	232
Cephalopoda	1	1	1	2	0	0	1	2
Scaphopoda	2	2	2	4	0	2	0	5
Polyplacophora	7	5	5	2	2	3	6	10
TOTALS	491	571	317	473	295	469	372	826

TABLE 2.   Species Appearing Most Characteristic of the Yucatán Area.

Those listed below are both widely distributed and relatively abundant in all of the ecologically distinguished geographic areas. Numbers indicate the percent of the localities from which the species listed has been found relative to the total number of localities in each of the areas.

Molluscan species	I	II	III	IV	V	VI	VII
Diadora cayenensis (Lamarck)	59	57	74	50	50	67	50
Tegula (Agathistoma) fasciata (Born)	59	71	100	100	100	52	100
Tricolia affinis cruenta Robertson	80	50	100	100	83	77	50
Tricolia thalassicola Robertson	63	50	89	100	100	46	50
Neritina virginea (Linnaeus)	77	14	48	100	50	63	75
Smaragdia viridis viridemaris Maury	68	33	95	75	100	77	75
Alvania auberiana (Orbigny)	32	83	68	100	100	62	25
Rissoina (Schwartziella) bryerea (Montagu)	74	100	74	50	100	92	50
Rissoina (Phosinella) cancellata Philippi	80	50	80	100	100	54	50
Zebina browniana (Orbigny)	74	83	89	100	100	92	50
Caecum (Caecum) pulchellum Stimpson	100	83	100	100	100	54	75
Spiroglyphus annulatus Daudin	74	33	52	100	100	100	100
Modulus modulus (Linnaeus)	95	86	74	100	100	67	100
Cerithium (Thericium) eburneum Bruguière	82	86	74	100	75	67	100
Bittium varium Pfeiffer	84	83	89	100	100	69	75
Finella (Finella) dubia (Orbigny)	42	50	80	100	100	38	50
Alaba incerta (Orbigny)	84	100	100	100	100	62	50
Seila adamsii (Lea)	89	100	100	100	100	85	50
Triphora nigrocincta (C. B. Adams)	89	83	84	100	100	38	25
Crepidula (Crepidula) maculosa Conrad	100	100	100	100	88	44	100

Molluscan species	I	II	III	IV	V	VI	VII
Chicoreus (Phyllonotus) *pomum* (Gmelin)	73	57	85	50	75	56	100
Columbella mercatoria (Linnaeus)	95	86	81	100	100	93	100
Melongena melongen (Linnaeus)	86	100	81	75	50	55	25
Fasciolaria tulipa (Linnaeus)	100	86	92	100	100	22	100
Turbinella angulata (Lightfoot)	82	71	78	25	75	26	100
Prunum apicinum (Menke)	86	86	89	100	75	44	100
Utriculastra candei (Orbigny)	47	67	100	100	100	77	50
Bulla striata Bruguière	86	100	92	100	100	74	75
Melampus coffeus (Linnaeus)	32	71	78	100	75	38	75
BIVALVIA (PELECYPODA)							
Arca (Arca) *imbricata* Bruguière	86	43	100	100	75	59	100
Arca (Arca) *zebra* (Swainson)	82	43	100	100	75	41	50
Arcopsis adamsi (Dall)	64	57	63	75	75	41	100
Brachidontes modiolus (Linnaeus)	77	43	89	100	88	52	75
Codakia (Codakia) *orbicularis* (Linnaeus)	64	29	85	100	100	93	100
Lucina pectinata (Gmelin)	64	86	67	100	63	44	75
Chama macerophylla Gmelin	86	43	92	100	100	70	100
Trachycardium (Dallocardia) *muricatum* (Linnaeus)	91	57	89	75	88	37	50
Laevicardium laevigatum (Linnaeus)	91	57	92	50	100	44	75
Chione (Chione) *cancellata* (Linnaeus)	100	100	100	100	100	78	75
Anomalocardia auberiana (Orbigny)	100	100	100	100	100	48	50
Parastarte triquetra (Conrad)	36	100	100	100	100	62	25

The following species are thought to be diagnostic of the east coast fauna being represented in at least 50 percent of the locality collections and absent from the north and west coastal faunas, although they may occur in the eastern part of the transitional northeast area and most are also present on the offshore reefs:

GASTROPODA:

Fissurella (Cremides) barbadensis
  (Gmelin)
Fissurella (Cremides) nodosa (Born)
Fissurella (Clypidella) fascicularis
  Lamarck
Cittarium pica (Linnaeus)
Arene (Marevalvata) tricarinata (Stearns)
Nerita peloronta Linnaeus
Nerita versicolor Gmelin
Littorina ziczac (Gmelin)
Tectarius (Cenchritis) muricatus
  (Linnaeus)

GASTROPODA: (continued)

Strombus (Tricornis) gigas Linnaeus
Cyphoma gibbosum (Linnaeus)
Thais (Stramonita) rustica (Lamarck)
Thais (Mancinella) deltoidea (Lamarck)
Conus mus Hwass

BIVALVIA (PELECYPODA):

Barbatia cancellaria (Lamarck)
Tellina (Tellina) radiata Linnaeus
Tellina (Tellinella) listeri Röding

Species characteristic of the Gulf of Mexico shallow-water faunal areas, being represented in at least half of the 57 locality collections from this area and absent from our east coastal Caribbean collections, although some are present in the northeast corners' "Transition Fauna," include:

GASTROPODA:

Littoridina (Texadina) sphinctostoma
  Abbott & Ladd
Melanella (Balcis) conoidea Kurtz &
  Stimpson
Crucibulum planum Schumacher
Crepidula (Bostrycapulus) aculeata
  (Gmelin)
Strombus (Strombus) alatus Gmelin
Phalium (Tylocassis) inflatum (Shaw)
Chicoreus (Chicoreus) dilectus (A. Adams)
Anachis (Costoanachis) lafresnayi (Fischer
  & Bernardi)
Anachis (Suturoglypta) hotessieriana
  (Orbigny)
Anachis (Parvanachis) obesa (C. B.
  Adams)
Mitrella (Astyris) lunata (Say)

GASTROPODA: (continued)

Mitrella (Astyris) raveneli (Dall)
Cantharus multangulus (Philippi)
Busycon (Sinistrofulgur) contrarium
  (Conrad)
Busycon (Fulguropsis) spiratum (Lamarck)
Nassarius vibex (Say)
Fasciolaria (Cinctura) lilium Fischer de
  Waldheim
Pleuroploca gigantea (Kiener)
Conus spurius atlanticus Clench
Turbonilla (Strioturbonilla) dalli Bush

BIVALVIA (PELECYPODA):

Anadara (Larkinia) transversa (Say)
Noetia (Eontia) ponderosa (Say)—present
  only in west coast areas, absent on
  north.

BIVALVIA (continued)

Modiolus modiolus squamosus Beauperthuy

Atrina (Atrina) rigida (Lightfoot)

Lucina (Callucina) keenae Chavan

Anodontia (Pegophysema) alba Link

Carditamera floridana Conrad

Dinocardium robustum vanhyningi Clench & L. C. Smith

Mulinia lateralis (Say)

Tagelus (Mesopleura) divisus (Spengler)

Mercenaria campechiensis (Gmelin)

Macrocallista (Megapitaria) maculata (Linnaeus)

Dosinia elegans Conrad

Rupellaria typica (Jonas)

A number of the species in the above list are known from other parts of the Caribbean area; their absence from the east coastal Yucatán collections may be a result of ecologic factors.

Acknowledgments

I was joined as co-investigator by my wife, Emily H. Vokes, Professor of Earth Sciences, Newcomb College, Tulane University, who has done much research and published many papers on various groups of gastropod mollusks. We both wish to express our sincere appreciation to Joann M. Andrews (Mrs. E. Wyllys IV) not only for her warm hospitality during our collecting trips but also for her logistical aid and for the many collections that she independently made for us. We also wish to acknowledge the assistance of George Herman for additional collections, especially from areas along the Caribbean coast.

REFERENCES

ANDREWS, E. WYLLYS IV
  1969.   The archaeological use and distribution of Mollusca in the Maya low-
  [1970]   lands.   Middle Amer. Res. Inst., Tulane Univ., Publ. 34, 115 pp.,
          illus.

BAKER, FRANK C.
  1891.   Notes on a collection of shells from southern Mexico.   Acad. Nat. Sci.,
          Philadelphia, Proc., vol. 43, pp. 45-55.

JAUME, MIGUEL L.
  1946.   Moluscos marinos litorales del Cabo Catoche, Yucatán, Mexico.   Rev.
          Soc. Malac, 'Carlos de la Torre,' vol. 4, no. 3, pp. 95-110.

WEISBORD, NORMAN E.
  1926.   Notes on marine mollusks from the Yucatán Peninsula, Mexico.
          Nautilus, vol. 39, pp. 81-87.

HAROLD E. VOKES

Structure and Function of a
Freshwater Tidal-Marsh Ecosystem

Principal Investigators: Dennis F. Whigham, Chesapeake Bay Center for Environmental Studies, Smithsonian Institution, Edgewater, Maryland; and Robert L. Simpson, Rider College, Lawrenceville, New Jersey.

Grant No. 1313: For a study of the structure and function of a freshwater tidal-marsh ecosystem (Hamilton Marshes, Delaware River).[1]

In 1973 we began a series of investigations of ecological characteristics of a Delaware River freshwater tidal marsh. At that time, there had been few studies of freshwater tidal marshes (McCormick, Grant, and Patrick, 1970; McCormick, 1970; McCormick and Ashbaugh, 1972; Walton and Patrick, 1973) even though they are widespread in tidal portions of eastern North American rivers. Initially our studies were centered on the floristics of the marsh vegetation. Our primary objectives were to determine which species occurred in tidally influenced freshwater marshes and how the species segregated into community types. Additionally we wanted to determine whether or not freshwater tidal marshes were as productive as estuarine brackish marshes. Based on preliminary data, Walton and Patrick (1970) had suggested that freshwater tidal marshes were efficient nutrient processors. Therefore, a second phase of our work centered on the patterns of nutrient movement through and within the marshes by analyzing seasonal patterns of selected water quality parameters, particularly nitrogen and phosphorus.

The research was conducted in the 500-hectare Hamilton Marshes (fig. 1), which are the northernmost tidal marshes in the Delaware River. In addition to the marshes, located near Trenton, New Jersey, there are lowland forests, tidally influenced shrub forests, and a few shallow impoundments (Whigham, 1974). Table 1 summarizes the coverage and production data for the major marsh vegetation types.

---

[1] In addition to the National Geographic Society, we extend our thanks to the Hamilton Township Environmental Commission for its financial support and to the following students whose work on the project was supported by the Society's grant: Paula Bozowski, Herbert Grover, Barie Kline, Thomas Leslie, and David West.

TABLE 1.   Aerial Extent and Total Aboveground Production Estimates for
Dominant Vegetation Associations of the Hamilton Marshes

Vegetation type	Coverage	Annual aboveground production (t/ha)*	Total production (t)
Mixed	137	9.1	1246.7
Cattail	19	13.2	250.8
Giant ragweed	3	11.6	34.8
Arrow arum	11	6.5	71.5
Spiked loosestrife	10	21.0	210.0
Wildrice	24	9.4	225.6
Yellow waterlily	58	7.8	452.4
TOTALS	262	X = 9.5	2491.8

*t = ton, ha= hectare.

Structurally the marsh consists of several distinct habitats, including stream banks, high marsh, and pondlike areas. The most extensive habitat is the high marsh, which is usually flooded to a depth of half a meter or less only during 3 hours of a 12-hour tide cycle. There are several recognizable community types in this habitat even though most species are widespread and occur throughout the high marsh. The most common high-marsh community consists of sweetflag *(Acorus calamus)*, arrow arum *(Peltandra virginica)*, tear-thumb *(Polygonum arifolium)*, bur marigold *(Bidens laevis)*, touch-me-not *(Impatiens capensis)*, wildrice *(Zizania aquatica)*, and arrowhead *(Sagittaria latifolia)*. Phenologically, sweetflag and arrow arum dominate the marsh landscape in the early part of the growing season, but they are eventually overtopped by wildrice, which dominates in July and August, and finally by bur marigold, which dominates until the end of the growing season. Several additional species, including giant ragweed *(Ambrosia trifida)*, cattail *(Typha angustifolia* and *T. latifolia)*, and purple loosestrife *(Lythrum salicaria)*, become dominant in other high-marsh communities (Whigham et al., 1978).

Stream-bank communities are dominated by waterlily *(Nuphar advena)*, pickerelweed *(Pontederia cordata)*, waterhemp *(Acnida cannabina)*, smartweed *(Polygonum punctatum)*, and wildrice *(Zizania aquatica)*. One large marsh area (site 4B in fig. 1) is pondlike and flooded to a depth of 1 meter at high tide and drained only at low tide. Waterlily, arrow arum, wildrice, cattail, smartweed, and pickerelweed dominate in this habitat.

In areas adjacent to upland habitats, the open marsh is replaced by a shrub forest, which is inundated at high tide. All the herbaceous species found in

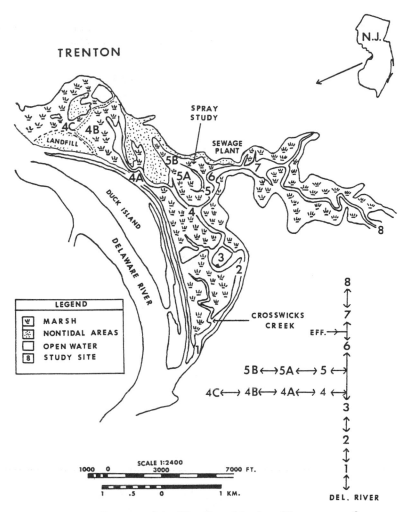

FIG. 1. Schematic diagram of the Hamilton Marshes. The pattern of water movement into and out of the marsh is shown at the lower right.

the open marsh plus several woody shrubs, the most common being arrow-wood *(Viburnum dentatum)*, red maple *(Acer rubrum)*, alder *(Alnus serrulata)*, and buttonbush *(Cephalanthus occidentalis)*, occur in this transition zone.

Compared to salt marshes, the outstanding floristic characteristics of freshwater tidal marshes are high diversity and abundance, and, in some cases dominance, of annuals. The latter are virtually excluded from salt marshes, and whereas species richness is normally approximately 30 vascular plants in Delaware River salt marshes, there may be more than 60 species in freshwater

TABLE 2.   Summary of Production Values for Marsh Plants

Community type (dominant)	Aboveground net production (g/m²/yr)	Locale	Reference
	(1) Freshwater Tidal Marshes		
Wildrice	605-1547	Pa.	McCormick, 1970
(*Zizania aquatica*)	659-1125	N.J.	Present study
	1390	N.J.	McCormick and Ashbaugh, 1972
Giant Ragweed	1211-1250	Pa.	McCormick, 1970
(*Ambrosia trifida*)	1160	N.J.	Present study
Yellow Waterlily	1166-1188	Pa.	McCormick, 1970
(*Nuphar advena*)	516	N.J.	McCormick and Ashbaugh, 1972
	775	N.J.	Present study
	245	Va.	Wass and Wright, 1969
Cattail	874-2063	Pa.	McCormick, 1970
(*Typha* sp.)	987	N.J.	McCormick and Ashbaugh, 1972
	1119-1528	N.J.	Present study
	930	Va.	Wass and Wright, 1969
Mixed	516- 897	Pa.	McCormick, 1970
(*Bidens laevis*)	756-1162	N.J.	Present study
Primrose willow	403- 583	Pa.	McCormick, 1970
(*Jussiaea repens*)			
Arrowhead	628	Pa.	McCormick, 1970
(*Sagittaria* sp.)			
Arrow arum	269	Pa.	McCormick, 1970
(*Peltandra virginica*)	500- 800	N.J.	Present study
Sweetflag	712- 940	N.J.	Present study
(*Acorus calamus*)			
Loosestrife	1749	Pa.	McCormick, 1970
(*Lythrum salicaria*)	2104	N.J.	Present study
Waterhemp	762	Pa.	McCormick, 1970
(*Acnida cannabina*)			
	(2) Salt Marshes between New York and Virginia		
Saltwater cordgrass	1332	Va.	Wass and Wright, 1969
(*Spartina alterniflora*)	445	Del.	M. H. Morgan, 1961
	300	N.J.	Good, 1965
Salt-meadow grass	805	Va.	Wass and Wright, 1969
(*Spartina patens*)			
Spike grass	360	Va.	Wass and Wright, 1969
(*Fimbristylis* sp.)			

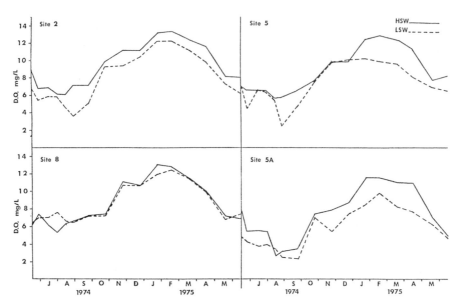

FIG. 2.   Changes in dissolved oxygen (D.O.) at sites 2, 8, 5, and 5A in the Hamilton
Marshes between May 1974 and July 1975. Solid lines represent high slack water
(HSW) and dashed lines low slack water (LSW). Refer to figure 1 for location of sam-
pling stations.

tidal marshes. Most likely the higher level of species richness is due to the lack
of salt stress that is a normal feature in salt-marsh environments.

Table 2 shows biomass data for Delaware and Chesapeake Bay salt
marshes and freshwater tidal marshes along the Delaware River from south of
Philadelphia (Tinicum Marshes) to the Hamilton Marshes. It is apparent that,
compared to saline marshes, a great number of community types occur in the
freshwater tidal marshes. Even though the biomass data given for the freshwater marshes in table 2 represent underestimates of net production because of
the seasonal changes in dominance (Whigham et al., 1978), it is obvious that
freshwater tidal marshes are extremely productive and that they are probably
more productive than salt marshes at the same latitude. We estimated a mean
production of 950 g/m^2/yr in the Hamilton Marshes. Purple-loosestrife communities were the most productive (2100 g/m^2), while waterlily-dominated
areas were the least productive (450 g/m^2).

The marshes are metabolically active throughout the year (Simpson et al.,
1978), as shown in figures 2 and 3. Flood-tide waters from the Delaware River are consistently higher in oxygen and lower in carbon dioxide than waters

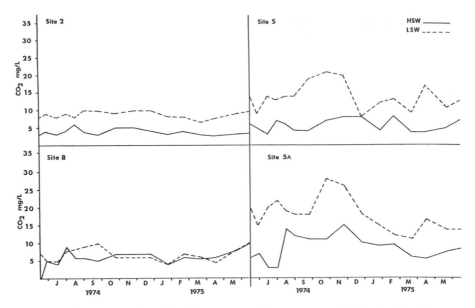

FIG. 3. Changes in carbon-dioxide content at sites 2, 8, 5, and 5A in the Hamilton Marshes between May 1974 and July 1975. Solid lines represent high slack water (HSW) and dashed lines low slack water (LSW). Refer to figure 1 for location of sampling stations.

leaving the marsh at low slack water (compare site 2 of figs. 2 and 3). The highest carbon-dioxide levels occur in October (site 5 and 5A, fig. 3), corresponding with the fall dieback of vascular plants in the marsh, suggesting that heterotrophic activity is most pronounced at that time.

High levels of productivity should be indicative of efficient nutrient utilization. Our water-quality studies (Simpson and Whigham, 1975; Simpson et al., 1978) demonstrated that nitrogen and phosphorus are assimilated by all marsh habitats during the growing season. Figures 4 and 5 demonstrate the seasonal pattern of nitrogen and phosphorus for high-marsh site 5A (fig. 1). During the summer nitrate and ammonia nitrogen and inorganic phosphate are assimilated, whereas during the winter they are exported. The pondlike areas (site 4B) were interesting because they appeared to assimilate nitrogen and phosphorus during the entire year (figs. 4, 5). Nutrient assimilation in the summer months is performed primarily by vascular plants in both habitats. In the pondlike areas filamentous algae appear to be the assimilators during the winter months. It is obvious that this riverine freshwater marsh ecosystem is capable of assimilating nutrients, especially during the summer months when eutrophication is a problem, and that they play an important role in the over-all nutrient budgets of the Delaware River (Whigham and Simpson, 1978).

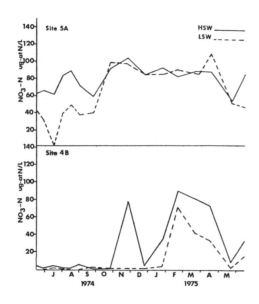

FIG. 4. Changes in nitrate nitrogen at sites 5A and 4B in the Hamilton Marshes. Refer to figure 1 for locations of sampling stations. Water samples were collected at high slack water (HSW) and low slack water (LSW) from May 1974 until July 1975.

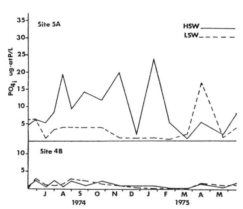

FIG. 5. Changes in inorganic phosphate at sites 5A and 4B in the Hamilton Marshes. Refer to figure 1 for locations of sampling stations. Water samples were collected at high slack water (HSW) and low slack water (LSW) from May 1974 until July 1975.

REFERENCES

GOOD, RALPH E.
    1965.   Salt marsh vegetation, Cape May, N.J.   Bull. New Jersey Acad. Sci., vol. 10, pp. 1-11.

McCORMICK, JACK
    1970.   The natural features of Tinicum Marsh, with particular emphasis on the vegetation.   Pp. 1-104 *in* "Two Studies of Tinicum Marsh, Delaware and Philadelphia Counties, Pa.," J. F. McCormick, R. R. Grant, Jr., and R. Patrick, eds.   Conservation Foundation, Washington, D. C.

McCormick, Jack, and Ashbaugh, T.
    1972.   Vegetation of a section of Oldmans Creek tidal marsh and related areas in Salem and Gloucester Counties, New Jersey.   Bull. New Jersey Acad. Sci., vol. 17, pp. 31-37.
McCormick, Jack; Grant, R. R., Jr.; and Patrick, R.
    1970.   Two studies of Tinicum Marsh, Delaware and Philadelphia Counties, Pa., 123 pp.   Conservation Foundation, Washington, D. C.
Simpson, Robert L., and Whigham, Dennis F.
    1976.   Seasonal distribution of selected water chemical parameters in a Delaware River freshwater tidal marsh.   American Society of Limnology and Oceanography, Savannah, Georgia. (Abstract.)
Simpson, Robert L.; Whigham, Dennis F.; and Walker, R.
    1978.   Seasonal patterns of nutrient movement in a freshwater tidal marsh.   Pp. 242-258 *in* "Freshwater Wetlands: Ecological Process and Potential," R. E. Good, D. F. Whigham, and R. L. Simpson, eds. Academic Press, New York.
Walton, T., and Patrick, R.
    1973.   Delaware River estuarine marsh survey.   *In* "Delaware Estuary System: Environmental Impacts and Socio-economic Effects," 177 pp. A report prepared for the National Science Foundation (raan).   Academy of Natural Sciences of Philadelphia.
Wass, Marvin L., and Wright, Thomas D.
    1969.   Coastal wetlands of Virginia. Interim report to the Governor and General Assembly.   Virginia Inst. Mar. Sci. Spec. Rpt. in Appl. Mar. Sci. and Ocean Eng., no. 10, 154 pp.
Whigham, Dennis F.
    1974.   Preliminary ecological studies of the Hamilton Marshes: Progress report for the period ending January 1974, 66 pp.   Rider College, Lawrenceville, New Jersey.
Whigham, Dennis F.; McCormick, Jack; Good, Ralph E.; and Simpson, Robert L.
    1978.   Biomass and primary production in freshwater tidal wetlands of the Middle Atlantic Coast.   Pp. 1-20 *in* "Freshwater Wetlands: Ecological Process and Management Potential," R. E. Good, D. F. Whigham, and R. L. Simpson, eds.   Academic Press, New York.
Whigham, Dennis F., and Simpson, Robert L.
    1975.   Ecological studies of the Hamilton Marshes: Progress report for the period June, 1974-January, 1975, 185 pp.   Rider College, Lawrenceville, New Jersey.
    1976.   The potential use of freshwater tidal marshes in the management of water quality in the Delaware River.   Pp. 173-186 *in* "Biological Control of Water," Joachim Tourbier and Robert W. Pierson, Jr., eds.   University of Pennsylvania Press.
    1978.   Nitrogen and phosphorus movement in a freshwater tidal wetland receiving sewage effluent.   Pp. 2089-2203 *in* "Coastal 78: Symposium on Technical, Environmental, Socioeconomic, and Regulatory Aspects of Coastal Zone Management." American Society of Civil Engineers, Minneapolis, Minnesota.

Dennis F. Whigham

Ecology of the Nez Perce Bighorn Sheep Herd

Principal Investigator: E. Earl Willard, University of Montana, Missoula, Montana.

Grant nos. 1363 and   To study the population characteristics and seasonal habitats
1548.   of the Nez Perce Creek bighorn sheep herd.

This report summarizes investigations of the sheep population which occurs in isolation within the Bitterroot Mountains of Montana and Idaho. Final interpretations and conclusions have been developed into an M.S. thesis by the junior author.

The Rocky Mountain bighorn sheep *(Ovis canadensis canadensis)* in the vicinity of Watchtower and Sheephead Creeks, Montana, are remnants of a population which once occupied the entire Bitterroot Range. Information about the herd prior to the study was limited to the general location of the summer range, analysis of the rumen contents of a hunter-killed ram (Firebaugh, 1973), and a population estimate of at least 50 sheep (Firebaugh, 1971). The area had been cursorily censused by air each winter but no sheep were observed. Speculations were that they migrated into the Selway or Salmon River drainages of Idaho during the winter.

This population is in a relatively undisturbed region, especially the Selway-Bitterroot Wilderness Area. Few people venture into their range; thus, the sheep are mostly free from human interference. Buechner (1960) stated that a thorough investigation might reveal a considerable population in this area. This particular population then represented an opportunity to study food habits, seasonal habitats, and migration patterns of native sheep in near pristine conditions.

Lewis and Clark were told by Indians that there were large numbers of bighorn sheep present in the Bitterroot Mountains, with the greatest density along the main divide (Buechner, 1960). The Lewis and Clark party shot at sheep near Traveller's Rest (Lolo Creek) (Thewaites, 1969). There has been relatively little information about sheep numbers since that time.

This investigation was conducted from June 1974 through June 1976. Specific objectives were to investigate: 1, sheep distribution, seasonal key-use areas and migration routes; 2, population characteristics; 3, bighorn habitat use along the Selway River drainage from Indian Creek to Snake Creek; 4, winter diet; and 5, physical condition and vigor of the population.

Study Area

The study area lies near the south end of the Bitterroot Mountains of Montana and Idaho. Much of the bighorn sheep range lies within the Selway-Bitterroot Wilderness Area. The summer range includes rugged mountains; deep, steep-sided canyons; long, open ridges; extensive forested areas in mid to low elevations; and alpine to subalpine grassy meadows within which small lakes are common. The winter range was found to be mostly on lower ridges along the Selway River in Idaho. The area contains large brush fields, open grasslands, cliffs and some forested sites.

Fire has played an important role in the ecology of the area. A review of the major fires of the area from 1889-1976 indicates that the sheep range has been repeatedly burned. This fire history is expressed in the presence of large areas of brush and grasslands.

Materials and Methods

Censusing.   Bighorn sheep were censused periodically on the summer and winter ranges of the study area between June 8, 1974, and June 10, 1976. During each observation, physiographic characteristics, group structure, behavior, climatic conditions, and vegetation were recorded on datum forms. Only one record was made daily for each group, but additional notes were made in a diary on behavior, habitat use, and reobservations.

During spring, summer, and fall when sheep were at high elevations, 4- to 10-day backpacking trips were made into upper drainages. Hikes were then made daily from the base camp. This arrangement kept the observer constantly in sheep habitat and had little apparent impact on the sheep.

During the course of the study it was observed that at least some of the bighorn sheep were wintering along the lower slopes of the Selway River in Idaho. Thus, from December 6, 1975, to May 27, 1976, a camp was established near the mouth of Sheep Creek, Idaho, for observing the sheep. The sheep were little disturbed by man since the road is now plowed and the only access is a 64-kilometer snowmobile trip. Depending on snow conditions, daylong hiking, snowshoeing, or cross-country skiing trips were made over the sheep's winter range.

Standardized census routes were walked approximately once a week to obtain population estimates of the winter-spring range and an index of habitat selection. Sheep observations were made at distances from 18 to 3,200 meters, using 8 x 30 binoculars and a 20X-45X variable spotting scope. Sex and age groups were recorded as described by Geist (1971).

At various times of the year, fixed-wing aircraft were used to supplement ground observations.

Capture, Marking and Telemetry. An attempt was made to capture and mark bighorn sheep for documentation of daily and seasonal movements and to obtain an unbiased estimate of habitat use. During July 1974, a clover trap was erected at the natural mineral lick near Sheephead Creek, Montana. The trap was baited with a block of salt.

Attempts were made to tranquilize sheep on the summer range. Difficulties were encountered in obtaining a large number of sheep because of the problems in locating sheep in such a large area, and in approaching to within range of a tranquilizer gun.

Tranquilized animals were measured and marked with braided rope collars and radio transmitters attached to webbing collars placed around the sheeps' necks.

Sheep having transmitters were sighted on their summer range or located by radio telemetry from an airplane with a Yagi antenna attached to each wing strut. On winter range, marked animals were located visually and by radio telemetry from the ground. A loop antenna was then used with the receiver.

Group Fidelity. Group constancy was calculated for observed sheep as described by Knight (1970) and was expressed as the probability of two animals occurring together by Cole's (1949) coefficient. The degree of association between two sheep was calculated for each season of the year.

Centers of Activity. Centers of activity for individually marked animals were located on a USFS base map using a 0.16-square kilometer grid overlay. The centers of activity were then used to calculate the animal's seasonal standard diameter ($SD = D^2N$), where D is twice the distance from the center of activity to each of N relocations (Harrison, 1958). The standard diameter is the diameter of a circle whose center is the center of activity and which contains 68.26 percent of all relocations of the animals.

Lungworms. Three hunters contributed fecal samples from their trophies harvested during the 1974-1976 hunting seasons. Between February 2 and March 11, 1976, 20 fecal samples were collected from animals of unknown age and sex. Additional samples were collected from two class II rams on June 8, 1976. All samples were analyzed for the presence of lungworm larvae.

Food Habits. Feeding sites were examined on the sheep's winter range from December 1975 through March 1976. Each feeding site contained between 50 and 500 instances of use as measured in bites. Because mule deer, elk, and bighorn sheep used the same terrain, data were collected when enough snow was on the ground to determine that only sheep had recently fed on a given plant.

Analysis of all food habits data followed the mean percentage method of Martin et al. (1946).

Habitat Selection.   Habitat use was determined by sheep observations from census routes and from radio telemetry locations. The total area available was determined by connecting peripheral locations of all sheep observations as described by Dalke (1942), Craighead and Craighead (1956), and Marcum (1975); then the entire slope they fell on was included. In this manner, boundaries for areas of availability were drawn along ridge lines. The upper elevation of the winter range was determined from the location of the highest sighting.

Areas of habitat components were measured from topographical maps by use of a dot grid. Selection for or against a specific component was determined by the Z-statistic (Neu et al., 1974).

Results and Discussion

Capturing Sheep.   Trapping at a mineral lick near Sheephead Creek, Montana, was unsuccessful after 13 trap days. Although this was the most promising location for a trap, it was not certain whether sheep visited the lick. The mineral lick is heavily used by deer and elk, but the location may not be used for trapping sheep. However, two animals were immobilized and fitted with radio collars at other locations.

Movements of Radioed Sheep.   Ewe 142 was radiotracked between June 14, 1975, and December 1, 1976. Ram 363 was followed from June 26, 1975, to April 23, 1976. The ram was later found dead. When the summer locations for 1975 and 1976 are combined, the standard diameters for the ewe and ram were 9.6 and 9.3 kilometers, respectively. The winter standard diameter for each was 3.4 and 1.8 kilometers.

Animal Movements.   Seasonal movement patterns can be constructed from locations of marked sheep and observations of sheep in general. The ewes move from the winter-spring range, located along the Selway River in Idaho, to Montana ranges in late May or early June. The migration route leads from the Selway over the Bitterroot Divide and down Sheephead Creek drainage to the Nez Perce Fork of the Bitterroot River. Sheep initially range over the lower elevations of the habitat in Montana. As the snow melts, they move to higher elevations. During the summer months, sheep are located primarily in the high subalpine basins along the Divide, but some sheep can always be found along the Nez Perce Road and other areas at lower elevations. This movement pattern can be interpreted as sheep following the retreating snow line and the emergence of green vegetation.

Rams presumably follow a similar pattern. During early summer they are at lower elevations in Montana. Later in the summer, one group of rams centers its activity around Mount Jerusalem; another group of four to five rams remains along the Nez Perce Road above Sheephead Creek.

Sheep migrate from the upper portion of Sheep Creek, Idaho, in late May and follow the south-facing slope of Schofield Creek to the Bitterroot Divide. They then cross the Divide at Watchtower Pass and follow the Divide to the head of the North Fork of Sheephead Creek, which they follow down to the Nez Perce Fork of the Bitterroot River. They cross the Bitterroot River and journey to Castle Rock and to the head of Fale's Creek. No evidence was found for a migration route to the Salmon River. This migration route is vital to the sheep and should be maintained at all costs. Few sheep could survive an average to harsh winter on the summer range because of the deep, dense snowpack. The present migration route allows sheep to winter under relatively mild conditions along lower, open slopes and to summer on excellent, high-elevation ranges.

Habitat Selection. Within a season, there are shifts in preference from one area of availability to another. During winter, cliff cover type is being used at random within the concentrated use region but it is highly preferred within the maximum winter range. This region presumably has the proper juxtaposition of habitat components they desire, since it contains 72% of the observations.

Habitat preferences shift from winter to spring. Bunchgrass and savanna types are used more during spring. Rock outcrop and scree types are used less in spring than winter. More habitat types and land types were used in spring than during winter because of a change in availability and because of a real change in habitat preference.

In general, sheep selected vegetation types with little forest overstory and a predominantly grass understory. Types with high forest and shrub canopy coverage were avoided. Cliffs and south-facing slopes with much rock were heavily used. There are apparently two rutting areas, one located in Montana and another in the vicinity of Sheep Creek, Idaho. Visual observations of class III and IV rams and the locations of 11 rams killed by hunters were used as indicators of rutting grounds. In 1975, rams were located on both the Selway winter range and on the Montana side during the period of the rut, approximately November 20 to December 15. However, most of the rutting activity took place on the Idaho rutting ground.

Five mineral licks were found on the study area. Sheep were observed using the ones located on the winter-spring range, which were cave-like areas in cliffs.

Inferences concerning lambing grounds were made from locations of ewes between May 20 and June 10. The locations are mainly on very steep cliffs. Important areas are the cliffs of Stewart Creek and the early summer range in Montana.

Cliffs are important in both winter and spring. During winter, cliffs slough snow; thus they are mainly snow-free, allowing sheep to feed without having to paw through a deep, dense snowpack. Cliffs also offer lambs relative safety from predators during the spring. These advantages are reflected by strong selection for this type both winter and spring.

Boundaries of winter and spring ranges were drawn from observations of the ewe-lamb-young ram groups during the winter of 1975-76. Most class III and IV rams left Sheep Creek between January 2 and 10, 1976, and all were gone by January 20. They did not return until April 8, 1976, when four class III rams returned and remained throughout that month.

Sheep had previously been reported wintering on the Montana side. The area around Fale's Flat, Montana, was checked during the winter of 1975 by skiing into the area. Tracks of what probably were sheep were observed near Peyton Rock, and in the Sheephead Creek drainage in January 1975. No other signs were observed in the area during that winter. On March 5, 1976, the Montana portion of the study area was aerially censused under good conditions for seeing sheep. During March 1976 aerial surveys were made at all locations on the Montana side where sheep might occur. The only location where tracks were seen was Sheephead Creek; these later proved to be the tracks of four sheep. The other areas had very deep snow cover.

Information on summer range was obtained only in Montana, from Nez Perce Pass to Nelson Creek. However, sheep were reported near Cuneo Point, Idaho. Much of the higher elevations of White Cap, Canyon, and Cooper Creeks, Idaho, are probably used by bighorn sheep during the summer.

Most bighorn sheep in North America winter on climax steppe vegetation communities. Such winter ranges have been reported by Stelfox (1975) for Alberta; Schallenberger (1966) for the Sun River, Montana; Smith (1954) for the Middle Fork of the Salmon River, Idaho; Morgan (1970) for other parts of the Salmon River; Berwick (1968) for Rock Creek, Montana; Oldemeyer et al. (1971) for Yellowstone National Park; and Buechner (1960) for Colorado and Wyoming. Sheep in the Bitterroot Mountains, those near Thompson Falls, Montana (Tilton, 1977), and a herd in British Columbia (Demarchi, 1975) do not have steppe communities; thus, winter ranges are seral fire communities of the Douglas-fir forest. The winter range in the Bitterroot Mountains was repeatedly burned early in this century and extensive areas are in early seral stages. Without repeated burning these openings will slowly revert to forests.

Thus, some form of burning program is necessary to maintain suitable winter range.

Food Habits.   Information on winter food habits is presented in Table 1. The two most important forage species were bluebunch wheatgrass *(Agropyron spicatum)* and greenbush *(Glossopetalon nevadense)*. Bluebunch wheatgrass was most used in December, after which use declined somewhat during the winter. Greenbush was also important during December, but use was heaviest during late winter. Use of grasses in mid and late winter declined, when use of shrubs and forbs increased.

Food habits of sheep vary among populations, depending on the vegetation available. Smith (1954) found 56% use of grasses and 39% of forbs and shrubs for the Salmon River winter range. Morgan (1970) reported 69% grasses, 4% forbs, and 27% browse for Morgan Creek, Idaho, during winter. The sheep on the winter range near West Rosebud Creek in the Beartooths of Montana used 47% grasses, 13% forbs, and 40% shrubs (Stewart, 1975). Those sheep on the Stillwater winter range in the Beartooths utilized 50%, 15%, and 34% grasses, forbs, and shrubs, respectively (Stewart, 1975). The sheep that winter in the Gallatin Canyon, Montana, ate 72%, 17%, and 8% grasses, forbs, and browse, respectively (Constan, 1967). Schallenberger (1966) reported 37% grass, 21% forbs, and 42% browse eaten during the winter in the Sun River area of Montana. Brown (1974) reported the winter food habits near Thompson Falls, Montana, as 5%, 3%, and 92% grasses, forbs, and shrubs, respectively.

Range Condition.   Poor range condition was apparent on the winter range. Grasses, including bluebunch wheatgrass, Idaho fescue *(Festuca idahoensis)*, Junegrass *(Koeleria cristata)* and bluegrasses *(Poa* spp.) were heavily grazed, leaving little old growth at the basal crowns by spring. Greenbush was so heavily browsed and clubbed that its height was only 8 to 10 centimeters tall. Other palatable shrubs, chokecherry *(Prunus virginiana)*, serviceberry *(Amelanchier alnifolia)*, and mountain maple *(Acer glabrum)* were severely hedged, appeared as single stalks, or had mostly grown out of reach of herbivores.

Poor range condition is often reflected in high lungworm larvae output (Buechner, 1960; Uhazy et al., 1973; Stelfox, 1975). In the Bitterroots, larvae output is lower than in other parts of Montana (Forrester and Senger, 1964; Brown, 1974; Stewart, 1975; Worley et al., 1976), possibly due to limited concentrations of sheep.

Population Characteristics.   During the rut, which occurred in early December, the highest count was made of 90 individuals (50 ewes, 25 lambs, 9 class II rams, 6 class III rams). Long distance observations resulted in underes-

TABLE 1. Bighorn Sheep Winter Food Habits from the
Examination of 37 Feeding Sites

Plant species	Number of sites			
	December 10	January 13	February 7	March 7
Grasses:				
Agropyron spicatum	42.3	31.9	26.7	28.1
Bromus tectorum		0.2		
Danthonia spicata	0.5			
Festuca idahoensis	17.6	1.7	2.2	2.7
Festuca scabrella		3.2		
Koeleria cristata	8.4	2.5		0.2
Poa secunda	0.4	0.2	2.3	
Total for grasses	69.2	39.8	31.3	31.0
Forbs:				
Achillea millefolium		0.1		0.0
Agoseris glauca	4.4	1.8		
Antennaria rosea	0.2	0.8	26.0	12.1
Eriogonum heracleoides	3.0	2.9	2.2	8.2
Lomatium sp.		2.0	2.8	2.4
Potentilla sp.	0.5	0.8	0.4	
Tragapogon dubius	0.2			
Total for forbs	8.4	8.4	31.0	23.2
Shrubs:				
Acer glabrum		1.8		
Amelanchier alnifolia		0.6	0.9	1.4
Cercocarpus ledifolius	3.8	15.7	2.6	4.7
Chrysothamnus nauseosus		7.0		
Glossopetalon nevadense	18.6	25.7	23.5	34.4
Holodiscus discolor			1.1	
Philadelphus lewisii			2.8	0.6
Physocarpus malvaceus		0.0		
Prunus virginiana		0.7	4.8	4.8
Ribes sp.		0.2	2.1	
Total for shrubs	22.4	51.8	37.8	45.9

timating horn size, so the ewe-lamb ratio is actually higher and the rams should be spread over classes I through IV. Following the rut, there is a gradual emigration of rams and presumably some ewes. Rams and ewes return to Sheep and Stewart Creeks in April, during which 70 individuals were counted in one day. The population begins migrating to summer range in May.

Monthly average group size was calculated for the winter range. Except for February, there is a steady decline in group size from the rut in December (9.6 sheep/group) to lambing in May (4.1 sheep/group). Beginning in June, the group size again increased through the rut.

Prior to winter observations, the ewe-lamb ratio was 65 lambs per 100 ewes. During the rut, the ratio was 52 lambs per 100 ewes and steadily decreased throughout the winter. A regression analysis indicated a significant ($p<0.025$) decrease in the number of lambs. Approximately 50% of the lamb crop died between December 1 and May 30. The observed ewe-lamb ratio is normal compared to many populations (Smith, 1954, Schallenberger, 1966; Constan, 1967; Morgan, 1970; Frisina, 1974; Stelfox, 1975).

Animal Health. Of the fecal samples, 80% showed light larvae output while only 4% (one sample) had a heavy output. Average output of ova was 3.6 larvae per gram. But if the one sample of heavy infection is omitted, the average output is only 0.66 larvae per gram.

Three lower jaws from sheep were obtained: a hunter-killed ram, one ewe found dead, and ram 363. In all cases, there were abnormalities in the teeth. Ram 363 had necrotic stomatitis under PM4. The other two sheep had abnormal wear of the molariform teeth; the ewe had an especially severe case.

Two sheep carcasses were found. A ewe fed upon by coyotes had severe tooth wear and was in good condition as judged by the color and consistency of femur marrow. She was located beneath a cliff, so she may have died either by accident or predation. Ram 363 was found dead near the stream bottom of the South Fork of Sheep Creek. He was in poor physical condition and suffered from necrotic stomatitis, but he may have been killed by a mountain lion.

REFERENCES

BERWICK, S. H.
   1968.   Observations on the decline of the Rock Creek, Montana, population of bighorn sheep, 245 pp.   Unpubl. M.S. Thesis, Univ. of Montana, Missoula.
BROWN, G. W.
   1974.   Distribution and population characteristics of bighorn sheep near Thompson Falls in northwestern Montana, 134 pp.   M.S. Thesis, Univ. of Montana, Missoula.

BUECHNER, H. K.
  1960.   The bighorn sheep in the United States, its past, present and future, 174
           pp.   Wildl. Monogr. no. 4.
COLE, L. C.
  1949.   The measurement of interspecific association.   Ecology, vol. 30, no. 4,
           pp. 411-424.
CONSTAN, K.
  1967.   Bighorn sheep range use, food habits and relationship to mule deer and
           elk in Gallatin Canyon, 43 pp.   Job Comp. Rep., Proj. W-98-R-7, 8,
           Montana Fish & Game Dept., Helena.
CRAIGHEAD, J. J., and CRAIGHEAD, F. C., JR.
  1956.   Hawks, owls and wildlife, 443 pp.   Stackpole Co., Harrisburg, Pa.
           and Wildlife Management Inst., Washington, D. C.
DALKE, P. D.
  1942.   The cottontail rabbits in Connecticut. 97 pp.   Connecticut State Geol.
           Nat. Hist. Surv. Bull. 65.
DEMARCHI, D. A.
  1975.   Report from British Columbia.   Pp. 23-27 *in* "The Wild Sheep in
           Modern North America," J. B. Trefethen, ed., 302 pp.   Boone and
           Crockett Club in cooperation with the Winchester Press, N. Y.
FIREBAUGH, J. E.
  1971.   Big game survey and inventory, Bitterroot Unit, 68 pp.   Job Prog.
           Rep., Proj. W-130-R-4, Montana Fish & Game Dept., Helena.
  1973.   Big game survey and inventory, Bitterroot Unit, 78 pp.   Job. Prog.
           Rep., Proj. W-130-R-4, Montana Fish & Game Dept., Helena.
FORRESTER, D. J., and SENGER, C. M.
  1964.   A survey of lungworm infection in bighorn sheep of Montana.   Journ.
           Wildl. Man., vol. 28, pp. 481-491.
FRISINA, M. R.
  1974.   Ecology of bighorn sheep in the Sun River area of Montana during fall
           and spring, 68 pp.   Job Comp. Rep., Proj. W-120-4, 5, Montana Fish
           & Game Dept., Helena.
GEIST, V.
  1971.   Mountain sheep—a study in behavior and evolution, 383 pp.
           Univ. Chicago Press, Chicago.
HARRISON, J. L.
  1958.   Range movement of some Malayan rats.   Journ. Mammal., vol. 39,
           no. 2, pp. 180-206.
KNIGHT, R. R.
  1970.   The Sun River elk herd, 66 pp.   Wildl. Monogr. no. 23.
MARCUM, C. L.
  1975.   Summer-fall habitat selection and use by a western Montana elk herd,
           188 pp.   Ph.D. Thesis, Univ. of Montana, Missoula.
MARTIN, A. C.; GENSCH, R. H.; and BROWN, C. P.
  1946.   Alternate methods in upland game bird food analysis.   Journ. Wildl.
           Man., vol. 10, no. 1, pp. 8-12.

MORGAN, J. K.
  1970. Ecology of the Morgan Creek and East Fork of the Salmon River bighorn sheep herds and management of bighorn sheep in Idaho. Job Comp. Rep., Proj. W-142-R-1, Idaho Fish & Game Dept., Boise.
NEU, C. W.; BYERS, C. R.; and PEEK, J. M.
  1974. A technique for analysis of utilization-availability data. Journ. Wildl. Man., vol. 38, no. 3, pp. 541-545.
OLDEMEYER, J. L.; BARMORE, W. J.; and GILBERT, D. L.
  1971. Winter ecology of bighorn sheep in Yellowstone National Park. Journ. Wildl. Man., vol. 35, no. 2, pp. 257-269.
SCHALLENBERGER, A. D.
  1966. Food habits, range use and interspecific relationships of bighorn sheep in the Sun River area, west-central Montana, 44 pp. M.S. Thesis, Montana State Univ., Bozeman.
SMITH, D. R.
  1954. The bighorn sheep in Idaho, 154 pp. Wildl. Bull. No. 1, Idaho Fish & Game Dept., Boise.
STELFOX, J. G.
  1975. Range ecology of Rocky Mountain bighorn sheep in Canadian National Parks, 234 pp. Ph.D. Thesis, Univ. of Montana, Missoula.
STEWART, S. T.
  1975. Ecology of the West Rosebud and Stillwater bighorn sheep herd, Beartooth Mountains, Montana, 130 pp. Job Comp. Rep., Proj. W-120-R-6, 7, Montana Fish & Game Dept., Helena.
THEWAITES, R. G., ed.
  1969. Original journals of the Lewis and Clark expedition 1804-1806. Vol. 5, 395 pp. Arno Press, New York.
TILTON, M. E.
  1977. Habitat selection and use by bighorn sheep *(Ovis canadensis)* on a northwestern Montana winter range, 121 pp. Unpubl. M.S. Thesis, Univ. of Montana, Missoula.
UHAZY, L. S.; HOMES, J. C.; and STELFOX, J. G.
  1973. Lungworm in the Rocky Mountain bighorn sheep of western Canada. Canadian Journ. Zool., vol. 51, no. 8, pp. 817-824.
WORLEY, D. E.; STEWART, S. T.; and KAMBEREC, T.; (with the collaboration of R. STONEBERG, J. BROWN, K. G. KNOCHE, J. FIREBAUGH, and R. B. CAMPBELL)
  1976. Lungworm infection in Montana bighorn sheep—a reexamination. Proc. Northern Wild Sheep Council, Jackson, Wyoming, pp. 83-88.

E. EARL WILLARD
ROBERT W. KLAVER

A Study of Ant-following Birds of Northeastern Brazil

Principal Investigator: Edwin O'Neill Willis, Department of Biology, University of Miami, Coral Gables, Florida.

Grant No. 1377:   For a study of the ant-following birds of northeastern Brazil.

From Mexico to Argentina, birds follow swarms of army ants *(Eciton burchelli* or *Labidus praedator)* and capture insects flushed by the ants. Our studies had shown that birds that regularly follow ants increase from 0-4 species in Mexico and British Honduras to 5-10 in central Panama and western Colombia, and that diversities reach 7-12 species in Amazonian forests. Presumably aiversities decreased again to the southeast. From October to December, 1974, we traveled from Belém in the Brazilian state of Pará southeast to coastal Bahia to determine the pattern of the decrease.

Decreasing rainfall southeast from the mouth of the Amazon causes the natural vegetation to change from rain forest to dry forest in which babaçu palms *(Orbigyna mertensiana)* form a conspicuous element. One of the largest palm forests in the world, this dry-forested zone ranges from the Rio Pindaré of central Maranhão east nearly to the carnauba forests of the Rio Parnaiba of eastern Maranhão. Southward the babaçu is increasingly restricted to valleys, and a dry open forest takes over on the ridges into Piauí; but there are large areas of riverine babaçu south and west at least as far as the Rio Tocantins. (Marabá, Pará). Possibly Indian and later human use has resulted in the babaçu zone, for in less heavily populated areas such as the basin of the Itacaiunas River—in south Pará—the dry forest is a "liana forest," or "mata de cipó" with only scattered babaçu.

We found the babaçu zone extremely populated, and location of a seminatural forest very difficult. This vegetation zone certainly deserves a national park, for use of babaçu seeds for oil leads people to cut other trees out of the forest, leaving only babaçu. The babaçu itself is being replaced partly or wholly by grass and cattle in many areas of Maranhão, forcing people to move west along the Transamazonica and other roads and cut forests there. We found small patches of seminatural babaçu forest only at Fazenda Luiziana near Bacabal in north-central Maranhão.

Partly because of lines of swamp forest along the nearby Rio Mearim, these small patches have a surprisingly high diversity of ant-following birds.

745

Five species occur, a high fraction of the eight or so present in true Amazonian forests in eastern Pará. New southeastern records were obtained for three species—gray-headed tanagers *(Eucometis penicillata)*, black-spotted bare-eye *(Phlegopsis nigromaculata)*, and plain-brown woodcreeper *(Dendrocincla fuliginosa)*. A surprising northern extension of range came with the large planalto woodcreeper *(Dendrocolaptes platyrostris)*, which here works much like the barred woodcreeper *(Dendrocolaptes certhia)* of humid forests just to the west. As in Pará, white-backed fire-eyes *(Pyriglena leuconota)* form the main element in the ant-following assemblage. Southward in the babaçu and dry forest diversities are much lower; at Colinas and the nearby Fazenda Serra Negra in southern Maranhão we found only fire-eyes and Planalto woodcreepers. Thus, the main decrease in ant-following diversity occurs within the babaçu zone rather than at a sharp vegetation boundary.

Eastward from Maranhão, dry forests become "caatinga" or desert scrub in the rain shadow of a low "chapada" or plateau (900-1000 meters elevation) on the border between Piauí and Ceará. Previously, I had found army ants in dry vegetation in Sinaloa, Mexico. There, ants apparently move up the coast in riverine and coastal forests. The desert scrub of northeastern Brazil, however, is isolated between two rivers that run in very dry rain-shadow valleys— the Parnaiba and the São Francisco. We were unable to find army ants or ant-following birds in the forest reserve at the Chapada de Araripe in southern Ceará, and it may be that these ants are rare or absent from much of northeastern Brazil. An isolated population of fire-eyes reported from eastern Pernambuco suggests that ants may still occur in some areas, perhaps as remnants from an earlier wet period; but remnants of moist forest in the northeast have mostly been destroyed. We were unable to locate a suitable forest in the short time available, as parks and reserves are rare. The national park in caatinga at the falls of Paulo Afonso on the São Francisco has been destroyed for houses of a hydroelectric project, we found.

We therefore turned our attention to the coastal forests of southern Bahia. At the Plantation "Tres Pancadas" of the Firestone Rubber Co. near Ituberá on the coast of Bahia, rubber trees are being planted in secondary forest that was in sugarcane in days of slavery. In the remaining forest, we soon found army ants and studied for the first time birds characteristic of forests from southern Bahia to Argentina—white-shouldered fire-eyes *(Pyriglena leucoptera)* and thrushlike woodcreepers *(Dendrocincla turdina)*. Finding a southern species of fire-eye so far north forced us to return to patches of forest on Fazendas Timbó and Palma near Santo Amaro, north of the mouth of the Rio Paraguaçú into Baía de Todos os Santos. For eleven days we studied, recorded, and filmed the white-fringed fire-eye *(Pyriglena atra)*, which is in danger of extinction because it is restricted to these patches of forests near the rapidly growing city of Salvador. We hope to investigate the possibility of establishing a forest reserve at Santo Amaro or some other location within 100 kilometers of the city. Each year, zones of industry and cattle put biologists and others of the city farther from natural habitats.

Another endangered species, the slender antbird *(Rhopornis ardesiaca)* of interior Bahia, was the next species we studied. Known from three specimens from near the Rio das Contas, it was supposed to be a bird of caatinga. We found it common in the edges of remnants of mata de cipó on Fazenda Alvorada, atop the 900-meter ridges near Boa Nova; but it turned out not to be an ant-follower. It seems restricted to dry forest where it borders caatinga, for there the large bromeliads in which it feeds descend to the ground. Army ants at Boa Nova were attended by white-shouldered fire-eyes, thrushlike woodcreepers, and black-goggled tanagers *(Trichothraupis melanops)*—here studied for the first time. The mata de cipó of the Bahian coastal ridge is being transformed to pastures for cattle. It will be necessary to set up a forest reserve to protect slender antbirds; and cloud forests at 500 to 700 meters elevation on the rainy east slope of the ridge should also have a reserve.

From Boa Nova, we briefly checked other coastal forests in southern Bahia and Espirito Santo for future studies. The center for studies of cacao (CEPLAC) at Itabuna, Bahia, has mapped southern Bahian vegetation and found that only remnants of natural vegetation remain. The growth of lumber and cattle enterprises in recent years has been phenomenal, even though few people are living on diminishing resources. We visited the CEPLAC reserve of forest near Porto Seguro, the national park of Monte Pascoal, the forest reserves of Sooretama—Barra Seca near Linhares in Espirito Santo, several forest reserves due to the efforts of Dr. Augusto Ruschi near Santa Teresa, and the national park of Caparaó (where we found army ants and white-shouldered fire-eyes, thrushlike woodcreepers, and black-goggled tanagers at 1350 meters elevation, almost at the edge of alpine scrub).

These and other reserves, some in planning stages, represent a minute fraction of the original habitat but show that there is some conservation and at least a minimum level of human interest. North and west from Salvador into Amazonia, however, the number of reserves is inadequate even to preserve samples of major vegetation types, such as babaçu forest or dry forest. Southern Brazil, where we now work, has the problem that despite interest in conservation, many types of habitat are gone or under heavy pressure economically. Pointing to huge forests in Amazonia does no good when slender antbirds live not in Amazonia but in eastern zones.

Our studies and those of others indicate that fewer species of birds live in most of these regions than in Amazonian forests, and that the few species seem resistant to habitat alteration and restriction, but even resistant species disappear when all forests are cut.

It is unfortunate that there is little tradition of visiting even major parks, and that in parks there are practically no facilities available for people, sometimes not even paved roads. Caparaó, near major population centers, is inaccessible in wet weather. It is to be hoped that at least some areas of the many habitat types in northeastern Brazil can be opened to public uses rather than to private overuse, for there are few people in much of the northeast. The amount of land altered by these few people, however, is great. Even an easy question like that of presence of ant-following birds is difficult to answer when there are practically no areas of natural habitat or humans living at more than a subsistence level.

REFERENCES

WILLIS, EDWIN O.
  1976.   A possible reason for mimicry of a bird-eating hawk by an insect-eating
           kite.   Auk, vol. 93, p. 841.
WILLIS, EDWIN O., and ONIKI, Y.
  1981.   Notes on the slender antbird *(Rhopornis ardesiaca).*   Wilson Bull., vol.
           93, pp. 103-107.

EDWIN O. WILLIS
YOSHIKA O. WILLIS

Late Cretaceous Mammals of Western South Dakota, 1974

Principal Investigator: Robert W. Wilson, Professor Emeritus, South Dakota School of Mines and Technology, Rapid City, South Dakota.

Grant No. 1332:   For completion of a long-term study of Late Cretaceous mammals from South Dakota.

The first Late Cretaceous mammal (*Meniscoessus conquistus*) to be found in North America was obtained by J. L. Wortman in 1882 from western South Dakota, presumably in what is now Harding County (Van Valen, 1967). Ten years later in 1892, E. D. Cope found a second Late Cretaceous mammal (*Thlaeodon padanicus*) near the Grand River southeast of Black Horse, South Dakota (Wilson, 1965). From that time through 1962 only two or three additional specimens were found within the state so far as known. Beginning with 1963, important collections have been made by the Museum of Geology of the South Dakota School of Mines and Technology, and aside from a small collection made by Yale University from the Iron Lightning member of the Fox Hills Formation (Waage, 1968), are the only ones of significance. These are: (1) collection from the Eureka Quarry and vicinity southwest of Buffalo, South Dakota (Wilson, 1964; Szalay, 1965) in the Hell Creek Formation, and perhaps near the type locality of *Meniscoessus conquistus*—locality worked in 1962-1965; (2) collection from the Joe Painter Quarry, northwest of Buffalo, and also in the Hell Creek Formation—locality worked in 1966, 1970; and (3) collection from the Red Owl Quarry, in the Fox Hills Formation, but lower in the section than the Yale collection—locality worked in 1970-1972.

At one time even isolated finds of single teeth of Late Cretaceous mammals were subjects of papers. Modern methods of recovery, however, by means of washing large quantities of rock through screens have produced large collections of Cretaceous mammals at many places. Even so, the School of Mines collections are not insignificant, numbering as they do well over 600 teeth and some jaws. At least two, possibly three, distinct stratigraphic levels are represented. One is from the Fox Hills and one, possibly two, is from the Hell Creek. Although the Fox Hills and Hell Creek are in part lateral equivalents of each other, the School of Mines locality from Red Owl seems clearly older than anything in the Hell Creek of South Dakota, and yields the oldest known mammalian fauna from this state.

749

Most of the early fieldwork (1962-1965) by the School of Mines was supported by funds from National Science Foundation grant No. G43646. Funds for later fieldwork and laboratory processing came largely from the regular budget of the Museum of Geology (1970-1972), but also in a small amount from National Geographic Society grant No. 549 (1966). Finally, the National Geographic Society supplied funds (grant no. 1157) which permitted the principal investigator to go on a part-time teaching basis in the academic year 1974-1975, in order to research the Cretaceous collections.

Eureka Quarry and Vicinity

The Eureka Quarry is 14 miles southwest of Buffalo in Harding County. Approximately 25,000 pounds of matrix were processed by underwater screening, resulting in the obtaining of 173 isolated teeth and 10 jaw fragments of mammals. Sixteen additional teeth were found by surface prospecting in an area up to a half mile distant from the quarry, and through about 100 feet of section. Although dinosaurs seemingly diminished in variety in this 100 feet (e.g., disappearance of anatosaurs at quarry level which is at top of local section), mammalian remains were too few to indicate any change in this interval. The quarry faunal list follows:

EUREKA QUARRY MAMMALIAN FAUNA

Meniscoessus robustus?	*Alphadon* sp.
Mesodma thompsoni	*Pediomys hatcheri*
Mesodma hensleighi?	*Pediomys elegans*
Mesodma formosa	*Pediomys florencae*
Cimolomys gracilis?	*Didelphodon* cf. *D. vorax*
Cimolodon nitidus?	*Gypsonictops hypoconus*

The above faunal list is essentially an abridged version of the classic Lance Creek fauna of Wyoming, consisting of abundant multituberculates and marsupials, but with only rare eutherians. The rather common occurrence of *Cimolomys* and the rarity of *Alphadon* are distinctions. The similarity to the Lance is perhaps as much owing to correspondence in environment as correspondence in age. The partially deciduous premolar dentition described by Szalay (1965) was assigned by him to *Cimolodon*. At present this assignment might be questioned because of the rarity of *Cimolodon* at the quarry site, and lack of information on the upper premolars in *Cimolomys* from the Eureka Quarry.

Joe Painter Quarry

The Joe Painter Quarry is located near the head of Jones Creek in northern Harding County. Individual teeth are not abundant in the quarry, but there is a relatively high proportion of jaw fragments. About 50 determinable teeth are from this locality, and about a half-dozen jaw fragments. A faunal list follows:

JOE PAINTER QUARRY FAUNA

Meniscoessus robustus	*Pediomys hatcheri*
Mesodma thompsoni	*Pediomys elegans*
Mesodma hensleighi	*Pediomys krejcii*
Mesodma formosa	*Didelphodon?* sp.
Alphadon marshi?	*Gypsonictops hypoconus*

No *Cimolomys* or *Cimolodon* seem present. The Joe Painter Quarry is in the Hell Creek Formation, but its stratigraphic relation to the Eureka Quarry is difficult to determine. Both quarries are presumably in the Lower Hell Creek because dinosaur remains seem absent from the Upper Hell Creek in Harding County. The Painter Quarry site appears to be exposed as an erosion window in the Upper Hell Creek, and hence may be quite high in the lower division of the formation. It may be either the same age as the Eureka Quarry or somewhat younger.

Red Owl Quarry

The Red Owl Quarry is situated 3 miles north and 1 mile east of Red Owl, Meade County, South Dakota, in the Stoneville facies of the Fox Hills (Pettyjohn, 1967). It seems to be about at the level of the Fox Hills at the Lance Creek type locality. Mammal remains are abundant but consist almost entirely of isolated teeth. Several hundred such teeth have been recovered, but jaw fragments are usually toothless, or rarely with a single tooth. The mammalian fauna follows:

RED OWL QUARRY FAUNA

Meniscoessus, n. sp.	*Alphadon marshi*
Mesodma thompsoni?	*Alphadon lulli?*
Mesodma hensleighi	*Pediomys hatcheri*
Mesodma formosa	*Pediomys* cf. *P. krejcii*
Cimolodon nitidus	*Pediomys cooki*
?Cimexomys sp.	*Didelphodon* cf. *D. vorax*
Multituberculate, n. gen. and sp.	*Gypsonictops hypoconus*

The Red Owl fauna is distinctive in the small size of the species of *Meniscoessus,* the presence of a new and gigantic Mesozoic multituberculate, and the absence of *Pediomys elegans.* In addition, there seem to be differences not revealed by the formal nomenclature, as for example, the presence of a distinctly atypical population here referred tentatively to *Mesodma formosa.*

The three quarry faunas are alike in having *Alphadon* associated with *Pediomys.* They also all have *Didelphodon,* although not necessarily the same species. All three have nominally the same three species of *Mesodma* although, in actual fact, the situation may be more complicated than would appear from the nomenclatural assignments. Lastly, they agree in the rarity of eutherians which at this stage in the Late Cretaceous may be more because of environmental similarity than temporal closeness. An extended taxonomic treatment of the collections is being prepared for publication in the near future.

REFERENCES

PETTYJOHN, WAYNE A.
  1967.   New members of Upper Cretaceous Fox Hills Formation in South Dakota, representing delta deposits.   Amer. Assoc. Petrol. Geologists, Bull. 51, pp. 1361-1367, Tulsa.
SZALAY, FREDERICK S.
  1965.   First evidence of tooth replacement in the Subclass Allotheria (Mammalia).   Amer. Mus. Novitates, no. 2226, pp. 1-12, New York City.
VAN VALEN, LEIGH
  1967.   The first discovery of a Cretaceous mammal.   Amer. Mus. Novitates, no. 2285, pp. 1-4, New York City.
WAAGE, KARL M.
  1968.   The type Fox Hills Formation, Cretaceous (Maestrichtian), South Dakota, Part 1. Stratigraphy and paleoenvironments.   Bull. Peabody Mus. Nat. Hist., vol. 27, pp. 1-175, New Haven.
WILSON, ROBERT W.
  1964.   Late Cretaceous mammals from South Dakota.   Proc. S. Dak. Acad. Sci., vol. 43, p. 210 (abstract), Vermillion.
  1965.   Type localities of Cope's Cretaceous mammals.   Proc. S. Dak. Acad. Sci., vol. 44, pp. 88-90, Vermillion.

ROBERT W. WILSON

Brooding and Aggregating Behavior of the Treehopper, *Umbonia crassicornis*

Principal Investigator: Thomas K. Wood, Wilmington College, Wilmington, Ohio.[1]

Grant No. 1391:   For study of the brooding and aggregating behavior of *Umbonia crassicornis* (Membracidae: Homoptera).

The research supported by the National Geographic Society is part of a comparative study to determine the extent and types of presocial behavior (parental care) in the insect family Membracidae. It is divided into factors associated with presocial behavior of *Umbonia crassicornis,* and with interactions with *Anolis carolinensis,* a vertebrate predator. Parental care was suggested as early as 1887, but was not accepted by authorities on the group (Funkhouser, 1951). Casual observations of female behavior with offspring suggested membracids had unusual biologies, but were never verified by intensive observation or experiment until recently (Wood, 1974). The parent-offspring chemical communication in *U. crassicornis* reported here is the first example of this type of interaction in the membracids (Wood, 1976a).

The bizarre shapes of the Membracidae (Insecta) were explained in terms of protective functions such as mimicry and crypsis, but until recently (Wood, 1975a, b; Wood and Morris, 1974) lacked experimental verification. This report establishes conclusive evidence that the pronotum (structure responsible for bizarre shapes) of the treehopper *Umbonia crassicornis* provides potential protection from vertebrate predation. Vertebrate antipredator defense in this species involves specialized behavior, taste factors, coloration, and hardness of the pronotum. The importance of each factor varies with stages in the life history.

Presocial Behavior

Defense Behavior of Females. The major findings reported by Wood (1976a) are as follows: Adult females of *U. crassicornis* provide protection to eggs and first instars from insect predators; parent females disperse reduviids,

---

[1] Currently at University of Delaware, Newark, Delaware.

syrphid larvae, and coccinellid beetles with directed aggressive movements; visual stimuli from the predators and alarm pheromones released from injured nymphs evoke the aggressive response of brooding females; aggregates of nymphs and adults of three other membracid species respond to alarm pheromones (Nault et at., 1974), but this is the first substantiated example of parent-offspring communication.

Females with Eggs.   Studies were made to determine whether females removed from eggs returned, and what stimuli were necessary for successful egg brooding.

Under field conditions, 15 females were removed and released 30 centimeters below their egg mass. Females remained at the release site for varied periods, but within 10 minutes all females moved at least 10 centimeters. Two females found eggs in 10 minutes, while 10 others found them within 30 minutes after release. At the end of 90 minutes, 14 females were on egg masses; the remaining female located an unmarked egg mass.

In the greenhouse, 9 marked females were removed and placed back on eggs, while 9 others were placed on a plant without eggs and surrounded by plants with unoccupied egg masses. Females placed back on eggs remained to egg hatch (10 to 15 days). Females on the plants without eggs stayed for various periods. After 24 hours, 6 of 9 females were still on the plant, but 1 female moved at least 90 centimeters to another plant and eggs (not her own). One other female found eggs 48 hours after release. Only 2 females found eggs at the end of 5 days. The remainder of the females were placed on eggs, where they stayed to egg hatch (5 to 10 days).

To determine the receptors used for the perception of egg masses, 40 females were removed from eggs, marked, and divided into 4 treatments of 10 insects each: 1, untreated; 2, surgically blinded; 3, ablated antennae; and 4, ablated eyes and antennae. Females were placed on eggs, with the number on eggs recorded at 4, 24, and 96 hours. Nine untreated females remained on eggs for 96 hours. Females with ablated eyes and antennae were active; the number on eggs dropped from 4 (4 hours) to 1 after 96 hours. Females (7) without antennae did not move from eggs, with 8 on eggs at 96 hours. Initially, blinded females were active, with only 3 on eggs at 4 hours but the number increased to 6 at 24 and 96 hours. Insects not associated with eggs were located on other plants.

A tentative hypothesis to explain how females find and remain on eggs is that females probe the host plant with mouthparts to detect physiological changes in the host plant. Egg deposition may initiate these changes and establish a physiological gradient below the egg mass.

Role of Females in the Maintenance and Reaggregation of Nymphs. Nymphs failed to mature (Wood, 1974, 1976a) in the absence of parent females. Nymphal aggregates were maintained in part by females tapping them on the back with front tarsi to stop movement. If tactile contact was the only mechanism to maintain nymphal aggregates, then removal of females should trigger dispersal of nymphs.

To test this, 21 branches with 1st to 5th instar nymphs were selected. Before removal of females, the number of nymphs and length of branch occupied were recorded. Changes in these variables at 24 and 48 hours were compared to values before removal of female ("t" test for paired observations). Removal of females failed to trigger immediate dispersal of nymphs, with no statistical change in the number of nymphs or length of branch surface at 24 and 48 hours. There was a slight drop in numbers and increase in branch surface occupied, that was accounted for by natural mortality or molting.

Since aggregates were maintained without females, the following experiment was designed to determine if disrupted nymphs reaggregate, and what the female role was in nymphal reaggregation. Nymphs were placed on branches (28) in a release site which was 5 to 3 centimeters long. Original females (14) were placed on branches below the release site but not on the remaining (14) branches. Nymphs in aggregates varied, but their ages were the same in each treatment. Statistical comparisons ("t" test) on the net change in nymphs and branch surfaces were made at 1, 24, and 48 hours after release. Females (14) remained with aggregates for 48 hours; nymphs tended to remain near the release site but extended the aggregation toward the apex of the branch. Several aggregates without females remained near the release site but most moved up the branch 7 to 45 centimeters. After 48 hours, 81.63 percent of released nymphs (728) with females were in aggregates, compared to 68.93 percent of those (631) without females; this indicated nymphs must detect other nymphs. At each sampling period there were significantly more nymphs with females than those without. Branch surface occupied at 1 hour was the same in both treatments, but increased on branches without females at 24 and 48 hours. Some females moved below or above the release site but maintained no apparent physical contact with nymphs, while others at the release site tapped nymphs with their tarsi.

Females enhance nymphal reaggregation but are not essential. This suggests that they may provide stimuli other than tactile (i.e., visual or chemical). Nymphs may use chemical, tactile, or visual stimuli from each other, since they failed to disperse and established aggregates in the absence of females.

Adult Aggregations. Teneral adults form conspicuous aggregates which may be accompanied by parent females. Adults (0-4 days old) from already established aggregates were sexed (1:1) and released on new branches. Two treatments (with and without parent females) were replicated 5 times with 30 individuals per replicate. The number of insects per linear centimeter of branch in the 2 treatments was compared by means of a "t" test at 1, 24, and 48 hours after release. After 48 hours, only 58 to 60 percent of the insects in the 2 treatments remained, but aggregates with parent females were more compact than those without. Adult reaggregation is enhanced by females but they are not essential to it.

Defensive Role of the Pronotum and Adult Aggregates. Defense of adult *Umbonia crassicornis* against vertebrate predators involves behavior, unpalatability, and coloration and hardness of the pronotum. Vertebrate predators which search plants for prey create branch movements or vibrations that trigger catalepsy of individuals in aggregates. Cataleptic behavior is a highly adaptive tactic by prey sought by vertebrate predators that capture moving prey. Physical contact with insects by a predator, such as walking or sitting on aggregates, does not cause dispersal. Individual insects that walk or fly in response to the predator may enhance the probability of their capture and may provide a search image to the predator for the remainder of the aggregate.

In my experiments, anoles showed degrees of aggressiveness in how they captured test insects. Anoles in some cases would gently place their mouths around the insect, and at other times simply grab it. The factors associated with this aggressive behavior have not been studied but probably depend on hunger levels and previous experience. *Umbonia crassicornis* must be pulled with some force by the predator to free it from the branch. Anoles may pull on an insect several times, during which they will encounter the taste factors associated with the pronotum. Rejected captured insects may survive if not seriously injured but, if swallowed, provide an immediate learning experience to anoles which enhances avoidance of other individuals. Availability of alternate movable prey in the field could easily distract visually oriented predators from the treehoppers and decrease the incidence of capture (Wood, 1977a).

The pronota of adults as they mature turn dark green, which is associated with increased sclerotization and loss of the taste factor. Individuals in aggregates, as they approach sexual maturity, are more sensitive to disturbance, and they disperse. Premating pairs display movements which may attract predators. The sharp, hard pronotal processes provide protection to individuals during these vulnerable stages. Insects of this age group presented to anoles were rejected alive (Wood, 1975b, 1977a). Although some of these insects were severely injured, others survived several days under laboratory conditions. Rejected insects are often tossed some distance, placing the insect some distance from the predator.

Females on eggs are essentially sessile, their color blending with the host plant, and they cling to branches with great tenacity. Force used to pull insects off branches may push the pronotal processes into the tissue of the mouth and cause rejection. Encounters of this type may inhibit predators from applying the force necessary to pull the insect from the branch. Insects of this age group are readily rejected by anoles. Although not tested, females with nymphs may use aggressive displays (Wood, 1976a) to distract predators from nymphs. Again, the pronotum may provide a deterrent that may enhance female survival and subsequent rearing of nymphs. Nymphs (5th instar) are sufficiently unpalatable that all anoles, after eating one, may temporarily at least avoid the remainder. This certainly could provide time to distract predators to more palatable prey.

The presocial behavior of *Umbonia crassicornis* is with this report the best documented of all membracid species. Recent work with *Entylia bactriana* (Wood, 1977b, Nault et al., 1974), *Publilia concava, Platycotis vittata* (Wood, 1976b), H. E. Hinton's (1977) studies of tropical species, and those by Brown (1976) indicate the Membracoidea are unique among Hemipterous insects. Parental care appears to differ in its form and obligatory nature, but is also complicated by mutualistic relationships with ants (Wood 1977b).

REFERENCES

BROWN, RICHARD L.
    1976.   Behavioral observations of *Aethalion reticulatum* (Hem., Aethalonidae) and associated ants.   Insect. Soc., vol. 23, pp. 99-107.

FUNKHOUSER, W. D.
    1951.   Homoptera Family Membracidae.   Genera Insecta, no. 208, 383 pp., 14 pl., 9 text-figs.

HINTON, H. E.
    1977.   Subsocial behavior and biology of some Mexican membracid bugs. Ecological Entomol., vol. 2, pp. 61-79.

NAULT, L. R.; WOOD, T. K.; and GOFF, A. M.
    1974.   Treehopper (Membracidae) alarm pheromones.   Nature, vol. 149, pp. 387-388.

WOOD, THOMAS K.
    1974.   Aggregating behavior of *Umbonia crassicornis* (Homoptera: Membracidae).   Can. Ent., vol. 106, pp. 169-173.
    1975a.   Studies on the function of the membracid pronotum (Homoptera). II. Histology.   Proc. Ent. Soc. Washington, vol. 77, pp. 78-82.
    1975b.   Defense in two presocial membracids (Homoptera: Membracidae). Can. Ent., vol. 107, pp. 1227-1231.

WOOD, THOMAS K. (continued)

1976a.   Alarm behavior of brooding female *Umbonia crassicornis* (Homoptera: Membracidae).   Ann. Ent. Soc. Amer., vol. 69, pp. 304-343.

1976b.   Biology and presocial behavior of *Platycotis vittata* F. (Homoptera: Membracidae).   Ann. Ent. Soc. Amer., vol. 69, pp. 807-811.

1977a.   Defense in *Umbonia crassicornis:* Role of the pronotum and adult aggregations (Homoptera: Membracidae).   Ann. Ent. Soc. Amer., vol. 70, pp. 524-528.

1977b.   Role of parent females and attendant ants in the maturation of the treehopper, *Entylia bactriana* (Homoptera: Membracidae). Sociobiology, vol. 2 (4), pp. 257-272.

WOOD, T. K., and MORRIS, G. K.

1974.   Studies on the function of the membracid pronotum (Homoptera). Occurrence and distribution of articulated hairs.   Can. Ent., vol. 106, pp. 143-148.

THOMAS K. WOOD

Biological Survey of Haiti: Status of the Endangered Birds and Mammals

Principal Investigator: Charles A. Woods, University of Vermont, Burlington, Vermont.[1]

Grant Nos. 1367,   For biological field studies in Haiti, particularly relating to
1552, 1565.   endangered species of mammals and birds.

The research under these grants was conducted in the Département du Sud, Haiti, which is located on the western half of the Southern Peninsula (Tiburon Peninsula). The Département du Sud stretches 160 kilometers from Miragoâne to the western tip of the Republic and is the most remote and undeveloped area of the country. On some recent maps of Haiti it is divided into the Département de la Grande Ause, to the North, and the Département du Sud, to the south.

The mammalian fauna of Haiti has changed dramatically since Columbus landed there in 1492. Most of the original natural fauna except for bats has become extinct, mainly as a result of hunting, habitat destruction, the introduction of rats, mice, and mongooses, and overgrazing by domestic animals. The only examples of the endemic mammalian fauna that survive in Haiti are bats, the Haitian hutia *(Plagiodonta aedium),* and the solenodon *(Solenodon paradoxus).* This investigation was initiated in 1974 particularly to find out more about the rare Haitian hutia. The animal was originally described in 1836 by Cuvier, who discussed one of two specimens collected between 1826 and 1830 in "Saint-Dominique" by Alexander Ricord. Cuvier reported that the animals were even then becoming "very rare." These may have been the same that Columbus referred to as "hutias" and reported eating on several occasions. The animals Columbus discussed, however, may have been *Isolobodon portoricensis,* which are now extinct but were commonly kept as domestic animals by the Arawak Indians. The Haitian hutia was not found alive again until 1947 and 1949, when two were collected near Miragoâne. As of 1974, only four *confirmed* Haitian hutias had been found alive, and of these only two are known *for sure* to have come from the Southern Peninsula.

The primary objective of this project was to look for the Haitian hutia and to establish: (1) How abundant the species is; (2) where it is distributed in the

---

[1] Currently (1981) at Florida State Museum, University of Florida, Gainesville.

Département du Sud; (3) why it has so rarely been seen in the past; and (4) how the animal lives (natural history).

In addition, a biological survey of the Southern Peninsula was conducted to learn more about this unique and isolated region. We searched for the solenodon, banded North American migrant birds, collected cave material in search of fossil mammals, and collected bats, amphibians, and reptiles.

We made four trips to Haiti between August 1974 and June 1975 and spent a total of 26 weeks in the field. Field assistants on these expeditions were Carl Butterfield, Richard C. Rosen, David Barrington, Betsy Howland, Bill Howland of the University of Vermont, and Jean-Pierre Lebel of McGill University. David Klingener of the University of Massachusetts participated in two of the expeditions. Our work in Haiti was aided by Joseph Wainwright, Chef de Service de Conservation du Sol, des Forets et de la Protection de la Faune, who provided permits and technical assistance, and by Ekke Lemke and Michel Mezile. Mr. and Mrs. A. G. Butterfield and the Reynolds Haitian Mines, Inc., were especially helpful.

In our trips in southern Haiti we made a special effort to duplicate the trips made in 1931 by Alexander Wetmore of the United States National Museum and in 1934 by Philip Darlington of Harvard University. We flew over the region in a small plane, just as Dr. Wetmore did on April 3, 1931, and hiked into the high, rugged mountains of Morne la Hotte, following the same routes as both Wetmore and Darlington. This information is especially valuable when compared with the published accounts by Wetmore and Darlington of the region as they found it in the early 1930's (Wetmore and Lincoln, 1933).

Status of the Haitian Hutia

The information about the Haitian hutia *Plagiodontia aedium* (fig. 1) was gathered in many ways. Mountain farmers were interviewed, and cards with a drawing of the hutia were handed out all over the Southern Peninsula. Town officials and army and government personnel were interviewed. Expeditions were made to remote regions where the habitat was still "relatively" undisturbed.

The hutia is rare. Eighteen living specimens were located or could be reliably documented (see fig. 2). Hutias are most abundant in forested, rocky, mountain areas between 300 and 1,800 meters in elevation. They spend most of their time on the ground, but some individuals prefer vine-covered trees. The species is so rare that most Haitians have never seen one, even though they live close to the land and work in the fields every day. Reports indicate

FIG. 1.   Drawing of *Plagiodontia aedium*.

that hutias were more common in the Miragoâne, L'Asile, and Anse-à-Veau regions at the turn of the century when forests in these areas were heavier. They are now confined in these areas to steep, vegetated valleys surrounded by dry, barren mountains. The hutia is currently most abundant in the interior mountains between Aux Cayes and Jérémie. Nowhere in the Southern Peninsula, however, is the hutia "common." Seeing a hutia, even for a peasant working in the best of habitats, is a rare event. Even on the slopes of Pic de Macaya, where conditions are most favorable for hutias, the animal is so rare that most peasants do not recognize a drawing of one.

The hutia is vulnerable to predation because it is slow-moving and unwary, and it can easily be handled soon after being captured. Mountain farmers kill them because they eat crops in their gardens and because the animal is good to eat. In rocky areas where the animal can climb into a hole it is safe, but on nonrocky hillsides or when the animal climbs into a tree to escape it is easily captured. As the population has moved into even the most remote mountain areas of Haiti, the last unmolested hutia habitats have disappeared. The animal is not in *immediate* danger of becoming extinct. It is nocturnal and difficult to find during the daylight hours. Its general habitats are such that

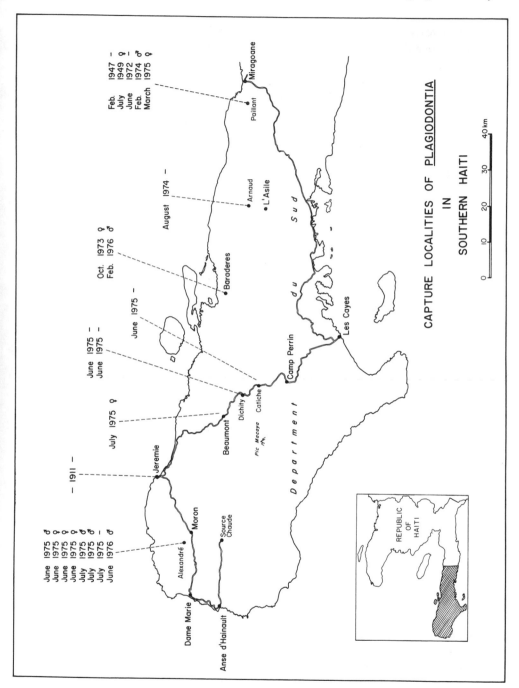

CAPTURE LOCALITIES OF PLAGIODONTIA
IN
SOUTHERN HAITI

even 150 years ago it was considered rare. It is possible for the hutia to be around moderate peasant populations and go unnoticed unless driven from its habitat among the rocks.

The most immediate problem for the hutia is the clearing of forested mountain slopes for hillside gardens. Large areas of southern Haiti have been burned over and the steep slopes planted in malanga, mazumbelle, potato, corn, and other crops. Many hutias are killed by the fires. The gardens are good sources of food for hutias, but the exposed areas are more frequented by humans and the chances of a hutia being killed are greater. Finally, the heavy rains soon wash the soil out of the gardens and hutias are left behind on dry, sun-baked mountains with no suitable habitat except the steep ravines. Such a pattern is illustrated in the La Hotte region where Pic de la Grande Colline has gone through this sequence over the past 10 years. Today it is a 2,060-meter mountain without any vegetation. Nearby 2,300-meter Pic de Macaya is rapidly following the same pattern. All the mountains between Beaumont and Miragoâne have followed this pattern in the past 30 years. Hutias survive for a number of years in habitats such as this, as indicated by the remaining population of hutias in the Miragoâne region, but slowly the populations drift down to critically low levels.

In the mountains of Haiti between Jérémie and Anse d'Hainault the animal is still common enough that three of the four female hutias we captured were pregnant. The largest population of hutias remaining in Haiti is found in the region west of Pic de Macaya. In this region the habitat is rocky, well forested, and only moderately inhabited. It is in this region that a national reserve is most possible.

Much remains to be learned of the habits of the Haitian hutia. The animal lives in burrows and shallow caves, which can be identified as being inhabited by the piles of fecal pellets at the entrance and worn trails leading from the opening. The Haitian hutia, like the Jamaican hutia, usually spends the daylight hours in these small caves. Harold E. Anthony used dogs to locate burrows of the Jamaican hutia in the remote John Crow Mountains of eastern Jamaica. He reported hearing a "birdlike chirping" coming from the burrows of animals cornered by dogs. The Haitian hutias we have in captivity also make a birdlike chirp or "zee chirp" when alarmed. All but one of the captive hutias spend the day inside their nest boxes rather than in the branches of trees provided for them. Hutias are reasonably good climbers. The tail is not prehensile.

FIG. 2.   Map of southern Haiti showing capture localities and dates of capture of all known specimens of *Plagiodontia aedium*.

FIG. 3.   Drawing of *Solenodon paradoxus.*

The animal is vocal. In addition to the birdlike chirps reported above, hutias chatter their teeth and make sounds resembling a snore (= *greeer*) and a loud resonant honk.

Hutias usually have one young. Reliable reports by mountain farmers who have killed hutias indicate seeing only one fetus inside, and the females we encountered all had one young. The breeding season is not known for sure, but the gestation period is between 125 and 150 days.

The name for the hutia in most regions is "zagouti." In the region of Morne Deux Mamelles it is called "agouti." Other names sometimes encountered were "cochon d'Inde" and "rat de terre."

The natural food of the hutia is unknown. It is known to dig for root tubers and eat bark, leaves, and peasants' garden crops. The most frequently eaten cultivated plants are stems and roots of malanga *(Xanthosoma sagittaefolium),* mazumbelle *(Colocasia esculenta),* and yam.

A general review of the status of *Plagiodontia* in Haiti has recently been published (Woods, 1981).

Status of the Solenodon

Information about the solenodon was gathered in the same manner as it was for the hutia. Based on this information we conclude that *Solenodon paradoxus* (fig. 3) is in imminent danger of becoming extinct. The animal was still locally common as recently as 1946, especially in the regions south of Moron and east of Les Irois. The forest cover of this region at the tip of the Southern Peninsula was destroyed mainly by the devastating hurricanes of the 1950's and 1960's. The opened interior encouraged increases in human populations and gardens and has resulted in a near complete extermination of the animal.

We estimate that fewer than 100 individuals survive in the remote mountains of southern Haiti and that there is no hope of saving this species without protection in a well-patrolled natural preserve. Even if such a park can be established within the next five years, it may be too late to save existing stocks of the animal in Haiti. We found two juveniles in a valley in the mountains northwest of Les Cayes in 1975 (Woods, 1975a), and these were the only reliable indications of the presence of *Solenodon* that we encountered during our entire stay in Haiti. An all-out effort is needed to save this esoteric and unique creature from extinction.

Recent surveys (Woods, 1980a, 1981) indicate that a significant population of *Solenodon* is still to be found in southern Haiti.

Status of Wintering North American Migrant Birds

Mist netting and banding of North American migrant birds during the periods we were in Haiti enabled us to compare the avifauna in the various regions of the Département du Sud. This work resulted in findings of an unusually specific return of warblers to the same regions of Haiti. It also revealed differential use of habitats by male and female black-throated blue warblers. Female warblers are concentrated in the higher slopes of mountains while males are confined to the wooded valleys. (Woods, 1975b.)

Status of the Bats of Haiti

Bats were collected in the same mist nets that were used to net birds during the day. An excellent series of bats from all locales was collected; these have been deposited in the collections of the American Museum of Natural History. Fifteen different species were collected of a total of 20 that are suspected to occur in Haiti. These have been analyzed as to age and reproductive status, and comparison has been made with the bat faunas of Central America (Klingener et al., 1978). This work revealed several important differences between the reproductive biology of island versus mainland populations.

Cave Work

More than 25 caves were investigated for the presence of barn owls and fossil-bearing deposits. The owls feed on small mammals and then cough up a pellet of undigested hair and bones when they roost in a cave. The owl, therefore, is an excellent collector of the small vertebrate fauna of a region. Owls have been roosting in some caves for centuries, and it is possible to reconstruct the kinds of mammals that lived in the area in the recent past by analyzing these pellets and the debris on the cave floor. Over a thousand mandibles and crania of three species of small insectivorous mammals of the genus *Nesophontes* were collected by sifting debris on the cave floor. The forms have been compared with material from Cuba and from earlier collections in the Dominican Republic. The work, now in manuscript form and ready for publication, discusses the pattern of distribution of *Nesophontes* on Hispaniola and the relationship of these animals to the *Nesophontes* found in Cuba. A search for living specimens of *Nesophontes* was not successful.

Other specimens were found that represent remains of early endemic hystricognath rodents. This material has been compared to specimens from the Dominican Republic in an effort to document the adaptive radiation of the endemic rodents of Hispaniola (Woods, 1980b; 1981; in press). We have currently finished investigating the nature of head region in fossil and living forms (Woods and Howland, 1979).

Conservation Efforts

One result of our work has been an awareness of how important it is for Haiti to take strong measures to save what is left of its endemic fauna. After hiking through most remote sections of the Département du Sud, and making three separate surveys of the region by airplane, we conclude that the only hope of saving these rare mammals and a number of birds, reptiles, and mammals from extinction is to have Haiti set aside several large national preserves. With this in mind, we have met with officials of the Département de l'Agriculture, des Resources Naturelles, et du Développement Rural, as well as several international conservation agencies. Haiti is aware of the plight of its fauna and is anxious to find some effective and reasonable way to protect these animals. Three reports have been submitted to the government (Woods, 1975c; Woods and Rosen, 1977a, 1977b), and a number of locations that would be suitable as national parks or national preserves have been recommended. We hope that Haiti will choose two of these locations as national parks and concentrate on creating a safe environment within these regions where *Plagiodontia aedium, Solenodon paradoxus,* and other rare Haitian animals can survive. It will be necessary to reintroduce individuals of these species into the parks and to manage carefully the populations for a period of time before it can be said with confidence that *Plagiodontia* and *Solenodon* will not become extinct as wild mammals in Haiti. Since neither species breeds or survives well in captivity, there is little long-term hope for the survival of the species by breeding the animals in captivity.

We appreciate the assistance from the National Geographic Society in supporting many months of fieldwork in Haiti. I thank also Al and Natalie Butterfield for their continual support in Haiti, and Missy, Stott, Patty, and Bry for their understanding, love, and support. They all know the truth of the Creole proverb "Deyè mòn gê mòn" (beyond the mountains there are more mountains again).

REFERENCES

CUVIER, GEORGES LEOPOLD FREDERIC
  1836. Characters du genre Plagiodonte et description du *Plagiodonte* des habitation, *Plagiodonte aedium*.   Ann. Sci. Nat., Paris, ser. 2, vol. 6, pp. 347-353.
DARLINGTON, PHILIP J.
  1935. West Indian Carabidae II: Itinerary of 1934; forests of Haiti; new species; and a new key to *Colpodes*.   Psyche, vol. 42, no. 4, pp. 167-215.
KLINGENER, DAVID; GENOWAYS, H. H.; and BAKER, R. J.
  1978. Bats from Southern Haiti.   Ann. Carnegie Mus., vol. 47, pp. 81-99.
WETMORE, ALEXANDER, and LINCOLN, FREDERICK C.
  1933. Additional notes on the birds of Haiti and the Dominican Republic.   Proc. U. S. Nat. Mus., vol. no. 83, no. 2966, pp. 1-68.
WOODS, CHARLES A.
  1975a. *Solenodon paradoxus* in Southern Haiti.   Journ. Mamm., vol. 57, no. 3, pp. 591-592.
  1975b. Banding and recapture of wintering warblers in Haiti.   Bird Banding, vol. 46, no. 4, pp. 344-346.
  1975c. The natural history of the Haitian Hutia: A preliminary report.   (Manuscript submitted to the Départment de l'Agriculture, Republic d'Haiti, 15 pp.)
  1980a. El *Solenodon paradoxus* en el Sur de Haiti, 5 pp.   Dept. Agric. Spec. Publ., Santo Domingo.
  1980b. Collecting fossil mammals in the Greater Antilles: An immense journey.   Plaster Jacket, vol. 34, pp. 4-13.
  1981. Last endemic mammals in Hispaniola.   Oryx, vol. 16, pp. 146-152.
  _____. Evolution and systematics of South American hystricognath rodents.   Spec. Publ., Pymatuning Lab., Univ. Pittsburgh. (In press.)
WOODS, CHARLES A., and HOWLAND, E. B.
  1979. Adaptive radiation of capromyid rodents. I. Anatomy of the masticatory apparatus.   Journ. Mamm., vol. 60, pp. 95-116.
WOODS, CHARLES A., and ROSEN, R. C.
  1977a. Summary of the conservation work by Charles A. Woods and Richard C. Rosen in Southern Haiti.   (Manuscript submitted to the Department de l'Agriculture, Republic d'Haiti, 8 pp. + 10 attachments.) (French and English versions.)

WOODS, CHARLES A., and ROSEN, R. C. (continued)

1977b.   Biological survey of Haiti; Status of *Plagiodontia aedium* and *Solenodon paradoxus* and recommendations concerning natural preserves and National Parks.   (Bound manuscript submitted to the Department de l'Agriculture, Republic d'Haiti, 32 pp. + 6 maps and 31 photographs.) (French and English versions.)

CHARLES A. WOODS

Larval Development and Geographical Distribution of Coral-reef Asteroids

Principal Investigator: Masashi Yamaguchi, Marine Laboratory, University of Guam, Agana, Guam.

Grant No. 1406:   For a study of larval development and geographical distribution of coral-reef asteroids.

The purpose of this investigation was twofold. First it was desired to augment zoogeographical information with regard to asteroids distributed in Palau so that a critical comparison of asteroid fauna between Palau and Guam could be made. Second, larval development of asteroids was observed in order to elucidate differences of distribution ranges among different species. In my earlier paper (Yamaguchi, 1975) I noted that there are some peculiarities in asteroid fauna of Palau in comparison to that of the rest of Micronesian islands, i.e., some of the species occurring in Palau appear not to have extended their geographical range eastward. Apparently the larval stage is of primary importance in dispersal of such benthic animals.

Methods and Materials

I collected specimens from various parts of Palau during two trips, in August 1974 (one week) and from May to July 1975 (eight weeks). Most specimens were examined for sexual ripeness with 1-methyladenine, which is a spawning-inducing substance for asteroids (Kanatani, 1969). Whenever I collected ripe gametes of both sexes, I attempted rearing of larvae using plastic culture beakers. Larvae were transferred to fresh sea water daily, and their concentration was maintained at less than 50 per 750 milliliters so that the natural food particle could support growth of the plankton-feeding larvae.

Collected asteroid specimens were preserved in formalin and then dried, except for those of *Ophidiaster granifer,* which required careful dissection so that the condition of gonads could be examined critically, because this species appears to be parthenogenetic in Guam.

769

Summary of Results

There is little endemism in asteroid fauna of oceanic islands in the Indo-West Pacific region (Marsh, 1974; Yamaguchi, 1975). However, there is a pattern of geographic distribution in which two groups of species may be distinguished: those distributed across the oceanic islands and those restricted to the continental land masses and proximal islands.

The asteroid species (23) recorded from Palau in this study (Yamaguchi, 1977) and those (26) from Guam (Yamaguchi, 1975) were markedly different in species composition, with only 13 species in common. The abundant or common species of Palau such as *Archaster typicus, Protoreaster nodosus, Fromia monilis,* and *Nardoa tuberculata* did not occur in Guam, a fact reflecting their restricted distribution.

Larval development of four species, *Protoreaster nodosus, Archaster typicus, Culcita novaeguineae,* and *Acanthaster planci,* was observed in the laboratory at Palau. The first two species represented those restricted in distribution (continental species) and the latter two those widely distributed (oceanic species). Sizes of eggs and embryos, pattern of larval development, and rates of growth in the larval body were similar among the four species and thus between the two groups. Larvae settled and metamorphosed slightly earlier in the two continental species (14 days) than in the two oceanic species (16 to 18 days), but this difference was not sufficient to account for the marked segregation of distribution patterns between the two groups.

A marked difference in the larval swimming behavior, negative geotaxis in larvae of the oceanic species and positive geotaxis in those of the continental species, was considered to be an important factor in restricting the continental species from oceanic dispersal by pelagic larvae.

REFERENCES

KANATANI, H.
  1969.   Induction of spawning and oocyte maturation by 1-methyladenine in starfishes.   Exp. Cell. Res., vol. 57, pp. 333-337.
MARSH, L. M.
  1974.   Shallow-water asterozoans of southeastern Polynesia, I: Asterozoa. Micronesica, vol. 10, pp. 65-104.
YAMAGUCHI, MASASHI
  1975.   Coral-reef asteroids of Guam.   Biotropica, vol. 7, pp. 12-23.
  1977.   Larval behavior and geographic distribution of coral reef asteroids in the Indo-West Pacific.   Micronesica, vol. 13, pp. 283-296.

MASASHI YAMAGUCHI

APPENDIX

List of Grants for Research and Exploration Made by the National Geographic Society in 1981

2288: To Dr. Charles C. Porter, Fordham University, Bronx, New York, to study biosystematics of North and Middle American Thyreodon.

2289: To Dr. Walter F. Heiligenberg, Scripps Institution of Oceanography, La Jolla, California, to study social communication in gymnotoid electric fish.

2290: To Dr. Anthony F. Aveni, Colgate University, Hamilton, New York, for the preliminary investigation of geometric and astronomical order in Nazca lines.

2291: To Dr. Jack L. Davis, University of Illinois at Chicago Circle, Chicago, Illinois, for an archeological survey of the Greek island of Keos.

2292: To Dr. Christopher B. Donnan, University of California, Los Angeles, California, for the excavation of an ancient Peruvian legend—Chotuna and Chornancap.

2293: To Dr. David H. Thomas, American Museum of Natural History, New York, New York, to study high altitude desert ecology at Barker Creek Village.

2294: To Drs. Bruce H. Dahlin and Raymond T. Matheny, Catholic University, Washington, D. C. and Brigham Young University, Provo, Utah, for the El Mirador archeological project.

2295: To Dr. Craig Packer, Allee Laboratory of Animal Behavior, Chicago, Illinois, to study the formation of male coalitions in lions.

2296: To Dr. Frank C. Craighead, Jr., Environmental Research Institute, Moose, Wyoming, for tracking migrating eagles by satellite.

2297: To Dr. Norman Herz, University of Georgia, Athens, Georgia, to study stable isotopic signatures applied to problems of classical Greek marble.

2298: To Dr. José F. Bonaparte, Museo Argentino de Ciencias Naturales, Buenos Aires, Argentina, to study Jurassic and Cretaceous terrestrial vertebrates of South America.

2299: To Dr. John A. Gifford, University of Minnesota, Duluth, Minnesota, to take core samples of submerged Holocene sediments off Franchthi Cave, Greece.

2300: Dr. Stephens Williams, Peabody Museum of Archaeology and Ethnology, Cambridge, Massachusetts, for an archeological study of culture contact and change among the Natchez Indians.

2301: To Mr. Robert L. Stephenson, University of South Carolina, Columbia, South Carolina, for the excavation of a portion of the city of Santa Elena.

2302: To Dr. Willem Meijer, University of Kentucky, Lexington, Kentucky, to explore for Tiliaceae (Basswood Family) in Cameroon (West Africa).

2303: To Dr. Alwyn H. Gentry, Missouri Botanical Garden, St. Louis, Missouri, to study patterns of plant community diversity in paleontropical forests.

2304: To Dr. James H. Brown, University of Arizona, Tucson, Arizona, to study pollination ecology of *Agave sebastiana* on Cedros Island, Mexico.

2305: To Dr. Frances S. Chew, Tufts University, Medford, Massachusetts, to study ecological interactions among cabbage butterflies from adjacent biogeographic regions.

2306: To Dr. William C. Mahaney, Atkinson College, York University, Downsview, Ontario, Canada, for radiometric dating of Quaternary glacial and nonglacial deposits on Mount Kenya in East Africa.

2307: To Joseph B. MacInnis, Toronto, Ontario, Canada, for underwater scientific and photographic survey in Lancaster Sound, Northwest Passage, Canadian Arctic.

2308: To Dr. Peter Dodson, University of Pennsylvania, Philadelphia, Pennsylvania, to study paleoecology of the Oldman Formation (Cretaceous) in Dinosaur Provincial Park, Alberta, Canada.

2309: To Mr. Frank L. Lambrecht, University of Arizona, Tucson, Arizona, for the re-evaluation of *Glossina* fossils from Florissant, Colorado.

2310: To Dr. Farish A. Jenkins, Jr., Harvard University, Cambridge, Massachusetts, to study the earliest mammals yet found in the New World.

2311: To Dr. Iain Douglas-Hamilton, African Elephant Specialist Group, Nairobi, Kenya, to study the behavior and ecology of the African elephant.

2312: To Dr. Rosevelt L. Pardy, University of Nebraska-Lincoln, Lincoln, Nebraska, for the expedition to Palau to study *Prochloron*-ascidian symbioses.

2313: To Dr. Myrna E. Watanabe, New York College of Podiatric Medicine, New York, New York, for behavioral study and population survey of the Chinese alligator.

2314: To Dr. Robert E. Ricklefs, University of Pennsylvania, Philadelphia, Pennsylvania, to study the energetics, reproduction, and population biology of Midway Island seabirds.

2315: To Dr. Norman W. Ten Brink, Grand Valley State Colleges, Allendale, Michigan, for the Alaska Range Quaternary Mapping Program.

2316: To Dr. Lewis T. Nielsen, University of Utah, Salt Lake City, Utah, for a comparative taxonomic and distributional study of Holarctic *Aedes* mosquitoes.

2317: To Dr. Edwin O. Willis, University of Miami, Coral Gables, Florida, for a survey of birds that follow driver ants.

2318: To Dr. Birute M. F. Galdikas, Orangutan Research and Conservation Project, Tanjung Puting Reserve, Indonesia, for the Orangutan Research and Conservation Project, Tanjung Puting Reserve.

2319: To Dr. Timothy E. Gregory, Ohio State University, Columbus, Ohio, for the Ohio Boeotia Expedition exploration of the Thisbe Basin.

2320: To Dr. Patrick E. McGovern, University of Pennsylvania, Philadelphia, Pennsylvania, for additional test soundings of magnetometer anomalies at the Baqcah Valley Project.

2321: To Dr. Walter E. Rast, Valparaiso University, Valparaiso, Indiana, to study Bronze Age life patterns along the southeastern Dead Sea, Jordan.

2322: To Dr. George F. Bass, Institute of Nautical Archaeology, College Station, Texas, for the Program of Nautical Archaeology in the New World.

2323: To Dr. Alister G. MacDonald, University of Aberdeen, Aberdeen, Scotland, to measure the pressure tolerance of deep sea animals.

2324: To Dr. Peter Dodson, University of Pennsylvania, Philadelphia, Pennsylvania, to study the paleoecology of the Oldman Formation (Cretaceous) in Dinosaur Provincial Park, Alberta, Canada.

2325: To Dr. Mary D. Leakey, Nairobi, Kenya, for the final preparation of monographs on Laetoli and beds III-IV, Olduvai.

2326: To Dr. Grant H. Heiken, Los Alamos Scientific Laboratory, Los Alamos, New Mexico, to study the geology and geography of Thera, Greece, before the volcanic eruption of 1450 B.C.

2327: To Dr. Kevin Padian, University of California, Berkeley, California, for a preliminary biostratigraphic-sedimentologic exploration of the Kayenta Formation of Arizona.

2328: To Dr. Karel L. Rogers, Adams State College, Alamosa, Colorado, for paleontological investigations of the Alamosa Formation.

2329: To Dr. Kenneth E. Campbell, Natural History Museum of Los Angeles County, Los Angeles, California, to study the evolution of teratorns.

2330: To Dr. Robert R. Jackson, University of Canterbury, Christchurch, New Zealand, to study the biology of primitive web-building jumping spiders.

2331: To Dr. Thomas J. Cade, Cornell University, Ithaca, New York, to study the population ecology of the Gyrfalcon in Iceland.

2332: To Dr. Arthur H. Bankoff, Brooklyn College, Brooklyn, New York, for the Morava Valley Project: Novacka Cuprija excavation.

2333: To Dr. Myrna E. Watanabe, New York College of Podiatric Medicine, New York, New York, for a behavioral study and population survey of the Chinese alligator.

2334: To Dr. Iain Douglas-Hamilton, African Elephant Specialist Group, Nairobi, Kenya, to study the behavior and ecology of the African elephant.

2335: To Dr. Kenan T. Erim, New York University, New York, New York, for study, research, and restoration activities at Aphrodisias.

2336: To Ms. Ann M. Odasz, University of Colorado, Boulder, Colorado, to study vegetation dynamics of the treelimit ecotone, Upper Alatna drainage in Central Brooks Range, Alaska.

2337: To Dr. Francis R. Fosberg, Smithsonian Institution, Washington, D. C., for the search for plant species found on Cook and Flinders voyages.

2338: To Dr. William G. Reeder, University of Texas, Austin, Texas, to study population ecology of the green turtle in the Galápagos Archipelago.

2339: To Mr. R. Lance Grande, American Museum of Natural History, New York, New York, for the study of community paleoecology and biogeography of the Green River fish fauna.

2340: To Dr. Rollin E. Coville, University of California, Berkeley, California, to study the behavior ecology of spider wasps in the genus *Trypoxylon* subgenus *Trypargilum*.

2341: To Dr. John G. H. Cant, University of Colorado, Colorado Springs, Colorado, to study adaptive strategies of primates and the evolution of suspensory locomotion.

2342: To Dr. Marvin J. Allison, Medical College of Virginia, Richmond, Virginia, for the study of Pre-Columbian American diseases.

2343: To Dr. Robert E. Ackerman, Washington State University, Pullman, Washington, for an archeological survey of the Central Kuskokwim region.

2344: To Dr. Dennis J. Stanford, National Museum of Natural History, Smithsonian Institution, Washington, D. C., for the Lamb Springs Early Man Project II.

2345: To Dr. Philip Sze, Georgetown University, Washington, D. C., to study algal communities in tidepools on the New England coast.

2346: To Dr. Richard L. Hay, University of California, Berkeley, California, for a geological study of Laetoli and Olduvai Gorge.

2347: To Dr. David M. Armstrong, University of Colorado, Boulder, Colorado, to study desert buttes and to perform natural experiments for testing island biogeography theories.

2348: To Dr. Frank A. Pitelka, University of California, Berkeley, California, to study the social organization and ecology in Lawes's six-wired bird of paradise.

2349: To Mr. Rodney M. Jackson, Bodega Bay Institute, Berkeley, California, for radio-tracking snow leopards in the Himalaya.

2350: To Dr. John M. Bird, Cornell University, Ithaca, New York, to study native iron of Disko Island in western Greenland.

2351: To Dr. Judith L. Hannah, U. S. Geological Survey, Denver, Colorado, to study mobility of trace elements during alteration of basaltic rocks.

2352: To Dr. F. Clark Howell, University of California, Berkeley, California, to investigate human occupation of the early prehistoric site of Ambrona (Soria Province, Spain).

2353: To Dr. William A. Clemens, University of California, Berkeley, California, to study vertebrate paleontology and biogeography, Judith River Formation, Montana.

2354: To Dr. Stanley C. Finney, Northern Arizona University, (now at Oklahoma State University, Stillwater, Oklahoma), to study Ordovician graptolite biostratigraphy of Bolivia.

2355: To Dr. Joseph M. Wunderle, Jr., North Carolina State University, Raleigh, North Carolina, to study the uncertainty and foraging behavior of Bananaquits on artificial flowers.

2356: To Dr. Paul M. Taylor, United States Museum of Natural History, Smithsonian Institution, Washington, D. C., to study the ethnobiology of the highland Tugutil (Halmahera Island, Indonesia).

2357: To Dr. Robert J. Braidwood, University of Chicago, Chicago, Illinois, for continued excavation of an early-village site in southeastern Turkey.

2358: To Dr. Trude Dothan, Institute of Archaeology, The Hebrew University of Jerusalem, Jerusalem, Israel, to support the Deir el-Balah regional archeological project.

2359: To Dr. Edward J. Dixon, Jr., University of Alaska Museum, University of Alaska, Fairbanks, Alaska, for 1981 archeological survey and testing of Pleistocene cave, eolian, and alluvial deposits, along the Porcupine River, Alaska.

2360: To Dr. Dennis J. Stanford, National Museum of Natural History, Smithsonian Institution, Washington, D. C., to carry out the Lamb Springs Early Man archeological project II.

2361: To Dr. Iain Douglas-Hamilton, African Elephant Specialist Group, IUCN Regional Representative, East Africa, to study the behavior and ecology of the African elephant.

2362: To Dr. Robert D. Ballard, Woods Hole Oceanographic Institution, Woods Hole, Massachusetts, for deep-sea exploration using large-area imaging.

2363: To Dr. Richard E. Leakey, National Museums of Kenya, Nairobi, Kenya, for geological and paleontological research at Lake Turkana.

2364: To Dr. Nicholas Hotton III, National Museum of Natural History, Smithsonian Institution, Washington, D. C., for field study of Popo Agie vertebrates (Late Triassic).

2365: To Dr. Steven M. Stanley, The Johns Hopkins University, Baltimore, Maryland, to study the pattern of Neogene mass extinction of Western Atlantic bivalve mollusks.

2366: To Dr. Kenneth D. Rose, The Johns Hopkins University School of Medicine, Baltimore, Maryland, to study the anatomy and adaptations of early Eocene mammals.

2367: To Dr. Thomas F. Hornbein, University of Washington, Seattle, Washington, to study human cerebral function at extreme high altitude.

2368: To Dr. John W. Hardy, The Florida State Museum, University of Florida, Gainesville, Florida, to investigate a new species of Nightjar in Peru.

2369: To Dr. Don R. Davis, National Museum of Natural History, Smithsonian Institution, Washington, D. C., for biological investigations on the Microlepidoptera (small moths) of Chile.

2370: To Dr. Robert S. O. Harding, University of Pennsylvania, Philadelphia, Pennsylvania, to study the primates of the Outamba-Kilimi National Park, Sierra Leone.

2371: To Dr. John G. Frazier, Smithsonian Institution, Washington, D. C., to study the biology of the olive Ridley sea turtle.

2372: To Mr. Elias J. Mujica, National Institute of Culture in Lima, Peru (now at Cornell University, Ithaca, New York), to study the cultural chronology in the Titicaca Basin, South-Central Andes.

2373: To Dr. Mehmet C. Ozdogan, University of Istanbul, Istanbul, Turkey, for a surface survey for prehistoric and early historic sites in northwestern Turkey.

2374: To Dr. Izumi Shimada, Princeton University, Princeton, New Jersey, to study the technological and cultural dimensions of central Andean metallurgy at Batan Grande.

2375: To Dr. Naguib Kanawati, Macquarie University, North Ryde, New South Wales, Australia, for excavations at Akhmim, Upper Egypt.

2376: To Dr. John J. Craighead, Wildlife-Wildlands Institute, Missoula, Montana, for a computer extrapolation of LANDSAT spectral signatures to classify vegetation over a large biogeographic area.

2377: To Dr. Frank Oldfield, University of Liverpool, Liverpool, England, for magnetic studies of lake sediments and sources at Mirror Lake.

2378: To Dr. James D. Howard, Skidaway Institute of Oceanography (University System of Georgia), Savannah, Georgia, to investigate Proterozoic trace fossils in the Godavari Valley, India.

2379: To Ms. Amy R. McCune, Yale University, New Haven, Connecticut, for adaptive radiations of Semionotus in Mesozoic Lakes.

2380: To Dr. Joyce R. Richardson, New Zealand Oceanographic Institute, Wellington North, New Zealand, to study evolution in brachiopods.

2381: To Dr. Gary L. Nuechterlein, University of Michigan, Ann Arbor, Michigan, to study the comparative behavior and nesting ecology of the hooded grebe.

2382: To Dr. David H. Ellis, Institute for Raptor Studies, Oracle, Arizona, to support the Patagonian falcon research expedition.

2383: To Dr. Phillip T. Robinson, Zoological Society of San Diego, San Diego, California, to survey wildlife resources in Sarpo National Park, Liberia.

2384: To Dr. Janet H. Johnson, University of Chicago, Chicago, Illinois, to support the Quseir archeological project.

2385: To Dr. Alan L. McPherron, University of Pittsburgh, Pittsburgh, Pennsylvania, for paleomagnetic dating of the earliest human occupations in Italy.

2386: To Dr. Carl D. Hopkins, University of Minnesota, Minneapolis, Minnesota, to study electric communication and species recognition in Mormyrid electric fish.

2387: To Ms. Caroline S. Harcourt, Cambridge University, Cambridge, England (now at Diani Beach, Kenya), to study competition and adaptation in nocturnal prosimians.

2388: To Dr. Donald R. Farrar, Iowa State University, Ames, Iowa, to study the origin and identity of tropical ferns in the eastern United States.

2389: To Dr. J. Alan Holman, Michigan State University, East Lansing, Michigan, for excavation of the Jaguar-fissure, Ladds Quarry, northwestern Georgia.

2390: To Dr. Robert M. West, University of Wisconsin-Milwaukee, Milwaukee, Wisconsin, to study vertebrate paleontology and geology of the Neogene Siwalik Group in western Nepal.

2391: To Dr. Dale P. Cruikshank, University of Hawaii, Honolulu, Hawaii, and Dr. Jay M. Pasachoff, Williams College, Williamstown, Massachusetts, for a spectroscopic study of volcanic gas and fume.

2392: To Dr. Gordon W. Frankie, University of California, Berkeley, California, for a comparative study of mating systems in *Centris* bees in Costa Rica (Hymenoptera: Anthophoridae)

2393: To Dr. Stanley J. Olsen, University of Arizona, Tucson, Arizona, to study the beginnings of animal domestication in China.

2394: To Dr. Luis Abel Orquera, University of Comahue, Buenos Aires, Argentina, to support the Túnel site archeological excavation.

2395: To Dr. Ralph M. Wetzel, University of Connecticut, Storrs, Connecticut, to study the evolution and distribution of Xenarthra (Edentata, Mammalia).

2396: To Dr. David A. West, Virginia Polytechnic Institute and State University, Blacksburg, Virginia, to study the ecological genetics of the polymorphic Brazilian swallowtail *Eurytides iysithous*.

2397: To Mr. Mark W. Moffett, Harvard University, Cambridge, Massachusetts, to study the sociobiology and systematics of the ant genus *Pheidologeton*.

2398: To Dr. John F. Eisenberg, National Zoological Park, Smithsonian Institution, Washington, D. C., to study the behavioral ecology of the giant panda in its native habitat.

2399: To Dr. James R. McDonald, Eastern Michigan University, Ypsilanti, Michigan, to study the development and implications of nuclear energy in France.

2400: To Dr. Dian J. Fossey, Cornell University, Ithaca, New York, to support the Karisoke Mountain Gorilla Research Centre, in Rwanda, Africa.

2401: To Dr. Francine G. Patterson, The Gorilla Foundation Research Center, Woodside, California, to study the linguistic and cognitive abilities of the lowland gorilla.

2402: To Dr. Frank E. Poirier, Ohio State University, Columbus, Ohio, to study paleoanthropology and primatology in Hubei Province, People's Republic of China.

2403: To Dr. Norman Hammond, Rutgers University, New Brunswick, New Jersey, to support the Nohmul project: The emergence of a classic Maya Regional Center.

2404: To Mr. Ricardo Praderi, Museo Nacional de Historia Natural, Montevideo, Uruguay, to support continuing research and conservation on dolphins incidentally caught in Uruguay II.

2405: To Mr. Steven L. Swartz, University of California, Santa Cruz, to study gray whales, *Eschrichtius robustus,* in Laguna San Ignacio.

2406: To Dr. Bernice M. Wenzel, University of California, Los Angeles, California, to study olfactory behavior and neurophysiology in procellariiform birds.

2407: To Dr. James C. Solomon, Missouri Botanical Garden, St. Louis, Missouri, for a botanical inventory of the Tariquia Forest, Tarija, Bolivia.

2408: To John J. Engel, Field Museum of Natural History, Chicago, Illinois, to support botanical exploration and collection of bryophytes in Bolivia.

2409: To Dr. Stephen E. Scheckler, Virginia Polytechnic Institute and State University, Blacksburg, Virginia, to study the paleoecology of pre-Carboniferous coal swamps in southern Appalachia.

2410: To Dr. Paul S. Martin, University of Arizona, Tucson, Arizona, to study the Holocene paleoecology of the packrat midden of Chaco Canyon, New Mexico.

2411: To Dr. Ramiro Matos, Universidad Nacional Mayor de San Marcos (now at University of California, Los Angeles, California), for an archeological investigation of Pachamachay Cave, Peru.

2412: To Dr. Bruce H. Dahlin, Catholic University, Washington, D. C., and Dr. Raymond T. Matheny, Brigham Young University, Provo, Utah, to support project El Mirador, Petén, Guatemala.

2413: To Dr. Laurence P. Madin, Woods Hole Oceanographic Institution, Woods Hole, Massachusetts, to support the nocturnal study of zooplankton behavior.

2414: To Dr. Leonard Muscatine, University of California, Los Angeles, California, to study the productivity of symbiotic jellyfish in marine lakes of Palau.

2415: To Mr. Pepper W. Trail, Cornell University, Ithaca, New York, to study the lek mating system of the cock-of-the-rock *(Rupicola rupicola).*

2416: To Dr. John C. Ogden, Fairleigh Dickinson University, St. Croix, Virgin Islands, to study foraging ecology of the green turtle *(Chelonia mydas).*

2417: To Dr. Geoffrey J. Martin, Southern Connecticut State College, New Haven, Connecticut, in support of a history of geography in North America.

2418: To Dr. Roger M. Selya, University of Cincinnati, Cincinnati, Ohio, to study the impact of industrial estates on rural areas in Taiwan.

2419: To Dr. Martin I. Glassner, Southern Connecticut State College, New Haven, Connecticut, to study Bolivia's access to the sea.

2420: To Dr. Stuart H. Hurlbert, San Diego State University, San Diego, California, to study ice islands and flamingos in salt lakes of the Andean puna.

Index

Africa:
Central Kalahari Desert, feeding ecology and social organization of brown hyenas of, 495-499

Kenya, behavior and conservation of Hippotragine antelopes in the Shimba Hills of, 179-202

Kenya, Gilgil baboon project in, 251-256

Kenya, Kitengela Conservation Unit adjoining Nairobi National Park, study of lions in, 565-571

Sudan, quaternary studies in the Western Desert of, 257

West, relic ports on the Grain Coast of, 629-639

Ager, Thomas A., 475

Alaska:
lepidoptera survey, to western North Slope and Victoria Island, 513-522

Nunivak Island, amphiboles from the mantle beneath, 143-144

Alligator mississippiensis, 337

Alvarez-Lopez, Humberto, 57, 58

Andes, evolution of distribution patterns of amphibians and reptiles in, 175-177

Anthropology:
Chambri of Papua New Guinea, exchange systems among, study of, 237-244

ethnomedicine of the Torres Strait Islanders, 577-581

Excavation of the Archaic habitation site on Huahine Island, 583-599

investigations at Quiriguá, Guatemala, 85-112

of the Tunica, 67-80

olive baboons in Gilgil, Kenya, study of the ecology and behavior of, 251-256

study of prehistoric habitat reconstruction by mammalian microfaunal analysis at Grasshopper Pueblo, Arizona, 387-402

Turner Farm project, North Haven, Maine, research at, 59-65

See also Paleoanthropology; Physical anthropology; and Social anthropology.

Archeological geology, Bronze Age eruption of Santorini (Thera) and the demise of Minoan civilization, 709-713

Archeology:
Central African megaliths project, 113-126

excavations of ancient canals at Edzna, Campeche, Mexico, 441-449

excavations of the Vaito'otia and Fa'ahia sites on Huahine Island, French Polynesia, 583-599

exploration and research (1974-1980) at Olduvai Gorge and Laetoli, Tanzania, 379-386

investigations at Quiriguá, Guatemala, 85-112

of the Tunica Indian sites, 67-80

prehistoric demography of coastal Ecuador, 695-704

quaternary studies in the Western Desert of Egypt and Sudan, 257-293

trial on the Yazoo and the Tunica Treasure II projects, 67-80

779